Great
Spy Stories

The Spy Who
Came in from the Cold
John Le Carré

The Mask of Dimitrios
Eric Ambler

The Naked Runner
Francis Clifford

Dr No
Ian Fleming

Sundial

The Spy Who Came in from the Cold
first published in Great Britain in 1963 by Victor Gollancz Ltd

The Mask of Dimitrios
first published in Great Britain in 1939 by Hodder & Stoughton Ltd

The Naked Runner
first published in Great Britain in 1966 by Hodder & Stoughton Ltd

Dr No
first published in Great Britain in 1958 by Jonathan Cape Limited

This edition first published in Great Britain in 1978 by

Sundial Publications Limited, 59 Grosvenor Street, London W.1.

in collaboration with

William Heinemann Limited, 15–16 Queen Street, London W.1.

and

Martin Secker & Warburg Limited, 14 Carlisle Street, London W.1.

ISBN 0 904230 70 8

Printed in Great Britain by
Richard Clay (The Chaucer Press) Ltd,
Bungay, Suffolk

Contents

The Spy Who
Came in from the Cold
9

The Mask of Dimitrios
175

The Naked Runner
359

Dr No
535

The Spy Who Came in from the Cold

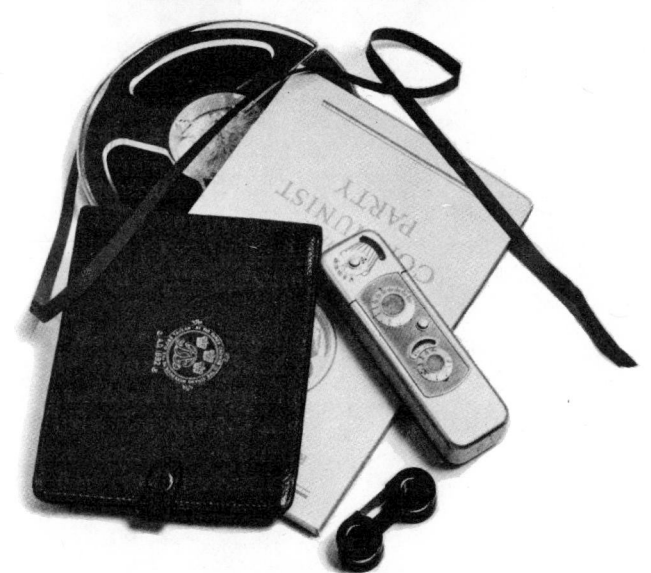

John Le Carré

CHAPTER 1

CHECKPOINT

The American handed Leamas another cup of coffee and said, 'Why don't you go back and sleep? We can ring you if he shows up.'

Leamas said nothing, just stared through the window of the checkpoint, along the empty street.

'You can't wait for ever, sir. Maybe he'll come some other time. We can have the polizei contact the Agency: you can be back here in twenty minutes.'

'No,' said Leamas, 'it's nearly dark now.'

'But you can't wait for ever; he's nine hours over schedule.'

'If you want to go, go. You've been very good,' Leamas added. 'I'll tell Kramer you've been damn' good.'

'But how long will you wait?'

'Until he comes.' Leamas walked to the observation window and stood between the two motionless policemen. Their binoculars were trained on the Eastern checkpoint.

'He's waiting for the dark,' Leamas muttered. 'I know he is.'

'This morning you said he'd come across with the workmen.'

Leamas turned on him.

'Agents aren't aeroplanes. They don't have schedules. He's blown, he's on the run, he's frightened. Mundt's after him, now, at this moment. He's only got one chance. Let him choose his time.'

The younger man hesitated, wanting to go and not finding the moment.

A bell rang inside the hut. They waited, suddenly alert. A policeman said in German, 'Black Opel Rekord, Federal registration.'

'He can't see that far in the dusk, he's guessing,' the American whispered and then he added: 'How did Mundt know?'

'Shut up,' said Leamas from the window. One of the policemen left the hut and walked to the sandbag emplacement two feet short of the white demarcation which lay across the road like the base line of a tennis court. The other waited until his companion was crouched behind the telescope in the emplacement, then put down his binoculars, took his black helmet from the peg by the door and carefully adjusted it on his head. Somewhere high above the checkpoint the arclights sprang to life, casting theatrical beams on to the road in front of them.

The policeman began his commentary. Leamas knew it by heart.

'Car halts at the first control. Only one occupant, a woman. Escorted to the Vopo hut for document check.' They waited in silence.

'What's he saying?' said the American. Leamas didn't reply. Picking up a spare pair of binoculars, he gazed fixedly towards the East German controls.

'Document check completed. Admitted to the second control.'

'Mr. Leamas, is this your man?' the American persisted. 'I ought to ring the Agency.'

'Wait.'

'Where's the car now? What's it doing?'

'Currency check, Customs,' Leamas snapped.

Leamas watched the car. There were two Vopos at the driver's door, one doing the talking, the other standing off, waiting. A third was sauntering round the car. He stopped at the boot, then walked back to the driver. He wanted the key. He opened the boot, looked inside, closed it, returned the key and walked thirty yards up the road to where, midway between the two opposing checkpoints, a solitary East German sentry was standing, a squat silhouette in boots and baggy trousers. The two stood together talking, self-conscious in the glare of the arclight.

With a perfunctory gesture they waved the car on. It reached the two sentries in the middle of the road and stopped again. They walked round the car, stood off and talked again; finally, almost unwillingly, they let it continue across the line to the Western sector.

'It is a man you're waiting for, Mr. Leamas?' asked the American.

'Yes, it's a man.'

Pushing up the collar of his jacket, Leamas stepped outside into the icy October wind. He remembered the crowd then. It was something you forgot inside the hut, this group of puzzled faces. The people changed but the expressions were the same. It was like the helpless crowd that gathers round a traffic accident, no one knowing how it happened, whether you should move the body. Smoke or dust rose through the beam of the arclamps, a constant shifting pall between the margins of light.

Leamas walked over to the car, and said to the woman, 'Where is he?'

'They came for him and he ran. He took the bicycle. They can't have known about me.'

'Where did he go?'

'We had a room near Brandenburg, over a pub. He kept a few things there, money, papers. I think he'll have gone there. Then he'll come over.'

'Tonight?'

'He said he would come tonight. The others have all been caught – Paul, Viereck, Ländser, Salomon. He hasn't got long.'

Leamas stared at her for a moment in silence.

'Ländser too?'

'Last night.'

A policeman was standing at Leamas' side.

'You'll have to move away from here,' he said. 'It's forbidden to obstruct the crossing point.'

Leamas half turned.

'Go to hell,' he snapped. The German stiffened, but the woman said: 'Get in. We'll drive down to the corner.'

He got in beside her and they moved slowly down the road to a side turning.

'I didn't know you had a car,' he said.

'It's my husband's,' she replied indifferently. 'Karl never told you I was married, did he?' Leamas was silent. 'My husband and I work for an optical firm. They let us over to do business. Karl only told you my maiden name. He didn't want me to be mixed up with . . . you.'

Leamas took a key from his pocket.

'You'll want somewhere to stay,' he said. His voice sounded flat. 'There's an apartment in the Albrecht-Dürer-Strasse, next to the Museum. Number 28A. You'll find everything you want. I'll telephone you when he comes.'

'I'll stay here with you.'

'I'm not staying here. Go to the flat. I'll ring you. There's no point in waiting here now.'

'But he's coming to this crossing point.'

Leamas looked at her in surprise.

'He told you that?'

'Yes. He knows one of the Vopos there, the son of his landlord. It may help. That's why he chose this route.'

'And he told *you* that?'

'He trusts me. He told me everything.'

'Christ.'

He gave her the key and went back to the checkpoint hut, out of the cold. The policemen were muttering to each other as he entered; the larger one ostentatiously turned his back.

'I'm sorry,' said Leamas. 'I'm sorry I bawled you out.' He opened a tattered briefcase and rummaged in it until he found what he was looking for: a half bottle of whisky. With a nod the elder man accepted it, half filled each coffee mug and topped them up with black coffee.

'Where's the American gone?' asked Leamas.

'Who?'

'The CIA boy. The one who was with me.'

'Bed time,' said the elder man and they all laughed.

Leamas put down his mug and said:

'What are your rules for shooting to protect a man coming over? A man on the run.'

'We can only give covering fire if the Vopos shoot into our sector.'

'That means you can't shoot until a man's over the boundary?'

The older man said, 'We can't give covering fire, Mr. . . .'

'Thomas,' Leamas replied, 'Thomas.' They shook hands, the two policemen pronouncing their own names as they did so.

'We can't give covering fire. That's the truth. They tell us there'd be war if we did.'

'It's nonsense,' said the younger policeman, emboldened by the whisky. 'If the allies weren't here the Wall would be gone by now.'

'So would Berlin,' muttered the elder man.

'I've got a man coming over tonight,' said Leamas abruptly.

'Here? At this crossing point?'

'It's worth a lot to get him out. Mundt's men are looking for him.'

'There are still places where you can climb,' said the younger policeman.

'He's not that kind. He'll bluff his way through; he's got papers, if the papers are still good. He's got a bicycle.'

There was only one light in the checkpoint, a reading lamp with a green shade, but the glow of the arclights, like artificial moonlight, filled the cabin. Darkness had fallen, and with it silence. They spoke as if they were afraid of being overheard. Leamas went to the window and waited, in front of him the road and to either side the Wall, a dirty, ugly thing of breeze blocks and strands of barbed wire, lit with cheap yellow light, like the backdrop for a concentration camp. East and west of the Wall lay the unrestored part of Berlin, a half-world of ruin, drawn in two dimensions, crags of war.

The damned woman, thought Leamas, and that fool Karl who'd lied about her. Lied by omission, as they all do, agents the world over. You teach them to cheat, to cover their tracks, and they cheat you as well. He'd only produced her once, after that dinner in the Schürzstrasse last year. Karl had just had his big scoop and Control had wanted to meet him. Control always came in on success. They'd had dinner together – Leamas, Control and Karl. Karl loved that kind of thing. He turned up looking like a Sunday School boy, scrubbed and shining, doffing his hat and all respectful. Control had shaken his hand for five minutes and said: 'I want you to know how pleased we are, Karl, damn' pleased.' Leamas had watched and thought, 'That'll cost us another couple of hundred a year.' When they'd finished dinner Control pumped their hands again, nodded significantly and implying that he had to go off and risk his life somewhere else, got back into his chauffeur-driven car. Then Karl had laughed, and Leamas had laughed with him, and they'd finished the champagne, still laughing about Control. Afterwards they'd gone to the 'Alter Fass', Karl had insisted on it and there Elvira was waiting for them, a forty-year-old blonde, tough as nails.

'This is my best kept secret, Alec,' Karl had said, and Leamas was furious. Afterwards they'd had a row.

'How much does she know? Who is she? How did you meet her?' Karl sulked and refused to say. After that things went badly. Leamas tried to alter the routine, change the meeting places and the catch words, but Karl didn't like it. He knew what lay behind it and he didn't like it.

'If you don't trust her it's too late anyway,' he'd said, and Leamas took the hint and shut up. But he went carefully after that, told Karl much less, used more of the hocus-pocus of espionage technique. And there she was, out there in her car, knowing everything, the whole network, the safe house, everything; and Leamas swore, not for the first time, never to trust an agent again.

He went to the telephone and dialled the number of his flat. Frau Martha answered.

'We've got guests at the Dürer-Strasse,' said Leamas, 'a man and a woman.'

'Married?' asked Martha.

'Near enough,' said Leamas, and she laughed that frightful laugh. As he put down the receiver one of the policemen turned to him.

'Herr Thomas! Quick!' Leamas stepped to the observation window.

'A man, Herr Thomas,' the younger policeman whispered, 'with a bicycle.' Leamas picked up the binoculars.

It was Karl, the figure was unmistakable even at that distance, shrouded in an old Wehrmacht macintosh, pushing his bicycle. He's made it, thought Leamas, he must have made it, he's through the document check, only currency and customs to go. Leamas watched Karl lean his bicycle against the railing, walk casually to the Customs hut. Don't overdo it, he thought. At last Karl came out, waved cheerfully to the man on the barrier, and the red and white pole swung slowly upwards. He was through, he was coming towards them, he had made it. Only the Vopo in the middle of the road, the line and safety.

At that moment Karl seemed to hear some sound, sense danger; he glanced over his shoulder, began to pedal furiously, bending low over the handlebars. There was still the lonely sentry on the bridge, and he had turned and was watching Karl. Then, totally unexpected, the searchlights went on, white and brilliant, catching Karl and holding him in their beam like a rabbit in the headlights of a car. There came the see-saw wail of a siren, the sound of orders wildly shouted. In front of Leamas the two policemen dropped to their knees, peering through the sandbagged slits, deftly flicking the rapid load on their automatic rifles.

The East German sentry fired, quite carefully, away from them, into his own sector. The first shot seemed to thrust Karl forward, the second to pull him back. Somehow he was still moving, still on the bicycle, passing the sentry, and the sentry was still shooting at him. Then he sagged, rolled to the ground, and they heard quite clearly the clatter of the bike as it fell. Leamas hoped to God he was dead.

CHAPTER 2

THE CIRCUS

He watched the Templehof runway sink beneath him.

Leamas was not a reflective man and not a particularly philosophical one. He knew he was written off – it was a fact of life which he would henceforth live with, as a man must live with cancer or imprisonment. He knew there was no kind of preparation which could have bridged the gap between then and now. He met failure as one day he would probably meet death, with cynical resentment and the courage of a solitary. He'd lasted longer than most; now he was beaten. It is said a dog lives as long as its teeth; metaphorically, Leamas' teeth had been drawn; and it was Mundt who had drawn them.

Ten years ago he could have taken the other path – there were desk jobs in that anonymous government building Cambridge Circus which Leamas could have taken and kept till he was God knows how old; but Leamas wasn't made that way. You might as well have asked a jockey to become a totalisator clerk as expect Leamas to abandon operational life for the tendentious theorising and clandestine self-interest of Whitehall. He had stayed on in Berlin, conscious that Personnel had marked his file for review at the end of every year – stubborn, wilful, contemptuous of instruction, telling himself that something would turn up. Intelligence work was one moral law – it is justified by results. Even the sophistry of Whitehall paid court to that law, and Leamas got results. Until Mundt came.

It was odd how soon Leamas had realised that Mundt was the writing on the wall.

Hans-Dieter Mundt, born forty-two years ago in Leipzig. Leamas knew his dossier, knew the photograph on the inside of the cover; the blank, hard face beneath the flaxen hair; knew by heart the story of Mundt's rise to power as second man in the Abteilung and effective head of operations. Mundt was hated even within his own department. Leamas knew that from the evidence of defectors, and from Riemeck, who as a member of the SED Praesidium sat on security committees with Mundt, and dreaded him. Rightly as it turned out, for Mundt had killed him.

Until 1959 Mundt had been a minor functionary of the Abteilung, operating in London under the cover of the East German Steel Mission. He returned to Germany in a hurry after murdering two of his own agents to save his skin and was not heard of for more than a year. Quite suddenly he reappeared at the Abteilung's headquarters in Leipzig as head of the Ways and Means Department, responsible for allocating currency, equipment and personnel for special tasks. At the end of that year came the big struggle for power within the Abteilung. The number and influence of Soviet liaison officers were drastically reduced, several of the old guard were dismissed on ideological grounds and three men emerged: Fiedler as head of counter intelligence, Jahn took over from Mundt as head of facilities, and Mundt himself got the plum – deputy director of operations – at the age of forty-one. Then the new style began. The first agent Leamas lost was a girl. She was only a small link in the network; she was used for courier jobs. They shot her dead in the street as she left a West Berlin cinema. The police never found the murderer and Leamas was at first inclined to write the incident off as unconnected with her work. A month later a railway porter in Dresden, a discarded agent from Peter Guillam's network, was found dead and mutilated beside a railway track. Leamas knew it wasn't coincidence any longer. Soon after that two members of another network under Leamas' control were arrested and summarily sentenced to death. So it went on: remorseless and unnerving.

And now they had Karl, and Leamas was leaving Berlin as he had come – without a single agent worth a farthing. Mundt had won.

Leamas was a short man with close, iron-grey hair, and the physique of a swimmer. He was very strong. This strength was discernible in his back and shoulders, in his neck, and in the stubby formation of his hands and fingers.

He had a utilitarian approach to clothes, as he did to most other things and even the spectacles he occasionally wore had steel rims. Most of his suits were of artificial fibre, none of them had waistcoats. He favoured shirts of the American kind with buttons on the points of the collars, and suede shoes with rubber soles.

He had an attractive face, muscular, and a stubborn line to his thin mouth. His eyes were brown and small; Irish, some said. It was hard to place Leamas. If he were to walk into a London club the porter would certainly not mistake him for a member; in a Berlin night club they usually gave him the best table. He looked like a man who could make trouble, a man who looked after his money, a man who was not quite a gentleman.

The air hostess thought he was interesting. She guessed he was North Country, which he might have been, and rich, which he was not. She put his age at fifty, which was about right. She guessed he was single, which was half true. Somewhere long ago there had been a divorce; somewhere there were children, now in their teens, who received their allowance from a rather odd private bank in the City.

'If you want another whisky,' said the air hostess, 'you'd better hurry. We shall be at London airport in twenty minutes.'

'No more.' He didn't look at her; he was looking out of the window at the grey-green fields of Kent.

Fawley met him at the airport and drove him to London.

'Control's pretty cross about Karl,' he said, looking sideways at Leamas. Leamas nodded.

'How did it happen?' asked Fawley.

'He was shot. Mundt got him.'

'Dead?'

'I should think so, by now. He'd better be. He nearly made it. He should never have hurried, they couldn't have been sure. The Abteilung got to the checkpoint just after he'd been let through. They started the siren and a Vopo shot him twenty yards short of the line. He moved on the ground for a moment, then lay still.'

'Poor bastard.'

'Precisely,' said Leamas.

Fawley didn't like Leamas, and if Leamas knew he didn't care.

Fawley was a man who belonged to Clubs and wore representative ties, pontificated on the skills of sportsmen and assumed a service rank in office correspondence. He thought Leamas suspect, and Leamas thought him a fool.

'What section are you in?' asked Leamas.

'Personnel.'

'Like it?'

'Fascinating.'

'Where do I go now? On ice?'

'Better let Control tell you, old boy.'

'Do you know?'

'Of course.'

'Then why the hell don't you tell me?'

'Sorry, old man,' Fawley replied, and Leamas suddenly very nearly lost his temper. Then he reflected that Fawley was probably lying anyway.

'Well, tell me one thing, do you mind? Have I got to look for a bloody flat in London?'

Fawley scratched at his ear: 'I don't think so, old man, no.'

'No? Thank God for that.'

They parked near Cambridge Circus, at a parking meter, and went together into the hall.

'You haven't got a pass, have you? You'd better fill in a slip, old man.'

'Since when have we had passes? McCall knows me as well as his own mother.'

'Just a new routine. Circus is growing, you know.'

Leamas said nothing, nodded at McCall and got into the lift without a pass.

Control shook his hand rather carefully, like a doctor feeling the bones.

'You must be awfully tired,' he said apologetically, 'do sit down.' That same dreary voice, the donnish bray.

Leamas sat down in a chair facing an olive green electric fire with a bowl of water balanced on the top of it.

'Do you find it cold?' Control asked. He was stooping over the fire rubbing his hands together. He wore a cardigan under his black jacket, a shabby brown one. Leamas remembered Control's wife, a stupid little woman called Mandy who seemed to think her husband was in the Coal Board. He supposed she had knitted it.

'It's so dry, that's the trouble,' Control continued. 'Beat the cold and you parch the atmosphere. Just as dangerous.' he went to the desk and pressed a button. 'We'll try and get some coffee,' he said, 'Ginnie's on leave, that's the trouble. They've given me some new girl. It really is too bad.'

He was shorter than Leamas remembered him; otherwise, just the same. The same affected detachment, the same donnish conceits; the same horror of draughts; courteous according to a formula miles removed from Leamas' experience. The same milk-and-water smile, the same elaborate diffidence, the same apologetic adherence to a code of behaviour which he pretended to find ridiculous. The same banality.

He brought a packet of cigarettes from the desk and gave one to Leamas.

"You're going to find these more expensive,' he said, and Leamas nodded dutifully. Slipping the cigarettes into his pocket, Control sat down. There was a pause; finally Leamas said:

'Riemeck's dead.'

'Yes, indeed,' Control declared, as if Leamas had made a good point. 'It is very unfortunate. Most . . . I suppose that girl blew him – Elvira?'

'I suppose so.' Leamas wasn't going to ask him how he knew about Elvira.

'And Mundt had him shot,' Control added.

'Yes.'

Control got up and drifted round the room looking for an ash-tray. He found one and put it awkwardly on the floor between their two chairs.

'How did you feel? When Riemeck was shot, I mean? You saw it, didn't you?'

Leamas shrugged. 'I was bloody annoyed,' he said.

Control put his head on one side and half closed his eyes. 'Surely you felt more than that? Surely you were upset? That would be more natural.'

'I was upset. Who wouldn't be?'

'Did you like Riemeck – as a man?'

'I suppose so,' said Leamas helplessly. 'There doesn't seem much point in going into it,' he added.

'How did you spend the night, what was left of it, after Riemeck had been shot?'

'Look, what is this?' Leamas asked hotly; 'what are you getting at?'

'Riemeck was the last,' Control reflected, 'the last of a series of deaths. If my memory is right it began with the girl, the one they shot in Wedding, outside the cinema. Then there was the Dresden man, and the arrests at Jena. Like the ten little niggers. Now Paul, Viereck and Ländser – all dead. And finally Riemeck.' He smiled deprecatingly;

'that is quite a heavy rate of expenditure. I wondered if you'd had enough.'

'What do you mean – enough?'

'I wondered whether you were tired. Burnt out.' There was a long silence.

'That's up to you,' Leamas said at last.

'We have to live without sympathy, don't we? That's impossible of course. We act it to one another, all this hardness; but we aren't like that really, I mean . . . one can't be out in the cold all the time; one has to come in from the cold . . . d'you see what I mean?'

Leamas saw. He saw the long road outside Rotterdam, the long straight road beside the dunes, and the stream of refugees moving along it; saw the little aeroplane miles away, the procession stop and look towards it; and the plane coming in, nearly over the dunes; saw the chaos, the meaningless hell, as the bombs hit the road.

'I can't talk like this, Control,' Leamas said at last. 'What do you want me to do?'

'I want you to stay out in the cold a little longer.' Leamas said nothing, so Control went on: 'The ethic of our work, as I understand it, is based on a single assumption. That is, we are never going to be aggressors. Do you think that's fair?'

Leamas nodded. Anything to avoid talking.

'Thus we do disagreeable things, but we are *defensive*. That, I think, is still fair. We do disagreeable things so that ordinary people here and elsewhere can sleep safely in their beds at night. Is that too romantic? Of course, we occasionally do very wicked things'; he grinned like a schoolboy. 'And in weighing up the moralities, we rather go in for dishonest comparisons; after all, you can't compare the ideals of one side with the methods of the other, can you, now?'

Leamas was lost. He'd heard the man talk a lot of drivel before getting the knife in, but he'd never heard anything like this before.

'I mean you've got to compare method with method, and ideal with ideal. I would say that since the war, our methods – ours and those of the opposition – have become much the same. I mean you can't be less ruthless than the opposition simply because your government's *policy* is benevolent, can you now?' He laughed quietly to himself: 'That would *never* do,' he said.

For God's sake, thought Leamas, it's like working for a bloody clergyman. What *is* he up to?

'That is why,' Control continued, 'I think we ought to try and get rid of Mundt. . . . Oh really,' he said, turning irritably towards the door,

'Where is that damned coffee?'

Control crossed to the door, opened it and talked to some unseen girl in the outer room. As he returned he said: 'I really think we *ought* to get rid of him if we can manage it.'

'Why? We've got nothing left in East Germany, nothing at all. You just said so – Riemeck was the last. We've nothing left to protect.'

Control sat down and looked at his hands for a while.

'That is not altogether true,' he said finally; 'but I don't think I need to bore you with the details.'

Leamas shrugged.

'Tell me,' Control continued, 'are you tired of spying? Forgive me if I repeat the question. I mean that is a phenomenon we understand here, you know. Like aircraft designers . . . metal fatigue, I think the term is. Do say if you are.'

Leamas remembered the flight home that morning and wondered.

'If you were,' Control added, 'we would have to find some other way of taking care of Mundt. What I have in mind is a little out of the ordinary.'

The girl came in with the coffee. She put the tray on the desk and poured out two cups. Control waited till she had left the room.

'Such a *silly* girl,' he said, almost to himself. 'It seems extraordinary they can't find good ones any more. I do wish Ginnie wouldn't go on holiday at times like this.' He stirred his coffee disconsolately for a while.

'We really must discredit Mundt,' he said. 'Tell me, do you drink a lot? Whisky and that kind of thing?'

Leamas had thought he was used to Control.

'I drink a bit. More than most I suppose.'

Control nodded understandingly. 'What do you know about Mundt?'

'He's a killer. He was here a year or two back with the East German Steel Mission. We had an Adviser here then: Maston.'

'Quite so.'

'Mundt was running an agent, the wife of an F.O. man. He killed her.'

'He tried to kill George Smiley. And of course he shot the woman's husband. He is a very distasteful man. Ex Hitler-Youth and all that kind of thing. Not at all the intellectual kind of Communist. A practitioner of the cold war.'

'Like us,' Leamas observed drily. Control didn't smile.

'George Smiley knew the case well. He isn't with us any more, but I think you ought to ferret him out. He's doing things on seventeenth-century Germany. He lives in Chelsea, just behind Sloane Square. Bywater Street, do you know it?'

'Yes.'

'And Guillam was on the case as well. He's in Satellites Four, on the first floor. I'm afraid everything's changed since your day.'

'Yes.'

'Spend a day or two with them. They know what I have in mind. Then I wondered if you'd care to stay with me for the weekend. My wife,' he added hastily, 'is looking after her mother, I'm afraid. It will be just you and I.'

'Thanks. I'd like to.'

'We can talk about things in comfort then. It would be very nice. I think you might make a lot of money out of it. You can have whatever you make.'

'Thanks.'

'That is, of course, if you're *sure you want* to . . . no metal fatigue or anything?'

'If it's a question of killing Mundt, I'm game.'

'Do you really feel that?' Control enquired politely. And then, having looked at Leamas thoughtfully for a moment he observed: 'Yes, I really think you do. But you mustn't feel you *have* to say it. I mean in our world we pass so quickly out of the register of hate or love – like certain sounds a dog can't hear. All that's left in the end is a kind of nausea; you never want to cause suffering again. Forgive me, but isn't that rather what you felt when Karl Riemeck was shot? Not hate for Mundt, nor love for Karl, but a sickening jolt like a blow on a numb body. . . . They tell me you walked all night – just walked through the streets of Berlin. Is that right?'

'It's right that I went for a walk.'

'All night?'

'Yes.'

'What happened to Elvira?'

'God knows . . . I'd like to take a swing at Mundt,' he said.

'Good . . . good. Incidentally, if you should meet any old friends in the meantime, I don't think there's any point in discussing this with them. In fact,' Control added after a moment, 'I should be rather short with them. Let them think we've treated you badly. It's as well to begin as one intends to continue, isn't it?'

CHAPTER 3

DECLINE

It surprised no one very much when they put Leamas on the shelf. In the main, they said, Berlin had been a failure for years, and someone had to take the rap. Besides, he was old for operational work, where your reflexes often had to be as quick as those of a professional tennis player. Leamas had done good work in the war, everyone knew that. In Norway and Holland he had somehow remained demonstrably alive, and at the end of it they gave him a medal and let him go. Later, of course, they got him to come back. It was bad luck about his pension, decidedly bad luck. Accounts Section had let it out, in the person of Elsie. Elsie said in the canteen that poor Alec Leamas would only have £400 a year to live on because of his interrupted service. Elsie felt it was a rule they really ought to change; after all, Mr. Leamas had *done* the service, hadn't he? But there they were with Treasury on their backs, not a bit like the old days, and what could they do? Even in the bad days of Maston they'd managed things better.

Leamas, the new men were told, was the old school; blood, guts and cricket and School Cert. French. In Leamas' case this happened to be unfair, since he was bilingual in German and English and his Dutch was admirable; he also disliked cricket. But it was true that he had no degree.

Leamas' contract had a few months to run, and they put him in Banking to do his time. Banking Section was different from Accounts; it dealt with overseas payments, financing agents and operations. Most of the jobs in Banking could have been done by an office boy were it not for the high degree of secrecy involved, and thus Banking was one of several Sections of the Service which were regarded as laying-out places for officers shortly to be buried.

Leamas went to seed.

The process of going to seed is generally considered to be a protracted one, but in Leamas this was not the case. In the full view of his colleagues he was transformed from a man honourably put aside to a resentful, drunken wreck – and all within a few months. There is a kind of stupidity among drunks, particularly when they are sober, a kind of disconnection which the unobservant interpret as vagueness and which Leamas seemed to acquire with unnatural speed. He developed small dishonesties, borrowed insignificant sums from secretaries and neglected to return them, arrived late or left early under some mumbled pretext. At first his colleagues treated him with indulgence; perhaps his decline scared them in the same way as we are scared by cripples, beggars and invalids because we fear we could ourselves become them; but in the end his neglect, his brutal, unreasoning malice isolated him.

Rather to people's surprise, Leamas didn't seem to mind being put on the shelf. His will seemed suddenly to have collapsed. The débutante secretaries, reluctant to believe that Intelligence Services are peopled by ordinary mortals, were alarmed to notice that Leamas had become definitely seedy. He took less care of his appearance and less notice of his surroundings, he lunched in the canteen which was normally the preserve of junior staff, and it was rumoured that he was drinking. He became a solitary, belonging to that tragic class of active men prematurely deprived of activity; swimmers barred from the water or actors banished from the stage.

Some said he had made a mistake in Berlin, and that was why his network had been rolled up; no one quite knew. All agreed that he had been treated with unusual harshness, even by a personnel department not famed for its philanthropy. They would point to him covertly as he went by, as men will point to an athlete of the past, and say: 'That's Leamas. He put up a black in Berlin. Pathetic the way he's let himself go.'

And then one day he had vanished. He said good-bye to no one, not even, apparently, Control. In itself that was not surprising. The nature of the Service precluded elaborate farewells and the presentation of gold watches, but even by these standards Leamas' departure seemed abrupt. So far as could be judged, his departure occurred before the statutory termination of his contract. Elsie, of Accounts Section, offered one or two crumbs of information: Leamas had drawn the balance of his pay in cash, which, if Elsie knew anything, meant he was having trouble with his bank. His gratuity was to be paid at the turn of the month, she couldn't say how much but it wasn't four figures, poor lamb. His National Insurance card had been sent on. Personnel had an address for him, Elsie added with a sniff, but of course they weren't revealing it, not Personnel.

Then there was the story about the money. It leaked out – no one, as usual, knew where from – that Leamas' sudden departure was connected with irregularities in the accounts of Banking Section. A largish sum was missing (not three figures but four, according to a lady with blue hair who worked in the telephone room) and they'd got it back, nearly all of it, and they'd stuck a lien on his pension. Others said they didn't believe it – if Alec had wanted to rob the till, they said, he'd know better ways of doing it than fiddling with H.Q. accounts. Not that he wasn't capable of it – he'd just have done it better. But those less impressed by Leamas' criminal potential pointed at his large consumption of alcohol, at the expense of maintaining a separate household, at the fatal disparity between pay at home and allowances abroad and above all at the temptations put in the way of a man handling large sums of hot money when he knew that his days in the Service were numbered. All agreed that if Alec had dipped his hands in the honey pot he was finished for all time – the Resettlement people wouldn't look at him and Personnel would give him no reference – or one so icy cold that the most enthusiastic employer would shiver at the sight of it. Peculation was the one sin Personnel would never let you forget – and they never forgot it themselves. If it was true that Alec had robbed the Circus, he would take the wrath of Personnel with him to the grave – and Personnel would not so much as pay for the shroud.

For a week or two after his departure, a few people wondered what had become of him. But his former friends had already learnt to keep clear of him. He had become a resentful bore, constantly attacking the Service and its administration, and what he called the 'Cavalry boys' who, he said, managed its affairs as if it were a regimental club. He never missed an opportunity of railing against the Americans and their intelligence agencies. He seemed to hate them more than the Abteilung, to which he seldom, if ever, referred. He would hint that it was they who had compromised his network; this seemed to be an obsession with him, and it was poor reward for attempts to console him, it made him bad company, so that those who had known and even tacitly liked him, wrote him off. Leamas' departure caused only a ripple on the water; with other winds and the changing of the seasons it was soon forgotten.

His flat was small and squalid, done in brown paint with photographs of Clovelly. It looked directly on to the grey backs of three stone warehouses, the windows of which were drawn, for aesthetic reasons, in creosote. Above the warehouse there lived an Italian family, quarrelling at night and beating carpets in the morning. Leamas had few possessions with which to brighten his rooms. He bought some shades to cover the light bulbs, and two pairs of sheets to replace the hessian squares provided by the landlord. The rest Leamas tolerated: the flower pattern curtains, not lined or hemmed, the fraying brown carpets and the clumsy darkwood furniture, like something from a seamen's hostel. From a yellow, crumbling geyser he obtained hot water for a shilling.

He needed a job. He had no money, none at all. So perhaps the stories of embezzlement were true. The offers of resettlement which the Service made had seemed to Leamas lukewarm and peculiarly unsuitable. He tried first to get a job in commerce. A firm of industrial adhesive manufacturers showed interest in his application for the post of assistant manager and personnel officer. Unconcerned by the inadequate reference with which the Service provided him, they demanded no qualifications, and offered him six hundred a year. He stayed for a week, by which time the foul stench of decaying fish oil had permeated his clothes and hair, lingering in his nostrils like the smell of death. No amount of washing would remove it, so that in the end Leamas had his hair cut short to the scalp and threw away two of his best suits. He spent another week trying to sell encyclopaedias to suburban housewives, but he was not a man that housewives liked or understood; they did not want Leamas, let alone his encyclopaedias. Night after night he returned wearily to his flat, his ridiculous sample under his arm. At the end of a week he telephoned the company and told them he had sold nothing. Expressing no surprise, they reminded him of his obligation to return the sample if he discontinued acting on their behalf, and rang off. Leamas stalked out of the telephone booth in a fury, leaving the sample behind him, went to a pub and got very drunk at a cost of twenty-five shillings, which he could not afford. They threw him out for shouting at a woman who tried to pick him up. They told him never to come back, but they'd forgotten all about it a week later. They were beginning to know Leamas there.

They were beginning to know him elsewhere too, the grey, shambling figure from the Mansions. Not a wasted word did he speak, not a friend, neither man, woman nor beast did he have. They guessed he was in trouble, run away from his wife like as not. He never knew the price of anything, never remembered it when he was told. He patted all his pockets whenever he looked for change, he never remembered to bring a basket, always buying carrier bags. They didn't like him in the Street, but they were almost sorry for him. They thought he was dirty too, the way he didn't shave weekends, and his shirts all grubby. A Mrs. McCaird from Sudbury Avenue cleaned for him for a week, but having never received a civil word from him withdrew her labour. She was an important source of information in the Street, where tradesmen told one another that they needed to know in case he asked for credit. Mrs. McCaird's advice was against credit. Leamas never had a letter, she said, and they agreed that that was serious. He'd no pictures and only a few books; she thought one of the books was dirty but couldn't be sure because it was in foreign writing. It was her opinion he had a bit to live on, and that that bit was running out. She knew he drew Benefit on Thursdays. Bayswater was warned, and needed no second warning. They heard from Mrs. McCaird that he drank like a fish: this was confirmed by the publican. Publicans and charwomen are not in the way of accommodating their clients with credit; but their information is treasured by those who are.

CHAPTER 4

LIZ

Finally he took the job in the library. The Labour Exchange had put him on to it each Thursday morning as he drew his unemployment benefit, and he'd always turned it down.

'It's not really your cup of tea,' Mr. Pitt said, 'but the pay's fair and the work's easy for an educated man.'

'What sort of library?' Leamas asked.

'It's the Bayswater Library for Psychic Research. It's an endowment. They've got thousands of volumes, all sorts, and they've been left a whole lot more. They want another helper.'

He took his dole and the slip of paper. 'They're an odd lot,' Mr. Pitt added, 'but then you're not a stayer anyway, are you? I think it's time you gave them a try, don't you?'

It was odd about Pitt. Leamas was certain he'd seen him before somewhere. At the Circus, during the war.

The library was like a church hall, and very cold. The black oil stoves at either end made it smell of paraffin. In the middle of the room was a cubicle like a witness-box and inside it sat Miss Crail, the librarian.

It had never occured to Leamas that he might have to work for a woman. No one at the Labour Exchange had said anything about that.

'I'm the new help,' he said; 'my name's Leamas.'

Miss Crail looked up sharply from her card index, as if she had heard a rude word. 'Help? What do you mean, help?'

'Assistant. From the Labour Exchange. Mr. Pitt.' He pushed across the counter a roneoed form with his particulars entered in a sloping hand. She picked it up and studied it.

'You are Mr. Leamas.' This was not a question, but the first stage of a laborious fact-finding investigation.

'And you are from the Labour Exchange.'

'No. I was sent by the Exchange. They told me you needed an assistant.'

'I see.' A wooden smile.

At that moment the telephone rang: she lifted the receiver and began arguing with somebody, fiercely. Leamas guessed they argued all the time; there were no preliminaries. Her voice just rose a key and she began arguing about some tickets for a concert. He listened for a minute or two and then drifted towards the bookshelves. He noticed a girl in one of the alcoves standing on a ladder sorting large volumes.

'I'm the new man,' he said, 'my name's Leamas.'

She came down from the ladder and shook his hand a little formally.

'I'm Liz Gold. How d'you do. Have you met Miss Crail?'

'Yes, but she's on the phone at the moment.'

'Arguing with her mother I expect. What are you going to do?'

'I don't know. Work.'

'We're marking at the moment; Miss Crail's started a new index.'

She was a tall girl, ungainly, with a long waist and long legs. She wore flat, ballet type shoes to reduce her height. Her face, like her body, had large components which seemed to hesitate between plainness and beauty. Leamas guessed she was twenty-two or three, and Jewish.

'It's just a question of checking that all the books are in the shelves. This is the reference bit, you see. When you've checked you pencil in the new reference and mark it off on the index.'

'What happens then?'

'Only Miss Crail's allowed to ink in the reference. It's the rule.'

'Whose rule?'

'Miss Crail's. Why don't you start on the archaeology?'

Leamas nodded and together they walked to the next alcove where a shoe-box full of cards lay on the floor.

'Have you done this kind of thing before?' she asked.

'No,' He stooped and picked up a handful of cards and shuffled through them. 'Mr. Pitt sent me. From the Exchange.' He put the cards back.

'Is Miss Crail the only person who can ink the cards, too?' Leamas enquired.

'Yes.'

She left him there, and after a moment's hesitation he took out a book and looked at the fly-leaf. It was called *Archaeological Discoveries in Asia Minor*, Volume four. They only seemed to have volume four.

It was one o'clock and Leamas was very hungry, so he walked over to where Liz Gold was sorting and said:

'What happens about lunch?'

'Oh, I bring sandwiches.' She looked a little embarrassed. 'You can have some of mine if that would help. There's no café for miles.'

Leamas shook his head.

'I'll go out, thanks. Got some shopping to do.' She watched him push his way through the swing doors.

It was half past two when he came back. He smelt of whisky. He had one carrier bag full of vegetables and another containing groceries. He put them down in a corner of the alcove and wearily began again on the archaeology books. He'd been marking for about ten minutes when he became aware that Miss Crail was watching him.

'*Mister* Leamas.' He was half-way up the ladder, so he looked down over his shoulder and said:

'Yes?'

'Do you know where these carrier bags come from?'

'They're mine.'

'I see. They are yours.' Leamas waited. 'I regret,' she continued at last, 'that we do not allow it, bringing shopping in to the library.'

'Where else can I put it? There's nowhere else I *can* put it.'

'Not in the library,' she replied. Leamas ignored her, and returned his attention to the archaeology section.

'If you only took the normal lunch break,' Miss Crail continued, 'you would not have time to go shopping. Neither of *us* does, Miss Gold or myself; *we* do not have time to shop.'

'Why don't you take an extra half-hour?' Leamas asked, 'you'd have time then. If you're pushed you can work another half-hour in the evening. If you're pressed.'

She stayed for some moments, just watching him and obviously thinking of something to say. Finally she announced:

'I shall discuss it with Mr. Ironside,' and went away.

At exactly half past five Miss Crail put on her coat and, with a pointed: 'Good night, Miss Gold', left. Leamas guessed she had been brooding on the carrier bags all afternoon. He went in to the next alcove where Liz Gold was sitting on the bottom rung of her ladder reading what looked like a tract. When she saw Leamas she dropped it guiltily into her handbag and stood up.

'Who's Mr. Ironside?' Leamas asked.

'I don't think he exists,' she replied. 'He's her big gun when she's stuck for an answer. I asked her once who he was. She went all shifty and mysterious and said "never mind". I don't think he exists.'

'I'm not sure Miss Crail does,' said Leamas and Liz Gold smiled.

At six o'clock she locked up and gave the keys to the curator, a very old man with first war shellshock who, said Liz, sat awake all night in case the Germans made a counterattack. It was bitterly cold outside.

'Got far to go?' asked Leamas.

'Twenty minutes walk. I always walk it. Have you?'

'Not far,' said Leamas. 'Good night.'

He walked slowly back to the flat. He left himself in and turned the light switch. Nothing happened. He tried the light in the tiny kitchen and finally the electric fire that plugged in by his bed. On the door mat was a letter. He picked it up and took it out into the pale, yellow light of the staircase. It was the electricity company, regretting that the area manager had no alternative but to cut off the electricity until the outstanding account of nine pounds four shillings and eightpence had been settled.

He had become an enemy of Miss Crail, and enemies were what Miss Crail liked. Either she scowled at him or she ignored him, and when he came close, she began to tremble, looking to left and right, either for something with which to defend herself, or perhaps for a line of escape. Occasionally she would take immense umbrage, such as when he hung his macintosh on *her* peg, and she stood in front of it shaking, for fully five minutes, until Liz spotted her and called Leamas. Leamas went over to her and said:

'What's troubling you, Miss Crail?'

'Nothing,' she replied in a breathy, clipped way, 'nothing at all.'

'Something wrong with my coat?'

'Nothing at all.'

'Fine,' he replied, and went back to his alcove. She quivered all that day, and conducted a telephone call in a stage whisper for half the morning.

'She's telling her mother,' said Liz. 'She always tells her mother. She tells her about me too.'

Miss Crail developed such an intense hatred for Leamas that she found it impossible to communicate with him. On pay days he would come back from lunch and find an envelope on the third rung of his ladder with his name misspelt on the outside. The first time it happened he took the money over to her with the envelope and said, 'It's L-E-A, Miss Crail, and only one S,' whereupon she was seized with a veritable palsy, rolling her eyes and fumbling erratically with her pencil until

Leamas went away. She conspired into the telephone for hours after that.

About three weeks after Leamas began work at the library Liz asked him to supper. She pretended it was an idea that had come to her quite suddenly, at five o'clock that evening; she seemed to realise that if she were to ask him for tomorrow or the next day he would forget or just not come, so she asked him at five o'clock. Leamas seemed reluctant to accept, but in the end he did.

They walked to her flat through the rain and they might have been anywhere – Berlin, London, any town where paving stones turn to lakes of light in the evening rain, and the traffic shuffles despondently through wet streets.

It was the first of many meals which Leamas had at her flat. He came when she asked him, and she asked him often. He never spoke much. When she discovered he would come, she took to laying the table in the morning before leaving for the library. She even prepared the vegetables beforehand and had the candles on the table, for she loved candlelight. She always knew that there was something deeply wrong with Leamas, and that one day, for some reason she could not understand, he might break and she would never see him again. She tried to tell him she knew; she said to him one evening:

'You must go when you want. I'll never follow you, Alec,' and his brown eyes rested on her for a moment: 'I'll tell you when,' he replied.

Her flat was just a bed-sitting room and a kitchen. In the sitting-room were two armchairs, a divan bed, and a bookcase full of paper-back books, mainly classics which she had never read.

After supper she would talk to him, and he would lie on the divan, smoking. She never knew how much he heard, she didn't care. She would kneel by the bed holding his hand against her cheek, talking.

Then one evening she said to him:

'Alec, what do you believe in? Don't laugh – tell me.' She waited and at last he said:

'I believe an eleven bus will take me to Hammersmith. I don't believe it's driven by Father Christmas.'

She seemed to consider this and at last she asked again:

'But what do you believe in?'

Leamas shrugged.

'You must believe in something,' she persisted: 'something like God – I know you do, Alec; you've got that look sometimes, as if you'd got something special to do, like a priest. Alec, don't smile, it's true.'

He shook his head.

'Sorry, Liz, you've got it wrong. I don't like Americans and public schools. I don't like military parades and people who play soldiers.' Without smiling he added, 'And I don't like conversations about Life.'

'But, Alec, you might as well say—'

'I should have added,' Leamas interrupted, 'that I don't like people who tell me what I ought to think.' She knew he was getting angry but she couldn't stop herself any more.

'That's because you don't *want* to think, you don't dare! There's some poison in your mind, some hate. You're a fanatic, Alec, I know you are, but I don't know what about. You're a fanatic who doesn't want to convert people, and that's a dangerous thing. You're like a man who's . . . sworn vengeance or something.' The brown eyes rested on her. When he spoke she was frightened by the menace in his voice.

'If I were you,' he said roughly, 'I'd mind my own business.'

And then he smiled, a roguish Irish smile. He hadn't smiled like that before and Liz knew he was putting on the charm.

'What does Liz believe in?' he asked, and she replied:

'I can't be had that easy, Alec.'

Later that night they talked about it again. Leamas brought it up – he asked her whether she was religious.

'You've got me wrong,' she said, 'all wrong. I don't believe in God.'

'Then what do you believe in?'

'History.'

He looked at her in astonishment for a moment, then laughed.

'Oh, Liz . . . oh *no*. You're not a bloody Communist?' She nodded, blushing like a small girl at his laughter, angry and relieved that he didn't care.

She made him stay that night and they became lovers. He left at five in the morning. She couldn't understand it; she was so proud and he seemed ashamed.

He left her flat and turned down the empty street towards the park. It was foggy. Some way down the road – not far, twenty yards, perhaps a bit more – stood the figure of a man in a raincoat, short and rather plump. He was leaning against the railings of the park, silhouetted in the shifting mist. As Leamas approached, the mist seemed to thicken, closing in around the figure at the railings, and when it parted the man was gone.

CHAPTER 5

CREDIT

Then one day about a week later, he didn't come to the library. Miss Crail was delighted; by half-past eleven she had told her mother, and on returning from lunch she stood in front of the archaeology shelves where he had been working since he came. She stared with theatrical concentration at the rows of books and Liz knew she was pretending to work out whether Leamas had stolen anything.

Liz entirely ignored her for the rest of that day, failed to reply when she addressed her and worked with assiduous application. When the evening came she walked home and cried herself to sleep.

The next morning she arrived early at the library. She somehow felt that the sooner she got there, the sooner Leamas might come; but as the morning dragged on her hopes faded, and she knew he would never come. She had forgotten to make sandwiches for herself that day so she decided to take a bus to the Bayswater Road and go to the A.B.C. She felt sick and empty, but not hungry. Should she go and find him? She had promised never to follow him, but he had promised to tell her; should she go and find him?

She hailed a taxi and gave his address.

She made her way up the dingy staircase and pressed the bell of his door. The bell seemed to be broken; she heard nothing. There were three bottles of milk on the mat and a letter from the electricity company. She hesitated a moment, then banged on the door, and she heard the faint groan of a man. She rushed downstairs to the flat below, hammered and rang at the door. There was no reply so she ran down another flight and found herself in the back room of a grocer's shop. An old woman sat in a corner, rocking back and forth in her chair.

'The top flat,' Liz almost shouted, 'somebody's very ill. Who's got a key?'

The old woman looked at her for a moment, then called towards the front room, where the shop was.

'Arthur, come in here, Arthur, there's a girl here!'

A man in a brown overall and grey trilby hat looked round the door and said:

'Girl?'

'There's someone seriously ill in the top flat,' said Liz, 'he can't get to the front door to open it. Have you got a key?'

'No,' replied the grocer, 'but I've got a hammer,' and they hurried up the stairs together, the grocer, still in his trilby, carrying a heavy screwdriver and a hammer. He knocked on the door sharply, and they waited breathless for an answer. There was none.

'I heard a groan before, I promise I did,' Liz whispered.

'Will you pay for this door if I bust it?'

'Yes.'

The hammer made a terrible noise. With three blows he had wrenched out a piece of the frame and the lock came with it. Liz went in first and the grocer followed. It was bitterly cold in the room and dark, but on the bed in the corner they could make out the figure of a man.

'Oh God,' thought Liz, 'if he's dead I don't think I can touch him,' but she went to him and he was alive. Drawing the curtains, she knelt beside the bed.

'I'll call you if I need you, thank you,' she said without looking back, and the grocer nodded and went downstairs.

'Alec, what is it, what's making you ill? What is it, Alec?'

Leamas moved his head on the pillow. His sunken eyes were closed. The dark beard stood out against the pallor of his face.

'Alec, you must tell me, please, Alec.' She was holding one of his hands in hers. The tears were running down her cheeks. Desperately she wondered what to do; then, getting up, she ran to the tiny kitchen and put on a kettle. She wasn't quite clear what she would make, but it comforted her to do something. Leaving the kettle on the gas she picked up her handbag, took Leamas' key from the bedside table and ran downstairs, down the four flights into the street, and crossed the road to Mr. Sleaman, the Chemist. She bought some calvesfoot jelly, some essence of beef and a bottle of aspirin. She got to the door, then went back and bought a packet of rusks. Altogether it cost her sixteen shillings, which left four shillings in her handbag and eleven pounds in her post office book, but she couldn't draw any of that till tomorrow. By the time she returned to his flat the kettle was just boiling.

She made the beef tea like her mother used to, in a glass with a teaspoon in to stop it cracking, and all the time she glanced towards him, as if she were afraid he was dead.

She had to prop him up to make him drink the tea. He only had one pillow and there were no cushions in the room, so taking his overcoat down from the back of the door she made a bundle of it and arranged it behind the pillow. It frightened her to touch him, he was drenched in sweat, so that his short grey hair was damp and slippery. Putting the cup beside the bed she held his head with one hand, and fed him the tea with the other. After he had taken a few spoonfuls, she crushed two aspirin and gave them to him in the spoon. She talked to him as if he were a child, sitting on the edge of the bed looking at him, sometimes letting her fingers run over his head and face, whispering his name over and over again, 'Alec, Alec.'

Gradually his breathing became more regular, his body more relaxed as he drifted from the taut pain of fever to the calm of sleep; Liz, watching him, sensed that the worst was over. Suddenly she realised it was almost dark.

Then she felt ashamed, because she knew she should have cleaned and tidied. Jumping up, she fetched the carpet sweeper, and a duster from the kitchen and set to work with feverish energy. She found a clean teacloth and spread it neatly on the bedside table and she washed up the odd cups and saucers which lay around the kitchen. When everything was done she looked at her watch and it was half past eight. She put the kettle on and went back to the bed. Leamas was looking at her.

'Alec, don't be cross, please don't,' she said. 'I'll go, I promise I will, but let me make you a proper meal. You're ill, you can't go on like this, you're . . . oh, Alec,' and she broke down and wept, holding both hands over her face, the tears running between her fingers like the tears of a child. He let her cry, watching her with his brown eyes, his hands holding the sheet.

She helped him wash and shave and she found some clean bed-clothes. She gave him some calvesfoot jelly, and some breast of chicken from the jar she'd bought at Mr. Sleaman's. Sitting on the bed she watched him eat, and she thought she had never been so happy before.

Soon he fell asleep, and she drew the blanket over his shoulders and went to the window. Parting the threadbare curtains, she raised the sash and looked out. Two other windows in the courtyard were lit. In one she could see the flickering blue shadow of a television screen, the figures round it held motionless in its spell; in the other a woman, quite young, was arranging curlers in her hair. Liz wanted to weep at the crabbed delusion of their dreams.

She fell asleep in the armchair and did not wake until it was nearly light, feeling stiff and cold. She went to the bed: Leamas stirred as she looked at him and she touched his lips with the tip of her finger. He did not open his eyes but gently took her arm and drew her down on to the bed and suddenly she wanted him terribly, and nothing mattered, and she kissed him again and again and when she looked at him he seemed to be smiling.

She came every day for six days. He never spoke to her much and once, when she asked him if he loved her, he said he didn't believe in fairy tales. She would lie on the bed, her head against his chest, and sometimes he would put his thick fingers in her hair, holding it quite tight, and Liz laughed and said it hurt. On the Friday evening she found him dressed but not shaved and she wondered why he hadn't shaved. For some imperceptible reason she was alarmed. Little things were missing from the room – his clock and the cheap portable wireless that had been on the table. She wanted to ask and did not dare. She had bought some eggs and ham and she cooked them for their supper while Leamas sat on the bed and smoked one cigarette after another. When it was ready he went to the kitchen and came back with a bottle of red wine.

He hardly spoke at supper, and she watched him, her fear growing until she could bear it no more and she cried out suddenly:

'Alec . . . oh, Alec . . . what is it? Is it good-bye?'

He got up from the table, took her hands, and kissed her in a way he'd never done before and spoke to her softly for a long time, told her things she only dimly understood, only half heard because all the time she knew it was the end and nothing mattered any more.

'Good-bye, Liz,' he said. 'Good-bye,' and then: 'Don't follow me. Not again.'

Liz nodded and muttered: 'Like we said.' She was thankful for the biting cold of the street and for the dark which hid her tears.

It was the next morning, the Saturday, that Leamas asked at the grocer's for credit. He did it without much artistry, in a way not calculated to ensure him success. He ordered half a dozen items – they didn't come to more than a pound – and when they had been wrapped and put into the carrier bag he said:

'You'd better send me that account.'

The grocer smiled a difficult smile and said:

'I'm afraid I can't do that'; the 'Sir' was definitely missing.

'Why the hell not?' asked Leamas, and the queue behind him stirred uneasily.

'Don't know you,' replied the grocer.

'Don't be bloody silly,' said Leamas, 'I've been coming here for four months.' The grocer coloured.

'We always ask for a banker's reference before giving credit,' he said, and Leamas lost his temper.

'Don't talk bloody cock,' he shouted; 'Half your customers have never seen the inside of a bank and never bloody well will.' This was heresy beyond bearing, since it was true.

'I don't know you,' the grocer repeated thickly, 'and I don't like you. Now get out of my shop.' And he tried to recover the parcel which unfortunately Leamas was already holding. Opinions later differed as to what happened next. Some said the grocer, in trying to recover the bag, pushed Leamas; others say he did not. Whether he did or not, Leamas hit him, most people think twice, without disengaging his right hand, which still held the carrier bag. He seemed to deliver the blow not with the fist but with the side of the left hand, and then, as part of the same phenomenally rapid movement, with the left elbow; and the grocer fell straight over and lay as still as a rock. It was said in court later, and not contested by the defence, that the grocer had two injuries – a fractured cheek bone from the first blow and a dislocated jaw from the second. The coverage in the daily press was adequate, but not over-elaborate.

CHAPTER 6

CONTACT

At night he lay on his bunk listening to the sounds of the prisoners. There was a boy who sobbed and an old lag who sang 'On Ilkley Moor bar t'at' beating out the time on his food tin. There was a warder who shouted, 'Shut up, George, you miserable sod', after each verse, but no one took any notice. There was an Irishman who sang songs about the IRA, though the others said he was in for rape.

Leamas took as much exercise as he could during the day in the hope that he would sleep at night; but it was no good. At night you knew you were in prison: at night there was nothing, no trick of vision or self-delusion which saved you from the nauseating enclosure of the cell. You could not keep out the taste of prison, the smell of prison uniform, the stench of prison sanitation heavily disinfected, the noises of captive men. It was then, at night, that the indignity of captivity became urgently insufferable, it was then that Leamas longed to walk in the friendly sunshine of a London park. It was then that he hated the grotesque steel cage that held him, had to force back the urge to fall upon the bars with his bare fists, to split the skulls of his gaolers and burst into the free, free space of London. Sometimes he thought of Liz. He would direct his mind towards her briefly like the shutter of a camera, recall for a moment the soft-hard touch of her long body, then put her from his memory. Leamas was not a man accustomed to living on dreams.

He was contemptuous of his cell mates, and they hated him. They hated him because he succeeded in being what each in his heart longed to be: a mystery. He preserved from collectivisation some discernible part of his personality; he could not be drawn at moments of sentiment to talk of his girl, his family or his children. They knew nothing of Leamas; they waited, but he did not come to them. New prisoners are largely of two kinds – there are those who for shame, fear or shock wait in fascinated horror to be initiated into the lore of prison life, and there are those who trade on their wretched novelty in order to endear themselves to the community. Leamas did neither of these things. He seemed pleased to despise them all, and they hated him because, like the world outside, he did not need them. After about ten days they had had enough. The great had had no homage, the small had had no comfort, so they crowded him in the dinner queue. Crowding is a prison ritual akin to the eighteenth-century practice of jostling. It was the virtue of an apparent accident, in which the prisoner's mess tin is upturned, and its contents spilt on his uniform. Leamas was barged from one side, while from the other an obliging hand descended on his forearm, and the thing was done. Leamas said nothing, looked thoughtfully at the two men on either side of him, and accepted in silence the filthy rebuke of a warder who knew quite well what had happened.

Four days later, while working with a hoe on the prison flower-bed, he seemed to stumble. He was holding the hoe with both hands across his body, the end of the handle protruding about six inches from his right fist. As he strove to recover his balance the prisoner to his right doubled up with a grunt of agony, his arms across his stomach. There was no more crowding after that.

Perhaps the strangest thing of all about prison was the brown paper parcel when he left. In a ridiculous way it reminded him of the marriage service – with this ring I thee wed, with this paper parcel I return thee to society. They handed it to him and made him sign for it, and it contained all he had in the world. There was nothing else. Leamas felt it the most dehumanising moment of the three months, and he determined to throw the parcel away as soon as he got outside.

He seemed a quiet prisoner. There had been no complaints against him. The Governor, who was vaguely interested in his case, secretly put the whole thing down to the Irish blood he swore he could detect in Leamas.

'What are you going to do,' he asked, 'when you leave here?' Leamas replied, without a ghost of a smile, that he thought he would make a new start, and the Governor said that was an excellent thing to do.

'What about your family?' he asked. 'Couldn't you make it up with your wife?'

'I'll try,' Leamas had replied indifferently; 'but she's remarried.'

The probation officer wanted Leamas to become a male nurse at a mental home in Buckinghamshire and Leamas agreed to apply. He even took down the address and noted the train times from Marylebone.

'The rail's electrified as far as Great Missenden, now,' the probation officer added, and Leamas said that would be a help. So they gave him the parcel and he left. He took a bus to Marble Arch and walked. He had a bit of money in his pocket and he intended to give himself a decent meal. He thought he would walk through Hyde Park to Piccadilly, then through Green Park and St. James's Park to Parliament Square, then wander down Whitehall to the Strand where he could go to the big café near Charing Cross station and get a reasonable steak for six shillings.

London was beautiful that day. Spring was late and the parks were filled with crocuses and daffodils. A cool, cleaning wind was blowing from the south; he could have walked all day. But he still had the parcel and he had to get rid of it. The litter baskets were too small; he'd look absurd trying to push his parcel into one of those. He supposed there were one or two things he ought to take out – his wretched pieces of paper – insurance card, driving licence and his E.93 (whatever that was) in a buff OHMS envelope, but suddenly he couldn't be bothered. He sat down on a bench and put the parcel beside him, not too close and moved a little away from it. After a couple of minutes he walked back towards the footpath, leaving the parcel where it lay. He had just reached the footpath when he heard a shout; he turned, a little sharply perhaps, and saw a man in an army macintosh beckoning to him, holding the brown paper parcel in the other hand.

Leamas had his hands in his pockets and he left them there, and stood, looking back over his shoulder at the man in the macintosh. The man hesitated, evidently expecting Leamas to come to him or give some sign of interest, but Leamas gave none. Instead, he shrugged and continued along the footpath. He heard another shout and ignored it, and he knew the man was coming after him. He heard the footsteps on the gravel, half running, approaching rapidly, and then a voice, a little breathless, a little aggrieved:

'Here, you – I say!' and then he had drawn level, so that Leamas stopped, turned and looked at him.

'Yes?'

'This is your parcel, isn't it? You left it on the seat. Why didn't you stop when I called you?'

Tall, with rather curly brown hair; orange tie and pale green shirt; a little bit petulant, a little bit of a pansy, thought Leamas. Could be a schoolmaster, ex L.S.E. and runs a suburban drama club. Weak-eyed.

'You can put it back,' said Leamas. 'I don't want it.'

The man coloured:

'You can't just leave it there,' he said, 'it's litter.'

'I bloody well can,' Leamas replied. 'Somebody will find a use for it.' He was going to move on, but the stranger was still standing in front of him, holding the parcel in both arms as if it were a baby. 'Get out of the light,' said Leamas. 'Do you mind?'

'Look here,' said the stranger, and his voice had risen a key, 'I was trying to do you a favour; why do you have to be so damned rude?'

'If you're so anxious to do me a favour,' Leamas replied, 'why have you been following me for the last half hour?'

He's pretty good, thought Leamas. He hasn't flinched, but he must be shaken rigid.

'I thought you were somebody I once knew in Berlin, if you must know.'

'So you followed me for half an hour?'

Leamas' voice was heavy with sarcasm, his brown eyes never left the other's face.

'Nothing like half an hour. I caught sight of you in Marble Arch and I thought you were Alec Leamas, a man I borrowed some money from. I used to be in the B.B.C. in Berlin and there was this man I borrowed some money from. I've had a conscience about it ever since and that's why I followed you. I wanted to be sure.'

Leamas went on looking at him, not speaking, and thought he wasn't all that good but he was good enough. His story was scarcely plausible – that didn't matter. The point was that he'd produced a new one and stuck to it after Leamas had wrecked what promised to be a classic approach.

'I'm Leamas,' he said at last, 'who the hell are you?'

He said his name was Ashe, with an 'E' he added quickly, and Leamas knew he was lying. He pretended not to be quite sure that Leamas really was Leamas, so over lunch they opened the parcel and looked at the

National Insurance card like, thought Leamas, a couple of cissies looking at a dirty post card. Ashe ordered lunch with just a fraction too little regard for expense, and they drank some Frankenwein to remind them of the old days. Leamas began by insisting he couldn't remember Ashe, and Ashe said he was surprised. He said it in the sort of tone that suggested he was hurt. They met at a party, he said, which Derek Williams gave in his flat off the Kudamm (he got that right) and all the press boys had been there; surely Alec remembered that? No, Leamas did not. Well, surely he remembered Derek Williams from the *Observer*, that *nice* man who gave such lovely pizza parties? Leamas had a lousy memory for names, after all they were talking about fifty-four; a lot of water had flowed under the bridge since then. . . . Ashe remembered (his christian name was William, by the by, most people called him Bill). Ashe remembered *vividly*. They'd been drinking stingers, brandy and crème de menthe, and were all rather tiddly, and Derek had provided some really gorgeous girls, half the cabaret from the Malkasten, *surely* Alec remembered now? Leamas thought it was probably coming back to him, if Bill would go on a bit.

Bill did go on, *ad lib.* no doubt, but he did it well, playing up the sex side a little, how they'd finished up in a night club with three of these girls; Alec, a chap from the political adviser's office and Bill, and Bill had been so embarrassed because he hadn't any money on him and Alec had paid, and Bill had wanted to take a girl home and Alec had lent him another tenner. . . .

'Christ,' said Leamas, 'I remember now, of course I do.'

'I *knew* you would,' said Ashe happily, nodding at Leamas over his glass, 'look, do let's have the other half this is *such* fun.'

Ashe was typical of that strata of mankind which conducts its human relationships according to a principle of challenge and response. Where there was softness, he would advance; where he found resistance, retreat. Having himself no particular opinions or tastes he relied upon whatever conformed with those of his companion. He was as ready to drink tea at Fortnum's as beer at the Prospect of Whitby; he would listen to military music in St. James's Park or jazz in a Compton Street cellar; his voice would tremble with sympathy when he spoke of Sharpeville, or with indignation at the growth of Britain's coloured population. To Leamas this observably passive role was repellent; it brought out the bully in him, so that he would lead the other gently into a position where he was committed, and then himself withdraw, so that Ashe was constantly scampering back from some cul-de-sac into which Leamas had enticed him. There were moments that afternoon when Leamas was so brazenly perverse that Ashe would have been justified in terminating their conversation – not least since he was paying for it; but he did not. The little sad man with spectacles who sat alone at the neighbouring table, deep in a book on the manufacture of ball bearings, might have deduced, had he been listening, that Leamas was indulging a sadistic nature – or perhaps (if he had been a man of particular subtlety) that Leamas was proving to his own satisfaction that only a man with a strong ulterior motive would put up with that kind of treatment.

It was nearly four o'clock before they ordered the bill and Leamas tried to insist on paying his half. Ashe wouldn't hear of it, paid the bill and took out his cheque book in order to settle his debt to Leamas.

'Twenty of the best,' he said, and filled in the date on the cheque form. Then he looked up at Leamas, all wide-eyed and accommodating.

'I say, a cheque is all right by you, isn't it?'

Colouring a little, Leamas replied:

'I haven't got a bank at the moment – only just back from abroad, something I've got to fix up. Better give me a cheque and I'll cash it at your bank.'

'My dear chap, I wouldn't *dream* of it! You'd have to go to Rotherhithe to cash this one!' Leamas shrugged and Ashe laughed, and they agreed to meet at the same place on the following day, at one o'clock, when Ashe would have the money in cash.

Ashe took a cab at the corner of Compton Street, and Leamas waved at it until it was out of sight. When it was gone, he looked at his watch. It was four o'clock. He guessed he was still being followed, so he walked down to Fleet Street and had a cup of coffee in the Black and White. He looked at bookshops, read the evening papers displayed in the show windows of newspaper offices, and then quite suddenly, as if the thought had occurred to him at the last minute, he jumped on a bus. The bus went to Ludgate Hill, where it was held up in a traffic jam near a tube station; he dismounted and caught a tube. He bought a sixpenny ticket, stood in the end carriage and alighted at the next station. He caught another train to Euston, trekked back to Charing Cross. It was nine o'clock when he reached the station and it had turned rather cold. There was a van waiting in the forecourt; the driver was fast asleep. Leamas glanced at the number, went over and called through the window:

'Are you from Clements?' The driver woke up with a start and asked:

'Mr. Thomas?'

'No,' replied Leamas. 'Thomas couldn't come. I'm Amies from Hounslow.'

'Hop in, Mr. Amies,' the driver replied, and opened the door. They drove west, towards the King's Road. The driver knew the way.

Control opened the door.

'George Smiley's out,' he said. 'I've borrowed his house. Come in.' Not until Leamas was inside and the front door closed, did Control put on the hall light.

'I was followed till lunch time,' Leamas said. They went into the little drawing-room. There were books everywhere. It was a pretty room; tall, with eighteenth-century mouldings, long windows and a good fireplace.

'They picked me up this morning. A man called Ashe.' He lit a cigarette. 'A pansy. We're meeting again tomorrow.'

Control listened carefully to Leamas' story, stage by stage, from the day he hit Ford, the grocer, to his encounter that morning with Ashe.

'How did you find prison?' Control enquired. He might have been asking whether Leamas had enjoyed his holiday. 'I am sorry we couldn't improve conditions for you, provide little extra comforts, but that would never have done.'

'Of course not.'

'One must be consistent. At every turn one must be consistent. Besides, it would be wrong to break the spell. I understand you were ill. I am sorry. What was the trouble?'

'Just fever.'

'How long were you in bed?'

'About ten days.'

'How very distressing; and nobody to look after you, of course.'

There was a very long silence.

'You know she's in the Party, don't you?' Control asked quietly.

'Yes,' Leamas replied. Another silence. 'I don't want her brought into this.'

'Why should she be?' Control asked sharply and for a moment, just for a moment, Leamas thought he had penetrated the veneer of academic detachment. 'Who suggested she should be?'

'No one,' Leamas replied, 'I'm just making the point. I know how these things go – all offensive operations. They have by-products, take sudden turns in unexpected directions. You think you've caught one fish and you find you've caught another. I want her kept clear of it.'

'Oh, quite, quite.'

'Who's that man in the Labour Exchange – Pitt? Wasn't he in the Circus during the war?'

'I know no one of that name. Pitt, did you say?'

'Yes.'

'No, not a name to me. In the Labour Exchange?'

'Oh, for God's sake,' Leamas muttered audibly.

'I'm sorry,' said Control, getting up, 'I'm neglecting my duties as deputy host. Would you care for a drink?'

'No. I want to get away tonight, Control. Go down to the country and get some exercise. Is the House open?'

'I've arranged a car,' he said. 'What time do you see Ashe tomorrow – one o'clock?'

'Yes.'

'I'll ring Haldane and tell him you want some squash. You'd better see a doctor, too. About that fever.'

'I don't need a doctor.'

'Just as you like.'

Control gave himself a whisky and began looking idly at the books in Smiley's shelf.

'Why isn't Smiley here?' Leamas asked.

'He doesn't like the operation,' Control replied indifferently. 'He finds it distasteful. He sees the necessity but he wants no part in it. His fever,' Control added with a whimsical smile, 'is recurrent.'

'He didn't exactly receive me with open arms.'

'Quite. He wants no part in it. But he told you about Mundt; gave you the background?'

'Yes.'

'Mundt is a very *hard* man,' Control reflected. 'We should never forget that. And a good intelligence officer.'

'Does Smiley know the reason for the operation. The special interest?'

Control nodded and took a sip of whisky.

'And he still doesn't like it?'

'It isn't a question of moralities. He is like the surgeon who has grown tired of blood. He is content that others should operate.'

'Tell me,' Leamas continued, 'how are you so certain this will get us where we want? How do you know the East Germans are on to it – not the Czechs or the Russians?'

'Rest assured,' Control said a little pompously, 'that that has been taken care of.'

As they got to the door, Control put his hand lightly on Leamas' shoulder.

'This is your last job,' he said. 'Then you can come in from the cold. About that girl – do you want anything done about her, money or anything?'

'When it's over. I'll take care of it myself then.'

'Quite. It would be very insecure to do anything now.'

'I just want her left alone,' Leamas repeated with emphasis. 'I just don't want her to be messed about. I don't want her to have a file or anything. I want her forgotten.'

He nodded to Control and slipped out into the night air. Into the cold.

CHAPTER 7

KIEVER

On the following day Leamas arrived twenty minutes late for his lunch with Ashe, and smelt of whisky. Ashe's pleasure on catching sight of Leamas was, however, undiminished. He claimed that he had himself only that moment arrived, he'd been a little late getting to the bank. He handed Leamas an envelope.

'Singles,' said Ashe. 'I hope that's all right.'

'Thanks,' Leamas replied, 'let's have a drink.' He hadn't shaved and his collar was filthy. He called the waiter and ordered drinks, a large whisky for himself and a pink gin for Ashe. When the drinks came Leamas' hand trembled as he poured the soda into the glass, almost slopping it over the side.

They lunched well, with a lot of drink, and Ashe made most of the running. As Leamas had expected he first talked about himself, an old trick but not a bad one.

'To be quite frank, I've got on to rather a good thing recently,' said Ashe; 'free-lancing English features for the foreign press. After Berlin I made rather a mess of things at first – the Corporation wouldn't renew the contract and I took a job running a dreary toffee-shop weekly about hobbies for the over-sixties. Can you *imagine* anything more frightful? That went under in the first printing strike – I can't tell you how relieved I was. Then I went to live with my mama in Cheltenham for a time, she runs an antique shop, does very nicely thank you, as a matter of fact. Then I got a letter from an old friend, Sam Kiever his name is actually, who was starting up a new agency for small features on English life specially slanted for foreign papers. You know the sort of thing – six hundred words on Morris dancing. Sam had a new gimmick, though; he sold the stuff already translated and do you know, it makes a hell of a difference. One always imagines anyone can pay a translator or do it themselves, but if you're looking for a half column in-fill for your foreign features you don't *want* to waste time and money on translation. Sam's gambit was to get in touch with the editors direct – he traipsed round Europe like a gypsy, poor thing, but it's paid hands *down*.'

Ashe paused, waiting for Leamas to accept the invitation to speak about himself, but Leamas ignored it. He just nodded dully and said: 'Bloody good'. Ashe had wanted to order wine, but Leamas said he'd stick to whisky and by the time the coffee came he'd had four large ones. He seemed to be in bad shape; he had the drunkard's habit of ducking his mouth towards the rim of his glass just before he drank, as if his hand might fail him and the drink escape.

Ashe fell silent for a moment.

'You don't know Sam, do you?' he asked.

'Sam?'

A note of irritation entered Ashe's voice.

'Sam Kiever, my boss. The chap I was telling you about.'

'Was he in Berlin too?'

'No. He knows Germany well, but he's never lived in Berlin. He did a bit of devilling in Bonn, free-lance stuff. You might have met him. He's a dear.'

'Don't think so.' A pause.

'What do you do these days, old chap?' asked Ashe.

Leamas shrugged.

'I'm on the shelf,' he replied, and grinned a little stupidly. 'Out of the bag and on the shelf.'

'I forget what were you doing in Berlin? Weren't you one of the mysterious cold warriors?' My God, thought Leamas, you're stepping things up a bit.

Leamas hesitated, then coloured and said savagely, 'Office boy for the bloody Yanks, like the rest of us.'

'You know,' said Ashe, as if he had been turning the idea over for some time, 'you ought to meet Sam. You'd like him,' and then, all of a bother, 'I say Alec – I don't even know where to get hold of you!'

'You can't,' Leamas replied listlessly.

'I don't get you, old chap. Where are you staying?'

'Around the place. Roughing it a bit. I haven't got a job. Bastards wouldn't give me a proper pension.'

Ashe looked horrified.

'But, Alec, that's awful; why didn't you *tell* me? Look, why not come and stay at my place? It's only tiny but there's room for one more if you don't mind a camp bed. You can't just live in the trees, my dear chap!'

'I'm all right for a bit,' Leamas replied, tapping at the pocket which contained the envelope. 'I'm going to get a job,' he nodded with determination; 'get one in a week or so. Then I'll be all right.'

'What sort of job?'

'Oh, I don't know. Anything.'

'But you can't just throw yourself away, Alec! You speak German like a native, I remember you do. There must be all sorts of things you can do!'

'I've done all sorts of things. Selling encyclopaedias for some bloody American firm, sorting books in a psychic library, punching work tickets in a stinking glue factory. What the hell *can* I do?' He wasn't looking at Ashe but at the table before him, his agitated lips moving quickly. Ashe responded to his animation, leaning forward across the table, speaking with emphasis, almost triumph.

'But Alec, you need *contacts*, don't you see? I know what it's like, I've been on the breadline myself. That's when you need to *know* people. I don't know what you were doing in Berlin, I don't want to know, but it wasn't the sort of job where you could meet people who matter, was it? If I hadn't met Sam at Poznan five years ago I'd *still* be on the breadline. Look, Alec, come and stay with me for a week or so. We'll ask Sam round and perhaps one or two of the old press boys from Berlin if any of them are in town.'

'But I can't write,' said Leamas. 'I couldn't write a bloody thing.' Ashe had his hand on Leamas' arm: 'Now, don't fuss,' he said soothingly; 'let's just take things one at a time. Where are your bits and pieces?'

'My what?'

'Your things: clothes, baggage and what not?'

'I haven't got any. I've sold what I had – except the parcel.'

'What parcel?'

'The brown paper parcel you picked up in the park. The one I was trying to throw away.'

Ashe had a flat in Dolphin Square. It was just what Leamas had expected – small and anonymous with a few hastily assembled curios from Germany: beer mugs, a peasant's pipe and a few pieces of second-rate Nymphenburg.

'I spend the weekends with my mother in Cheltenham,' he said. 'I just use this place mid week. It's pretty handy,' he added deprecatingly. They fixed the camp bed up in the tiny drawing-room. It was about four-thirty.

'How long have you been here?' asked Leamas.

'Oh – about a year or more.'

'Find it easily?'

'They come and go, you know, these flats. You put your name down and one day they ring you up and tell you you've made it.'

Ashe made tea and they drank it, Leamas sullen, like a man not used to comfort. Even Ashe seemed a little piano. After tea Ashe said: 'I'll go out and do a spot of shopping before the shops close, then we'll decide what to do about everything. I might give Sam a tinkle later this evening – I think the sooner you two get together the better. Why don't you get some sleep – you look all in.'

Leamas nodded. 'It's bloody good of you——' he made an awkward gesture with his hand, '—all this.' Ashe gave him a pat on the shoulder, picked up his army macintosh and left.

As soon as Leamas reckoned Ashe was safely out of the building, he put the front door of the flat carefully on the latch and made his way downstairs to the centre hall where there were two telephone cabins. He dialled a Maida Vale number and asked for Mr. Thomas' secretary. Immediately a girl's voice said, 'Mr. Thomas' secretary speaking.'

'I'm ringing on behalf of Mr. Sam Kiever,' Leamas said, 'he has accepted the invitation and hopes to contact Mr. Thomas personally this evening.'

'I'll pass that on to Mr. Thomas. Does he know where to get in touch with you?'

'Dolphin Square,' Leamas replied, and gave the address. 'Good-bye.'

After making some enquiries at the reception desk he returned to Ashe's flat, and sat on the camp bed looking at his clasped hands. After a while he lay down. He decided to accept Ashe's advice and get some rest. As he closed his eyes he remembered Liz lying beside him in the flat in Bayswater, and he wondered vaguely what had become of her.

He was woken up by Ashe, accompanied by a small, rather plump man with long, greying hair swept back and a double breasted suit. He spoke with a slight central European accent; German perhaps, it was hard to tell. He said his name was Kiever – Sam Kiever.

They had a gin and tonic, Ashe doing most of the talking. It was just like old times, he said, in Berlin: the boys together and the night their oyster. Kiever said he didn't want to be too late; he had to work tomorrow. They agreed to eat at a Chinese restaurant that Ashe knew of – it was opposite Limehouse police station and you brought your own wine. Oddly enough Ashe had some Burgundy in the kitchen, and they took that with them in the taxi.

Dinner was very good and they drank both bottles of wine. Kiever opened up a little on the second: he'd just come back from a tour of West Germany and France. France was in a hell of a mess, de Gaulle was on the way out and God alone knew what would happen then. With a hundred thousand demoralised *colons* returning from Algeria he reckoned Fascism was on the cards.

'What about Germany?' asked Alec, prompting him.

'It's just a question of whether the Yanks can hold them.' Kiever looked invitingly at Leamas.

'What do you mean?' asked Leamas.

'What I say. Dulles gave them a foreign policy with one hand, Kennedy takes it away with the other. They're getting waspish.'

Leamas nodded abruptly and said, 'Bloody typical Yank.'

'Alec doesn't seem to like our American cousins,' said Ashe, stepping in heavily, and Kiever, with complete disinterest, murmured, 'Oh, really?' Kiever played it, Leamas reflected, very long. Like someone used to horses, he let you come to him. He conveyed to perfection a man who suspected that he was about to be asked a favour, and was not easily won.

After dinner Ashe said, 'I know a place in Wardour Street – you've been there, Sam. They do you all right there. Why don't we summon a barouche and go along?'

'Just a minute,' said Leamas, and there was something in his voice which made Ashe look at him quickly; 'just tell me something will you? Who's paying for this jolly?'

'I am,' said Ashe quickly, 'Sam and I.'

'Have you discussed it?'

'Well – no.'

'Because I haven't got any bloody money; you know that, don't you? None to throw about anyway.'

'Of course, Alec. I've looked after you up till now, haven't I?'

'Yes,' Leamas replied; 'yes, you have.'

He seemed to be going to say something else, and then to change his mind. Ashe looked worried, not offended, and Kiever as inscrutable as before.

Leamas refused to speak in the taxi. Ashe attempted some conciliatory remark and he just shrugged irritably. They arrived at Wardour Street and dismounted, neither Leamas nor Kiever making any attempt to pay for the cab. Ashe led them past a shop window full of 'girlie' magazines, down a narrow alley, at the far end of which shone a tawdry neon sign: 'Pussywillow Club. Members Only.' On either side of the door were photographs of girls, and pinned across each was a thin, hand-printed strip of paper which read, 'Nature Study. Members only.'

Ashe pressed the bell. The door was at once opened by a very large man in a white shirt and black trousers.

'I'm a member,' Ashe said. 'These two gentlemen are with me.'

'See your card?'

Ashe took a buff card from his wallet and handed it over.

'Your guests pay a quid a head temporary membership. Your recommendation, right?' He held out the card and as he did so, Leamas stretched past Ashe and took it. He looked at it for a moment, then handed it back to Ashe.

Taking two pounds from his hip pocket Leamas put them into the waiting hand of the man at the door.

'Two quid,' said Leamas, 'for the guests,' and ignoring the astonished protests of Ashe he guided them through the curtained doorway into the dim hallway of the club. He turned to the doorman.

'Find us a table,' said Leamas, 'and a bottle of Scotch. And see we're left alone.' The doorman hesitated for a moment, decided not to argue, and escorted them downstairs. As they descended they heard the subdued moan of unintelligible music.

They got a table on their own at the back of the room. A two-piece band was playing and girls sat around in twos and threes. Two got up as they came in but the big doorman shook his head.

Ashe glanced at Leamas uneasily while they waited for the whisky. Kiever seemed slightly bored. The waiter brought a bottle and three tumblers and they watched in silence as he poured a little whisky into each glass. Leamas took the bottle from the waiter and added as much again to each. This done, he leant across the table and said to Ashe, 'Now perhaps you'll tell me what the bloody hell's going on?'

'What do you mean?' Ashe sounded uncertain. 'What *do* you mean, Alec?'

'You followed me from prison the day I was released,' he began quietly, 'with some bloody silly story of meeting me in Berlin. You gave me money you didn't owe me. You've bought me expensive meals and you're putting me up in your flat.'

Ashe coloured and said, 'If that's the . . .'

'Don't interrupt,' said Leamas fiercely. 'Just damn' well wait till I've finished, do you mind? Your membership card for this place is made out for someone called Murphy. Is that your name?'

'No, it is not.'

'I suppose a friend called Murphy lent you his membership card?'

'No he didn't as a matter of fact. If you must know I come here occasionally to find a girl. I used a phoney name to join the club.'

'Then why,' Leamas persisted ruthlessly, 'is Murphy registered as the tenant of your flat?'

It was Kiever who finally spoke.

'You run along home,' he said to Ashe. 'I'll look after this.'

A girl performed a striptease, a young, drab girl with a dark bruise on her thigh. She had that pitiful, spindly nakedness which is embarrassing because it is not erotic; because it is artless and undesiring. She turned slowly, jerking sporadically with her arms or legs as if she only heard the music in snatches, and all the time she looked at them with the precocious interest of a child in adult company. The tempo of the music increased abruptly, and the girl responded like a dog to the whistle, scampering back and forth. Removing her brassière on the last note, she held it above her head, displaying her meagre body with its three tawdry patches of tinsel hanging from it like old Christmas decorations.

They watched in silence, Leamas and Kiever.

'I suppose you're going to tell me that we've seen better in Berlin,' Leamas suggested at last, and Kiever saw that he was still very angry.

'I expect *you* have,' Kiever replied pleasantly. 'I have often been to Berlin, but I am afraid I dislike night clubs.'

Leamas said nothing.

'I'm no prude, mind, just rational. If I want a woman I know cheaper ways of finding one; if I want to dance I know better places to do it.'

Leamas might not have been listening.

'Perhaps you'll tell me why that cissy picked me up,' he suggested. Kiever nodded.

'By all means. I told him to.'

'Why?'

'I am interested in you. I want to make you a proposition, a journalistic proposition.'

There was a pause.

'Journalistic,' Leamas repeated, 'I see.'

'I run an agency, an international feature service. It pays well – very well – for interesting material.'

'Who publishes the material?'

'It pays so well, in fact, that a man with your kind of experience of . . . the international scene, a man with your background, you understand, who provided convincing, factual material, could free himself in a comparatively short time from further financial worry.'

'Who publishes the material, Kiever?' There was a threatening edge to Leamas' voice, and for a moment, just for a moment, a look of apprehension seemed to pass across Kiever's smooth face.

'International clients. I have a correspondent in Paris who disposes of a good deal of my stuff. Often I don't even know who *does* publish. I confess,' he added with a disarming smile, 'that I don't awfully care. They pay and they ask for more. They're the kind of people, you see, Leamas, who don't fuss about awkward details; they pay promptly, and they're happy to pay into foreign banks, for instance, where no one bothers about things like tax.'

Leamas said nothing. He was holding his glass with both hands, staring into it.

Christ, they're rushing their fences, Leamas thought; it's indecent. He remembered some silly musical hall joke – 'This is an offer no respectable girl could accept – and besides, I don't know what it's worth.' Tactically, he reflected, they're right to rush it. I'm on my uppers, prison experience still fresh, social resentment strong. I'm an old horse, I don't need breaking in; I don't have to pretend they've offended my honour as an English gentleman. On the other hand they would expect *practical* objections. They would expect him to be afraid; for his Service pursued traitors as the eye of God followed Cain across the desert.

And finally, they would know it was a gamble. They would know that inconsistency in human decision can make nonsense of the best-planned espionage approach; that cheats, liars and criminals may resist every blandishment while respectable gentleman have been moved to appalling treasons by watery cabbage in a Departmental canteen.

'They'd have to pay a hell of a lot,' Leamas muttered at last. Kiever gave him some more whisky.

'They are offering a down-payment of fifteen thousand pounds. The money is already lodged at the Banque Cantonale in Bern. On production of a suitable identification, with which my clients will provide you, you can draw the money. My clients reserve the right to put questions to you over the period of one year on payment of another five thousand pounds. They will assist you with any . . . resettlement problems that may arise.'

'How soon do you want an answer?'

'Now. You are not expected to commit all your reminiscences to paper. You will meet my client and he will arrange to have the material . . . ghost written.'

'Where am I supposed to meet him?'

'We felt for everybody's sake it would be simplest to meet outside the United Kingdom. My client suggested Holland.'

'I haven't got my passport,' Leamas said dully.

'I took the liberty of obtaining one for you,' Kiever replied suavely; nothing in his voice or his manner indicated he had done other than negotiate an adequate business arrangement. 'We're flying to the Hague tomorrow morning at nine forty-five. Shall we go back to my flat and discuss any other details?'

Kiever paid and they took a taxi to a rather good address not far from St. James's Park.

Kiever's flat was luxurious and expensive, but its contents somehow gave the impression of having been hastily assembled. It is said there are shops in London which will sell you bound books by the yard, and interior decorators who will harmonise the colour scheme of the walls with that of a painting. Leamas, who was not particularly receptive to such subtleties, found it hard to remember that he was in a private flat and not an hotel. As Kiever showed him to his room (which looked on to a dingy inner courtyard and not on to the street) Leamas asked him:

'How long have you been here?'

'Oh, not long,' Kiever replied lightly, 'a few months, not more.'

'Must cost a packet. Still, I suppose you're worth it.'

'Thanks.'

There was a bottle of Scotch in his room and a syphon of soda on a silver-plated tray. A curtained doorway at the further end of the room led to a bathroom and lavatory.

'Quite a little love nest. All paid for by the great Worker State?'

Shut up,' said Kiever savagely, and added, 'If you want me, there's an internal telephone to my room. I shall be awake.'

'I think I can manage my buttons now,' Leamas retorted.

'Then good night,' said Kiever shortly, and left the room. He's on edge, too, thought Leamas.

Leamas was woken by the telephone at his bedside. It was Kiever.

'It's six o'clock,' he said, 'breakfast at half past.'

'All right,' Leamas replied, and rang off. He had a headache.

Kiever must have telephoned for a taxi, because at seven o'clock the door bell rang and Kiever asked, 'Got everything?'

'I've no luggage,' Leamas replied, 'except a toothbrush and a razor.'

That is taken care of. And are you ready otherwise?'

Leamas shrugged. 'I suppose so. Have you got any cigarettes?'

'No,' Kiever replied, 'but you can get some on the plane. You'd better look through this,' he added, and handed Leamas a British passport. It was made out in his name with his own photograph mounted in it, embossed by the deep press Foreign Office seal running across the corner. It was neither old nor new; it described Leamas as a clerk, and gave his status as single. Holding it in his hand for the first time, Leamas was a little nervous. It was like getting married: whatever happend, things would never be the same again.

'What about money?' Leamas asked.

'You won't need any. It's on the firm.'

CHAPTER 8

LE MIRAGE

It was cold that morning; the light mist was damp and grey, pricking the skin. The airport reminded Leamas of the war: machines, half hidden in the fog, waiting patiently for their masters; the resonant voices and their echoes, the sudden shout and the incongruous clip of a girl's heels on a stone floor; the roar of an engine that might have been at your elbow. Everywhere that air of conspiracy which generates among people who have been up since dawn – of superiority almost, derived from the common experience of having seen the night disappear and the morning come. The staff had that look which is informed by the mystery of dawn and animated by the cold, and they treated the passengers and their baggage with the remoteness of men returned from the front: ordinary mortals had nothing for them that morning.

Kiever had provided Leamas with luggage. It was a nice detail: Leamas admired it. Passengers without luggage attracted attention, and it was not part of Kiever's plan to do that. They checked in at the airline desk and followed the signs to passport control. There was a ludicrous moment when they lost the way and Kiever was rude to a porter. Leamas supposed Kiever was worried about the passport – he needn't be, thought Leamas, there's nothing wrong with it.

The passport officer was a youngish, little man with an Intelligence Corps tie and some mysterious badge in his lapel. He had a ginger moustache, and a North Country accent which was his life's enemy.

'Going to be away for a long time, Sir?' he asked Leamas.

'A couple of weeks,' Leamas replied.

'You'll want to watch it, Sir. Your passport's due for renewal on the 31st.'

'I know,' said Leamas.

They walked side by side into the passengers' waiting room. On the way Leamas said: 'You're a suspicious sod, aren't you, Kiever,' and the other laughed quietly.

'Can't have you on the loose, can we? Not part of the contract,' he replied.

They still had twenty minutes to wait. They sat down at a table and ordered coffee. 'And take these things away,' Kiever added to the waiter, indicating the used cups, saucers and ash-trays, on the table. 'There's a trolley coming round,' the waiter replied.

'Take them,' Kiever repeated, angry again. 'It's disgusting, leaving dirty crockery there like that.'

The waiter just turned and walked away. He didn't go near the service counter and he didn't order their coffee. Kiever was white, ill with anger. 'For Christ's sake,' Leamas muttered, 'let it go. Life's too short.'

'Cheeky bastard, that's what he is,' said Kiever.

'All right, all right, make a scene; you've chosen a good moment. They'll never forget us here.'

The formalities at the airport at The Hague provided no problem. Kiever seemed to have recovered from his anxieties. He became jaunty and talkative as they walked the short distance between the plane and the Customs sheds. The young Dutch officer gave a perfunctory glance at their luggage and passports and announced in awkward throaty English: 'I hope you have a pleasant stay in the Netherlands.'

'Thanks,' said Kiever, almost too gratefully, 'thanks very much.'

They walked from the Customs shed along the corridor to the reception hall on the other side of the airport buildings. Kiever led the way to the main exit, between the little groups of travellers staring vaguely at kiosk displays of scent, cameras and fruit. As they pushed their way through the revolving glass door, Leamas looked back. Standing at the newspaper kiosk, deep in a copy of the *Continental Daily Mail*, stood a small, frog-like figure in glasses, an earnest, worried little man. He looked like a civil servant. Something like that.

A car was waiting for them in the car park, a Volkswagen with a Dutch registration, driven by a woman who ignored them. She drove slowly, always stopping if the lights were amber, and Leamas guessed she had been briefed to drive that way and that they were being followed by another car. He watched the off-side wing mirror, trying to recognise the car but without success. Once he saw a black Peugeot with a CD number, but when they turned the corner there was only a furniture van behind them. He knew The Hague quite well from the war, and he tried to work out where they were heading. He guessed they were travelling north-west towards Scheveningen. Soon they had left the suburbs behind them and were approaching a colony of villas bordering the dunes along the sea front.

Here they stopped. The woman got out, leaving them in the car, and rang the front door bell of a small cream coloured bungalow which stood at the near end of the row. A wrought iron sign hung on the porch with the words 'Le Mirage' in pale blue Gothic script. There was a notice in the window which proclaimed that all the rooms were taken.

The door was opened by a kindly, plump woman who looked past the driver towards the car. Her eyes still on the car, she came down the drive towards them, smiling with pleasure. She reminded Leamas of an old aunt he once had who beat him for wasting string.

'How nice that you have come,' she declared; 'we are so *pleased* that you have come!' They followed her into the bungalow, Kiever leading the way. The driver got back into the car. Leamas glanced down the road which they had just travelled; three hundred yards away a black car, a Fiat perhaps, or a Peugeot, had parked. A man in a raincoat was getting out.

Once in the hall the woman shook Leamas warmly by the hand. 'Welcome, welcome to Le Mirage. Did you have a good journey?'

'Fine,' Leamas replied.

'Did you fly or come by sea?'

'We flew,' Kiever said; 'a very smooth flight.' He might have owned the airline.

'I'll make your lunch,' she declared; 'a special lunch. I'll make you something specially good. What shall I bring you?'

'Oh, for God's sake,' said Leamas under his breath, and the door bell rang. The woman went quickly into the kitchen; Kiever opened the front door.

He was wearing a macintosh with leather buttons. He was about Leamas' height, but older. Leamas put him at about fifty-five. His face had a hard, grey hue and sharp furrows; he might have been a soldier. He held out his hand.

'My name is Peters,' he said. The fingers were slim and polished.

'Did you have a good journey?'

'Yes,' said Kiever quickly, 'quite uneventful.'

'Mr. Leamas and I have a lot to discuss; I do not think we need to keep you, Sam. You could take the Volkswagen back to town.'

Kiever smiled. Leamas saw the relief in his smile.

'Good-bye, Leamas,' said Kiever, his voice jocular; 'good luck, old man.'

Leamas nodded, ignoring Kiever's hand.

'Good-bye,' Kiever repeated and let himself quietly out of the front door.

Leamas followed Peters into a back room. Heavy lace curtains hung on the window, ornately fringed and draped. The window-sill was covered with potted plants; great cacti, tobacco plant and some curious tree with wide, rubbery leaves. The furniture was heavy, pseudo-antique. In the centre of the room was a table with two carved chairs. The table was covered with a rust-coloured counterpane more like a carpet; on it before each chair was a pad of paper and a pencil. On a sideboard there was whisky and soda. Peters went over to it and mixed them both a drink.

'Look,' said Leamas suddenly, 'from now on I can do without the goodwill; do you follow me? We both know what we're about; both professionals You've got a paid defector – good luck to you. For Christ's sake don't pretend you've fallen in love with me.' He sounded on edge, uncertain of himself.

Peters nodded, 'Kiever told me you were a proud man,' he observed dispassionately. Then he added without smiling, 'After all, why else does a man attack tradesmen?'

Leamas guessed he was Russian, but he wasn't sure. His English was nearly perfect, he had the ease and habits of a man long used to civilised comforts.

They sat at the table.

'Kiever told you what I am going to pay you?' Peters enquired.

'Yes. Fifteen thousand pounds to be drawn on a Bern bank.'

'Yes.'

'He said you might have follow-up questions during the next year,' said Leamas, 'you would pay another five thousand if I kept myself available.'

Peters nodded.

'I don't accept that condition,' Leamas continued. 'You know as well as I do it wouldn't work. I want to draw the fifteen thousand and get clear. Your people have a rough way with defected agents; so have mine. I'm not going to sit on my fanny in St. Moritz while you roll up every network I've given you. They're not fools; they'd know who to look for. For all you and I know they're on to us now.'

Peters nodded: 'You could, of course, come somewhere . . . safer, couldn't you?'

'Behind the Curtain?'

'Yes.'

Leamas just shook his head and continued: 'I reckon you'll need about three days for a preliminary interrogation. Then you'll want to refer back for a detailed brief.'

'Not necessarily,' Peters replied.

Leamas looked at him with interest:

'I see,' he said, 'they've sent the expert. Or isn't Moscow Centre in on this?'

Peters was silent; he was just looking at Leamas, taking him in. At last he picked up the pencil in front of him and said:

'Shall we begin with your war service?'

Leamas shrugged:

'It's up to you.'

'That's right. We'll begin with your war service. Just talk.'

'I enlisted in the Engineers in 1939. I was finishing my training when a notice came round inviting linguists to apply for specialist service abroad. I had Dutch and German and a good deal of French and I was fed up with soldiering, so I applied. I knew Holland well; my father had a machine tool agency at Leiden; I'd lived there for nine years. I had the usual interviews and went off to a school near Oxford where they taught me the usual monkey tricks.'

'Who was running that set-up?'

'I didn't know till later. Then I met Steed-Asprey, and an Oxford don called Fielding. They were running it. In forty-one they dropped me into Holland and I stayed there nearly two years. We lost agents quicker than we could find them in those days – it was bloody murder. Holland's a wicked country for that kind of work – it's got no real rough country, nowhere out of the way you can keep a headquarters or a radio set. Always on the move, always running away. It made it a very dirty game. I got out in forty-three and had a couple of months in England, then I had a go at Norway – that was a picnic by comparison. In forty-five they paid me off and I came over here again, to Holland, to try and catch up on my father's old business. That was no good, so I joined up with an old friend who was running a travel agency business in Bristol. That lasted eighteen months then we were sold up. Then out of the blue I got a letter from the Department: would I like to go back? But I'd had enough of all that, I thought, so I said I'd think about it and rented a cottage on Lundy Island. I stayed there a year contemplating my stomach, then I got fed up again so wrote to them. By late forty-nine I was back on the payroll. Broken service of course – reduction of pension rights and the usual crabbing. Am I going too fast?'

'Not for the moment,' Peters replied, pouring him some more whisky; 'we'll discuss it again of course, with names and dates.'

There was a knock at the door and the woman came in with lunch, an enormous meal of cold meats and bread and soup. Peters pushed his notes aside and they ate in silence. The interrogation had begun.

Lunch was cleared away. 'So you went back to the Circus,' said Peters.

'Yes. For a while they gave me a desk job, processing reports, making assessments of military strengths in Iron Curtain countries, tracing units and that kind of thing.'

'Which section?'

'Satellites Four. I was there from February fifty to May fifty-one.'

'Who were your colleagues?'

'Peter Guillam, Brian de Grey and George Smiley. Smiley left us in early fifty-one and went over to Counter Intelligence. In May fifty-one I was posted to Berlin as DCA – Deputy-Controller of Area. That meant all the operational work.'

'Who did you have under you?' Peters was writing swiftly. Leamas guessed he had some home-made shorthand.

'Hackett, Sarrow and de Jong. De Jong was killed in a traffic accident in fifty-nine. We thought he was murdered but we could never prove it. They all ran networks and I was in charge. Do you want details?' he asked drily.

'Of course, but later. Go on.'

'It was late fifty-four when we landed our first big fish in Berlin: Fritz Feger, second man in the DDR Defence Ministry. Up till then it had been heavy going – but in November fifty-four we got on to Fritz. He lasted almost exactly two years then one day we never heard any more. I hear he died in prison. It was another three years before we found anyone to touch him. Then, in 1959, Karl Riemeck turned up. Karl was on the Praesidium of the East German Communist Party. He was the best agent I ever knew.'

'He is now dead,' Peters observed.

A look of something like shame passed across Leamas' face:

'I was there when he was shot,' he muttered. 'He had a mistress who came over just before he died. He'd told her everything – she knew the whole damned network. No wonder he was blown.'

'We'll return to Berlin later. Tell me this. When Karl died you flew back to London. Did you remain in London for the rest of your service?'

'What there was of it, yes.'

'What job did you have in London?'

'Banking section; supervision of agents' salaries, overseas payments for clandestine purposes. A child could have managed it. We got our orders and we signed the drafts. Occasionally there was a security headache.'

'Did you deal with agents direct?'

'How could we? The Resident in a particular country would make a requisition. Authority would put a hoofmark on it and pass it to us to make the payment. In most cases we had the money transferred to a convenient foreign bank where the Resident could draw it himself and hand it to the agent.'

'How were agents described? By cover names?'

'By figures. The Circus calls them combinations. Every network was given a combination; every agent was described by a suffix attached to the combination. Karl's combination was eight A stroke one.'

Leamas was sweating. Peters watched him coolly, appraising him like a professional gambler across the table. What was Leamas worth? What would break him, what attract or frighten him? What did he hate, above all, what did he know? Would he keep his best card to the end and sell it dear? Peters didn't think so; Leamas was too much off balance to monkey about. He was a man at odds with himself, a man who knew one life, one confession, and had betrayed them. Peters had seen it before. He had seen it, even in men who had undergone a complete ideological reversal, who in the secret hours of the night had found a new creed, and alone, compelled by the internal power of their convictions, had betrayed their calling, their families, their countries. Even they, filled as they were with new zeal and new hope, had had to struggle against the stigma of teachery; even they wrestled with the almost physical anguish of saying that which they had been trained never, never to reveal. Like apostates who feared to burn the Cross, they hesitated between the instinctive and the material; and Peters, caught in the same polarity, must give them comfort and destroy their pride. It was a situation of which they were both aware; thus Leamas had fiercely rejected a human relationship with Peters, for his pride precluded it. Peters knew that for those reasons, Leamas would lie; lie perhaps only by omission, but lie all the same, for pride, from defiance or through the sheer perversity of his profession; and he, Peters, would have to nail the lies. He knew, too, that the very fact that Leamas was a professional could militate against his interests, for Leamas would select where Peters wanted no selection; Leamas would anticipate the type of intelligence which Peters required – and in doing so might pass by some casual scrap which could be of vital interest to the evaluators. To all that, Peters added the capricious vanity of an alcoholic wreck.

'I think,' he said, 'we will now take your Berlin service in some detail. That would be from May 1951 to March 1961. Have another drink.'

Leamas watched him take a cigarette from the box on the table, and light it. He noticed two things: that Peters was left handed, and that once again he had put the cigarette in his mouth with the maker's name away from him, so that it burnt first. It was a gesture Leamas liked: it indicated that Peters, like himself, had been on the run.

Peters had an odd face, expressionless and grey. The colour must have left it long ago – perhaps in some prison in the early days of the Revolution – and now his features were formed and Peters would look like that till he died. Only the stiff, grey hair might turn to white, but his face would not change. Leamas wondered vaguely what Peters' real name was, whether he was married. There was something very orthodox about him which Leamas liked. It was the orthodoxy of strength, of confidence. If Peters lied there would be a reason. The lie would be a calculated, necessary lie, far removed from the fumbling dishonesty of Ashe.

Ashe, Kiever, Peters; that was a progression in quality, in authority, which to Leamas was axiomatic of the hierarchy of an intelligence network. It was also, he suspected, a progression in ideology. Ashe, the mercenary, Kiever the fellow traveller, and now Peters, for whom the end and the means were identical.

Leamas began to talk about Berlin. Peters seldom interrupted, seldom asked a question or made a comment, but when he did, he displayed a technical curiosity and expertise which entirely accorded with Leamas' own temperament. Leamas even seemed to respond to the dispassionate professionalism of his interrogator – it was something they had in common.

It had taken a long time to build a decent East Zone network from Berlin, Leamas explained. In the earlier days the city had been thronging with second-rate agents: intelligence was discredited and so much a part of the daily life of Berlin that you could recruit a man at a cocktail party, brief him over dinner and he would be blown by breakfast. For a professional it was a nightmare: dozens of agencies, half of them penetrated by the opposition, thousands of loose ends; too many leads, too few sources, too little space to operate. They had their break with Feger in 1954, true enough. But by '56 when every Service department was screaming for high-grade intelligence, they were becalmed. Feger had spoilt them for second-rate stuff that was only one jump ahead of the news. They needed the real thing – and they had to wait another three years before they got it.

Then one day de Jong went for a picnic in the woods on the edge of East Berlin. He had a British military number plate on his car, which he parked, locked, in an unmade road beside the canal. After the picnic his children ran on ahead, carrying the basket. When they reached the car they stopped, hesitated, dropped the basket and ran back. Somebody had forced the car door – the handle was broken and the door was slightly open. De Jong swore, remembering that he had left his camera in the glove compartment. He went and examined the car. The handle had been forced; de Jong reckoned it had been done with a piece of steel tubing, the kind of thing you can carry in your sleeve. But the camera was still there, so was his coat, so were some parcels belonging to his wife. On the driving seat was a tobacco tin, and in the tin was a small nickel cartridge. De Jong knew exactly what it contained: it was the film cartridge of a sub-miniature camera, probably a Minox.

De Jong drove home and developed the film. It contained the minutes of the last meeting of the Praesidium of the East German Communist Party, the SED. By an odd coincidence there was collateral from another source; the photographs were genuine.

Leamas took the case over then. He was badly in need of a success. He'd produced virtually nothing since arriving in Berlin, and he was getting past the usual age limit for full time operational work. Exactly a week later he took de Jong's car to the same place and went for a walk.

It was a desolate spot that de Jong had chosen for his picnic: a strip of canal with a couple of shell-torn pillboxes, some parched, sandy fields and on the Eastern side a sparse pine wood, lying about two hundred yards from the gravel road which bordered the canal. But it had the virtue of solitude – something that was hard to find in Berlin – and surveillance was impossible. Leamas walked in the woods. He made no attempt to watch the car because he did not know from which direction the approach might be made. If he was seen watching the car from the woods, the chances of retaining his informant's confidence were ruined.

He need not have worried.

When he returned there was nothing in the car so he drove back to West Berlin, kicking himself for being a damned fool; the Praesidium was not due to meet for another fornight. Three weeks later he borrowed de Jong's car and took a thousand dollars in twenties in a picnic case. He left the car unlocked for two hours and when he returned there was a tobacco tin in the glove compartment. The picnic case had gone.

The films were packed with first grade documentary stuff. In the next six weeks he did it twice more, and the same thing happened.

Leamas knew he had hit a gold mine. He gave the source the cover name of 'Mayfair' and sent a pessimistic letter to London. Leamas knew that if he gave London half an opening they would control the case direct, which he was desperately anxious to avoid. This was probably the only kind of operation which could save him from superannuation, and it was just the kind of thing that was big enough for London to want to take over for itself. Even if he kept them at arm's length there was still the danger that the Circus would have theories, make suggestions, urge caution, demand action. They would want him to give only new dollar bills in the hope of tracing them, they would want the film cartridges sent home for examination, they would plan clumsy tailing operations and tell the Departments. Most of all they would want to tell the Departments; and that, said Leamas, would blow the thing sky-high. He worked like a madman for three weeks. He combed the personality files of each member of the Praesidium. He drew up a list of all the clerical staff who might have had access to the minutes. From the distribution list on the last page of the facsimiles he extended the total of possible informants to thirty-one, including clerks and secretarial staff.

Confronted with the almost impossible task of identifying an informant from the incomplete records of thirty-one candidates, Leamas returned to the original material, which, he said, was something he should have done earlier. It puzzled him that in none of the photostat minutes he had so far received were the pages numbered, that none was stamped with a security classification, and that in the second and fourth copy words were crossed out in pencil or crayon. He came finally to an important conclusion: that the photocopies related not to the minutes themselves, but to the *draft* minutes. This placed the source in the Secretariat and the Secretariat was very small. The draft minutes had been well and carefully photographed: that suggested that the photographer had had time and a room to himself.

Leamas returned to the personality index. There was a man called Karl Riemeck in the Secretariat, a former corporal in the Medical

Corps, who had served three years as a prisoner of war in England. His sister had been living in Pomerania when the Russians overran it, and he had never heard of her since. He was married and had one daughter named Carla.

Leamas decided to take a chance. He found out from London Riemeck's prisoner of war number, which was 29012, and the date of his release which was November 10th, 1945. He bought an East German children's book of science fiction and wrote in the fly leaf in German in an adolescent hand: 'This book belongs to Carla Riemeck, born December 10th, 1945, in Bideford, North Devon. Signed Moonspace-woman 29012', and underneath, he added, 'Applicants wishing to make space flights should present themselves for instruction to C. Riemeck in person. An application form is enclosed. Long live the Peoples' Republic of Democratic Space!'

He ruled some lines on a sheet of writing paper, made columns for name, address and age, and wrote at the bottom of the page:

'Each candidate will be interviewed personally. Write to the usual address stating when and where you wish to be met. Applications will be considered in seven days. C.R.'

He put the sheet of paper inside the book. Leamas drove to the usual place, still in de Jong's car, and left the book on the passenger seat with five used one hundred dollar bills inside the cover. When Leamas returned the book had gone, and there was a tobacco tin on the seat instead. It contained three rolls of film. Leamas developed them that night: one film contained as usual the minutes of the Praesidium's last meeting; the second showed a draft revision of the East Germans' relationship to COMECON and the third a breakdown of the East German Intelligence Service, complete with functions of departments and details of personalities.

Peters interrupted: 'Just a minute,' he said. 'Do you mean to say all this intelligence came from Riemeck?'

'Why not? You know how much he saw.'

'It's scarcely possible,' Peters observed, almost to himself; 'he must have had help.'

'He did have later on; I'm coming to that.'

'I know what you are going to tell me. But did you never have the feeling he got assistance from *above* as well as from the agents he afterwards acquired?'

'No. No, I never did. It never occurred to me.'

'Looking back on it now, does it seem likely?'

'Not particularly.'

'When you sent all this material back to the Circus, they never suggested that even for a man in Riemeck's position, the intelligence was phenomenally comprehensive?'

'No.'

'Did they ever ask where Riemeck got his camera from, who instructed him in document photography?'

Leamas hesitated.

'No . . . I'm sure they never asked.'

'Remarkable,' Peters observed drily. 'I'm sorry – do go on. I did not mean to anticipate you.'

Exactly a week later, Leamas continued, he drove to the canal and this time he felt nervous. As he turned into the unmade road he saw three bicycles lying in the grass and two hundred yards down the canal, three men fishing. He got out of the car as usual and began walking towards the line of trees on the other side of the field. He had gone about twenty yards when he heard a shout. He looked round and caught sight of one of the men beckoning to him. The other two had turned and were looking at him too. Leamas was wearing an old macintosh; he had his hands in the pockets, and it was too late to take them out. He knew that the men on either side were covering the man in the middle and that if he took his hands out of his pockets they would probably shoot him; they would think he was holding a revolver in his pocket. Leamas stopped ten yards from the centre man.

'You want something?' Leamas asked.

'Are you Leamas?' He was a small, plump man, very steady. He spoke English.

'Yes.'

'What is your British national identity number?'

'PRT stroke L 58003 stroke one.'

'Where did you spend VJ night?'

'At Leiden in Holland in my father's workshop, with some Dutch friends.'

'Let's go for a walk, Mr. Leamas. You won't need your macintosh. Take it off and leave it on the ground where you are standing. My friends will look after it.'

Leamas hesitated, shrugged and took off his macintosh. Then they walked together briskly towards the wood.

'You know as well as I do who he was,' said Leamas wearily, 'third man in the Ministry of the Interior, Secretary to the SED Praesidium, head of the Co-ordinating Committee for the Protection of the People. I suppose that was how he knew about de Jong and me: he'd seen our counter intelligence files in the Abteilung. He had three strings to his bow: the Praesidium, straightforward internal political and economic reporting and access to the files of the East German Security Service.'

'But only *limited* access. They'd never give an outsider the run of all their files,' Peters insisted.

Leamas shrugged.

'They did,' he said.

'What did he do with his money?'

'After that afternoon I didn't give him any. The Circus took that over straight away. It was paid into a West German bank. He even gave me back what I'd given him. London banked it for him.'

'How much did you tell London?'

'Everything after that. I had to; then the Circus told the Departments. After that,' Leamas added venomously, 'it was only a matter of time before it packed up. With the Departments at their backs, London got greedy. They began pressing us for more, wanted to give him more money. Finally we had to suggest to Karl that he recruited other sources and we took them on to form a network. It was bloody stupid, it put a strain on Karl, endangered him, undermined his confidence in us. It was the beginning of the end.'

'How much did you get out of him?'

Leamas hesitated.

'How much? Christ, I don't know. It lasted an unnaturally long time. I think he was blown long before he was caught. The standard dropped in the last few months; think they'd begun to suspect him by then and kept him away from the good stuff.'

'Altogether, what did he give you?' Peters persisted.

Piece by piece, Leamas recounted the full extent of all Karl Riemeck's work. His memory was, Peters noted approvingly, remarkably precise considering the amount he drank. He could give dates and names, he could remember the reaction from London, the nature of corroboration where it existed. He could remember sums of money demanded and paid, the dates of the conscription of other agents into the network.

'I'm sorry,' said Peters at last, 'but I do not believe that one man, however well placed, however careful, however industrious, could have acquired such a range of detailed knowledge. For that matter, even if he had he would never have been able to photograph it.'

'He *was* able,' Leamas persisted, suddenly angry, 'he bloody well did and that's all there is to it.'

'And the Circus never told you to go into it with him, exactly how and when he saw all this stuff.'

'No,' snapped Leamas, 'Riemeck was touchy about that, and London was content to let it go.'

'Well, well,' Peters mused.

After a moment Peters said: 'You heard about that woman, incidentally?'

'What woman?' Leamas asked sharply.

'Karl Riemeck's mistress, the one who came over to West Berlin the night Riemeck was shot.'

'Well?'

'She was found dead a week ago. Murdered. She was shot from a car as she left her flat.'

'It used to be my flat,' said Leamas mechanically.

'Perhaps,' Peters suggested, 'she knew more about Riemeck's network than you did.'

'What the hell do you mean?' Leamas demanded.

Peters shrugged.

'It's all very strange,' he observed. 'I wonder who killed her.'

When they had exhausted the case of Karl Riemeck, Leamas went on to talk of other less spectacular agents, then of the procedure of his Berlin office, its communications, its staff, its secret ramifications – flats, transport, recording and photographic equipment. They talked long into the night and throughout the next day and when at last Leamas stumbled into bed the following night he knew he had betrayed all that he knew of Allied Intelligence in Berlin, and drunk two bottles of whisky in two days.

One thing puzzled him: Peters' insistence that Karl Riemeck must have had help – must have had a high-level collaborator. Control had asked him the same question – he remembered now – Control had asked about Riemeck's access. How could they both be so sure Karl hadn't managed alone? He'd had helpers, of course; like the guards by the canal the day Leamas met him. But they were small beer – Karl had told him about them. But Peters – and Peters, after all, would know precisely how much Karl had been able to get his hands on – Peters had refused to believe Karl had managed alone. On this point, Peters and Control were evidently agreed.

Perhaps it was true. Perhaps there was somebody else. Perhaps this was the Special Interest whom Control was so anxious to protect from Mundt. That would mean that Karl Riemeck had collaborated with this special interest and provided what both of them had together obtained. Perhaps that was what Control had spoken to Karl about, alone, that evening in Leamas' flat in Berlin.

Anyway, tomorrow would tell. Tomorrow he would play his hand.

He wondered who had killed Elvira. And he wondered *why* they had killed her. Of course – here was a point, here was a possible explanation – Elvira, knowing the identity of Riemeck's special collaborator, had been murdered *by* that collaborator. . . . No, that was too far-fetched. It overlooked the difficulty of crossing from East to West: Elvira had after all been murdered in West Berlin.

He wondered why Control had never told him Elvira had been murdered. So that he would react suitably when Peters told him? It was useless speculating. Control had his reasons; they were usually so bloody tortuous it took you a week to work them out.

As he fell asleep he muttered, 'Karl was a damn' fool. That woman did for him, I'm sure she did.' Elvira was dead now, and serve her right. He remembered Liz.

CHAPTER 9

THE SECOND DAY

Peters arrived at eight o'clock the next morning, and without ceremony they sat down at the table and began.

'So you came back to London. What did you do there?'

'They put me on the shelf. I knew I was finished when that ass in Personnel met me at the airport. I had to go straight to Control and report about Karl. He was dead – what else was there to say?'

'What did they do with you?'

'They said at first I could hang around in London and wait till I was qualified for a proper pension. They were so bloody decent about it I got angry – I told them that if they were so keen to chuck money at me why didn't they do the obvious thing and count in all my time instead of bleating about broken service. Then they got cross when I told them that. They put me in Banking with a lot of women. I can't remember much about that part – I began hitting the bottle a bit. Had rather a bad patch.'

He lit a cigarette. Peters nodded.

'That was why they gave me the push, really. They didn't like me drinking.'

'Tell me what you *do* remember about Banking Section,' Peters suggested.

'It was a dreary set-up. I never was cut out for desk work, I knew that. That's why I hung on in Berlin. I knew when they recalled me I'd be put on the shelf, but, Christ . . .!'

'What did you do?'

Leamas shrugged.

'Sat on my behind in the same room as a couple of women. Thursby and Larrett. I called them Thursday and Friday.' He grinned rather stupidly. Peters looked uncomprehending.

'We just pushed paper. A letter came down from Finance: 'the payment of seven hundred dollars to so and so is authorised with effect from so and so. Kindly get on with it' – that was the gist of it. Thursday and Friday would kick it about a bit, file it, stamp it and I'd sign a cheque or get the bank to make a transfer.'

'What bank?'

'Blatt and Rodney, a chichi little bank in the City. There's a sort of theory in the Circus that Etonians are discreet.'

'In fact, then, you knew the names of agents all over the world?'

'Not necessarily. That was the cunning thing. I'd sign the cheque, you see, or the order to the bank, but we'd leave a space for the name of the payee. The covering letter or what have you was all signed and then the file would go *back* to Special Despatch.'

'Who are they?'

'They're the general holders of agents' particulars. They put in the names and posted the order. Bloody clever, I must say.'

Peters looked disappointed.

'You mean you had no way of knowing the names of the payees?'

'Not usually, no.'

'But occasionally?'

'We got pretty near the knuckle now and again. All the fiddling about between Banking, Finance and Special Despatch led to cock-ups, of course. Too elaborate. Then occasionally we came in on special stuff which brightened one's life a bit.'

Leamas got up. 'I've made a list,' he said, 'of all the payments I can remember. It's in my room. I'll get it.'

He walked out of the room, the rather shuffling walk he had affected since arriving in Holland. When he returned he held in his hand a couple of sheets of lined paper torn from a cheap notebook.

'I wrote these down last night,' he said; 'I thought it would save time.'

Peters took the notes and read them slowly and carefully. He seemed impressed.

'Good,' he said, 'very good.'

'Then I remember best a thing called Rolling Stone. I got a couple of trips out of it. One to Copenhagen and one to Helsinki. Just dumping money at banks.'

'How much?'

'Ten thousand dollars in Copenhagen, forty thousand D-Marks in Helsinki.'

Peters put down his pencil.

'Who for?' he asked.

'God knows. We worked Rolling Stone on a system of deposit accounts. The Service gave me a phoney British passport; I went to the Royal Scandinavian Bank in Copenhagen and the National Bank of Finland in Helsinki, deposited the money and drew a pass book on a joint account – for me in my alias and for someone else – the agent, I suppose, in his alias. I gave the banks a sample of the co-holder's signature. I'd got that from Head Office. Later the agent was given the pass book and a false passport which he showed at the bank when he drew the money. All I knew was the alias.' He heard himself talking and it all sounded so ludicrously improbable.

'Was this procedure common?'

'No. It was a special payment. It had a subscription list.'

'What's that?'

'It had a code name known to very few people.'

'What was the code name?'

'I told you – Rolling Stone. The operation covered irregular payments of ten thousand dollars in different currencies and in different capitals.'

'Always in capital towns?'

'Far as I know. I remember reading in the file that there had been other Rolling Stone payments before I came to the section, but in those cases Banking Section got the local Resident to do it.'

'These other payments that took place before you came: where were they made?'

'One in Oslo. I can't remember where the other was.'

'Was the alias of the agent always the same?'

'No. That was an added security precaution. I heard later we pinched the whole technique from the Russians. It was the most elaborate payment scheme I'd met. In the same way I used a different alias and of course a different passport for each trip.' That would please him; help him to fill in the gaps.

'These faked passports the agent was given so that he could draw the money: did you know anything about them: how they were made out and despatched?'

'No. Oh, except that they had to have visas in them for the country where the money was deposited. And entry stamps.'

'*Entry stamps?*'

'Yes. I assumed the passports were never used at the border – only presented at the bank for identification purposes. The agent must have travelled on his own passport, quite legally entered the country where the bank was situated, then used the faked passport at the bank. That was my guess.'

'Do you know of a reason why earlier payments were made by the Residents, and later payments by someone travelling out from London?'

'I know the reason. I asked the women in Banking Section, Thursday and Friday. Control was anxious that——'

'*Control?* Do you mean to say Control himself was running the case?'

'Yes, he was running it. He was afraid the Resident might be recognised at the bank. So he used a postman: me.'

'When did you make your journeys?'

'Copenhagen on the fifteenth of June. I flew back the same night. Helsinki at the end of September. I stayed two nights there, flew back around the twenty-eighth. I had a bit of fun in Helsinki.' He grinned but Peters took no notice.

'And the other payments – when were they made?'

'I can't remember. Sorry.'

'But one was definitely in Oslo?'

'Yes, in Oslo.'

'How much time separated the first two payments, the payments made by the Residents?'

'I don't know. Not long, I think. Maybe a month. A bit more perhaps.'

'Was it your impression that the agent had been operating for some time before the first payment was made? Did the file show that?'

'No idea. The file simply covered actual payments. First payments early '59. There was no other data on it. That is the principle that operates where you have a limited subscription. Different files handle different bits of a single case. Only someone with the master file would be able to put it all together.'

Peters was writing all the time now. Leamas assumed there was a tape recorder hidden somewhere in the room but the subsequent transcription would take time. What Peters wrote down now would provide the background for this evening's telegram to Moscow, while in the Soviet Embassy in The Hague the girls would sit up all night telegraphing the verbatim transcript on hourly schedules.

'Tell me,' said Peters; 'these are large sums of money. The arrangements for paying them were elaborate and very expensive. What did you make of it yourself?'

Leamas shrugged.

'What could I make of it? I thought Control must have a bloody good source, but I never saw the material so I don't know. I didn't like the way it was done – it was too high-powered, too complicated, too clever. Why couldn't they just meet him and give him the money in cash? Did they really let him cross borders on his own passport with a forged one in his pocket? I doubt it,' said Leamas. It was time he clouded the issue, let him chase a hare.

'What do you mean?'

'I mean, that for all I know the money was never drawn from the bank. Supposing he was a highly placed agent behind the Curtain – the money would be on deposit for him when he could get at it. That was what I reckoned anyway. I didn't think about it all that much. Why should I? It's part of our work only to know pieces of the whole set-up. You know that. If you're curious, God help you.'

'If the money wasn't collected, as you suggest, why all the trouble with passports?'

'When I was in Berlin we made an arrangement for Karl Riemeck in case he ever needed to run and couldn't get hold of us. We kept a bogus West German passport for him at an address in Düsseldorf. He could collect it any time by following a pre-arranged procedure. It never expired – Special Travel renewed the passport and the visas as they expired. Control might have followed the same technique with this man. I don't know – it's only a guess.'

'How do you know for certain that passports were issued?'

'There were minutes on the file between Banking section and Special Travel. Special Travel is the section which arranged false identity papers and visas.'

'I see.' Peters thought for a moment and then he asked: 'What names did you use in Copenhagen and Helsinki?'

'Robert Lang, electrical engineer from Derby. That was in Copenhagen.'

'When exactly were you in Copenhagen?' Peters asked.

'I told you, June the fifteenth. I got there in the morning at about eleven-thirty.'

'Which bank did you use?'

'Oh, for Christ's sake, Peters,' said Leamas, suddenly angry, 'the Royal Scandinavian. You've got it written down.'

'I just wanted to be sure,' the other replied evenly, and continued writing. 'And for Helsinki, what name?'

'Stephen Bennett, marine engineer from Plymouth. I was there,' he added sarcastically, 'at the end of September.'

'You visited the bank on the day you arrived?'

'Yes. It was the 24th or 25th, I can't be sure, as I told you.'

'Did you take the money with you from England?'

'Of course not. We just transferred it to the Resident's account in each case. The Resident drew it, met me at the airport with the money in a suitcase and I took it to the bank.'

'Who's the Resident in Copenhagen?'

'Peter Jensen, a bookseller in the University bookshop.'

'And what were the names which would be used by the agent?'

'Horst Karlsdorf in Copenhagen. I think that was it, yes it was, I remember. Karlsdorf. I kept on wanting to say Karlshorst.'

'Description?'

'Manager, from Klagenfurt in Austria.'

'And the other? The Helsinki name?'

'Fechtmann. Adolf Fechtmann from St. Gallen, Switzerland. He had a title – yes, that's right: Doctor Fechtmann, archivist.'

'I see; both German-speaking?'

'Yes, I noticed that. But it can't be a German.'

'Why not?'

'I was head of the Berlin set-up, wasn't I? I'd have been in on it. A high-level agent in East Germany would have to be run from Berlin. I'd have known.' Leamas got up, went to the sideboard and poured himself some whisky. He didn't bother about Peters.

'You said yourself there were special precautions, special procedures in this case. Perhaps they didn't think you needed to know.'

'Don't be bloody silly,' Leamas rejoined shortly; 'of course I'd have known.' This was the point he would stick to through thick and thin; it made them feel they knew better, gave credence to the rest of his information. 'They will want to deduce *in spite of you*,' Control had said. 'We must give them the material and remain sceptical to their conclusions. Rely on their intelligence and conceit, on their suspicion of one another – that's what we must do.'

Peters nodded as if he were confirming a melancholy truth. 'You are a very proud man, Leamas,' he observed once more.

Peters left soon after that. He wished Leamas good day and walked down the road along the sea-front. It was lunchtime.

CHAPTER 10

THE THIRD DAY

Peters didn't appear that afternoon, nor the next morning. Leamas stayed in, waiting with growing irritation for some message, but none came. He asked the housekeeper but she just smiled and shrugged her heavy shoulders. At about eleven o'clock the next morning he decided to go out for a walk along the front, bought some cigarettes and stared dully at the sea.

There was a girl standing on the beach throwing bread to the seagulls. Her back was turned to him. The sea wind played with her long black hair and pulled at her coat, making an arc of her body, like a bow strung towards the sea. He knew what it was then that Liz had given him; the thing that he would have to go back and find if ever he got home to England: it was the caring about little things – the faith in ordinary life; that simplicity that made you break up a bit of bread into a paper bag, walk down to the beach and throw it to the gulls. It was this respect for triviality which he had never been allowed to possess; whether it was bread for the seagulls or love, whatever it was he would go back and find it; he would make Liz find it for him. A week, two weeks perhaps, and he would be home. Control had said he could keep whatever they paid – and that would be enough. With fifteen thousand pounds, a gratuity and a pension from the Circus, a man – as Control would say – can afford to come in from the cold.

He made a detour and returned to the bungalow at a quarter to twelve. The woman let him in without a word, but when he had gone into the back room he heard her lift the receiver and dial a telephone number. She only spoke for a few seconds. At half past twelve she brought him lunch, and, to his pleasure, some English newspapers, which he read contentedly until three o'clock. Leamas who normally read nothing, read newspapers slowly and with concentration. He remembered details, like the names and addresses of people who were the subject of small news items. He did it almost unconsciously as a kind of private pelmanism, and it absorbed him entirely.

At three o'clock Peters arrived, and as soon as Leamas saw him he knew that something was up. They did not sit at the table; Peters did not take off his macintosh.

'I've got bad news for you,' he said, 'they're looking for you in England. I heard this morning. They're watching the ports.'

Leamas replied impassively: 'On what charge?'

'Nominally for failing to report to a police station within the statutory period after release from prison.'

'And in fact?'

'The word is going around that you're wanted for an offence under the Official Secrets Act. Your photograph's in all the London evening papers. The captions are very vague.'

Leamas was standing very still.

Control had done it. Control had started the hue and cry. There was no other explanation. If Ashe or Kiever had been pulled in, if they had talked – even then, the responsibility for the hue and cry was still Control's. 'A couple of weeks,' he'd said; 'I expect they'll take you off somewhere for the interrogation – it may even be abroad. A couple of weeks should see you through, though. After that, the thing should run itself. You'll have to lie low over here while the chemistry works itself out; but you won't mind that I'm sure. I've agreed to keep you on operational subsistence until Mundt is eliminated: that seemed the fairest way.'

And now this.

This wasn't part of the bargain; this was different. What the hell was he supposed to do? By pulling out now, by refusing to go along with Peters, he was wrecking the operation. It was just possible that Peters was lying, that this was the test – all the more reason that he should agree to go. But if he went, if he agreed to go east, to Poland, Czechoslovakia or God knows where, there was no good reason why they should ever let him out – there was no good reason (since he was notionally a wanted man in the West) why he should *want* to be let out.

Control had done it – he was sure. The terms had been too generous, he'd known that all along. They didn't throw money about like that for nothing – not unless they thought they might lose you. Money like that was a *douceur* for discomfort and dangers Control would not openly admit to. Money like that was a warning; Leamas had not heeded the warning.

'Now how the devil,' he asked quietly, 'could they get on to that?' A thought seemed to cross his mind and he said, 'Your friend Ashe could have told them, of course, or Kiever. . . .'

'It's possible,' Peters replied. 'You know as well as I do that such things are always possible. There is no certainty in our job. The fact is,' he added with something like impatience, 'that by now every country in Western Europe will be looking for you.'

Leamas might not have heard what Peters was saying. 'You've got me on the hook now, haven't you, Peters?' he said. 'Your people must be laughing themselves sick. Or did they give the tip off themselves?'

'You overrate your own importance,' Peters said sourly.

'Then why do you have me followed, tell me that? I went for a walk this morning. Two little men in brown suits, one twenty yards behind the other, trailed me along the sea front. When I came back the housekeeper rang you up.'

'Let us stick to what we know,' Peters suggested. 'How your own authorities have got on to you does not at the moment acutely concern us. The fact is, they have.'

'Have you brought the London evening papers with you?'

'Of course not. They are not available here. We received a telegram from London.'

'That's a lie. You know perfectly well your apparatus is only allowed to communicate with Centre.'

'In this case a direct link between two outstations was permitted,' Peters retorted angrily.

'Well, well,' said Leamas with a dry smile, 'you must be quite a big wheel. Or' – a thought seemed to strike him – 'isn't Centre in on this?'

Peters ignored the question.

'You know the alternative. You let us take care of you, let us arrange your safe passage, or you fend for yourself – with the certainty of eventual capture. You've no false papers, no money, nothing. Your British passport will have expired in ten days.'

'There's a third possibility. Give me a Swiss passport and some money and let me run. I can look after myself.'

'I am afraid that is not considered desirable.'

'You mean you haven't finished the interrogation. Until you have I am not expendable?'

'That is roughly the position.'

'When you have completed the interrogation, what will you do with me?'

Peters shrugged. 'What do you suggest?'

'A new identity. Scandinavian passport perhaps. Money.'

'It's very academic,' Peters replied, 'but I will suggest it to my superiors. Are you coming with me?' Leamas hesitated then he smiled a little uncertainly and asked:

'If I didn't, what would you do? After all I've quite a story to tell, haven't I?'

'Stories of that kind are hard to substantiate. I shall be gone tonight. Ashe and Kiever . . .' he shrugged, 'what do they add up to?'

Leamas went to the window. A storm was gathering over the grey North Sea. He watched the gulls wheeling against the dark clouds. The girl had gone.

'All right,' he said at last, 'fix it up.'

'There's no plane East until tomorrow. There's a flight to Berlin in an hour. We shall take that. It's going to be very close.'

Leamas' passive role that evening enabled him once again to admire the unadorned efficiency of Peters' arrangements. The passport had been put together long ago – Centre must have thought of that. It was made out in the name of Alexander Thwaite, travel agent, and filled with visas and frontier stamps – the old, well-gingered passport of the professional traveller. The Dutch frontier guard at the airport just nodded and stamped it for form's sake – Peters was three or four behind him in the queue and took no interest in the formalities.

As they entered the 'passengers only' enclosure Leamas caught sight of a bookstall. A selection of international newspapers was on show: *Figaro, Monde, Neue Zürcher Zeitung, die Welt* and half a dozen British dailies and weeklies. As he watched, the girl came round to the front of the kiosk and pushed an *Evening Standard* into the rack. Leamas hurried across to the bookstall and took the paper from the rack.

'How much?' he asked. Thrusting his hand into his trouser pocket he suddenly realised that he had no Dutch currency.

'Thirty cents,' the girl replied. She was rather pretty; dark and jolly.

'I've only got two English shillings. That's a guilder. Will you take them?'

'Yes, please,' she replied, and Leamas gave her the florin. He looked back; Peters was still at the passport desk, his back turned to Leamas. Without hesitation he made straight for the men's lavatory. There he glanced rapidly but thoroughly at each page, then shoved the paper in the little basket and re-emerged. It was true: there was his photograph with the vague little passage underneath. He wondered if Liz had seen it. He made his way thoughtfully to the passengers' lounge. Ten minutes later they boarded the plane for Hamburg and Berlin. For the first time since it all began, Leamas was frightened.

CHAPTER 11

FRIENDS OF ALEC

The men called on Liz the same evening.

Liz Gold's room was at the northern end of Bayswater. It had two single beds in it, and a gas fire, rather a pretty one in charcoal grey, which made a modern hiss instead of an old fashioned bubble. She used to gaze into it sometimes when Leamas was there, when the gas fire shed the only light in the room. He would lie on the bed, hers, the one furthest from the door, and she would sit beside him and kiss him, or watch the gas fire with her face pressed against his. She was afraid to think of him too much now because then she forgot what he looked like, so she let her mind think of him for brief moments like running her eyes across a faint horizon, and then she would remember some small thing he had said or done, some way he had looked at her, or, more often, ignored her. That was the terrible thing, when her mind dwelled on it: she had nothing to remember him by – no photograph, no souvenir, nothing. Not even a mutual friend – only Miss Crail in the library, whose hatred of him had been vindicated by his spectacular departure. Liz had been round to his room once and seen the landlord. She didn't know why she did it quite, but she plucked up courage and went. The landlord was very kind about Alec; Mr. Leamas had paid his rent like a gentleman, right till the end, then there'd been a week or two owing and a chum of Mr. Leamas had dropped in and paid up handsome, no queries or nothing. He'd always said it of Mr. Leamas, always would, he was a gent. Not public school, mind, nothing arsy-tarsy but a real gent. He liked to scowl a bit occasionally, and of course he drank a drop more than was good for him, though he never acted tight when he came home. But this little bloke who come round, funny little shy chap with specs, *he* said Mr. Leamas had particularly requested, quite particularly, that the rent owing should be settled up. And if that wasn't gentlemanly the landlord was damned if he knew what was. Where he got the money from Heaven knows, but that Mr. Leamas was a deep one and no mistake. He only did to Ford the grocer what a good many had been wanting to do ever since the war. The room? Yes, the room had been taken – a gentleman from Korea, two days after they took Mr. Leamas away.

That was probably why she went on working at the library – because there, at least, he still existed; the ladders, shelves, the books, the card

index, were things he had known and touched, and one day he might
come back to them. He had said he would never come back, but she
didn't believe it. It was like saying you would never get better, to believe
a thing like that. Miss Crail thought he would come back: she had
discovered she owed him some money – wages underpaid – and it
infuriated her that her monster had been so unmonstrous as not to
collect it. After Leamas had gone, Liz had never given up asking herself
the same question; why did he hit Mr. Ford? She knew he had a terrible
temper, but that was different. He had intended to do it right from the
start as soon as he had got rid of his fever. Why else had he said good-bye
to her the night before? He knew that he would hit Mr. Ford on the
following day. She refused to accept the only other possible in-
terpretation: that he had grown tired of her and said good-bye, and the
next day, still under the emotional strain of their parting, had lost his
temper with Mr. Ford and struck him. She knew, she had always
known, that there was something Alec had got to do. He'd even told her
that himself. What it was she could only guess.

First, she thought he had a quarrel with Mr. Ford, some deep-rooted
hatred going back for years. Something to do with a girl, or Alec's family
perhaps. But you only had to look at Mr. Ford and it seemed ridiculous.
He was the archetypal *petit-bourgeois*, cautious, complacent, mean. And
anyway, if Alec had a vendetta on with Mr. Ford, why did he go for him
in the shop on a Saturday, in the middle of the weekend shopping rush,
when everyone could see?

They'd talked about it in the meeting of her party branch. George
Hanby, the branch treasurer, had actually been passing Ford the
grocer's as it happened, he hadn't seen much because of the crowd, but
he'd talked to a bloke who'd seen the whole thing. Hanby had been so
impressed that he'd rung the *Worker*, and they'd sent a man to the trial –
that was why the *Worker* had given it a middle page spread as a matter of
fact. It was just a straight case of protest – of sudden social awareness and
hatred against the boss class, as the *Worker* said. This bloke that Hanby
spoke to (he was just a little ordinary chap with specs, white collar type)
said it had been so sudden – spontaneous was what he meant – and it just
proved to Hanby once again how incendiary was the fabric of the
capitalist system. Liz had kept very quiet while Hanby talked: none of
them knew, of course, about her and Leamas. She realised then that she
hated George Hanby; he was a pompous, dirty-minded little man,
always leering at her and trying to touch her.

Then the men called.

She thought they were a little too smart for policemen: they came in a small black car with an aerial on it. One was short and rather plump. He had glasses and wore odd, expensive clothes; he was a kindly, worried little man and Liz trusted him somehow without knowing why. The other was smoother, but not glossy – rather a boyish figure, although she guessed he wasn't less than forty. They said they came from Special Branch, and they had printed cards with photographs in cellophane cases. The plump one did most of the talking.

'I believe you were friendly with Alec Leamas,' he began. She was prepared to be angry, but the plump man was so earnest that it seemed silly.

'Yes,' Liz answered. 'How did you know?'

'We found out quite by chance the other day. When you go to . . . prison, you have to give next of kin. Leamas said he hadn't any. That was a lie as a matter of fact. They asked him whom they should inform if anything happened to him in prison. He said you.'

'I see.'

'Does anyone else know you were friendly with him?'

'No.'

'Did you go to the trial?'

'No.'

'No press men called, creditors, no one at all?'

'No, I've told you. No one else knew. Not even my parents, no one. We worked together in the library, of course – the Psychical Research Library – but only Miss Crail, the librarian, would know that. I don't think it occurred to her that there was anything between us. She's queer,' Liz added simply.

The little man peered very seriously at her for a moment, then he asked:

'Did it surprise you when Leamas beat up Mr. Ford?'

'Yes, of course.'

'Why did you think he did it?'

'I don't know. Because Ford wouldn't give him credit, I suppose. But I think he always meant to.' She wondered if she was saying too much, but she longed to talk to somebody about it, she was so alone and there didn't seem any harm.

'But that night, the night before it happened, we talked together. We had supper, a sort of special one; Alec said we should and I knew that it was our last night. He'd got a bottle of red wine from somewhere; I didn't like it much. Alec drank most of it. And then I asked him, 'Is this good-bye?' – whether it was all over.'

'What did he say?'

'He said there was a job he'd got to do. I didn't really understand it all, not really.'

There was a very long silence and the little man looked more worried than ever. Finally he asked her:

'Do you believe that?'

'I don't know.' She was suddenly terrified for Alec, and she didn't know why. The man asked:

'Leamas has got two children by his marriage, did he tell you?' Liz said nothing. 'In spite of that he gave your name as next of kin. Why do you think he did that?' The little man seemed embarrassed by his own question. He was looking at his hands, which were pudgy and clasped together on his lap. Liz blushed.

'I was in love with him,' she replied.

'Was he in love with you?'

'Perhaps. I don't know.'

'Are you still in love with him?'

'Yes.'

'Did he ever say he would come back?' asked the younger man.

'No.'

'But he did say good-bye to you?' the other asked quickly.

'Did he say good-bye to you?' The little man repeated his question slowly, kindly. 'Nothing more can happen to him, I promise you. But we want to help him, and if you have any idea of why he hit Ford, if you have the slightest notion from something he said, perhaps casually, or something he did, then tell us for Alec's sake.'

Liz shook her head.

'Please go,' she said, 'please don't ask any more questions. Please go now.'

As he got to the door, the elder man hesitated, then took a card from his wallet and put it on the table, gingerly, as if it might make a noise. Liz thought he was a very shy little man.

'If you ever want any help – if anything happens about Leamas or . . . ring me up,' he said. 'Do you understand?'

'Who are you?'

'I'm a friend of Alec Leamas.' He hesitated. 'Another thing,' he added, 'one last question. Did Alec know you were . . . did Alec know about the Party?'

'Yes,' she replied, hopelessly, 'I told him.'

'Does the Party know about you and Alec?'

'I've told you. No one knew.' Then, white-faced, she cried out suddenly, 'Where is he; tell me where he is. Why won't you tell me where he is? I can help him, don't you see; I'll look after him . . . I wrote to him in prison; I shouldn't have done, I know. I just said he could come back any time. I'd wait for him always. . . .' She couldn't speak any more, just sobbed and sobbed, standing there in the middle of the room, her broken face buried in her hands; the little man watching her.

'He's gone abroad,' he said gently. 'We don't quite know where he is. He isn't mad, but he shouldn't have said all that to you. It was a pity.'

The younger man said:

'We'll see you're looked after. For money and that kind of thing.'

'Who are you?' Liz asked again.

'Friends of Alec,' the young man repeated; 'good friends.'

She heard them go quietly down the stairs and into the street. From her window she watched them get into a small black car and drive away in the direction of the park.

Then she remembered the card. Going to the table she picked it up and held it to the light. It was expensively done, more than a policeman could afford, she thought. Engraved. No rank in front of the name, no police station or anything. Just the name with 'Mister' – and whoever heard of a policeman living in Chelsea?

'Mr. George Smiley. 9 Bywater Street, Chelsea.' Then the telephone number underneath.

It was very strange.

CHAPTER 12

EAST

Leamas unfastened his seat-belt.

It is said that men condemned to death are subject to sudden moments of elation; as if, like moths in the fire, their destruction were coincidental with attainment. Following directly upon his decision, Leamas was aware of a comparable sensation; relief, short-lived but consoling, sustained him for a time. It was followed by fear and hunger.

He was slowing down. Control was right.

He'd noticed it first during the Riemeck case, early last year. Karl had sent a message: he'd got something special for him and was making one of his rare visits to Western Germany; some legal conference at Karlsruhe. Leamas had managed to get an air passage to Cologne, and picked up a car at the airport. It was still quite early in the morning and he'd hoped to miss most of the autobahn traffic to Karlsruhe but the heavy lorries were already on the move. He drove seventy kilometres in half an hour, weaving between the traffic, taking risks to beat the clock, when a small car, a Fiat probably, nosed its way out into the fast lane forty yards ahead of him. Leamas stamped on the brake, turning his headlights full on and sounding his horn, and by the grace of God he missed it; missed it by a fraction of a second. As he passed the car he saw out of the corner of his eye four children in the back, waving and laughing, and the stupid, frightened face of their father at the wheel. He drove on, cursing, and suddenly it happened; suddenly his hands were shaking feverishly, his face was burning hot, his heart palpitating wildly. He managed to pull off the road into a lay-by, scrambled out of the car and stood breathing heavily, staring at the hurtling stream of giant lorries. He had a vision of the little car caught among them, pounded and smashed, until there was nothing left, nothing but the frenetic whine of klaxons and the blue lights flashing; and the bodies of the children, torn, like the murdered refugees on the road across the dunes.

He drove very slowly the rest of the way and missed his meeting with Karl.

He never drove again without some corner of his memory recalling the tousled children waving to him from the back of that car, and their father grasping the wheel like a farmer at the shafts of a hand plough.

Control would call it fever.

He sat dully in his seat over the wing. There was an American woman next to him wearing high-heeled shoes in polythene wrappers. He had a momentary notion of passing her some note for the people in Berlin, but he discarded it at once. She'd think he was making a pass at her, Peters would see it. Besides, what was the point? Control knew what had happened; Control had made it happen. There was nothing to say.

He wondered what would become of him. Control hadn't talked about that – only about the technique:

'Don't give it to them all at once, make them work for it. Confuse them with detail, leave things out, go back on your tracks. Be testy, be cussed, be difficult. Drink like a fish; don't give way on ideology, they won't trust that. They want to deal with a man they've bought; they want the clash of opposites, Alec, not some half-cock convert. Above all, they want to *deduce*. The ground's prepared; we did it long ago, little things, difficult clues. You're the last stage in the treasure hunt.'

He'd had to agree to do it: you can't back out of the big fight when all the preliminary ones have been fought for you.

'One thing I can promise you: it's worth it. It's worth it for our special interest, Alec. Keep alive and we've won a great victory.'

He didn't think he could stand torture. He remembered a book by Koestler where the old revolutionary had conditioned himself for torture by holding lighted matches to his fingers. He hadn't read much but he'd read that and he remembered it.

It was nearly dark as they landed at Templehof. Leamas watched the lights of Berlin rise to meet them, felt the thud as the plane touched down, saw the Customs and immigration officials move forward out of the half light.

For a moment Leamas was anxious lest some former acquaintance should chance to recognise him at the airport. As they walked side by side, Peters and he, along the interminable corridors, through the cursory Customs and immigration check, and still no familiar face turned to greet him, he realised that his anxiety had in reality been hope; hope that somehow his tacit decision to go on would be revoked by circumstance.

It interested him that Peters no longer bothered to disown him; it was as if Peters regarded West Berlin as safe ground, where vigilance and security could be relaxed; a mere technical staging post to the East.

They were walking through the big reception hall to the main entrance when Peters suddenly seemed to alter his mind, abruptly changed direction and led Leamas to a smaller side entrance which gave on to a car park and taxi rank. There Peters hesitated a second, standing beneath the light over the door, then put his suitcase on the ground beside him, deliberately removed his newspaper from beneath his arm, folded it, pushed it into the left pocket of his raincoat and picked up his suitcase again. Immediately, from the direction of the car park, a pair of headlights sprang to life, were dipped and then extinguished.

'Come on,' said Peters and started to walk briskly across the tarmac, Leamas following more slowly. As they reached the first row of cars the rear door of a black Mercedes was opened from the inside, and the courtesy light went on. Peters, ten yards ahead of Leamas, went quickly to the car, spoke softly to the driver, then called to Leamas.

'Here's the car. Be quick.'

It was an old Mercedes 180 and he got in without a word. Peters sat beside him in the back. As they pulled out they overtook a small DKW with two men sitting in the front. Twenty yards down the road there was a telephone kiosk. A man was talking into the telephone, and he watched them go by, talking all the time. Leamas looked out of the back window and saw the DKW following them. Quite a reception, he thought.

They drove quite slowly. Leamas sat with his hands on his knees, looking straight in front of him. He didn't want to see Berlin that night. This was his last chance, he knew that. The way he was sitting now he could drive the side of his right hand into Peters' throat, smashing the promontory of the thyrax. He could get out and run, weaving to avoid the bullets from the car behind. He would be free – there were people in Berlin who would take care of him – he could get away.

He did nothing.

It was so easy crossing the sector border. Leamas had never expected it to be quite that easy. For about ten minutes they dawdled, and Leamas guessed that they had to cross at a pre-arranged time. As they approached the West German checkpoint, the DKW pulled out and overtook them with the ostentatious roar of a laboured engine, and stopped at the police hut. The Mercedes waited thirty yards behind. Two minutes later the red and white pole lifted to let through the DKW and as it did so both cars drove over together, the Mercedes engine screaming in second gear, the driver pressing himself back against his seat, holding the wheel at arms' length.

As they crossed the fifty yards which separated the two checkpoints, Leamas was dimly aware of the new fortifications on the Eastern side of the wall – dragons' teeth, observation towers and double aprons of barbed wire. Things had tightened up.

The Mercedes didn't stop at the second checkpoint; the booms were already lifted and they drove straight through, the Vopos just watching them through binoculars. The DKW had disappeared, and when Leamas sighted it ten minutes later it was behind them again. They were driving fast now – Leamas had thought they would stop in East Berlin, change cars perhaps, and congratulate one another on a successful operation, but they drove on eastwards through the city.

'Where are we going?' he asked Peters.

'We are there. The German Democratic Republic. They have arranged accommodation for you.'

'I thought we'd be going further east.'

'We are. We are spending a day or two here first. We thought the Germans ought to have a talk with you.'

'I see.'

'After all, most of your work has been on the German side. I sent them details from your statement.'

'And they asked to see me?'

'They've never had anything quite like you, nothing quite so . . . near the source. My people agreed that they should have the chance to meet you.'

'And from there? Where do we go from Germany?'

'East again.'

'Who will I see on the German side?'

'Does it matter?'

'Not particularly. I know most of the Abteilung people by name, that's all. I just wondered.'

'Who would you expect to meet?'

'Fiedler,' Leamas replied promptly, 'deputy head of security. Mundt's man. He does all the big interrogations. He's a bastard.'

'Why?'

'A savage little bastard. I've heard about him. He caught an agent of Peter Guillam's and bloody nearly killed him.'

'Espionage is not a cricket game,' Peters observed sourly and after that they sat in silence. So it is Fiedler, Leamas thought.

Leamas knew Fiedler all right. He knew him from the photographs on the file and the accounts of his former subordinates. A slim, neat man, quite young, smooth faced. Dark hair, bright brown eyes; intelligent and savage, as Leamas had said. A lithe, quick body containing a patient, retentive mind; a man seemingly without ambition for himself but remorseless in the destruction of others. Fiedler was a rarity in the Abteilung – he took no part in its intrigues, seemed content to live in Mundt's shadow without prospect of promotion. He could not be labelled as a member of this or that clique; even those who had worked close to him in the Abteilung could not say where he stood in its power complex. Fiedler was a solitary; feared, disliked and mistrusted. Whatever motives he had were concealed beneath a cloak of destructive sarcasm.

'Fiedler is our best bet,' Control had explained. They'd been sitting together over dinner – Leamas, Control and Peter Guillam – in the dreary little seven-dwarfs house in Surrey where Control lived with his beady wife, surrounded by carved Indian tables with brass tops. 'Fiedler is the acolyte who one day will stab the high priest in the back. He's the only man who's a match for Mundt' – here Guillam had nodded – 'and he hates his guts. Fiedler's a Jew of course, and Mundt is quite the other thing. Not at all a good mixture. It has been our job,' he declared, indicating Guillam and himself, 'to give Fiedler the weapon with which to destroy Mundt. It will be yours, my dear Leamas, to encourage him to use it. Indirectly, of course, because you'll never meet him. At least I certainly hope you won't.'

They'd all laughed then, Guillam too. It had seemed a good joke at the time; good by Control's standards anyway.

It must have been after midnight.

For some time they had been travelling an unmade road, partly through a wood and partly across open country. Now they stopped and a moment later the DKW drew up beside them. As he and Peters got out Leamas noticed that there were now three people in the second car. Two were already getting out. The third was sitting in the back seat looking at some papers by the light from the car roof, a slight figure half in shadow.

They had parked by some disused stables; the building lay thirty yards back. In the headlights of the car Leamas had glimpsed a low farmhouse with walls of timber and whitewashed brick. They got out. The moon was up, and shone so brightly that the wooded hills behind were sharply defined against the pale night sky. They walked to the house, Peters and Leamas leading and the two men behind. The other man in the second car had still made no attempt to move; he remained there, reading.

As they reached the door Peters stopped, waiting for the other two to catch them up. One of them carried a bunch of keys in his left hand, and while he fiddled with them the other stood off, his hands in his pockets, covering him.

'They're taking no chances,' Leamas observed to Peters, 'what do they think I am?'

'They are not paid to think,' Peters replied, and turning to one of them he asked in German:

'Is he coming?'

The German shrugged and looked back towards the car.

'He'll come,' he said; 'he likes to come alone.'

They went into the house, the man leading the way. It was got up like a hunting lodge, part old, part new. It was badly lit with pale overhead lights. The place had a neglected, musty air as if it had been opened for the occasion. There were little touches of officialdom here and there – a notice of what to do in case of fire, institutional green paint on the door and heavy spring-cartridge locks; and in the drawing-room, which was quite comfortably done, dark heavy furniture, badly scratched, and the inevitable photographs of Soviet leaders. To Leamas these lapses from anonymity signified the involuntary identification of the Abteilung with bureaucracy. That was something he was familiar with in the Circus.

Peters sat down, and Leamas did the same. For ten minutes, perhaps longer, they waited, then Peters spoke to one of the two men standing awkwardly at the other end of the room.

'Go and tell him we're waiting. And find us some food, we're hungry.' As the man moved towards the door Peters called, 'And whisky – tell them to bring whisky and some glasses.' The man gave an uncooperative shrug of his heavy shoulders and went out, leaving the door open behind him.

'Have you been here before?' asked Leamas.

'Yes,' Peters replied, 'several times.'

'What for?'

'This kind of thing. Not the same, but our kind of work.'

'With Fiedler?'

'Yes.'

'Is he good?'

Peters shrugged. 'For a Jew, he's not bad,' he replied, and Leamas, hearing a sound from the other end of the room, turned and saw Fiedler standing in the doorway. In one hand he held a bottle of whisky, and in the other, glasses and some mineral water. He couldn't have been more than five foot six. He wore a dark blue single-breasted suit; the jacket was cut too long. He was sleek and slightly animal; his eyes were brown and bright. He was not looking at them but at the guard beside the door.

'Go away,' he said. He had a slight Saxonian twang; 'Go away and tell the other one to bring us food.'

'I've told him,' Peters called; 'they know already. But they've brought nothing.'

'They are great snobs,' Fiedler observed drily in English. 'They think we should have servants for the food.'

Fiedler had spent the war in Canada. Leamas remembered that, now that he detected the accent. His parents had been German Jewish refugees, Marxists, and it was not until 1946 that the family returned home, anxious to take part, whatever the personal cost, in the construction of Stalin's Germany.

'Hello,' he added to Leamas, almost by the way, 'glad to see you.'

'Hello, Fiedler.'

'You've reached the end of the road.'

'What the hell d'you mean?' asked Leamas quickly.

'I mean that contrary to anything Peters told you, you are not going further east. Sorry.' He sounded amused.

Leamas turned to Peters.

'Is this true?' His voice was shaking with rage. 'Is it true? Tell me!'

Peters nodded: 'Yes. I am the go-between. We had to do it that way. I'm sorry,' he added.

'Why?'

'*Force majeure*,' Fiedler put in. 'Your initial interrogation took place in the West, where only an embassy could provide the kind of link we needed. The German Democratic Republic has no embassies in the West. Not yet. Our liaison section therefore arranged for us to enjoy facilities and communications and immunities which are at present denied to us.'

'You bastard,' hissed Leamas, 'you lousy bastard! You knew I wouldn't trust myself to your rotten Service; that was the reason, wasn't it? That was why you used a Russian.'

'We used the Soviet Embassy at The Hague. What else could we do? Up till then it was our operation. That's perfectly reasonable. Neither we nor anyone else could have known that your own people in England would get on to you so quickly.'

'No? Not even when you put them on to me yourselves? Isn't that what happened, Fiedler? Well, isn't it?' Always remember to dislike them, Control had said. Then they will treasure what they get out of you.

'That is an absurd suggestion,' Fiedler replied shortly. Glancing towards Peters he added something in Russian. Peters nodded and stood up.

'Good-bye,' he said to Leamas. 'Good luck.'

He smiled wearily, nodded to Fiedler, then walked to the door. He put his hand on the door handle, then turned and called to Leamas again:

'Good luck.' He seemed to want Leamas to say something, but Leamas might not have heard. He had turned very pale, he held his hands loosely across his body, the thumbs upwards as if he were going to fight. Peters remained standing at the door.

'I should have known,' said Leamas, and his voice had the odd, faulty note of a very angry man, 'I should have guessed you'd never have the guts to do your own dirty work, Fiedler. It's typical of your rotten little half-country and your squalid little Service that you get big uncle to do your pimping for you. You're not a country at all, you're not a government, you're a fifth-rate dictatorship of political neurotics.' Jabbing his finger in Fiedler's direction, he shouted:

'I know you, you sadistic bastard; it's typical of you. You were in Canada in the war, weren't you; a bloody good place to be then, wasn't it? I'll bet you stuck your fat head into Mummy's apron any time an aeroplane flew over. What are you now? A creeping little acolyte to Mundt and twenty-two Russian divisions sitting on your mother's doorstep. Well, I pity you, Fiedler, the day you wake up and find them gone. There'll be a killing then, and not Mummy or big uncle will save you from getting what you deserve.'

Fiedler shrugged.

'Regard it as a visit to the dentist, Leamas. The sooner it's all done, the sooner you can go home. Have some food and go to bed.'

'You know perfectly well I can't go home,' Leamas retorted. 'You've seen to that. You blew me sky high in England, you had to, both of you. You knew damn' well I'd never come here unless I had to.'

Fiedler looked at his thin, strong fingers.

'This is hardly the time to philosophise,' he said, 'but you can't really complain, you know. All our work – yours and mine – is rooted in the theory that the whole is more important than the individual. That is why a Communist sees his secret service as the natural extension of his arm, and that is why in your own country intelligence is shrouded in a kind of *pudeur anglaise*. The exploitation of individuals can only be justified by the collective need, can't it? I find it slightly ridiculous that you should be so indignant. We are not here to observe the ethical laws of English country life. After all,' he added silkily, 'your own behaviour has not, from the purist's point of view, been irreproachable.'

Leamas was watching Fiedler with an expression of disgust.

'I know your set-up. You're Mundt's poodle, aren't you? They say you want his job. I suppose you'll get it now. It's time the Mundt dynasty ended; perhaps this is it.'

'I don't understand,' Fiedler replied.

'I'm your big success, aren't I?' Leamas sneered. Fiedler seemed to reflect for a moment, then he shrugged and said, 'The operation was successful. Whether you were worth it is questionable. We shall see. But it was a good operation. It satisfied the only requirement of our profession: it worked.'

'I suppose you take the credit?' Leamas persisted, with a glance in the direction of Peters.

'There is no question of credit,' Fiedler replied crisply, 'none at all.' He sat down on the arm of the sofa, looked at Leamas thoughtfully for a moment and then said:

'Nevertheless you are right to be indignant about one thing. Who told your people we had picked you up? We didn't. You may not believe me, but it happens to be true. We didn't tell them. We didn't even want them to know. We had ideas then of getting you to work for us later – ideas which I now realise to be ridiculous. So who told them? You were lost, drifting around, you had no address, no ties, no friends. Then how the devil did they know you'd gone? Someone told them – scarcely Ashe or Kiever, since they are both now under arrest.'

'Under arrest?'

'So it appears. Not specifically for their work on your case, but there were other things. . . .'

'Well, well.'

'It is true, what I said just now. We would have been content with Peters' report from Holland. You could have had your money and gone. But you hadn't told us everything; and I want to know everything. After all, your presence here provides us with problems too, you know.'

'Well, you've boobed. I know damn' all – and you're welcome to it.'

There was a silence, during which Peters, with an abrupt and by no means friendly nod in Fiedler's direction, quietly let himself out of the room.

Fiedler picked up the bottle of whisky and poured a little into each glass.

'We have no soda, I'm afraid,' he said. 'Do you like water? I ordered soda, but they brought some wretched lemonade.'

'Oh, go to hell,' said Leamas. He suddenly felt very tired.

Fiedler shook his head.

'You are a very proud man,' he observed, 'but never mind. Eat your supper and go to bed.'

One of the guards came in with a tray of food – black bread, sausage and cold, green salad.

'It is a little crude,' said Fiedler, 'but quite satisfying. No potato, I'm afraid. There is a temporary shortage of potato.'

They began eating in silence, Fiedler very carefully, like a man who counted his calories.

The guards showed Leamas to his bedroom. They let him carry his own luggage – the same luggage that Kiever had given him before he left England – and he walked between them along the wide central corridor which led through the house from the front door. They came to a large double door, painted dark green, and one of the guards unlocked it; they beckoned to Leamas to go first. He pushed open the door and found himself in a small barrack bedroom with two bunk beds, a chair and a rudimentary desk. It was like something in prison camp. There were pictures of girls on the walls and the windows were shuttered. At the far end of the room was another door. They signalled him forward again. Putting down his baggage he went and opened the door. The second room was identical to the first, but there was one bed and the walls were bare.

'You bring those cases,' he said; 'I'm tired.' He lay on the bed, fully dressed, and within a few minutes he was fast asleep.

A sentry woke him with breakfast: black bread and *ersatz* coffee. He got out of bed and went to the window.

The house stood on a high hill. The ground fell steeply away from beneath his window, the crowns of pine trees visible above the crest. Beyond them, spectacular in their symmetry, unending hills, heavy with trees, stretched into the distance. Here and there a timber gully or fire-break formed a thin brown divide between the pines, seeming like Aaron's rod miraculously to hold apart massive seas of enroaching forest. There was no sign of man; not a house or church, not even the ruin of some previous habitation – only the road, the yellow unmade road, a crayon line across the basin of the valley. There was no sound. It seemed incredible that anything so vast could be so still. The day was cold but clear. It must have rained in the night; the ground was moist, and the whole landscape so sharply defined against the white sky that Leamas could distinguish even single trees on the furthest hills.

He dressed slowly, drinking the sour coffee meanwhile. He had nearly finished dressing and was about to start eating the bread when Fiedler came into the room.

'Good morning,' he said cheerfully. 'Don't let me keep you from your breakfast.' He sat down on the bed. Leamas had to hand it to Fiedler; he had guts. Not that there was anything brave about coming to see him –

the sentries, Leamas supposed, were still in the adjoining room. But there was an endurance, a defined purpose in his manner which Leamas could sense and admire.

'You have presented us with an intriguing problem,' he observed.

'I've told you all I know.'

'Oh no.' He smiled. 'Oh no, you haven't. You have told us all you are *conscious* of knowing.'

'Bloody clever,' Leamas muttered pushing his food aside and lighting a cigarette – his last.

'Let me ask *you* a question,' Fiedler suggested with the exaggerated bonhomie of a man proposing a party game. 'As an experienced intelligence officer, what would *you* do with the information you have given us?'

'What information?'

'My dear Leamas, you have only given us one piece of intelligence. You have told us about Riemeck: we knew about Riemeck. You have told us about the dispositions of your Berlin organisation, about its personalities and its agents. That, if I may say so, is old hat. Accurate – yes. Good background, fascinating reading, here and there good collateral, here and there a little fish which we shall take out of the pool. But not – if I may be crude – not fifteen thousand pounds' worth of intelligence. Not,' he smiled again, 'at current rates.'

'Listen,' said Leamas, 'I didn't propose this deal – you did. You, Kiever and Peters. I didn't come crawling to your cissy friends, peddling old intelligence. You people made the running, Fiedler; you named the price and took the risk. Apart from that, I haven't had a bloody penny. So don't blame me if the operation's a flop.' Make them come to you, Leamas thought.

'It isn't a flop,' Fiedler replied, 'it isn't finished. It can't be. You haven't told us what you *know*. I said you had given us one piece of intelligence. I'm talking about Rolling Stone. Let me ask you again – what would *you* do if I, if Peters or someone like us, had told *you* a similar story?'

Leamas shrugged:

'I'd feel uneasy,' he said; 'it's happened before. You get an indication, several perhaps, that there's a spy in some department or at a certain level. So what? You can't arrest the whole government service. You can't lay traps for a whole department. You sit tight and hope for more. You bear it in mind. In Rolling Stone you can't even tell what country he's working in.'

'You are an operator, Leamas,' Fiedler observed with a laugh, 'not an evaluator. That is clear. Let me ask you some elementary questions.'

Leamas said nothing.

'The file – the actual file on operation Rolling Stone. What colour was it?'

'Grey with a red cross on it – that means limited subscription.'

'Was anything attached to the outside?'

'Yes, the Caveat. That's the subscription label. With a legend saying that any unauthorised person not named on this label finding the file in his possession must at once return it unopened to Banking Section.'

'Who was on the subscription list?'

'For Rolling Stone?'

'Yes.'

'P.A. to Control, Control, Control's secretary; Banking Section, Miss Bream of Special Registry and Satellites Four. That's all, I think. And Special Despatch, I suppose – I'm not sure about them.'

'Satellites Four? What do they do?'

'Iron Curtain countries excluding the Soviet Union and China. The Zone.'

'You mean the GDR?'

'I mean the Zone.'

'Isn't it unusual for a whole section to be on a subscription list?'

'Yes, it probably is. I wouldn't know – I've never handled limited subscription stuff before. Except in Berlin, of course; it was all different there.'

'Who was in Satellites Four at that time?'

'Oh, God. Guillam, Haverlake, de Jong, I think. De Jong was just back from Berlin.'

'Were they *all* allowed to see this file?'

'I don't know, Fiedler,' Leamas retorted irritably; 'and if I were you . . .'

'Then isn't it odd that a whole section was on the subscription list while all the rest of the subscribers are individuals?'

'I tell you I don't know – how could I know? I was just a clerk in all this.'

'Who carried the file from one subscriber to another?'

'Secretaries, I suppose – I can't remember. It's bloody months since . . .'

'Then why weren't the secretaries on the list? Control's Secretary was.' There was a moment's silence.

'No, you're right; I remember now,' Leamas said, a note of surprise in his voice; 'we passed it by hand.'

'Who else in Banking dealt with that file?'

'No one. It was my pigeon when I joined the section. One of the women had done it before, but when I came I took it over and they were taken off the list.'

'Then you alone passed the file by hand to the next reader?'

'Yes . . . yes, I suppose I did.'

'To whom did you pass it?'

'I . . . I can't remember.'

'*Think!*' Fiedler had not raised his voice, but it contained a sudden urgency which took Leamas by surprise.

'To Control's P.A., I think, to show what action we had taken or recommended.'

'Who brought the file?'

'What do you mean?' Leamas sounded off balance.

'Who brought you the file to read? Somebody on the list must have brought it to you.'

Leamas' fingers touched his cheek for a moment in an involuntary nervous gesture.

'Yes, they must. It's difficult, you see, Fiedler; I was putting back a lot of drink in those days'; his tone was oddly conciliatory. 'You don't realise how hard it is to . . .'

'I ask you again. Think. Who brought you the file?'

Leamas sat down at the table and shook his head.

'I can't remember. It may come back to me. At the moment I just can't remember, really I can't. It's no good chasing it.'

'It can't have been Control's girl, can it? You always handed the file *back* to Control's P.A. You said so. So those on the list must all have seen it *before* Control.'

'Yes, that's it, I suppose.'

'Then there is Special Registry, Miss Bream.'

'She was just the woman who ran the strong room for subscription list files. That's where the file was kept when it wasn't in action.'

'Then,' said Fiedler silkily, 'it must have been Satellites Four who brought it, mustn't it?'

'Yes, I suppose it must,' said Leamas helplessly, as if he were not quite up to Fiedler's brilliance.

'Which floor did Satellites Four work on?'

'The second.'

'And Banking?'

'The fourth. Next to Special Registry.'

'Do you remember *who* brought it up? Or do you remember, for instance, going downstairs ever to collect the file from them?'

In despair, Leamas shook his head; then suddenly he turned to Fiedler and cried:

'Yes, yes I do! Of course I do! I got it from Peter!' Leamas seemed to have woken up: his face was flushed, excited. 'That's it: I once collected the file from Peter in his room. We chatted together about Norway. We'd served there together, you see.'

'Peter Guillam?'

'Yes, Peter – I'd forgotten about him. He'd come back from Ankara a few months before. He was on the list! Peter was – of course! That's it. It was Satellite Four and PG in brackets, Peter's initials. Someone else had done it before and Special Registry had glued a bit of white paper over the old name and put Peter's initials.'

'What territory did Guillam cover?'

'The Zone. East Germany. Economic stuff; ran a small section, sort of backwater. He was the chap. He brought the file up to me once too, I remember that now. He didn't run agents though: I don't quite know how he came into it – Peter and a couple of others were doing some research job on food shortages. Evaluation really.'

'Did you not discuss it with him?'

'No, that's taboo. It isn't done with subscription files. I got a homily from the woman in Special Registry about it – Bream – no discussion, no questions.'

'But taking into account the elaborate security precautions surrounding Rolling Stone, it is possible, is it not, that Guillam's so-called research job might have involved the partial running of this agent, Rolling Stone?'

'I've told Peters,' Leamas almost shouted, banging his fist on the desk, 'it's just bloody silly to imagine that any operation could have been run against East Germany without my knowledge – without the knowledge of the Berlin organisation. I would have known, d'you see? How many times do I have to say that? I would have known!'

'Quite so,' said Fiedler softly, 'of course you would.' He stood up and went to the window.

'You should see it in the Autumn,' he said, looking out; 'it's magnificent when the beeches are on the turn.'

CHAPTER 13

PINS OR PAPER CLIPS

Fiedler loved to ask questions. Sometimes, because he was a lawyer, he asked them for his own pleasure alone, to demonstrate the discrepancy between evidence and perfective truth. He possessed, however, that persistent inquisitiveness which for journalists and lawyers is an end in itself.

They went for a walk that afternoon, following the gravel road down into the valley, then branching into the forest along a broad, pitted track lined with felled timber. All the time, Fiedler probed, giving nothing. About the building in Cambridge Circus, and the people who worked there. What social class did they come from, what parts of London did they inhabit, did husbands and wives work in the same Department? He asked about the pay, the leave, the morale, the canteen; he asked about their love-life, their gossip, their philosophy. Most of all he asked about their philosophy.

To Leamas that was the most difficult question of all.

'What do you mean, a philosophy?' he replied; 'we're not Marxists, we're nothing. Just people.'

'Are you Christians, then?'

'Not many, I shouldn't think. I don't know many.'

'What makes them do it, then?' Fiedler persisted; 'they must have a philosophy.'

'Why must they? Perhaps they don't know; don't even care. Not everyone has a philosophy,' Leamas answered, a little helplessly.

'Then tell me what is your philosophy?'

'Oh for Christ's sake,' Leamas snapped, and they walked on in silence for a while. But Fiedler was not to be put off.

'If they do not know what they want, how can they be so certain they are right?'

'Who the hell said they were?' Leamas replied irritably.

'But what is the justification then? What is it? For us it is easy, as I said to you last night. The Abteilung and organisations like it are the natural extension of the Party's arm. They are in the vanguard of the fight for Peace and Progress. They are to the party what the party is to socialism: they *are* the vanguard. Stalin said so' – he smiled drily, 'it is not fashionable to quote Stalin – but he said once 'half a million liquidated is

a statistic, and one man killed in a traffic accident is a national tragedy.'
He was laughing, you see, at the bourgeois sensitivities of the mass. He
was a great cynic. But what he meant is still true: a movement which
protects itself against counter-revolution can hardly stop at the
exploitation – or the elimination, Leamas – of a few individuals. It is all
one, we have never pretended to be wholly just in the process of
rationalising society. Some Roman said it, didn't he, in the Christian
Bible – it is expedient that one man should die for the benefit of many.'

'I expect so,' Leamas replied wearily.

'Then what do you think? What is your philosophy?'

'I just think the whole lot of you are bastards,' said Leamas savagely.

Fiedler nodded, 'That is a viewpoint I understand. It is primitive,
negative and very stupid – but it is a viewpoint, it exists. But what about
the rest of the Circus?'

'I don't know. How should I know?'

'Have you never discussed philosophy with them?'

'No. We're not Germans.' He hesitated, then added vaguely: 'I
suppose they don't like Communism.'

'And that justifies, for instance, the taking of human life? That justifies
the bomb in the crowded restaurant; that justifies your write-off rate of
agents – all that?'

Leamas shrugged. 'I suppose so.'

'You see, for us it does,' Fiedler continued, 'I myself would have put a
bomb in a restaurant if it brought us further along the road. Afterwards
I would draw the balance – so many women, so many children; and so
far along the road. But Christians – yours is a Christian society –
Christians may not draw the balance.'

'Why not. They've got to defend themselves, haven't they?'

'But they believe in the sanctity of human life. They believe every man
has a soul which can be saved. They believe in sacrifice.'

'I don't know. I don't much care,' Leamas added. 'Stalin didn't
either, did he?'

Fiedler smiled; 'I like the English,' he said, almost to himself; 'my
father did too. He was very fond of the English.'

'That gives me a nice, warm feeling,' Leamas retorted, and relapsed
into silence.

They stopped while Fiedler gave Leamas a cigarette and lit it for him.

They were climbing steeply now. Leamas liked the exercise, walking
ahead with long strides, his shoulders thrust forward. Fiedler followed,
slight and agile, like a terrier behind his master. They must have been
walking for an hour, perhaps more, when suddenly the trees broke

above them and the sky appeared. They had reached the top of a small hill, and could look down on the solid mass of pine broken only here and there by grey clusters of beech. Across the valley Leamas could glimpse the hunting lodge, perched below the crest of the opposite hill, low and dark against the trees. In the middle of the clearing was a rough bench beside a pile of logs and the damp remnants of a charcoal fire.

'We'll sit down for a moment,' said Fiedler, 'then we must go back.' He paused. 'Tell me: this money, these large sums in foreign banks – what did you think they were for?'

'What do you mean? I've told you, they were payments to an agent.'

'An agent from behind the Iron Curtain?'

'Yes, I thought so,' Leamas replied wearily.

'Why did you think so?'

'First, it was a hell of a lot of money. Then the complications of paying him; the special security. And of course, Control being mixed up in it.'

'What did you think the agent did with the money?'

'Look, I've told you – I don't know. I don't even know if he collected it. I didn't know anything – I was just the bloody office boy.'

'What did you do with the pass books for the accounts?'

'I handed them in as soon as I got back to London – together with my phoney passport.'

'Did the Copenhagen or Helsinki banks ever write to you in London – to your alias, I mean?'

'I don't know. I suppose any letters would have been passed straight to Control anyway.'

'The false signatures you used to open the accounts – Control had a sample of them?'

'Yes. I practised them a lot and they had samples.'

'More than one?'

'Yes. Whole pages.'

'I see. Then letters could have gone to the banks after you had opened the accounts. You need not have known. The signatures could have been forged and the letters sent without your knowledge.'

'Yes. That's right. I suppose that's what happened. I signed a lot of blank sheets too. I always assumed someone else took care of the correspondence.'

'But you never did actually *know* of such correspondence?'

Leamas shook his head: 'You've got it all wrong,' he said; 'you've got it all out of proportion. There was a lot of paper going around – this was just part of the day's work. It wasn't something I gave much thought to. Why should I? It was hush-hush, but I've been in on things all my life where you only know a little and someone else knows the rest. Besides, paper bores me stiff. I didn't lose any sleep on it. I liked the trips of course – I drew operational subsistence which helped. But I didn't sit at my desk all day, wondering about Rolling Stone. Besides,' he added a little shamefacedly, 'I was hitting the bottle a bit.'

'So you said,' Fiedler commented, 'and of course, I believe you.'

'I don't give a damn' whether you believe me or not,' Leamas rejoined hotly.

Fiedler smiled.

'I am glad. That is your virtue,' he said, 'that is your great virtue. It is the virtue of indifference. A little resentment here, a little pride there, but that is nothing: the distortions of a tape recorder. You are objective. It occurred to me,' Fiedler continued after a slight pause, 'that you could still help us to establish whether any of that money was ever drawn. There is nothing to stop you writing to each bank and asking for a current statement. We could say you were staying in Switzerland; use an accommodation address. Do you see any objection to that?'

'It might work. It depends on whether Control has been corresponding with the bank independently, over my forged signature. It might not fit in.'

'I do not see that we have much to lose.'

'What have you got to win?'

'If the money has been drawn, which I agree is doubtful, we shall know where the agent was on a certain day. That seems to be a useful thing to know.'

'You're dreaming. You'll never find him, Fiedler, not on that kind of information. Once he's in the West he can go to any Consulate, even in a small town and get a visa for another country. How are you any the wiser? You don't even know whether the man is East German. What are you after?'

Fiedler did not answer at once. He was gazing distractedly across the valley.

'You said you are accustomed to knowing only a little, and I cannot answer your question without telling you what you should not know.' He hesitated, 'but Rolling Stone was an operation against us, I can assure you.'

'Us?'

'The GDR.' He smiled, 'the Zone if you prefer. I am not really so sensitive.'

He was watching Fiedler now, his brown eyes resting on him reflectively.

'But what about me?' Leamas asked. 'Suppose I don't write the letters?' His voice was rising. 'Isn't it time to talk about me, Fiedler?'

Fiedler nodded.

'Why not?' he replied, agreeably. There was a moment's silence, then Leamas said:

'I've done my bit, Fiedler. You and Peters between you have got all I know. I never agreed to write letters to banks – it could be bloody dangerous, a thing like that. That doesn't worry you, I know. As far as you're concerned I'm expendable.'

'Now let me be frank,' Fiedler replied. 'There are, as you know, two stages in the interrogation of a defector. The first stage in your case is nearly complete: you have told us all we can reasonably record. You have not told us whether your Service favours pins or paper clips because we haven't asked you, and because you did not consider the answer worth volunteering. There is a process on both sides of unconscious selection. Now it is always possible – and this is the worrying thing, Leamas – it is always entirely possible that in a month or two we shall unexpectedly and quite desperately need to know about the pins and paper clips. That is normally accounted for in the second stage – that part of the bargain which you refused to accept in Holland.'

'You mean you're going to keep me on ice?'

'The profession of defector,' Fiedler observed with a smile, 'demands great patience. Very few are suitably qualified.'

'How long?' Leamas insisted.

Fiedler was silent.

'Well?'

Fiedler spoke with sudden urgency. 'I give you my word that as soon as I possibly can, I will tell you the answer to your question. Look – I could lie to you, couldn't I? I could say one month or less, just to keep you sweet. But I am telling you I don't know because that is the truth. You have given us some indications: until we have run them to earth I cannot listen to talk of letting you go. But afterwards if things are as I think they are, you will need a friend and that friend will be me. I give you my word as a German.'

Leamas was so taken aback that for a moment he was silent.

'All right,' he said finally, 'I'll play, Fiedler, but if you are stringing me along, somehow I'll break your neck.'

'That may not be necessary,' Fiedler replied evenly.

A man who lives a part, not to others but alone, is exposed to obvious psychological dangers. In itself, the practice of deception is not particularly exacting; it is a matter of experience, of professional expertise, it is a facility most of us can acquire. But while a confidence trickster, a play-actor or a gambler can return from his performance to the ranks of his admirers, the secret agent enjoys no such relief. For him, deception is first a matter of self-defence. He must protect himself not only from without but from within, and against the most natural of impulses; though he earn a fortune, his role may forbid him the purchase of a razor, though he be erudite, it can befall him to mumble nothing but banalities; though he be an affectionate husband and father, he must under all circumstances withhold himself from those in whom he should naturally confide.

Aware of the overwhelming temptations which assail a man permanently isolated in his deceit, Leamas resorted to the course which armed him best; even when he was alone, he compelled himself to live with the personality he had assumed. It is said that Balzac on his deathbed enquired anxiously after the health and prosperity of characters he had created. Similarly Leamas, without relinquishing the power of invention, identified himself with what he had invented. The qualities he exhibited to Fiedler, the restless uncertainty, the protective arrogance concealing shame, were not approximations but extensions of qualities he actually possessed; hence also the slight dragging of the feet, the aspect of personal neglect, the indifference to food, and an increasing reliance on alcohol and tobacco. When alone, he remained faithful to these habits. He would even exaggerate them a little, mumbling to himself about the iniquities of his Service.

Only very rarely, as now, going to bed that evening, did he allow himself the dangerous luxury of admitting the great lie he lived.

Control had been phenomenally right. Fiedler was walking like a man led in his sleep, into the net which Control had spread for him. It was uncanny to observe the growing identity of interest between Fiedler and Control: it was as if they had agreed on the same plan, and Leamas had been despatched to fulfil it.

Perhaps that was the answer. Perhaps Fiedler was the special interest Control was fighting so desperately to preserve. Leamas didn't dwell on that possibility. He did not want to know. In matters of that kind he was wholly uninquisitive: he knew that no conceivable good could come of his deductions. Nevertheless, he hoped to God it was true. It was possible, just possible in that case, that he would get home.

CHAPTER 14

LETTER TO A CLIENT

Leamas was still in bed the next morning when Fiedler brought him the letters to sign. One was on the thin, blue writing paper of the Seiler Hotel Alpenblick, Lake Spiez, Switzerland, the other from the Palace Hotel, Gstaad.

Leamas read the first letter:

> To the Manager,
> The Royal Scandinavian Bank Ltd.,
> Copenhagen.
>
> *Dear Sir,*
> *I have been travelling for some weeks and have not received any mail from England. Accordingly I have not had your reply to my letter of March 3rd requesting a current statement of the deposit account of which I am a joint signatory with Herr Karlsdorf. To avoid further delay, would you be good enough to forward a duplicate statement to me at the following address, where I shall be staying for two weeks beginning April 21st:*
> c/o Madame Y. de Sanglot,
> 13 Avenue des Colombes,
> Paris XII,
> France.
> *I apologise for this confusion,*
>   *Yours faithfully,*
>   (ROBERT LANG)

'What's all this about a letter of March 3rd?' he asked. 'I didn't write them any letter.'

'No, you didn't. As far as we know, no one did. That will worry the bank. If there is any inconsistency between the letter we are sending them now and letters they have had from Control, they will assume the solution is to be found in the *missing* letter of March 3rd. Their reaction will be to send you the statement as you ask, with a covering note regretting that they have not received your letter of the third.'

The second letter was the same as the first; only the names were different. The address in Paris was the same. Leamas took a blank piece of paper and his fountain pen and wrote half a dozen times in a fluent hand 'Robert Lang', then signed the first letter. Sloping his pen backwards he practised the second signature until he was satisfied with it, then wrote 'Stephen Bennett' under the second letter.

'Admirable,' Fiedler observed, 'quite admirable.'

'What do we do now?'

'They will be posted in Switzerland tomorrow, in Interlaken and Gstaad. Our people in Paris will telegraph the replies to me as soon as they arrive. We shall have the answer in a week.'

'And until then?'

'We shall be constantly in one another's company. I know that is distasteful to you, and I apologise. I thought we could go for walks, drive round in the hills a bit, kill time. I want you to relax and talk; talk about London, about Cambridge Circus and working in the Department; tell me the gossip, talk about the pay, the leave, the rooms, the paper and the people. The pins and the paper clips. I want to know all the little things that don't matter. Incidentally . . .' A change of tone.

'Yes?'

'We have facilities here for people, who . . . for people who are spending some time with us. Facilities for diversion and so on.'

'Are you offering me a woman?' he asked.

'Yes.'

'No, thank you. Unlike you, I haven't reached the stage where I need a pimp.'

Fiedler seemed indifferent to his reply. He went on quickly.

'But you had a woman in England, didn't you – the girl in the library?'

Leamas turned on him, his hands open at his sides.

'One thing!' he shouted. 'Just that one thing – don't ever mention that again, not as a joke, not as a threat, not even to turn the screws, Fiedler, because it won't work, not ever; I'd dry up, d'you see, you'd never get another bloody word from me as long as I lived. Tell that to them, Fiedler, to Mundt and Stammberger or whichever little alley-cat told you to say it – tell them what I said.'

'I'll tell them,' Fiedler replied; 'I'll tell them. It may be too late.'

In the afternoon they went walking again. The sky was dark and heavy, and the air warm.

'I've only been to England once,' Fiedler observed casually, 'that was on my way to Canada, with my parents before the war. I was a child then of course. We were there for two days.'

Leamas nodded.

'I can tell you this now,' Fiedler continued. 'I nearly went there a few years back. I was going to replace Mundt on the Steel Mission – did you know he was once in London?'

'I knew,' Leamas replied cryptically.

'I always wondered what it would have been like, that job.'

'Usual game of mixing with the other Bloc Missions I suppose. Certain amount of contact with British business – not much of that.' Leamas sounded bored.

'But Mundt got about all right: he found it quite easy.'

'So I hear,' said Leamas; 'he even managed to kill a couple of people.'

'So you heard about that too?'

'From Peter Guillam. He was in on it with George Smiley. Mundt bloody nearly killed George as well.'

'The Fennan Case,' Fiedler mused. 'It was amazing that Mundt managed to escape at all, wasn't it?'

'I suppose it was.'

'You wouldn't think that a man whose photograph and personal particulars were filed at the Foreign Office as a member of a Foreign Mission would have a chance against the whole of British Security.'

'From what I hear,' Leamas said, 'they weren't too keen to catch him anyway.'

Fiedler stopped abruptly.

'What did you say?'

'Peter Guillam told me he didn't reckon they wanted to catch Mundt, that's all I said. We had a different set-up then – an Adviser instead of an Operational Control – a man called Maston. Maston had made a bloody awful mess of the Fennan case from the start, that's what Guillam said. Peter reckoned that if they'd caught Mundt it would have made a hell of a stink – they'd have tried him and probably hanged him. The dirt that came out in the process would have finished Maston's career. Peter never knew quite what happened, but he was bloody sure there was no full-scale search for Mundt.'

'You are sure of that, you are sure Guillam told you that in as many words? No full-scale search?'

'Of course I am sure.'

'Guillam never suggested any other reason why they might have let Mundt go?'

'What do you mean?'

Fiedler shook his head and they walked on along the path.

'The Steel Mission was closed down after the Fennan case,' Fiedler observed a moment later, 'that's why I didn't go.'

'Mundt must have been mad. You may be able to get away with assassination in the Balkans – or here – but not London.'

'He did get away with it though, didn't he?' Fiedler put in quickly. 'And he did good work.'

'Like recruiting Kiever and Ashe? God help him.'

'They ran the Fennan woman for long enough.'

Leamas shrugged.

'Tell me something else about Karl Riemeck,' Fiedler began again. 'He met Control once, didn't he?'

'Yes, in Berlin about a year ago, maybe a bit more.'

'Where did they meet?'

'We all met together in my flat.'

'Why?'

'Control loved to come in on success. We'd got a hell of a lot of good stuff from Karl – I suppose it had gone down well with London. He came out on a short trip to Berlin and asked me to fix up for them to meet.'

'Did you mind?'

'Why should I?'

'He was your agent. You might not have liked him to meet other operators.'

'Control isn't an operator; he's head of Department. Karl knew that and it tickled his vanity.'

'Were you all three together, all the time?'

'Yes. Well, not quite. I left them alone for a quarter of an hour or so – not more. Control wanted that – he wanted a few minutes alone with Karl, God knows why, so I left the flat on some excuse, I forget what. Oh – I know, I pretended we'd run out of Scotch. I actually went and collected a bottle from de Jong in fact.'

'Do you know what passed between them while you were out?'

'How could I? I wasn't that interested, anyway.'

'Didn't Karl tell you afterwards?'

'I didn't ask him. Karl was a cheeky sod in some ways, always pretending he had something over me. I didn't like the way he sniggered about Control. Mind you, he had every right to snigger – it was a pretty ridiculous performance. We laughed about it together a bit, as a matter of fact. There wouldn't have been any point in pricking Karl's vanity; the whole meeting was supposed to give him a shot in the arm.'

'Was Karl depressed then?'

'No, far from it. He was spoilt already. He was paid too much, loved too much, trusted too much. It was partly my fault, partly London's. If we hadn't spoilt him he wouldn't have told that bloody woman of his about his network.'

'Elvira?'

'Yes.' They walked on in silence for a while, until Fiedler interrupted his own reverie to observe:

'I'm beginning to like you. But there's one thing that puzzles me. It's odd – it didn't worry me before I met you.'

'What's that?'

'Why you ever came. Why you defected.' Leamas was going to say something when Fiedler laughed. 'I'm afraid that wasn't very tactful, was it?' he said.

They spent that week walking in the hills. In the evenings they would return to the lodge, eat a bad meal washed down with a bottle of rank white wine, sit endlessly over their Steinhäger in front of the fire. The fire seemed to be Fiedler's idea – they didn't have it to begin with, then one day Leamas overheard him telling a guard to bring logs. Leamas didn't mind the evenings then; after the fresh air all day, the fire and the rough spirit, he would talk unprompted, rambling on about his service. Leamas supposed it was recorded. He didn't care.

As each day passed in this way Leamas was aware of an increasing tension in his companion. Once they went out in the DKW – it was late in the evening – and stopped at a call-box. Fiedler left him in the car with the keys and made a long phone call. When he came back Leamas said:

'Why didn't you ring from the house?' but Fiedler just shook his head. 'We must take care,' he replied; 'you too, you must take care.'

'Why? What's going on?'

'The money you paid into the Copenhagen bank – we wrote, you remember?'

'Of course I remember.'

Fiedler wouldn't say any more, but drove on in silence into the hills. There they stopped. Beneath them, half screened by the ghostly patchwork of tall pine trees, lay the meeting point of two great valleys. The steep wooded hills on either side gradually yielded their colours to the gathering dusk until they stood grey and lifeless in the twilight.

'Whatever happens,' Fiedler said, 'don't worry. It will be all right, do you understand?' His voice was heavy with emphasis, his slim hand rested on Leamas' arm. 'You may have to look after yourself a little, but it won't last long, do you understand?' he asked again.

'No. And since you won't tell me I shall have to wait and see. Don't worry too much for my skin, Fiedler.' He moved his arm, but Fiedler's hand still held him. Leamas hated being touched.

'Do you know Mundt?' asked Fiedler, 'do you know about him?'

'We've talked about Mundt.'

'Yes,' Fiedler repeated, 'we've talked about him. He shoots first and asks questions afterwards. The deterrent principle. It's an odd system in a profession where the questions are always supposed to be more important than the shooting.' Leamas knew what Fiedler wanted to tell him. 'It's an odd system unless you're frightened of the answers,' Fiedler continued under his breath.

Leamas waited. After a moment Fiedler said:

'He's never taken on an interrogation before. He's left it to me before, always. He used to say to me – "You interrogate them, Jens, no one can do it like you. I'll catch them and you make them sing." He used to say that people who do counter-espionage are like painters – they need a man with a hammer standing behind them to strike when they have finished their work, otherwise they forget what they're trying to achieve. "I'll be your hammer," he used to say to me. It was a joke between us, at first, then it began to matter; when he began to kill, kill them before they sang, just as you said: one here, another there, shot or murdered. I asked him, I begged him, "Why not arrest them? Why not let me have them for a month or two? What good to you are they when they are dead?" He just shook his head at me and said there was a law that thistles must be cut down before they flower. I had the feeling that he'd prepared the answer before I ever asked the question. He's a good operator, very good. He's done wonders with the Abteilung – you know that. He's got theories about it; I've talked to him late at night. Coffee he drinks – nothing else – just coffee all the time. He says Germans are too introspective to make good agents, and it all comes out in counter-intelligence. He says counter-intelligence people are like wolves chewing dry bones – you have to take away the bones and make them find new quarry – I see all that, I know what he means. But he's gone too far. Why did he kill Viereck? Why did he take him away from me? Viereck was fresh quarry, we hadn't even taken the meat from the bone, you see. So why did he take him? Why, Leamas, why?' The hand on Leamas' arm was clasping it tightly; in the total darkness of the car Leamas was aware of the frightening intensity of Fiedler's emotion.

'I've thought about it night and day. Ever since Viereck was shot, I've asked for a reason. At first it seemed fantastic. I told myself I was jealous, and that the work was going to my head, that I was seeing treachery behind every tree; we get like that, people in our world. But I couldn't help myself, Leamas, I had to work it out. There'd been other things before. He was afraid – he was afraid that we would catch one who would talk too much!'

'What are you saying? You're out of your mind,' said Leamas, and his voice held the trace of fear.

'It all held together, you see. Mundt escaped so easily from England; you told me yourself he did. And what did Guillam say to you? He said they didn't *want* to catch him! Why not? I'll tell you why – he was their man; they turned him, they caught him, don't you see and that was the price of his freedom – that and the money he was paid.'

'I tell you you're out of your mind!' Leamas hissed. 'He'll kill you if he ever thinks you make up this kind of stuff. It's sugar candy, Fiedler. Shut up and drive us home.' At last the hot grip on Leamas' arm relaxed.

'That's where you're wrong. You provided the answer, you yourself, Leamas. That's why we need one another.'

'It's not true!' Leamas shouted. 'I've told you again and again, they couldn't have done it. The Circus couldn't have run him against the Zone without my knowing! It just wasn't an administrative possibility. You're trying to tell me Control was personally directing the deputy head of the Abteilung without the knowledge of the Berlin station. You're mad, Fiedler, you're just bloody well off your head!' Suddenly he began to laugh quietly. 'You may want his job, you poor bastard; that's not unheard of, you know. But this kind of thing went out with bustles.' For a moment neither spoke.

'That money,' Fiedler said, 'in Copenhagen. The bank replied to your letter. The manager is very worred lest there has been a mistake. The money was drawn by your co-signatory exactly one week after you paid it in. The date it was drawn coincides with a two-day visit which Mundt paid to Denmark in February. He went there under an alias to meet an American agent we have who was attending a world scientists' conference.' Fiedler hesitated, then added, 'I suppose you ought to write to the bank and tell them everything is quite in order?'

CHAPTER 15

COME TO THE BALL

Liz looked at the letter from Party Centre and wondered what it was about. She found it a little puzzling. She had to admit she was pleased, but why hadn't they consulted her first? Had the District Committee put up her name, or was it Centre's own choice? But no one in Centre knew her, so far as she was aware. She'd met odd speakers of course, and at District Congress she'd shaken hands with the Party Organiser. Perhaps that man from Cultural Relations had remembered her – that fair, rather effeminate man who was so ingratiating. Ashe, that was his name. He'd taken a bit of interest in her and she supposed he might have handed her name on, or remembered her when the Scholarship came up. An odd man, he was; took her to the Black and White for coffee after the meeting and asked her about her boyfriends. He hadn't been amorous or anything – she'd thought he was a bit queer to be honest – but he asked her masses of questions about herself. How long had she been in the Party, did she get homesick living away from her parents? Had she lots of boy-friends or was there a special one she carried a torch for? She hadn't cared for him much but his talk had gone down quite well – the worker-state in the German Democratic Republic, the concept of the worker-poet and all that stuff. He certainly knew all about Eastern Europe, he must have travelled a lot. She'd guessed he was a schoolmaster, he had that rather didactic, fluent way with him. They'd had a collection for the Fighting Fund afterwards, and Ashe had put a pound in; she'd been absolutely amazed. That was it, she was sure now: it was Ashe, who'd remembered her. He'd told someone at London District, and District had told Centre or something like that. It still seemed a funny way to go about things, but then the Party always was secretive – it was part of being a revolutionary party, she supposed. It didn't appeal to Liz much, the secrecy, it seemed dishonest. But she supposed it was necessary, and Heaven knows, there were plenty who got a kick out of it.

She read the letter again. It was on Centre's writing paper, with the thick red print at the top and it began 'Dear Comrade', it sounded to military to Liz, and she hated that; she'd never quite got used to 'Comrade'.

Dear Comrade,

We have recently had discussions with our Comrades in the Socialist Unity Party of the German Democratic Republic on the possibility of effecting exchanges between party members over here and our comrades in democratic Germany. The idea is to create a basis of exchange at the rank and file level between our two parties. The S.U.P. is aware that the existing discriminatory measures by the British Home Office make it unlikely that their own delegates will be able to come to the United Kingdom in the immediate future, but they feel that an exchange of experiences is all the more important for this reason. They have generously invited us to select five Branch Secretaries with good experience and a good record of stimulating mass action at street level. Each selected comrade will spend three weeks attending Branch discussions, studying progress in industry and social welfare and seeing at first hand the evidence of fascist provocation by the West. This is a grand opportunity for our comrades to profit from the experience of a young socialist system.

We therefore asked District to put forward the names of young Cadre workers from your areas who might get the biggest advantage from the trip, and your name has been put forward. We want you to go if you possibly can, and carry out the second part of the scheme – which is to establish contact with a Party Branch in the GDR whose members are from similar industrial backgrounds and have the same kind of problems as your own. The Bayswater South Branch has been paired with Neuenhagen, a suburb of Leipzig. Freda Lüman, Secretary of the Neuenhagen branch, is preparing a big welcome. We are sure you are just the Comrade for the job, and that it will be a terrific success. All expenses will be paid by the GDR Cultural Office.

We are sure you realise what a big honour this is, and are confident you will not allow personal considerations to prevent you from accepting. The visits are due to take place at the end of next month, about the 23rd, but the selected Comrades will travel separately as their invitations are not all concurrent. Will you please let us know as soon as possible whether you can accept, and we will let you know further details.

The more she read it, the odder it seemed. Such short notice for a start – how could they know she could get away from the Library? Then to her surprise she recalled that Ashe had asked her what she did for her holidays, whether she had taken her leave this year, and whether she had to give a lot of notice if she wanted to claim free time. Why hadn't they told her who the other nominees were? There was no particular reason why they should, perhaps, but it somehow looked odd when they didn't. It was such a *long* letter, too. They were so hard up for secretarial help at Centre they usually kept their letters short, or asked Comrades to ring up. This was so efficient, so well typed it might not have been done at Centre at all. But it *was* signed by the Cultural Organiser; it was his signature all right, no doubt of that. She'd seen it at the bottom of roneoed notices masses of times. And the letter had that awkward, semi-bureaucratic, semi-Messianic style she had grown accustomed to without ever liking. It was stupid to say she had a good record of stimulating mass action at street level. She hadn't. As a matter of fact she hated that side of party work – the loudspeakers at the factory gates, selling the *Daily Worker* at the street corner, going from door to door at the local elections. Peace Work she didn't mind so much, it meant something to her, it made sense. You could look at the kids in the street as you went by, at the mothers pushing their prams and the old people standing in doorways, and you could say, 'I'm doing it for them.' That really *was* fighting for peace.

But she never quite saw the fighting for votes and the fighting for sales in the same way. Perhaps that was because it cut them down to size, she thought. It was easy when there were a dozen or so together at a Branch meeting to rebuild the world, march at the vanguard of socialism and talk of the inevitability of history. But afterwards she'd go out into the streets with an armful of *Daily Workers*, often waiting an hour, two hours, to sell a copy. Sometimes she'd cheat, as the others cheated, and pay for a dozen herself just to get out of it and go home. At the next meeting they'd boast about it – forgetting they'd bought them themselves – 'Comrade Gold sold eighteen copies on Saturday night – eighteen!' It would go in the Minutes then, and the Branch bulletin as well. District would rub their hands, and perhaps she'd get a mention in that little panel on the front page about the Fighting Fund. It was such a little world, and she wished they could be more honest. But she lied to herself about it all, too. Perhaps they all did. Or perhaps the others understood more *why* you had to lie so much. It seemed so odd they'd made her Branch Secretary. It was Mulligan who'd proposed it – 'Our young, vigorous *and* attractive comrade . . .' He'd thought she'd sleep with him if he got her made secretary. The others had voted for her because they liked her, and because she could type. Because she'd do the work and not try and make them go canvassing at weekends. Not too often anyway. They'd voted for her because they wanted a decent little club, nice and revolutionary and no fuss. It was all such a fraud. Alec had seemed to understand that; he just hadn't taken it seriously. 'Some people keep canaries, some people join the Party,' he'd said once, and it was true. In Bayswater South it was true anyway, and District knew that perfectly well. That's why it was so peculiar that she had been nominated; that was why she was extremely reluctant to believe that District had even had a hand in it. The explanation, she was sure, was Ashe. Perhaps he had a crush on her; perhaps he wasn't queer but just looked it.

Liz made a rather exaggerated shrug, the kind of overstressed gesture people do make when they are excited and alone. It was abroad anyway, it was free and it sounded interesting. She had never been abroad, and she certainly couldn't afford the fare herself. It would be rather fun. She had reservations about Germans, that was true. She knew, she had been told, that West Germany was militarist and revanchist, and that East Germany was democratic and peace loving. But she doubted whether all the good Germans were on one side and all the bad ones on the other. And it was the bad ones who had killed her father. Perhaps that was why the Party had chosen her – as a generous act of reconciliation. Perhaps that was what Ashe had had in mind when he asked her all those questions. Of course – that was the explanation. She was suddenly filled with a feeling of warmth and gratitude towards the Party. They really were decent people and she was proud and thankful to belong. She went to the desk and opened the drawer where, in an old school satchel, she kept the Branch stationery and the dues stamps. Putting a sheet of paper into her old Underwood typewriter – they'd sent it down from District when they heard she could type; it jumped a bit but otherwise was fine – she typed a neat, grateful letter of acceptance. Centre was such a wonderful thing – stern, benevolent, impersonal, perpetual. They were good, good people. People who fought for peace. As she closed the drawer she caught sight of Smiley's card.

She remembered that little man with the earnest, puckered face, standing at the doorway of her room and saying: 'Did the Party know about you and Alec?' How silly she was. Well, this would take her mind off it.

CHAPTER 16

ARREST

Fiedler and Leamas drove back the rest of the way in silence. In the dusk the hills were black and cavernous, the pinpoint lights struggling against the gathering darkness like the lights of distant ships at sea.

Fiedler parked the car in a shed at the side of the house and they walked together to the front door. They were about to enter the lodge when they heard a shout from the direction of the trees, followed by someone calling Fiedler's name. They turned, and Leamas distinguished in the twilight twenty yards away three men standing, apparently waiting for Fiedler to come.

'What do you want?' Fiedler called.

'We want to talk to you. We're from Berlin.'

'Fiedler hesitated. 'Where's that damn' guard?' he asked Leamas; 'there should be a guard on the front door.'

Leamas shrugged.

'Why aren't the lights on in the hall?' he asked again: then, still unconvinced, he began walking slowly towards the men.

Leamas waited a moment, then, hearing nothing, made his way through the unlit house to the annexe behind it. This was a shoddy barrack hut attached to the back of the building and hidden from all sides by close plantations of young pine trees. The hut was divided into three adjoining bedrooms; there was no corridor. The centre room had been given to Leamas, and the room nearest to the main building was occupied by two guards. Leamas never knew who occupied the third. He had once tried to open the connecting door between it and his own room, but it was locked. He had only discovered it was a bedroom by peering through a narrow gap in the lace curtains early one morning as he went for a walk. The two guards, who followed him everywhere at fifty yards, distance, had not rounded the corner of the hut, and he looked in at the window. The room contained a single bed, made, and a small writing-desk with papers on it. He supposed that someone, with what passes for German thoroughness, watched him from that bedroom. But Leamas was too old a dog to allow himself to be bothered by surveillance. In Berlin it had been a fact of life – if you couldn't spot it so much the worse: it only meant they were taking greater care, or you were losing your grip. Usually, because he was good at that kind of thing, because he was observant and had an accurate memory – because, in short, he was good at his job – he spotted them anyway. He knew the formations favoured by a shadowing team, he knew the tricks, the weaknesses, the momentary lapses that could give them away. It meant nothing to Leamas that he was watched, but as he walked through the improvised doorway from the lodge to the hut, and stood in the guards' bedroom, he had the distinct feeling that something was wrong.

The lights in the annexe were controlled from some central point. They were put on and off by an unseen hand. In the mornings he was often woken by the sudden blaze of the single overhead light in his room. At night he would be hastened to bed by perfunctory darkness. It was only nine o'clock as he entered the annexe, and the lights were already out. Usually they stayed on till eleven, but now they were out and the shutters had been lowered. He had left the connecting door from the house open, so that the pale twilight from the hallway reached, but scarcely penetrated, the guards' bedroom, and by it he could just see the two empty beds. As he stood there peering into the room, surprised to find it empty, the door behind him closed. Perhaps by itself, but Leamas made no attempt to open it. It was pitch dark. No sound accompanied the closing of the door, no click nor footstep. To Leamas, his instinct suddenly alert, it was as if the soundtrack had stopped. Then he smelt the cigar smoke. It must have been hanging in the air but he had not noticed it till now. Like a blind man, his senses of touch and smell were sharpened by the darkness.

There were matches in his pocket but he did not use them. He took one pace sideways, pressed his back against the wall and remained motionless. To Leamas there could only be one explanation – they were waiting for him to pass from the guards' room to his own and therefore he determined to remain where he was. Then from the direction of the main building whence he had come he heard clearly the sound of a footstep. The door which had just closed was tested, the lock turned and made fast. Still Leamas did not move. Not yet. There was no pretence: he was a prisoner in the hut. Very slowly, Leamas now lowered himself into a crouch, putting his hand in the side pocket of his jacket as he did so. He was quite calm, almost relieved at the prospect of action, but memories were racing through his mind. 'You've nearly always got a weapon: an ash-tray, a couple of coins, a fountain-pen – anything that will gouge or cut.' It was the favourite dictum of the mild little Welsh sergeant at that house near Oxford in the war; 'Never use both hands at once, not with a knife, a stick or a pistol; keep your left arm free, and hold it across the belly. If you can't find anything to hit with, keep the hands open and the thumbs stiff.' Taking the box of matches in his right hand he clasped it longways, and deliberately crushed it, so that the small, jagged edges of boxwood protruded from between his fingers. This done, he edged his way along the wall until he came to a chair which he knew was in the corner of the room. Indifferent now to the noise he made, he shoved the chair into the centre of the floor. Counting his footsteps as he moved back from the chair, he positioned himself in the angle of the two walls. As he did so, he heard the door of his own bedroom flung open. Vainly he tried to discern the figure who must be standing in the doorway, but there was no light from his own room either. The darkness was impenetrable. He dared not move forward to attack, for the chair was now in the middle of the room; it was his tactical advantage, for he knew where it was, and they did not. They must come for him, they must; he could not let them wait until their helper outside had reached the master switch and put on the lights.

'Come on, you windy bastards,' he hissed in German; 'I'm here, in the corner. Come and get me, can't you?' Not a move, not a sound.

'I'm here, can't you see me? What's the matter then? What's the matter, children, come on, can't you?' And then he heard one stepping forward, and another following; and then the oath of a man as he stumbled on the chair, and that was the sign that Leamas was waiting for. Tossing away the box of matches he slowly, cautiously crept forward, pace by pace, his left arm extended in the attitude of a man warding off twigs in a wood until, quite gently, he had touched an arm and felt the warm prickly cloth of a military uniform. Still with his left hand Leamas deliberately tapped the arm twice – two distinct taps – and heard a frightened voice whisper close to his ear in German:

'Hans, is it you?'

'Shut up, you fool,' Leamas whispered in reply, and in that same moment reached out and grasped the man's hair, pulling his head forward and down, then in a terrible cutting blow drove the side of his right hand on to the nape of the neck, pulled him up again by the arm, hit him in the throat with an upward thrust of his open fist, then released him to fall where the force of gravity took him. As the man's body hit the ground, the lights went on.

In the doorway stood a young captain of the Peoples' Police smoking a cigar, and behind him two men. One was in civilian clothes, quite young. He held a pistol in his hand. Leamas thought it was the Czech kind with a loading lever on the spine of the butt. They were all looking at the man on the floor. Somebody unlocked the outer door and Leamas turned to see who it was. As he turned, there was a shout – Leamas thought it was the captain – telling him to stand still. Slowly he turned back and faced the three men.

His hands were still at his side as the blow came. It seemed to crush his skull. As he fell, drifting warmly into unconsciousness, he wondered whether he had been hit with a revolver, the old kind with a swivel on the butt where you fastened the lanyard.

He was woken by the lag singing and the warder yelling at him to shut up. He opened his eyes and like a brilliant light the pain burst upon his brain. He lay quite still, refusing to close them, watching the sharp, coloured fragments racing across his vision. He tried to take stock of himself: his feet were icy cold and he was aware of the sour stench of prison denims. The singing had stopped and suddenly Leamas longed for it to start again, although he knew it never would. He tried to raise his hand and touch the blood that was caked on his cheek, but his hands were behind him, locked together. His feet too must be bound: the blood had left them, that was why they were cold. Painfully he looked about him, trying to lift his head an inch or two from the floor. To his surprise he saw his own knees in front of him. Instinctively he tried to stretch his legs and as he did so his whole body was seized with a pain so sudden and terrible that he screamed out a sobbing agonised cry of self-pity, like the last cry of a man upon the rack. He lay there panting, attempting to master the pain, then through the sheer perversity of his nature, he tried again, quite slowly, to straighten his legs. At once the agony returned, but Leamas had found the cause: his hands and feet were chained together behind his back. As soon as he attempted to stretch his legs the chain tightened, forcing his shoulders down and his damaged head on to the stone floor. They must have beaten him up while he was unconscious, his whole body was stiff and bruised and his groin ached. He wondered if he'd killed the guard. He hoped so.

Above him shone the light, large, clinical and fierce. No furniture, just whitewashed walls, quite close all round, and the grey steel door, a smart charcoal grey, the colour you see on clever London houses. There was nothing else. Nothing at all. Nothing to think about, just the savage pain.

He must have lain there hours before they came. It grew hot from the light, he was thirsty but he refused to call out. At last the door opened and Mundt stood there. He knew it was Mundt from the eyes. Smiley had told him about them.

CHAPTER 17

MUNDT

They untied him and let him try to stand. For a moment he almost succeeded, then, as the circulation returned to his hands and feet, and as the joints of his body were released from the contraction to which they had been subject, he fell. They let him lie there, watching him with the detachment of children looking at an insect. One of the guards pushed past Mundt and yelled at Leamas to get up. Leamas crawled to the wall and put the palms of his throbbing hands against the white brick. He was half-way up when the guard kicked him and he fell again. He tried once more and this time the guard let him stand with his back against the wall. He saw the guard move his weight on to his left leg and he knew he would kick him again. With all his remaining strength Leamas thrust himself forward, driving his lowered head into the guard's face. They fell together, Leamas on top. The guard got up and Leamas lay there waiting for the pay-off. But Mundt said something to the guard and Leamas felt himself being picked up by the shoulders and feet and heard the door of his cell close as they carried him down the corridor. He was terribly thirsty.

They took him to a small comfortable room, decently furnished with a desk and armchairs. Swedish blinds half covered the barred windows. Mundt sat at the desk and Leamas in an armchair, his eyes half closed. The guards stood at the door.

'Give me a drink,' said Leamas.

'Whisky?'

'Water.'

Mundt filled a carafe from a basin in the corner, and put it on the table beside him with a glass.

'Bring him something to eat,' he ordered, and one of the guards left the room, returning with a mug of soup and some sliced sausage. He drank and ate, and they watched him in silence.

'Where's Fiedler?' Leamas asked finally.

'Under arrest,' Mundt replied curtly.

'What for?'

'Conspiring to sabotage the security of the people.'

Leamas nodded slowly. 'So you won,' he said. 'When did you arrest him?'

'Last night.'

Leamas waited a moment, trying to focus again on Mundt.

'What about me?' he asked.

'You're a material witness. You will of course stand trial yourself later.'

'So I'm part of a put-up job by London to frame Mundt, am I?'

Mundt nodded, lit a cigarette and gave it to one of the sentries to pass to Leamas. 'That's right,' he said. The sentry came over, and with a gesture of grudging solicitude, put the cigarette between Leamas' lips.

'A pretty elaborate operation,' Leamas observed, and added stupidly, 'clever chaps these Chinese.'

Mundt said nothing. Leamas became used to his silences as the interview progressed. Mundt had rather a pleasant voice, that was something Leamas hadn't expected, but he seldom spoke. It was part of Mundt's extraordinary self-confidence perhaps, that he did not speak unless he specifically wished to, that he was prepared to allow long silences to intervene rather than exchange pointless words. In this he differed from professional interrogators who set story by initiative, by the evocation of atmosphere and the exploitation of that psychological dependency of a prisoner upon his inquisitor. Mundt despised technique: he was a man of fact and action. Leamas preferred that.

Mundt's appearance was fully consistent with his temperament. He looked an athlete. His fair hair was cut short. It lay mat and neat. His young face had a hard, clean line, and a frightening directness; it was barren of humour or fantasy. He looked young but not youthful; older men would take him seriously. He was well built. His clothes fitted him because he was an easy man to fit. Leamas found no difficulty in recalling that Mundt was a killer. There was a coldness about him, a rigorous self-sufficiency which perfectly equipped him for the business of murder. Mundt was a very hard man.

'The other charge on which you will stand trial, if necessary,' Mundt added quietly, 'is murder.'

'So the sentry died, did he?' Leamas replied.

A wave of intense pain passed through his head.

Mundt nodded: 'That being so,' he said, 'your trial for espionage is somewhat academic. I propose that the case against Fiedler should be publicly heard. That is also the wish of the Praesidium.'

'And you want my confession?'

'Yes.'

'In other words you haven't any proof.'

'We shall have proof. We shall have your confession.' There was no menace in Mundt's voice. There was no style, no theatrical twist.

'On the other hand, there could be mitigation in your case. You were blackmailed by British Intelligence; they accused you of stealing money and then coerced you into preparing a revanchist trap against myself. The court would have sympathy for such a plea.'

Leamas seemed to be taken off his guard.

'How did you know they accused me of stealing money?' But Mundt made no reply.

'Fiedler has been very stupid,' Mundt observed. 'As soon as I read the report of our friend Peters I knew why you had been sent, and I knew that Fiedler would fall into the trap. Fiedler hates me so much.' Mundt nodded, as if to emphasise the truth of his observation. 'Your people knew that of course. It was a very clever operation. Who prepared it, tell me. Was it Smiley? Did he do it?' Leamas said nothing.

'I wanted to see Fiedler's report of his own interrogation of you, you see. I told him to send it to me. He procrastinated and I knew I was right. Then yesterday he circulated it among the Praesidium, and did not send me a copy. Someone in London has been very clever.'

Leamas said nothing.

'When did you last see Smiley?' Mundt asked casually. Leamas hesitated, uncertain of himself. His head was aching terribly.

'When did you last see him?' Mundt repeated.

'I don't remember,' Leamas said at last; 'he wasn't really in the outfit any more. He'd drop in from time to time.'

'He is a great friend of Peter Guillam is he not?'

'I think so, yes.'

'Guillam, you thought, studied the economic situation in the GDR. Some odd little section in your Service; you weren't quite sure what it did.'

'Yes.' Sound and sight were becoming confused in the mad throbbing of his brain. His eyes were hot and painful. He felt sick.

'Well, when did you last see Smiley?'

'I don't remember . . . I don't remember.'

Mundt shook his head.

'You have a very good memory – for anything that incriminates me. We can all remember when we *last* saw somebody. Did you for instance see him after you returned from Berlin?'

'Yes, I think so. I bumped into him . . . in the Circus once, in London.' Leamas had closed his eyes and he was sweating. 'I can't go on, Mundt . . . not much longer, Mundt; I'm sick,' he said.

'After Ashe had picked you up, after he had walked into the trap that had been set for him, you had lunch together, didn't you?'

'Yes. Lunch together.'

'Lunch ended at about four o'clock. Where did you go then?'

'I went down to the City, I think. I don't remember for sure . . . for Christ's sake, Mundt,' he said holding his head with his hand, 'I can't go on. My bloody head's . . .'

'And after that where did you go? Why did you shake off your followers, why were you so keen to shake them off?'

Leamas said nothing: he was breathing in sharp gasps, his head buried in his hands.

'Answer this one question, then you can go. You shall have a bed. You can sleep if you want. Otherwise you must go back to your cell, do you understand? You will be tied up again and fed on the floor like an animal, do you understand? Tell me where you went.'

The wild pulsation of his brain suddenly increased, the room was dancing; he heard voices around him and the sound of footsteps; spectral shapes passed and re-passed, detached from sound and gravity; someone was shouting, but not at him; the door was open, he was sure someone had opened the door. The room was full of people, all shouting now, and then they were going, some of them had gone, he heard them marching away, the stamping of their feet was like the throbbing of his head; the echo died and there was silence. Then like the touch of mercy itself, a cool cloth was laid across his forehead, and kindly hands carried him away.

He woke on a hospital bed, and standing at the foot of it was Fiedler, smoking a cigarette.

CHAPTER 18

FIEDLER

Leamas took stock. A bed with sheets. A single ward with no bars in the windows, just curtains and frosted glass. Pale green walls, dark green linoleum; and Fiedler watching him, smoking.

A nurse brought him food: an egg, some thin soup and fruit. He felt like death, but he supposed he'd better eat it. So he did and Fiedler watched.

'How do you feel?' he asked.

'Bloody awful,' Leamas replied.

'But better?'

'I suppose so.' He hesitated, 'Those sods beat me up.'

'You killed a sentry, you know that?'

'I guessed I had. . . . What do they expect if they mount such a damn' stupid operation. Why didn't they pull us both in at once? Why put all the lights out? If anything was over-organised, that was.'

'I am afraid that as a nation we tend to over-organise. Abroad that passes for efficiency.'

Again there was a pause.

'What happened to you?' Leamas asked.

'Oh, I too was softened for interrogation.'

'By Mundt's men?'

'By Mundt's men *and* Mundt. It was a very peculiar sensation!'

'That's one way of putting it.'

'No, no; not physically. Physically it was a nightmare, but you see Mundt had a special interest in beating me up. Apart from the confession.'

'Because you dreamed up that story about——'

'Because I am a Jew.'

'Oh Christ,' said Leamas softly.

'That is why I got special treatment. All the time he whispered to me. It was very strange.'

'What did he say?'

Fiedler didn't reply. At last he muttered:

'That's all over.'

'Why? What's happened?'

'The day we were arrested I had applied to the Praesidium for a civil warrant to arrest Mundt as an enemy of the people.'

'But you're mad – I told you, you're raving mad, Fiedler! He'll never——'

'There was other evidence against him apart from yours. Evidence I have been accumulating over the last three years, piece by piece. Yours provided the proof we need; that's all. As soon as that was clear I prepared a report and sent it to every member of the Praesidium except Mundt. They received it on the same day that I made my application for a warrant.'

'The day we were pulled in.'

'Yes. I knew Mundt would fight. I knew he had friends on the Praesidium, or yes-men at least, people who were sufficiently frightened to go running to him as soon as they got my report. And in the end, I knew he would lose. The Praesidium had the weapon it needed to destroy him; they had the report, and for those few days while you and I were being questioned they read it and re-read it until they knew it was true and each knew the others knew. In the end they acted. Herded together by their common fear, their common weakness and their common knowledge they turned against him and ordered a Tribunal.'

'Tribunal?'

'A secret one, of course. It meets tomorrow. Mundt is under arrest.'

'What is this other evidence? The evidence you've collected.'

'Wait and see,' Fiedler replied with a smile. 'Tomorrow you will see.'

Fiedler was silent for a time, watching Leamas eat.

'This Tribunal,' Leamas asked, 'how is it conducted?'

'That is up to the President. It is not a People's Court – it is important to remember that. It is more in the nature of an enquiry – a committee of enquiry, that's it, appointed by the Praesidium to investigate and report upon a certain . . . subject. Its report contains a recommendation. In a case like this the recommendation is tantamount to a verdict, but remains secret, as a part of the proceedings of the Praesidium.'

'How does it work? Are there counsel and judges?'

'There are three judges,' Fiedler said; 'and in effect, there are counsel. Tomorrow I myself shall put the case against Mundt. Karden will defend him.'

'Who's Karden?'

Fiedler hesitated.

'A very tough man,' he said. 'Looks like a country doctor, small and benevolent. He was at Buchenwald.'

'Why can't Mundt defend himself?'

'It was Mundt's wish. It is said that Karden will call a witness.'

Leamas shrugged.

'That's your affair,' he said. Again there was silence. At last Fiedler said reflectively:

'I wouldn't have minded – I don't think I would have minded, not so much anyway – if he had hurt me for myself, for hate or jealousy. Do you understand that? That long, long pain and all the time you say to yourself, "Either I shall faint or I shall grow to bear the pain, nature will see to that" and the pain just increases like a violinist going up the E string. You think it can't get any higher and it does – the pain's like that, it rises and rises, and all that nature does is bring you on from note to note like a deaf child being taught to hear. And all the time he was whispering Jew . . . Jew. I could understand, I'm sure I could, If he had done it for the idea, for the Party, if you like, or if he had hated *me*. But it wasn't that; he hated——'

'All right,' said Leamas shortly, 'you should know. He's a bastard.'

'Yes,' said Fiedler, 'he is a bastard.' He seemed excited; he wants to boast to somebody, thought Leamas.

'I thought a lot about you,' Fiedler added. 'I thought about that talk we had – you remember – about the motor.'

'What motor?'

Fiedler smiled. 'I'm sorry, that is a direct translation. I mean '*Motor*', the engine, spirit, urge; whatever Christians call it.'

'I'm not a Christian.'

Fiedler shrugged. 'You know what I mean.' He smiled again, 'the thing that embarrasses you. . . . I'll put it another way. Suppose Mundt is right. He asked me to confess, you know; I was to confess that I was in league with British spies who were plotting to murder him. You see the argument – that the whole operation was mounted by British Intelligence in order to entice us – me, if you like – into liquidating the best man in the Abteilung. To turn our own weapon against us.'

'He tried that on me,' said Leamas indifferently. And he added, 'As if I'd cooked up the whole bloody story.'

'But what I mean is this: suppose you had done that, suppose it were true – I am taking an example, you understand, a hypothesis, would you kill a man, an innocent man——'

'Mundt's a killer himself.'

'Suppose he wasn't. Suppose it were me they wanted to kill: would London do it?'

'It depends . . . it depends on the need. . . .'

'Ah,' said Fiedler contentedly, 'it depends on the need. Like Stalin, in fact. The traffic accident and the statistics. That is a great relief.'

'Why?'

'You must get some sleep,' said Fiedler. 'Order what food you want. They will bring you whatever you want. Tomorrow you can talk.' As he reached the door he looked back and said, 'We're all the same, you know, that's the joke.'

Soon Leamas was asleep, content in the knowledge that Fiedler was his ally and that they would shortly send Mundt to his death. That was something which he had looked forward to for a very long time.

CHAPTER 19

BRANCH MEETING

Liz was happy in Leipzig. Austerity pleased her – it gave her the comfort of sacrifice. The little house she stayed in was dark and meagre, the food was poor and most of it had to go to the children. They talked politics at every meal, she and Frau Ebert, Branch Secretary for the Ward Branch of Leipzig-Hohengrün, a small, grey woman whose husband managed a gravel quarry on the outskirts of the city. It was like living in a religious community, Liz thought; a convent or a kibbutz or something. You felt the world was better for your empty stomach. Liz had some German which she had learnt from her aunt, and she was surprised how quickly she was able to use it. She tried it on the children first and they grinned and helped her. The children treated her oddly to begin with, as if she were a person of great quality or rarity value, and on the third day one of them plucked up courage and asked her if she had brought any chocolate from 'drüben' – from 'over there'. She'd never thought of that and she felt ashamed. After that they seemed to forget about her.

In the evenings there was Party Work. They distributed literature, visited Branch members who had defaulted on their dues or lagged behind in their attendance at meetings, called in at District for a discussion on 'Problems connected with the centralised distribution of agricultural produce' at which all local Branch Secretaries were present, and attended a meeting of the Workers' Consultative Council of a machine tool factory on the outskirts of the town.

At last, on the fourth day, the Thursday, came their own Branch Meeting. This was to be, for Liz at least, the most exhilarating experience of all; it would be an example of all that her own Branch in

Bayswater could one day be. They had chosen a wonderful title for the evening's discussions – 'Coexistence after two wars' – and they expected a record attendance. The whole ward had been circularised, they had taken care to see that there was no rival meeting in the neighbourhood that evening; it was not a late shopping day.

Seven people came.

Seven people and Liz and the Branch Secretary and the man from District. Liz put a brave face on it but she was terribly upset. She could scarcely concentrate on the speaker, and when she tried he used long German compounds that she couldn't work out anyway. It was like the meetings in Bayswater, it was like mid-week evensong when she used to go to church – the same dutiful, little group of lost faces, the same fussy self-consciousness, the same feeling of a great idea in the hands of little people. She always felt the same thing – it was awful, really, but she did – she wished no one would turn up, because that was absolute and it suggested persecution, humiliation – it was something you could react to.

But seven people were nothing: they were worse than nothing, because they were evidence of the inertia of the uncapturable mass. They broke your heart.

The room was better than the schoolroom in Bayswater, but even that was no comfort. In Bayswater it had been fun trying to *find* a room. In the early days they had pretended they were something else, not the Party at all. They'd taken back rooms in pubs, a committee room at the Ardena Café, or met secretly in one another's houses. Then Bill Hazel had joined from the Secondary School and they'd used his classroom. Even that was a risk – the headmaster thought Bill ran a drama group, so theoretically at least they might still be chucked out. Somehow that fitted better than this Peace Hall in pre-cast concrete with the cracks in the corners and the picture of Lenin. Why did they have that silly frame thing all round the picture? Bundles of organ pipes sprouting from the corners and the bunting all dusty. It looked like something from a fascist funeral. Sometimes she thought Alec was right – you believed in things because you needed to; what you believed in had no value of its own, no function. What did he say: 'A dog scratches where it itches. Different dogs itch in different places.' No, it was wrong, Alec was wrong – it was a wicked thing to say. Peace and freedom and equality – they were facts, of course they were. And what about history – all those laws the Party proved. No, Alec was wrong: truth existed outside people, it was demonstrated in history, individuals must bow to it, be crushed by it if necessary. The Party was the vanguard of history, the spearpoint in the fight for Peace . . . she went over the rubric a little uncertainly. She wished more people had come. Seven was so few. They looked so cross; cross and hungry.

The meeting over, Liz waited for Frau Ebert to collect the unsold literature from the heavy table by the door, fill in her attendance book and put on her coat, for it was cold that evening. The speaker had left – rather rudely, Liz thought – before the general discussion. Frau Ebert was standing at the door with her hand on the light switch when a man appeared out of the darkness, framed in the doorway. Just for a moment Liz thought it was Ashe. He was tall and fair and wore one of those raincoats with leather buttons.

'Comrade Ebert?' he enquired.

'Yes?'

'I am looking for an English Comrade, Gold. She is staying with you?'

'I'm Elizabeth Gold,' Liz put in, and the man came into the hall, closing the door behind him, so that the light shone full upon his face.

'I am Holten from District.' He showed some paper to Frau Ebert who was still standing at the door, and she nodded and glanced a little anxiously towards Liz.

'I have been asked to give a message to Comrade Gold from the Praesidium,' he said. 'It concerns an alteration in your programme; an invitation to attend a special meeting.'

'Oh,' said Liz rather stupidly. It seemed fantastic that the Praesidium should even have heard of her.

'It is a gesture,' Holten said. 'A gesture of goodwill.'

'But I – but Frau Ebert . . .' Liz began helplessly.

'Comrade Ebert, I am sure will forgive you under the circumstances.'

'Of course,' said Frau Ebert quickly.

'Where is the meeting to be held?'

'It will necessitate your leaving tonight,' Holten replied. 'We have a long way to go. Nearly to Görlitz.'

'To Görlitz. . . . Where's that?'

'East,' said Frau Ebert quickly. 'On the Polish border.'

'We can drive you home now. You can collect your things and we will continue the journey at once.'

'Tonight? Now?'

'Yes.' Holten didn't seem to consider Liz had much choice.

A large black car was waiting for them. There was a driver in the front and a flagpost on the bonnet. It looked rather a military car.

CHAPTER 20

TRIBUNAL

The court was no larger than a schoolroom. At one end, on the mere five or six benches which were provided, sat guards and warders and here and there among them spectators – members of the Praesidium and selected officials. At the other end of the room sat the three members of the Tribunal on tall-backed chairs at an unpolished oak table. Above them, suspended from the ceiling by three loops of wire, was a large red star made of plywood. The walls of the courtroom were white like the walls of Leamas' cell.

On either side, their chairs a little forward of the table, and turned inwards to face one another, sat two men; one was middle-aged, sixty perhaps, in a black suit and a grey tie, the kind of suit they wear in church in German country districts. The other was Fiedler.

Leamas sat at the back, a guard on either side of him. Between the heads of the spectators he could see Mundt, himself surrounded by police, his fair hair cut very short, his broad shoulders covered in the familiar grey of prison uniform. It seemed to Leamas a curious commentary on the mood of the court – or the influence of Fiedler – that he himself should be wearing his own clothes, while Mundt was in prison uniform.

Leamas had not long been in his place when the president of the Tribunal, sitting at the centre of the table, rang the bell. The sound directed his attention towards it, and a shiver passed over him as he realised that the president was a woman. He could scarcely be blamed for not noting it before. She was fiftyish, small-eyed and dark. Her hair was cut short like a man's, and she wore the kind of functional dark tunic favoured by Soviet wives. She looked sharply round the room, nodded to a sentry to close the door, and began at once without ceremony to address the court.

'You all know why we are here. The proceedings are secret, remember that. This is a Tribunal convened expressly by the Praesidium. It is to the Praesidium alone that we are responsible. We shall hear evidence as we think fit.' She pointed perfunctorily towards Fiedler. 'Comrade Fiedler, you had better begin.'

Fiedler stood up. Nodding briefly towards the table he drew from the brief-case beside him a sheaf of papers held together in one corner by a piece of black cord.

He talked quietly and easily, with a diffidence which Leamas had never seen in him before. Leamas considered it a good performance, well adjusted to the role of a man regretfully hanging his superior.

'You should know first, if you do not know already,' Fiedler began, 'that on the day that the Praesidium received my report on the activities of Comrade Mundt I was arrested, together with the defector Leamas. Both of us were imprisoned and both of us . . . invited, under extreme duress, to confess that this whole terrible charge was a fascist plot against a loyal comrade.

'You can see from the report I have already given you how it was that Leamas came to our notice: we ourselves sought him out, induced him to defect and finally brought him to Democratic Germany. Nothing could more clearly demonstrate the impartiality of Leamas than this: that he still refuses, for reasons I will explain, to believe that Mundt was a British agent. It is therefore grostesque to suggest that Leamas is a plant: the initiative was ours, and the fragmentary but vital evidence of Leamas provides only the final proof in a long chain of indications reaching back over the last three years.

'You have before you the written record of this case. I need do no more than interpret for you facts of which you are already aware.

'The charge against Comrade Mundt is that he is the agent of an imperialist power. I could have made other charges – that he passed information to the British Secret Service, that he turned his Department into the unconscious lackey of a bourgeois state, that he deliberately shielded revanchist anti-Party groups and accepted sums of foreign currency in reward. These other charges would derive from the first; that Hans-Dieter Mundt is the agent of an imperialist power. The penalty for this crime is death. There is no crime more serious in our penal code, none which exposes our state to greater danger, nor demands more vigilance of our Party organs.' Here he put the papers down.

'Comrade Mundt is forty-two years old. He is deputy head of the Department for the Protection of the People. He is unmarried. He has always been regarded as a man of exceptional capabilities, tireless in serving the Party's interests, ruthless in protecting them.

'Let me tell you some details of his career. He was recruited into the Department at the age of twenty-eight and underwent the customary instruction. Having completed his probationary period he undertook special tasks in Scandinavian countries – notably Norway, Sweden and

Finland – where he succeeded in establishing an intelligence network which carried the battle against fascist agitators into the enemy's camp. He performed this task well, and there is no reason to suppose that at that time he was other than a diligent member of his Department. But, Comrades, you should not forget this early connection with Scandinavia. The networks established by Comrade Mundt soon after the war provided the excuse, many years later, for him to travel to Finland and Norway, where his commitments became a cover enabling him to draw thousands of dollars from foreign banks in return for his treacherous conduct. Make no mistake: Comrade Mundt has not fallen victim to those who try to disprove the arguments of history. First cowardice, then weakness, then greed were his motives; the acquirement of great wealth his dream. Ironically, it was the elaborate system by which his lust for money was satisfied that brought the forces of justice on his trail.'

Fiedler paused, and looked round the room, his eyes suddenly alight with fervour. Leamas watched, fascinated.

'Let that be a lesson,' Fiedler shouted, 'to those other enemies of the state, whose crime is so foul that they must plot in the secret hours of the night!' A dutiful murmur rose from the tiny group of spectators at the back of the room.

'They will not escape the vigilance of the people whose blood they seek to sell!' Fiedler might have been addressing a large crowd rather than the handful of officials and guards assembled in the tiny, white-walled room.

Leamas realised at that moment that Fiedler was taking no chances: the deportment of the Tribunal, prosecutors and witnesses must be politically impeccable. Fiedler, knowing no doubt that the danger of a subsequent counter-charge was inherent in such cases, was protecting his own back: the polemic would go down in the record and it would be a brave man who set himself to refute it.

Fiedler now opened the file that lay on the desk before him.

'At the end of 1956 Mundt was posted to London as a member of the East German Steel Mission. He had the additional special task of undertaking counter-subversionary measures against *emigré* groups. In the course of his work he exposed himself to great dangers – of that there is no doubt – and he obtained valuable results.'

Leamas' attention was again drawn to the three figures at the centre table. To the President's left a youngish man, dark. His eyes seemed to be half closed. He had lank, unruly hair and the grey, meagre complexion of an ascetic. His hands were slim, restlessly toying with the corner of a bundle of papers which lay before him. Leamas guessed he was Mundt's man; he found it hard to say why. On the other side of the table sat a slightly older man, balding, with an open agreeable face. Leamas thought he looked rather an ass. He guessed that if Mundt's fate hung in the balance the young man would defend him and the woman condemn. He thought the second man would be embarrassed by the difference of opinion and side with the President.

Fiedler was speaking again.

'It was at the end of his service in London that recruitment took place. I have said that he exposed himself to great dangers; in doing so he fell foul of the British secret police, and they issued a warrant for his arrest. Mundt, who had no diplomatic immunity (NATO Britain does not recognise our sovereignty), went into hiding. Ports were watched, his photograph and description were distributed throughout the British Isles. Yet, after two days in hiding, Comrade Mundt took a taxi to London Airport and flew to Berlin. 'Brilliant,' you will say, and so it was. With the whole of Britain's police force alerted, her roads, railways, shipping and air routes under constant surveillance, Comrade Mundt takes a plane from London Airport. Brilliant indeed. Or perhaps you may feel, Comrades, with the advantage of hindsight, that Mundt's escape from England was a little *too* brilliant, a little *too* easy, that without the connivance of the British authorities it would never have been possible at all!' Another murmur, more spontaneous than the first, rose from the back of the room.

'The truth is this: Mundt *was* taken prisoner by the British; in a short historic interview they offered him the classic alternative. Was it to be years in an imperialist prison, the end of a brilliant career, or was Mundt to make a dramatic return to his home country, against all expectation, and fulfil the promise he had shown? The British, of course, made it a condition of his return that he should provide them with information, and they would pay him large sums of money. With the carrot in front and the stick behind, Mundt was recruited.

'It was now in the British interest to promote Mundt's career. We cannot yet prove that Mundt's success in liquidating minor Western intelligence agents was the work of his imperialist masters betraying their own collaborators – those who were expendable – in order that Mundt's prestige should be enhanced. We cannot prove it, but it is an assumption which the evidence permits.

'Ever since 1960 – the year Comrade Mundt became Head of the Counter Espionage section of the Abteilung – indications have reached us from all over the world that there was a highly-placed spy in our ranks. You all know Karl Riemeck was a spy; we thought when he was eliminated that the evil had been stamped out. But the rumours persisted.

'In late 1960 a former collaborator of ours approached an Englishman in the Lebanon known to be in contact with their Intelligence Service. He offered him – we found out soon afterwards – a complete breakdown of the two sections of the Abteilung for which he had formerly worked. His offer, after it had been transmitted to London, was rejected. That was a very curious thing. It could only mean that the British already possessed the intelligence they were being offered, *and that it was up to date.*

'From mid-1960 onwards we were losing collaborators abroad at an alarming rate. Often they were arrested within a few weeks of their despatch. Sometimes the enemy attempted to turn our own agents back on us, but not often. It was as if they could scarcely be bothered.

'And then – it was early 1961 if my memory is correct – we had a stroke of luck. We obtained by means I will not describe, a summary of the information which British Intelligence held about the Abteilung. It was complete, it was accurate, and it was astonishingly up to date. I showed it to Mundt, of course – he was my superior. He told me it came as no surprise to him: he had certain enquiries in hand and I should take no action for fear of prejudicing them. And I confess that at that moment the thought crossed my mind, remote and fantastic as it was, that Mundt himself could have provided the information. There were other indications too. . . .

'I need hardly tell you that the last, the very last person to be suspected of espionage is the head of the Counter Espionage section. The notion is so appalling, so melodramatic that few would entertain it, let alone give expression to it! I confess that I myself have been guilty of excessive reluctance in reaching such a seemingly fantastic deduction. That was erroneous.

'But, Comrades, the final evidence has been delivered into our hands. I propose to call that evidence now.' He turned, glancing towards the back of the room. 'Bring Leamas forward.'

The guards on either side of him stood up and Leamas edged his way along the row to the rough gangway which ran not more than two feet wide, down the middle of the room. A guard indicated to him that he should stand facing the table. Fiedler stood a bare six feet away from him. First the President addressed him.

'Witness, what is your name?' she easked.

'Alec Leamas.'

'What is your age?'

'Fifty.'

'Are you married?'

'No.'

'But you were.'

'I'm not married now.'

'What is your profession?'

'Assistant librarian.'

Fiedler angrily intervened. 'You were formerly employed by British Intelligence, were you not?' he snapped.

'That's right. Till a year ago.'

'The Tribunal has read the report of your interrogation,' Fiedler continued. 'I want you to tell them again about the conversation you had with Peter Guillam some time in May last year.'

'You mean when we talked about Mundt?'

'Yes.'

'I've told you. I was at the Circus, the office in London, our headquarters in Cambridge Circus. I bumped into Peter in the corridor. I knew he was mixed up with the Fennan case and I asked him what had become of George Smiley. Then we got talking about Dieter Frey, who died, and Mundt, who was mixed up in the thing. Peter said he thought that Maston – Maston was effectively in charge of the case then – had not wanted Mundt to be caught.'

'How did you interpret that?' asked Fiedler.

'I knew Maston had made a mess of the Fennan case. I supposed he didn't want any mud raked up by Mundt appearing at the Old Bailey.'

'If Mundt had been caught, would he have been legally charged?' the President put in.

'It depends who caught him. If the police got him they'd report it to the Home Office. After that no power on earth could stop him being charged.'

'And what if your Service had caught him?' Fiedler enquired.

'Oh, that's a different matter. I suppose they would either have interrogated him and then tried to exchange him for one of our own people in prison over here; or else they'd have given him a ticket.'

'What does that mean?'

'Get rid of him.'

'Liquidated him?' Fiedler was asking all the questions now, and the members of the Tribunal were writing diligently in the files before them.

'I don't know what they do. I've never been mixed up in that game.'

'Might they not have tried to recruit him as their agent?'

'Yes, but they didn't succeed.'

'How do you know that?'

'Oh, for God's sake, I've told you over and over again. I'm not a bloody performing seal. . . . I was head of the Berlin Command for four years. If Mundt had been one of our people, I would have known. I couldn't help knowing.'

'Quite.'

Fiedler seemed content with that answer, confident perhaps that the remainder of the Tribunal was not. He now turned his attention to Operation 'Rolling Stone', took Leamas once again through the special security complexities governing the circulation of the file, the letters to the Copenhagen and Helsinki banks and the one reply which Leamas had received. Addressing himself to the Tribunal, Fiedler commented:

'We had no reply from Helsinki. I do not know why. But let me recapitulate for you. Leamas deposited money at Copenhagen on June 15th. Among the papers before you there is the facsimile of a letter from the Royal Scandinavian Bank addressed to Robert Lang. Robert Lang was the name Leamas used to open the Copenhagen deposit account. From that letter (it is the twelfth serial in your files) you will see that the entire sum – ten thousand dollars – was drawn by the co-signatory to the account one week later. I imagine,' Fiedler continued, indicating with his head the motionless figure of Mundt in the front row, 'that it is not disputed by the Defendant that he was in Copenhagen on June 21st, nominally engaged on secret work on behalf of the Abteilung.' He paused and then continued:

'Leamas' visit to Helsinki – the second visit he made to deposit money – took place on about September 24th.' Raising his voice he turned and looked directly at Mundt. 'On the third of October Comrade Mundt made a clandestine journey to Finland – once more allegedly in the interests of the Abteilung.' There was silence. Fiedler turned slowly and addressed himself once more to the Tribunal. In a voice at once subdued and threatening he asked:

'Are you complaining that the evidence is circumstantial? Let me remind you of something more.' He turned to Leamas.

'Witness, during your activities in Berlin you became associated with Karl Riemeck, formerly Secretary to the Praesidium of the Socialist Unity Party. What was the nature of that association?'

'He was my agent, until he was shot by Mundt's men.'

'Quite so. He was shot by Mundt's men. One of several spies who were summarily liquidated by Comrade Mundt before they could be questioned. But before he was shot by Mundt's men he was an agent of the British Secret Service?'

Leamas nodded.

'Will you describe Riemeck's meeting with the man you call Control.'

'Control came over to Berlin from London to see Karl. Karl was one of the most productive agents we had, I think, and Control wanted to meet him.'

Fiedler put in: 'He was also one of the most trusted?'

'Yes, oh yes. London loved Karl; he could do no wrong. When Control came out I fixed up for Karl to come to my flat and the three of us dined together. I didn't like Karl coming there really, but I couldn't tell Control that. It's hard to explain but they get ideas in London, they're so cut off from it and I was frightened stiff they'd find some excuse for taking over Karl themselves – they're quite capable of it.'

'So you arranged for the three of you to meet,' Fiedler put in curtly, 'what happened?'

'Control asked me beforehand to see that he had a quarter of an hour alone with Karl, so during the evening I pretended to have run out of Scotch. I left the flat and went over to de Jong's place. I had a couple of drinks there, borrowed a bottle and came back.'

'How did you find them?'

'What do you mean?'

'Were Control and Riemeck talking still? If so, what were they talking about?'

'They weren't talking at all when I came back.'

'Thank you. You may sit down.'

Leamas returned to his seat at the back of the room. Fiedler turned to the three members of the Tribunal and began:

'I want to talk first about the spy Riemeck, who was shot: Karl Riemeck. You have before you a list of all the information which Riemeck passed to Alec Leamas in Berlin, so far as Leamas can recall it. It is a formidable record of treachery. Let me summarise it for you. Riemeck gave to his masters a detailed breakdown of the work and personalities of the whole Abteilung. He was able, if Leamas is to be believed, to describe the workings of our most secret sessions. As secretary to the Praesidium he gave minutes of its most secret proceedings.

'That was easy for him; he himself compiled the record of every meeting. But Riemeck's *access* to the secret affairs of the Abteilung is a different matter. Who at the end of 1959 co-opted Riemeck on to the Committee for the Protection of the People, that vital sub-committee of the Praesidium which co-ordinates and discusses the affairs of our security organs? Who proposed that Riemeck should have the privilege of access to the files of the Abteilung? Who at every stage in Riemeck's career *since* 1959 (the year Mundt returned from England, you remember) singled him out for posts of exceptional responsibility? I will tell you,' Fiedler proclaimed. 'The same man who was uniquely placed to shield him in his espionage activities: Hans-Dieter Mundt. Let us recall how Riemeck contacted the Western Intelligence Agencies in Berlin – how he sought out de Jong's car on a picnic and put the film inside it. Are you not amazed at Riemeck's foreknowledge? How could he have known where to find that car, and on that very day? Riemeck had no car himself, he could not have followed de Jong from his house in West Berlin. There was only one way he could have known – through the agency of our own Security police, who reported de Jong's presence as a matter of routine as soon as the car passed the Inter Sector checkpoint. That knowledge was available to Mundt, and Mundt made it available to Riemeck. *That* is the case against Hans-Dieter Mundt – I tell you, Riemeck was his creature, the link between Mundt and his imperialist masters?'

Fiedler paused, then added quietly:

'Mundt – Riemeck – Leamas: that was the chain of command, and it is axiomatic of intelligence technique the whole world over that each link of the chain be kept, as far as possible, in ignorance of the others. Thus it is *right* that Leamas should maintain he knows nothing to the detriment of Mundt: that is no more than the proof of good security by his masters in London.

'You have also been told how the whole case known as "Rolling Stone" was conducted under conditions of special secrecy, how Leamas knew in vague terms of an intelligence section under Peter Guillam which was supposedly concerned with economic conditions in our Republic – a section which surprisingly was on the distribution list of "Rolling Stone". Let me remind you that that same Peter Guillam was one of the several British security officers who were involved in the investigation of Mundt's activities while he was in England.'

The youngish man at the table lifted his pencil, and looking at Fiedler with his hard, cold eyes wide open he asked:

'Then why did Mundt liquidate Riemeck, if Riemeck was his agent?'

'He had no alternative. Riemeck was under suspicion. His mistress had betrayed him by boastful indiscretion. Mundt gave the order that he be shot on sight, got word to Riemeck to run, and the danger of betrayal was eliminated. Later, Mundt assassinated the woman.

'I want to speculate for a moment on Mundt's technique. After his return to Germany in 1959 British Intelligence played a waiting game. Mundt's willingness to co-operate with them had yet to be demonstrated, so they gave him instructions and waited, content to pay their money and hope for the best. At that time Mundt was not a senior functionary of our Service – nor of our party – but he saw a good deal, and what he saw he began to report. He was, of course, communicating with his masters unaided. We must suppose that he was met in West Berlin, that on his short journeys abroad to Scandinavia and elsewhere he was contacted and interrogated. The British must have been wary to begin with – who would not be? – they weighed what he gave them with painful care against what they already knew, they feared that he would play a double game. But gradually they realised they had hit a gold mine. Mundt took to his treacherous work with the systematic efficiency for which he is renowned. At first – this is my guess, but it is based, Comrades, on long experience of his work and on the evidence of Leamas – for the first few months they did not dare to establish any kind of network which included Mundt. They let him be a lone wolf, they serviced him, paid and instructed him independently of their Berlin organisation. They established in London, under Guillam (for it was he who recruited Mundt in England), a tiny undercover section whose function was not known even within the Service save to a select circle. They paid Mundt by a special system which they called Rolling Stone, and no doubt they treated the information he gave them with prodigious caution. Thus, you see, it is consistent with Leamas' protestations that the existence of Mundt was unknown to him although – as you will see – he not only paid him, but in the end *actually received from Riemeck and passed to London the intelligence which Mundt obtained.*

'Towards the end of 1959 Mundt informed his London masters that he had found within the Praesidium a man who would act as intermediary between them and Mundt. That man was Karl Riemeck.

'How did Mundt find Riemeck? How did he dare to establish Riemeck's willingness to co-operate? You must remember Mundt's exceptional position: he had access to all the security files, could tap telephones, open letters, employ watchers; he could interrogate anyone with undisputed right, and had before him the most detailed picture of their private life. Above all he could silence suspicion in a moment by turning against the people the very weapon' – Fiedler's voice was trembling with fury – 'which was designed for their protection.' Returning effortlessly to his former rational style, he continued:

'You can see now what London did. Still keeping Mundt's identity a close secret, they connived at Riemeck's enlistment and enabled indirect contact to be established between Mundt and the Berlin command. That is the significance of Riemeck's contact with de Jong and Leamas. *That* is how you should interpret Leamas' evidence, *that* is how you should measure Mundt's treachery.' He turned and, looking Mundt full in the face, he shouted:

'There is your saboteur, terrorist! There is the man who has sold the people's right!

'I have nearly finished. Only one more thing needs to be said. Mundt gained a reputation as a loyal and astute protector of the people, and he silenced for ever those tongues that could betray his secret. Thus he killed in the name of the people to protect his fascist treachery and advanced his own career within our Service. It is not possible to imagine a crime more terrible than this. That is why – in the end – having done what he could to protect Karl Riemeck from the suspicion which was gradually surrounding him he gave the order that Riemeck be shot on sight. That is why he arranged for the assassination of Riemeck's mistress. When you come to give your judgement to the Praesidium, do not shrink from recognising the full bestiality of this man's crime. For Hans-Dieter Mundt, death is a judgement of mercy.'

CHAPTER 21

THE WITNESS

The President turned to the little man in the black suit sitting directly opposite Fiedler.

'Comrade Karden, you are speaking for Comrade Mundt. Do you wish to examine the witness Leamas?'

'Yes, yes, I should like to in one moment,' he replied, getting laboriously to his feet and pulling the end of his gold-rimmed spectacles over his ears. He was a benign figure, a little rustic, and his hair was white.

'The contention of Comrade Mundt,' he began – his mild voice was rather pleasantly modulated – 'is that Leamas is lying; that Comrade Fiedler either by design or ill chance has been drawn into a plot to disrupt the Abteilung, and thus bring into disrepute the organs for the defence of our socialist state. We do not dispute that Karl Riemeck was a

British spy – there is evidence for that. But we dispute that Mundt was in league with him, or accepted money for betraying our Party. We say there is no objective evidence for this charge, that Comrade Fiedler is intoxicated by dreams of power and blinded to rational thought. We maintain that from the moment Leamas returned from Berlin to London he lived a part; that he simulated a swift decline into degeneracy, drunkenness and debt, that he assaulted a tradesman in full public view and affected anti-American sentiment – all solely in order to attract the attention of the Abteilung. We believe that British Intelligence has deliberately spun around Comrade Mundt a mesh of circumstantial evidence – the payment of money to foreign banks, its withdrawal to coincide with Mundt's presence in this or that country, the casual hearsay evidence from Peter Guillam, the secret meeting between Control and Riemeck at which matters were discussed that Leamas could not hear: these all provided a spurious chain of evidence and Comrade Fiedler, on whose ambitions the British so accurately counted, accepted it; and thus he became party to a monstrous plot to destroy – to murder in fact, for Mundt now stands to lose his life – one of the most vigilant defenders of our Republic.

'Is it not consistent with their record of sabotage, subversion and human trafficking that the British should devise this desperate plot? What other course lies open to them now that the rampart has been built across Berlin and the flow of Western spies has been checked? We have fallen victim to their plot; at best Comrade Fiedler is guilty of a most serious error; at worst of conniving with imperialist spies to undermine the security of the worker state, and shed innocent blood.

'We also have a witness.' He nodded benignly at the court. 'Yes. We too have a witness. For do you really suppose that all this time Comrade Mundt has been in ignorance of Fiedler's fevered plotting? Do you really suppose that? For months he has been aware of the sickness in Fiedler's mind. It was Comrade Mundt himself who authorised the approach that was made to Leamas in England: do you think he would have taken such an insane risk if he were himself to be implicated?

'And when the reports of Leamas' first interrogation in The Hague reached the Praesidium, do you suppose Comrade Mundt threw his away unread? And when, after Leamas had arrived in our country and Fiedler embarked on his own interrogation, no further reports were forthcoming, do you suppose Comrade Mundt was then so obtuse that he did not know what Fiedler was hatching? When the first reports came in from Peters in The Hague, Mundt had only to look at the dates of Leamas' visits to Copenhagen and Helsinki to realise that the whole thing was a plant – a plant to discredit Mundt himself. Those dates did indeed coincide with Mundt's visits to Denmark and Finland: they were chosen by London for that very reason. Mundt had known of those 'earlier indications' as well as Fiedler – remember that. Mundt too was looking for a spy within the ranks of the Abteilung. . . .

'And so by the time Leamas arrived in Democratic Germany, Mundt was watching with fascination how Leamas nourished Fiedler's suspicions with hints and oblique indications – never overdone, you understand, never emphasised, but dropped here and there with perfidious subtlety. And by then the ground had been prepared . . . the man in the Lebanon, the miraculous scoop to which Fiedler referred, both seeming to confirm the presence of a highly placed spy within the Abteilung. . . .

'It was wonderfully well done. It could have turned – it could still turn – the defeat which the British suffered through the loss of Karl Riemeck into a remarkable victory.

'Comrade Mundt took one precaution while the British, with Fiedler's aid, planned his murder.

'He caused scrupulous enquiries to be made in London. He examined every tiny detail of that double life which Leamas led in Bayswater. He was looking, you see, for some human error in a scheme of almost superhuman subtlety. Somewhere, he thought, in Leamas' long sojourn in the wilderness, he would have to break faith with his oath of poverty, drunkenness, degeneracy, above all of solitude. He would need a companion, a mistress perhaps; he would long for the warmth of human contact, long to reveal a part of the other soul within his breast. Comrade Mundt was right you see. Leamas, that skilled, experienced operator, made a mistake so elementary, so human that . . .' He smiled. 'You shall hear the witness, but not yet. The witness is here; procured by Comrade Mundt. It was an admirable precaution. Later I shall call – that witness.' He looked a trifle arch, as if to say he must be allowed his little joke. 'Meanwhile I should like, If I may, to put one or two questions to this reluctant incriminator, Mr. Alec Leamas.'

'Tell me,' he began, 'are you a man of means?'

'Don't be bloody silly,' said Leamas shortly: 'you know how I was picked up.'

'Yes, indeed,' Karden declared, 'it was masterly. I may take it, then, that you have no money at all?'

'You may.'

'Have you friends who would lend you money, give it to you perhaps?

Pay your debts?'

'If I had I wouldn't be here now.'

'You have none? You cannot imagine that some kindly benefactor, someone perhaps you have almost forgotten about, would ever concern himself with putting you on your feet . . . settling with creditors and that kind of thing?'

'No.'

'Thank you. Another question: do you know George Smiley?'

'Of course I do. He was in the Circus.'

'He has now left British Intelligence?'

'He packed it up after the Fennan case.'

'Ah yes – the case in which Mundt was involved. Have you ever seen him since?'

'Once or twice.'

'Have you seen him since you left the Circus?'

Leamas hesitated.

'No,' he said.

'He didn't visit you in prison?'

'No. No one did.'

'And before you went to prison?'

'No.'

'After you left prison – the day of your release in fact – you were picked up, weren't you, by a man called Ashe?'

'Yes.'

'You had lunch with him in Soho. After the two of you had parted, where did you go?'

'I don't remember. Probably I went to a pub. No idea.'

'Let me help you. You went to Fleet Street eventually and caught a bus. From there you seem to have zigzagged by bus, tube and private car, rather inexpertly for a man of your experience, to Chelsea. Do you remember that? I can show you the report if you like, I have it here.'

'You're probably right. So what?'

'George Smiley lives in Bywater Street, just off the King's Road, that is my point. Your car turned into Bywater Street and our agent reported that you were dropped at number nine. That happens to be Smiley's house.'

'That's drivel,' Leamas declared. 'I should think I went to the Eight Bells; it's a favourite pub of mine.'

'By private car?'

'That's nonsense too. I went by taxi, I expect. If I have money I spend it.'

'But why all the running about beforehand?'

'That's just cock. They were probably following the wrong man. That would be bloody typical.'

'Going back to my original question, you cannot imagine that Smiley would have taken any interest in your after you left the Circus?'

'God, no.'

'Nor in your welfare after you went to prison, nor spent money on your dependants, nor wanted to see you after you had met Ashe?'

'No. I haven't the least idea what you're trying to say, Karden, but the answer's no. If you'd ever met Smiley you wouldn't ask. We're about as different as we could be.'

Karden seemed rather pleased with this, smiling and nodding to himself as he adjusted his spectacles and referred elaborately to his file.

'Oh yes,' he said, as if he had forgotten something; 'when you asked the grocer for credit, how much money had you?'

'Nothing,' said Leamas carelessly. 'I'd been broke for a week. Longer, I should think.'

'What had you lived on?'

'Bits and pieces. I'd been ill; some fever. I'd hardly eaten anything for a week. I suppose that made me nervous too – tipped the scales.'

'You were, of course, still owed money at the library, weren't you?'

'How did you know that?' asked Leamas sharply. 'Have you been—
—'

'Why didn't you go and collect it? Then you wouldn't have had to ask for credit, would you, Leamas?'

He shrugged.

'I forget. Probably because the library was closed on Saturday mornings.'

'I see. Are you sure it was closed on Saturday mornings?'

'No, it's just a guess.'

'Quite. Thank you, that is all I have to ask.' Leamas was sitting down as the door opened, and a woman came in. She was large and ugly, wearing a grey overall with chevrons on one sleeve. Behind her stood Liz.

CHAPTER 22

THE PRESIDENT

She entered the court slowly, looking around her, wide-eyed, like a half-woken child entering a brightly-lit room. Leamas had forgotten how young she was. When she saw him sitting between two guards she stopped.

'Alec.'

The guard beside her put his hand on her arm and guided her forward to the spot where Leamas had stood. It was very quiet in the courtroom.

'What is your name, child?' the President asked abruptly. Liz's long hands hung at her sides, the fingers straight.

'What is your name?' she repeated, loudly this time.

'Elizabeth Gold.'

'You are a member of the British Communist Party?'

'Yes.'

'And you have been staying in Leipzig?'

'Yes.'

'When did you join the Party?'

'1955. No – fifty-four, I think it was——'

She was interrupted by the sound of movement; the screech of furniture forced aside, and Leamas' voice, hoarse, high-pitched, ugly, filling the room.

'You bastards! Leave her alone!'

Liz turned in terror and saw him standing, his white face bleeding and his clothes awry, saw a guard hit him with his fist, so that he half fell; then they were both upon him, had lifted him up, thrusting his arms high behind his back. His head fell forward on his chest, then jerked sideways in pain.

'If he moves again, take him out,' the President ordered, and she nodded to Leamas in warning, adding: 'You can speak again later if you want. Wait.' Turning to Liz she said sharply, 'Surely you know when you joined the Party?'

Liz said nothing, and after waiting a moment the President shrugged. Then leaning forward and staring at Liz intently she asked:

'Elizabeth, have you ever been told in your Party about the need for secrecy?'

Liz nodded.

'And you have been told never, never to ask questions of another Comrade on the organisation and dispositions of the Party?'

Liz nodded again. 'Yes,' she said, 'of course.'

'Today you will be severely tested in that rule. It is better for you, far better, that you should know nothing. Nothing,' she added with sudden emphasis. 'Let this be enough: we three at this table hold very high rank in the Party. We are acting with the knowledge of our Praesidium, in the interests of Party security. We have to ask you some questions, and your answers are of the greatest importance. By replying truthfully, and bravely you will help the cause of Socialism.'

'But *who*,' she whispered, '*who* is on trial? What's Alec done?'

The President looked past her at Mundt and said 'Perhaps no one is on trial. That is the point. Perhaps only the accusers. It can make no difference *who* is accused,' she added, 'it is a guarantee of your impartiality that you cannot know.'

Silence descended for a moment on the little room; and then, in a voice so quiet that the President instinctively turned her head to catch her words, she asked:

'Is it Alec? Is it Leamas?'

'I tell you,' the President insisted, 'it is better for you – far better – you should not know. You must tell the truth and go. That is the wisest thing you can do.'

Liz must have made some sign or whispered some words the others could not catch, for the President again leant forward and said, with great intensity:

'Listen, child, do you want to go home? Do as I tell you and you shall. But if you . . .' She broke off, indicated Karden with her hand and added cryptically, 'this Comrade wants to ask you some questions, not many. Then you shall go. Tell the truth.'

Karden stood again, and smiled his kindly, churchwarden smile.

'Elizabeth,' he enquired, 'Alec Leamas was your lover, wasn't he?'

She nodded.

'You met at the library in Bayswater, where you work.'

'Yes.'

'You had not met him before?'

She shook her head: 'We met at the library,' she said.

'Have you had many lovers, Elizabeth?'

Whatever she said was lost as Leamas shouted again: 'Karden, you swine,' but as she heard him she turned and said, quite loud:

'Alec, don't. They'll take you away.'

'Yes,' observed the President drily; 'they will.'

'Tell me,' Karden resumed smoothly, 'was Alec a Communist?'

'No.'

'Did he know you were a Communist?'

'Yes. I told him.'

'What did he say when you told him then, Elizabeth?'

She didn't know whether to lie, that was the terrible thing. The questions came so quickly she had no chance to think. All the time they were listening, watching, waiting for a word, a gesture, perhaps, that could do terrible harm to Alec. She couldn't lie unless she knew what was at stake; she would fumble on and Alec would die – for there was no doubt in her mind that Leamas was in danger.

'What did he say then?' Karden repeated.

'He laughed. He was above all that kind of thing.'

'Do you believe he was above it?'

'Of course.'

The young man at the Judges' table spoke for the second time. His eyes were half closed:

'Do you regard that as a valid judgement of a human being? That he is *above* the course of history and the compulsion of dialectic?'

'I don't know. It's what I believed, that's all.'

'Never mind,' said Karden; 'tell me, was he a *happy* person, always laughing and that kind of thing?'

'No. He didn't often laugh.'

'But he laughed when you told him you were in the Party. Do you know why?'

'I think he despised the Party.'

'Do you think he *hated* it?' Karden asked casually.

'I don't know,' Liz replied pathetically.

'Was he a man of strong likes and dislikes?'

'No . . . no; he wasn't.'

'But he assaulted a grocer. Now why did he do that?'

Liz suddenly didn't trust Karden any more. She didn't trust the caressing voice and the good-fairy face.

'I don't know.'

'But you thought about it?'

'Yes.'

'Well, what conclusion did you come to?'

'None,' said Liz flatly.

Karden looked at her thoughtfully, a little disappointed perhaps, as if she had forgotten her catechism.

'Did you,' he asked – it might have been the most obvious of questions

– 'did you *know* that Leamas was going to hit the grocer?'

'No,' Liz replied, perhaps too quickly, so that in the pause that followed Karden's smile gave way to a look of amused curiosity.

'Until now, until today,' he asked finally, 'when had you last seen Leamas?'

'I didn't see him again after he went to prison,' Liz replied.

'When did you see him last, then?' – the voice was kind but persistent. Liz hated having her back to the court; she wished she could turn and see Leamas, see his face perhaps; read in it some guidance, some sign telling how to answer. She was becoming frightened for herself; these questions which proceeded from charges and suspicions of which she knew nothing. They must know she wanted to help Alec, that she was afraid, but no one helped her – why would no one help her?

'Elizabeth, when was your last meeting with Leamas until today?' Oh that voice, how she hated it, that silken voice.

'The night before it happened,' she replied, 'the night before he had the fight with Mr. Ford.'

'The fight? It wasn't a fight, Elizabeth. The grocer never hit back, did he – he never had a chance. Very unsporting!' Karden laughed, and it was all the more terrible because no one laughed with him.

'Tell me, where did you meet Leamas that last night?'

'At his flat. He'd been ill, not working. He'd been in bed and I'd been coming in and cooking for him.'

'And buying the food? Shopping for him?'

'Yes.'

'How kind. It must have cost you a lot of money,' Karden observed sympathetically: 'could you afford to keep him?'

'I didn't keep him. I got it from Alec. He . . .'

'Oh,' said Karden sharply, 'so he *did* have some money?'

Oh God, thought Liz, oh God, oh dear God, what have I said?

'Not much,' she said quickly, 'not much, I know. A pound, two pounds, not more. He didn't have more than that. He couldn't pay his bills – his electric light and his rent – they were all paid afterwards, you see, after he'd gone, by a friend. A friend had to pay, not Alec.'

'Of course,' said Karden quietly, 'a friend paid. Came specially and paid all his bills. Some old friend of Leamas, someone he knew before he came to Bayswater perhaps. Did you ever meet this friend, Elizabeth?'

She shook her head.

'I see. What other bills did this good friend pay, do you know?'

'No . . . no.'

'Why do you hesitate?'

'I said I don't know,' Liz retorted fiercely.

'But you hesitated,' Karden explained, 'I wondered if you had second thoughts.'

'No.'

'Did Leamas ever speak of this friend? A friend with money who knew where Leamas lived?'

'He never mentioned a friend at all. I didn't think he had any friends.'

'Ah.'

There was a terrible silence in the courtroom, more terrible to Liz because like a blind child among the seeing she was cut off from all those around her; they could measure her answers against some secret standard, and she could not know from the dreadful silence what they had found.

'How much money do you earn, Elizabeth?'

'Six pounds a week.'

'Have you any savings?'

'A little. A few pounds.'

'How much is the rent of your flat?'

'Fifty shillings a week.'

'That's quite a lot, isn't it, Elizabeth? Have you paid your rent recently?'

She shook her head helplessly.

'Why not,' Karden continued. 'Have you no money?'

In a whisper she replied: 'I've got a lease. Someone bought the lease and sent it to me.'

'Who?'

'I don't know.' Tears were running down her face, 'I don't know. . . . Please don't ask any more questions. I don't know who it was . . . six weeks ago they sent it, a bank in the City . . . some Charity had done it . . . a thousand pounds. I swear I don't know who . . . a gift from a Charity they said. You know everything – you tell me who . . .'

Burying her face in her hands she wept, her back still turned to the court, her shoulders moving as the sobs shook her body. No one moved, and at length she lowered her hands but did not look up.

'Why didn't you enquire?' Karden asked simply, 'or are you used to receiving anonymous gifts of a thousand pounds?'

She said nothing and Karden continued: 'You didn't enquire because you guessed. Isn't that right?'

Raising her hand to her face again, she nodded.

'You guessed it came from Leamas, or from Leamas' friend, didn't you?'

'Yes,' she managed to say, 'I heard in the street that the grocer had got some money, a lot of money from somewhere after the trial. There was a lot of talk about it, and I knew it must be Alec's friend. . . .'

'How very strange,' said Karden almost to himself. 'How odd.' And then: 'Tell me, Elizabeth, did anyone get in touch with you after Leamas went to prison?'

'No,' she lied. She knew now, she was sure they wanted to prove something against Alec, something about the money or his friends; something about the grocer.

'Are you sure?' Karden asked, his eyebrows raised above the gold rims of his spectacles.

'Yes.'

'But your neighbour, Elizabeth,' Karden objected, patiently, 'says that men called – two men – quite soon after Leamas had been sentenced; or were they just lovers, Elizabeth? Casual lovers, like Leamas, who gave you money?'

'Alec *wasn't* a casual lover,' she cried, 'how can you . . .'

'But he gave you money. Did the men give you money, too?'

'Oh God,' she sobbed, 'don't ask . . .'

'Who were they?' She did not reply, then Karden shouted, quite suddenly; it was the first time he had raised his voice.

'*Who?*'

'I don't know. They came in a car. Friends of Alec.'

'*More* friends? What did they want?'

'I don't know. They kept asking me what he had told me . . . they told me to get in touch with them if . . .'

'*How? How* get in touch with them?'

At last she replied:

'He lived in Chelsea . . . his name was Smiley . . . George Smiley . . . I was to ring him.'

'And did you?'

'No!'

Karden had put down his file. A deathly silence had descended on the court. Pointing towards Leamas Karden said, in a voice more impressive because it was perfectly under control:

'Smiley wanted to know whether Leamas had told her too much, Leamas had done the one thing British Intelligence had never expected him to do: he had taken a girl and wept on her shoulder.' Then Karden laughed quietly, as if it were all such a neat joke:

'Just as Karl Riemeck did. He's made the same mistake.'

'Did Leamas ever talk about himself?' Karden continued.

'No.'

'You know nothing about his past?'

'No. I knew he'd done something in Berlin. Something for the government.'

'Then he did talk about his past, didn't he? Did he tell you he had been married?'

There was a long silence. Liz nodded.

'Why didn't you see him after he went to prison? You could have visited him.'

'I didn't think he'd want me to.'

'I see. Did you write to him?'

'No. Yes, once . . . just to tell him I'd wait. I didn't think he'd mind.'

'You didn't think he would want that either?'

'No.'

'And when he had served his time in prison, you didn't try and get in touch with him?'

'No.'

'Did he have anywhere to go, did he have a job waiting for him – friends who would take him in?'

'I don't know . . . I don't know.'

'In fact you were finished with him, were you?' Karden asked with a sneer. 'Had you found another lover?'

'No! I waited for him . . . I'll always wait for him.' She checked herself. 'I wanted him to come back.'

'Then why had you not written? Why didn't you try and find out where he was?'

'He didn't want me to, don't you see! He made me promise . . . never to follow him . . . never to . . .'

'*So he expected to go to prison, did he?*' Karden demanded triumphantly.

'No . . . I don't know. How can I tell you what I don't know. . . .'

'And on that last evening,' Karden persisted, his voice harsh and bullying, 'on the evening before he hit the grocer, did he make you renew your promise? . . . Well, did he?'

With infinite weariness, she nodded in a pathetic gesture of capitulation. 'Yes.'

'And you said good-bye?'

'We said good-bye.'

'After supper, of course. It was quite late. Or did you spend the night with him?'

'After supper. I went home . . . not straight home. . . . I went for a walk first, I don't know where. Just walking.'

'What reason did he give for breaking off your relationship?'

'He didn't break it off,' she said. 'Never. He just said there was something he had to do; someone he had to get even with, whatever it cost, and afterwards, one day perhaps, when it was all over . . . he would . . . come back, if I was still there and . . .'

'And you said,' Karden suggested with irony, 'that you would always wait for him, no doubt? That you would always love him?'

'Yes,' Liz replied simply.

'Did he say he would send you money?'

'He said . . . he said things weren't as bad as they seemed . . . that I would be . . . looked after.'

'And that was why you didn't enquire, wasn't it, afterwards, when some charity in the City casually gave you a thousand pounds?'

'Yes! Yes, that's right! Now you know everything – you knew it all already. . . . Why did you send for me if you knew?'

Imperturbably Karden waited for her sobbing to stop.

'That,' he observed finally to the Tribunal before him, 'is the evidence of the defence. I am sorry that a girl whose perception is clouded by sentiment and whose alertness is blunted by money, should be considered by our British comrades a suitable person for Party office.'

Looking first at Leamas and then at Fiedler he added brutally:

'She is a fool. It is fortunate, nevertheless, that Leamas met her. This is not the first time that a revanchist plot has been uncovered through the decadence of its architects.'

With a little precise bow towards the Tribunal, Karden sat down.

As he did so, Leamas rose to his feet, and this time the guards let him alone.

London must have gone raving mad. He'd told them – that was the joke – he'd told them to leave her alone. And now it was clear that from the moment, the very moment he left England – before that, even, as soon as he went to prison – some bloody fool had gone round tidying up – paying the bills, settling the grocer, the landlord; above all, Liz. It was insane, fantastic. What were they trying to do – kill Fiedler, kill their agent? Sabotage their own operation? Was it just Smiley – had his wretched little conscience driven him to this? There was only one thing to do – get Liz and Fiedler out of it and carry the can. He was probably written off anyway. If he could save Fiedler's skin – if he could do that – perhaps there was a chance that Liz would get away.

How the hell did they know so much? He was sure, he was absolutely sure, he hadn't been followed to Smiley's house that afternoon. And the money – how did they pick up the story about him stealing money from the Circus? That was designed for internal consumption only . . . then how? For God's sake, how?

Bewildered, angry and bitterly ashamed he walked slowly up the gangway, stiffly, like a man going to the scaffold.

CHAPTER 23

CONFESSION

'All right, Karden,' his face was white and hard as stone, his head tilted back, a little to one side, in the attitude of a man listening to some distant sound. There was a frightful stillness about him, not of resignation but of self-control, so that his whole body seemed to be in the iron grip of his will.

'All right, Karden, let her go.'

Liz was staring at him, her face crumpled and ugly, her dark eyes filled with tears.

'No, Alec . . . no,' she said. There was no one else in the room – just Leamas tall and straight like a soldier.

'Don't tell them,' she said, her voice rising, 'whatever it is, don't tell them just because of me. . . . I don't mind any more, Alec; I promise I don't.'

'Shut up, Liz,' said Leamas awkwardly. 'It's too late now.' His eyes turned to the President.

'She knows nothing. Nothing at all. Get her out of here and send her home. I'll tell you the rest.'

The President glanced briefly at the men on either side of her. She deliberated, then said:

'She can leave the court; but she cannot go home until the hearing is finished. Then we shall see.'

'She knows nothing, I tell you,' Leamas shouted. 'Karden's right, don't you see? It was an operation, a planned operation. How could she know that? She's just a frustrated little girl from a crackpot library – she's no good to you!'

'She is a witness,' replied the President shortly. 'Fiedler may want to question her.' It wasn't Comrade Fiedler any more.

At the mention of his name, Fiedler seemed to wake from the reverie into which he had sunk, and Liz looked at him consciously for the first time. His deep brown eyes rested on her for a moment, and he smiled very slightly, as if in recognition of her race. He was a small, forlorn figure, oddly relaxed she thought.

'She knows nothing,' Fiedler said. 'Leamas is right, let her go.' His voice was tired.

'You realise what you are saying?' the President asked. 'You realise what this means? Have *you* no questions to put to her?'

'She has said what she had to say.' Fiedler's hands were folded on his knees and he was studying them as if they interested him more than the proceedings of the court. 'It was all most cleverly done.' He nodded. 'Let her go. She cannot tell us what she does not know.' With a certain mock formality he added, 'I have no questions for the witness.'

A guard unlocked the door and called into the passage outside. In the total silence of the court they heard a woman's answering voice, and her ponderous footsteps slowly approaching. Fiedler abruptly stood up and taking Liz by the arm, he guided her to the door. As she reached the door she turned and looked back towards Leamas, but he was staring away from her like a man who cannot bear the sight of blood.

'Go back to England,' Fiedler said to her. 'You go back to England.' Suddenly Liz began to sob uncontrollably. The wardress put an arm round her shoulder, more for support than comfort, and led her from the room. The guard closed the door. The sound of her crying faded gradually to nothing.

'There isn't much to say,' Leamas began. 'Karden's right. It was a put-up job. When we lost Karl Riemeck we lost our only decent agent in the Zone. All the rest had gone already. We couldn't understand it – Mundt seemed to pick them up almost before we'd recruited them. I came back to London and saw Control. Peter Guillam was there and George Smiley. George was in retirement really, doing something clever. Philology or something.

'Anyway, they'd dreamed up this idea. Set a man to trap himself, that's what Control said. Go through the motions and see if they bite. Then we worked it out – backwards so to speak. 'Inductive' Smiley called it. If Mundt *were* our agent how would we have paid him, how would the files look, and so on. Peter remembered that some Arab had tried to sell us a breakdown of the Abteilung a year or two back and we'd sent him packing. Afterwards we found out we'd made a mistake. Peter had the idea of fitting that in – as if we'd turned it down because we already knew. That was clever.

'You can imagine the rest. The pretence of going to pieces; drink, money troubles, the rumours that Leamas had robbed the till. It all hung together. We got Elsie in Accounts to help with the gossip, and one or two others. They did it bloody well,' he added with a touch of pride. 'Then I chose a morning – a Saturday morning, lots of people about – and broke out. It made the local press – it even made the *Worker* I think – and by that time you people had picked it up. From then on,' he added with contempt, 'you dug your own graves.'

'Your grave,' said Mundt quietly. He was looking thoughtfully at Leamas with his pale, pale eyes. 'And perhaps Comrade Fiedler's.'

'You can hardly blame Fiedler,' said Leamas indifferently, 'he happened to be the man on the spot; he's not the only man in the Abteilung who'd willingly hang you, Mundt.'

'We shall hang you, anyway,' said Mundt reassuringly. 'You murdered a guard. You tried to murder me.'

Leamas smiled drily.

'All cats are alike in the dark, Mundt. . . . Smiley always said it could go wrong. He said it might start a reaction we couldn't stop. His nerve's gone – you know that. He's never been the same since the Fennan case – since the Mundt affair in London. They say something happened to him then – that's why he left the Circus. That's what I can't make out, why they paid off the bills, the girl and all that. It must have been Smiley wrecking the operation on purpose, it must have been. He must have had a crisis of conscience, thought it was wrong to kill or something. It was made after all that preparation, all that work, to mess up an operation that way.

'But Smiley hated you, Mundt. We all did, I think, although we didn't say it. We planned the thing as if it was all a bit of a game . . . it's hard to explain now. We knew we had our backs to the wall: we'd failed against Mundt and now we were going to try and kill him. But it was still a game.' Turning to the Tribunal he said: 'You're wrong about Fiedler; he's not ours. Why would London take this kind of risk with a man in Fiedler's position? They counted on him, I admit. They knew he hated Mundt – why shouldn't he? Fiedler's a Jew, isn't he? You know, you must know, all of you, what Mundt's reputation is, what he thinks about Jews.

'I'll tell you something, no one else will, so I'll tell you: Mundt had Fiedler beaten up, and all the time, while it was going on, Mundt baited him and jeered at him for being a Jew. You all know what kind of man Mundt is, and you put up with him because he's good at his job. But . . .' he faltered for a second, then continued: 'But for God's sake . . . enough people have got mixed up in all this without Fiedler's head going into the basket. Fiedler's all right, I tell you . . . ideologically sound, that's the expression, isn't it?'

He looked at the Tribunal. They watched him impassively, curiously almost, their eyes steady and cold. Fiedler, who had returned to his chair and was listening with rather studied detachment, looked at Leamas blandly for a moment:

'And you messed it all up, Leamas, is that it?' he asked. 'An old dog like Leamas, engaged in the crowning operation of his career, falls for a . . . what did you call her? . . . a frustrated little girl in a crackpot library? London must have known; Smiley couldn't have done it alone.' Fiedler turned to Mundt: 'Here's an odd thing, Mundt; they must have known you'd check up on every part of his story. That was why Leamas lived the life. Yet afterwards they sent money to the grocer, paid up the rent; and they bought the lease for the girl. Of all the extraordinary things for them to do . . . people of their experience . . . to pay a thousand pounds, to a girl – *to a member of the Party* – who was supposed to believe he was broke. Don't tell me Smiley's conscience goes that far. London must have done it. What a risk?'

Leamas shrugged.

'Smiley was right. We couldn't stop the reaction. We never expected you to bring me here – Holland yes – but not here.' He fell silent for a moment, then continued. 'And I never thought you'd bring the girl. I've been a bloody fool.'

'But Mundt hasn't,' Fiedler put in quickly. 'Mundt knew what to look for – he even knew the girl would provide the proof – very clever of Mundt I must say. He even knew about that lease – amazing really. I mean, how *could* he have found out; she didn't tell anyone. I know that girl; I understand her . . . she wouldn't tell anyone at all.' He glanced towards Mundt. 'Perhaps Mundt can tell us how he knew?'

Mundt hesitated, a second too long, Leamas thought.

'It was her subscription,' he said; 'a month ago she increased her Party contribution by ten shillings a month. I heard about it. And so I tried to establish how she could afford it. I succeeded.'

'A masterly explanation,' Fiedler replied coolly.

There was silence.

'I think,' said the President, glancing at her two colleagues, 'that the Tribunal is now in a position to make its report to the Praesidium. That is,' she added, turning her small, cruel eyes on Fiedler, 'unless you have anything more to say.'

Fiedler shook his head. Something still seemed to amuse him.

'In that case,' the President continued, 'my colleagues are agreed that Comrade Fiedler should be relieved of his duties until the disciplinary committee of the Praesidium has considered his position.

'Leamas is already under arrest. I would remind you all that the Tribunal has no executive powers. The peoples' prosecutor, in collaboration with Comrade Mundt, will no doubt consider what action is to be taken against a British *agent provocateur* and murderer.'

She glanced past Leamas at Mundt. But Mundt was looking at Fiedler with the dispassionate regard of a hangman measuring his subject for the rope.

And suddenly, with the terrible clarity of a man too long deceived, Leamas understood the whole ghastly trick.

CHAPTER 24

THE COMMISSAR

Liz stood at the window, her back to the wardress, and stared blankly into the tiny yard outside. She supposed the prisoners took their exercise there. She was in somebody's office; there was food on the desk beside the telephones but she couldn't touch it. She felt sick and terribly tired; physically tired. Her legs ached, her face felt stiff and raw from weeping. She felt dirty and longed for a bath.

'Why don't you eat?' the woman asked again. 'It's all over now.' She said this without compassion, as if the girl were a fool not to eat when the food was there.

'I'm not hungry.'

The wardress shrugged: 'You may have a long journey,' she observed, 'and not much the other end.'

'What do you mean?'

'The workers are starving in England,' she declared complacently. 'The capitalists let them starve.'

Liz thought of saying something but there seemed no point. Besides, she wanted to know; she had to know, and this woman could tell her.

'What is this place?'

'Don't you know?' the wardress laughed. 'You should ask them over there,' she nodded towards the window. 'They can tell you what it is.'

'Who are they?'

'Prisoners.'

'What kind of prisoners?'

'Enemies of the state,' she replied promptly. 'Spies, agitators.'

'How do you know they are spies?'

'The Party knows. The Party knows more about people than they know themselves. Haven't you been told that?' The wardress looked at her, shook her head and observed, 'The English! The rich have eaten your future and your poor have given them the food – that's what's happened to the English.'

'Who told you that?'

The woman smiled and said nothing. She seemed pleased with herself.

'And this is a prison for spies?' Liz persisted.

'It is a prison for those who fail to recognise Socialist reality; for those who think they have the right to err; for those who slow down the march. Traitors,' she concluded briefly.

'But what have they done?'

'We cannot build Communism without doing away with individualism. You cannot plan a great building if some swine builds his sty on your site.'

Liz looked at her in astonishment.

'Who told you all this?'

'I am Commissar here,' she said proudly, 'I work in the prison.'

'You are very clever,' Liz observed, approaching her.

'I am a worker,' the woman replied acidly. 'The concept of brain workers as a higher category must be destroyed. There are no categories, only workers; no antithesis between physical and mental labour. Haven't you read Lenin?'

'Then the people in this prison are intellectuals?'

The woman smiled. 'Yes,' she said, 'they are reactionaries who call themselves progressive: they defend the individual against the state. Do you know what Khruschev said about the counter-revolution in Hungary?'

Liz shook her head. She must show interest, she must make the woman talk.

'He said it would never have happened if a couple of writers had been shot in time.'

'Who will they shoot now?' Liz asked quickly. 'After the trial?'

'Leamas,' she replied indifferently, 'and the Jew, Fiedler.' Liz thought for a moment she was going to fall but her hand found the back of a chair and she managed to sit down.

'What has Leamas done?' she whispered. The woman looked at her with her small, cunning eyes. She was very large; her hair was scant, stretched over her head to a bun at the nape of her thick neck. Her face was heavy, her complexion flaccid and watery.

'He killed a guard,' she said.

'Why?'

The woman shrugged.

'As for the Jew,' she continued, 'he made an accusation against a loyal comrade.'

'Will they shoot Fiedler for that?' asked Liz incredulously.

'Jews are all the same,' the woman commented. 'Comrade Mundt knows what to do with Jews. We don't need their kind here. If they join the Party they think it belongs to them. If they stay out, they think it is conspiring against them. It is said that Leamas and Fiedler plotted together against Mundt. Are you going to eat that?' she enquired, indicating the food on the desk. Liz shook her head. 'Then I must,' she declared, with a grotesque attempt at reluctance. 'They have given you potato. You must have a lover in the kitchen.' The humour of this observation sustained her until she had finished the last of Liz's meal.

Liz went back to the window.

In the confusion of Liz's mind, in the turmoil of shame and grief and fear there predominated the appalling memory of Leamas, as she had last seen him in the courtroom, sitting stiffly in his chair, his eyes averted from her own. She had failed him and he dared not look at her before he died; would not let her see the contempt, the fear perhaps, that was written on his face.

But how could she have done otherwise? If Leamas had only told her what he had to do – even now it wasn't clear to her – she would have lied and cheated for him, anything, if he had only told her? Surely he understood that; surely he knew her well enough to realise that in the end she would do whatever he said, that she would take on his form and being, his will, life, his image, his pain, if she could; that she prayed for nothing more than the chance to do so? But how could she have known, if she was not told, how to answer those veiled, insidious questions? There seemed no end to the destruction she had caused. She remembered, in the fevered condition of her mind, how, as a child, she had been horrified to learn that with every step she made, thousands of minute creatures were destroyed beneath her foot; and now, whether she had lied or told the truth – or even, she was sure, had kept silent – she had been forced to destroy a human being; perhaps two, for was there not also the Jew, Fiedler, who had been gentle with her, taken her arm and told her to go back to England? They would shoot Fiedler; that's what the woman said. Why did it have to be Fiedler – why not the old man who asked the questions, or the fair one in the front row between the soldiers, the one who smiled all the time; whenever she turned round she had caught sight of his smooth, blond head and his smooth, cruel face smiling as if it were all a great joke. It comforted her that Leamas and Fiedler were on the same side. She turned to the woman again and asked:

'Why are we waiting here?'

The wardress pushed the plate aside and stood up.

'For instructions,' she replied. 'They are deciding whether you must stay.'

'Stay?' repeated Liz blankly.

'It is a question of evidence. Fiedler may be tried. I told you: they suspect conspiracy between Fiedler and Leamas.'

'But who against? How could he conspire in England? How did he come here? He's not in the Party.'

The woman shook her head.

'It is secret,' she replied. 'It concerns only the Praesidium. Perhaps the Jew brought him here.'

'But *you* know,' Liz insisted, a note of blandishment in her voice, 'you are Commissar at the prison. Surely they told *you*?'

'Perhaps,' the woman replied, complacently. 'It is very secret,' she repeated.

The telephone rang. The woman lifted the receiver and listened. After a moment she glanced at Liz.

'Yes, Comrade. At once,' she said, and put down the receiver.

'You are to stay,' she said shortly. 'The Praesidium will consider the case of Fiedler. In the meantime you will stay here. That is the wish of Comrade Mundt.'

'Who is Mundt?'

The woman looked cunning.

'It is the wish of the Praesidium,' she said.

'I don't want to stay,' Liz cried. 'I want . . .'

'The Party knows more about us than we know ourselves,' the woman replied. 'You must stay here. It is the Party's wish.'

'Who is Mundt?' Liz asked again, but still she did not reply.

Slowly Liz followed her along endless corridors, through grilles manned by sentries, past iron doors from which no sound came, down endless stairs, across whole courtyards far beneath the ground, until she thought she had descended to the bowels of hell itself, and no one would even tell her when Leamas was dead.

She had no idea what time it was when she heard the footstep in the corridor outside her cell. It could have been five in the evening – it could have been midnight. She had been awake, staring blankly into the pitch darkness, longing for a sound. She had never imagined that silence could be so terrible. Once she had cried out, and there had been no echo, nothing. Just the memory of her own voice. She had visualised the sound breaking against the solid darkness like a fist against a rock. She had moved her hands about her as she sat on the bed, and it seemed to her that the darkness made them heavy, as if she were groping in the water. She knew the cell was small; that it contained the bed on which she sat, a handbasin without taps and a crude table: she had seen them when she first entered. Then the light had gone out, and she had run wildly to where she knew the bed had stood, and struck it with her shins, and had remained there, shivering with fright. Until she heard the footsteps, and the door of her cell was opened abruptly.

She recognised him at once, although she could only discern his silhouette against the pale blue light in the corridor. The trim, agile figure, the clear line of the cheek and the short fair hair just touched by the light behind him.

'It's Mundt,' he said. 'Come with me, at once.' His voice was contemptuous yet subdued, as if he were not anxious to be overheard.

Liz was suddenly terrified. She remembered the wardress: 'Mundt knows what to do with Jews.' She stood by the bed, staring at him, not knowing what to do.

'Hurry, you fool.' Mundt had stepped forward and seized her wrist. 'Hurry.' She let herself be drawn into the corridor. Bewildered, she watched Mundt quietly relock the door of her cell. Roughly he took her arm and forced her quickly along the first corridor, half running, half walking. She could hear the distant whirr of air conditioners; and now and then the sound of other footsteps from passages branching from their own. She noticed that Mundt hesitated, drew back even, when they came upon other corridors, would go ahead and confirm that no one was coming, then signal her forward. He seemed to assume that she would follow, that she knew the reason. It was almost as if he was treating her as an accomplice.

And suddenly he had stopped, was thrusting a key into the keyhole of a dingy metal door. She waited, panic-stricken. He pushed the door savagely outwards and the sweet, cold air of a winter's evening blew against her face. He beckoned to her again, still with the same urgency, and she followed him down two steps on to a gravel path which led through a rough kitchen garden.

They followed the path to an elaborate Gothic gateway which gave on to the road beyond. Parked in the gateway was a car. Standing beside it was Alec Leamas.

'Keep your distance,' Mundt warned her as she started to move forward:

'Wait here.'

Mundt went forward alone and for what seemed an age she watched the two men standing together, talking quietly between themselves. Her heart was beating madly, her whole body shivering with cold fear. Finally Mundt returned.

'Come with me,' he said, and led her to where Leamas stood. The two men looked at one another for a moment.

'Good-bye,' said Mundt indifferently. 'You're a fool, Leamas,' he added. 'She's trash, like Fiedler.' And he turned without another word and walked quickly away into the twilight.

She put her hand out and touched him, and he half turned from her, brushing her hand away as he opened the car door. He nodded to her to get in, but she hesitated.

'Alec,' she whispered, 'Alec, what are you doing? Why is he letting you go?'

'Shut up!' Leamas hissed. 'Don't even think about it, d'you hear? Get in.'

'What was it he said about Fiedler? Alec, why is he letting us go?'

'He's letting us go because we've done our job. Get into the car, quick!' Under the compulsion of his extraordinary will she got into the car and closed the door. Leamas got in beside her.

'What bargain have you struck with him?' she persisted, suspicion and fear rising in her voice. 'They said you had tried to conspire against him, you and Fiedler. Then why is he letting you go?'

Leamas had started the car and was soon driving fast along the narrow road. On either side, bare fields; in the distance, dark monotonous hills were mingling with the gathering darkness. Leamas looked at his watch.

'We're five hours from Berlin,' he said. 'We've got to make Köpenick by quarter to one. We should do it easily.'

For a time Liz said nothing; she stared through the windscreen down the empty road, confused and lost in a labyrinth of half formed thoughts. A full moon had risen and the frost hovered in long shrouds across the fields. They turned on to an autobahn.

'Was I on your conscience, Alec?' she said at last. 'Is that why you made Mundt let me go?'

Leamas said nothing.

'You and Mundt are enemies, aren't you?'

Still he said nothing. He was driving fast now, the needle showed a hundred and twenty kilometres; the autobahn was pitted and bumpy. He had his headlights on full, she noticed, and didn't bother to dip for oncoming traffic on the other lane. He drove roughly, leaning forward, his elbows almost on the wheel.

'What will happen to Fiedler?' Liz asked suddenly and this time Leamas answered.

'He'll be shot.'

'Then why didn't they shoot you?' Liz continued quickly. 'You conspired with Fiedler against Mundt, that's what they said. You killed a guard. Why has Mundt let you go?'

'All right!' Leamas shouted suddenly. 'I'll tell you. I'll tell you what you were never, never to know, neither you nor I. Listen: Mundt is London's man, their agent; they bought him when he was in England. We are witnessing the lousy end to a filthy, lousy operation to save Mundt's skin. To save him from a clever little Jew in his own department who had begun to suspect the truth. They made us kill him, d'you see, kill the Jew. Now you know, and God help us both.'

CHAPTER 25

THE WALL

'If that is so, Alec,' she said at last, 'what was my part in all this?' Her voice was quite calm, almost matter-of-fact.

'I can only guess, Liz, from what I know and what Mundt told me before we left. Fiedler suspected Mundt; had suspected him ever since Mundt came back from England; he thought Mundt was playing a double game. He hated him, of course – why shouldn't he – but he was right too: Mundt was London's man. Fiedler was too powerful for Mundt to eliminate alone, so London decided to do it for him. I can see them working it out, they're so damned academic; I can see them sitting round a fire in one of their smart bloody clubs. They knew it was no good just eliminating Fiedler – he might have told friends, published accusations: they had to eliminate *suspicion*. Public rehabilitation, that's what they organised for Mundt.'

He swung into the left-hand lane to overtake a lorry and trailer. As he did so the lorry unexpectedly pulled out in front of him, so that he had to brake violently on the pitted road to avoid being forced into the crash-fence on his left.

'They told me to frame Mundt,' he said simply; 'they said he had to be killed, and I was game. It was going to be my last job. So I went to seed, and punched the grocer . . . you know all that.'

'And made love?' she asked quietly. Leamas shook his head. 'But this is the point, you see,' he continued, 'Mundt knew it all; he knew the plan; he had me picked up, he and Fiedler. Then he let Fiedler take over, because he knew in the end Fiedler would hang himself. My job was to let them think what in fact was the truth: that Mundt was a British spy.' He hesitated. 'Your job was to discredit me. Fiedler was shot and Mundt was saved, mercifully delivered from a fascist plot. It's the old principle of love on the rebound.'

'But how could they know about me; how could they know we would come together?' Liz cried. 'Heavens above, Alec, can they even tell when people will fall in love?'

'It didn't matter – it didn't depend on that. They chose you because you were young and pretty and in the Party, because they knew you would come to Germany if they rigged an invitation. That man in the Labour Exchange, Pitt, he sent me up there; they knew I'd work at the Library. Pitt was in the Service during the war and they squared him, I suppose. They only had to put you and me in contact, even for a day, it didn't matter; then afterwards they could call on you, send you the money, make it look like an affair even if it wasn't, don't you see? Make it look like an infatuation, perhaps. The only material point was that after bringing us together they should send you money as if it came at my request. As it was, we made it very easy for them. . . .'

'Yes, we did.' And then she added, 'I feel dirty, Alec, as if I'd been put out to stud.'

Leamas said nothing.

'Did it ease your Department's conscience at all? Exploiting . . . somebody in the Party, rather than just anybody?' Liz continued.

Leamas said, 'Perhaps. They don't really think in those terms. It was an operational convenience.'

'I might have stayed in that prison, mightn't I? That's what Mundt wanted, wasn't it? He saw no point in taking the risk – I might have heard too much, guessed too much. After all, Fiedler was innocent, wasn't he? But then he's a Jew,' she added excitedly. 'So that doesn't matter so much, does it?'

'Oh, for God's sake,' Leamas exclaimed.

'It seems odd that Mundt let me go, all the same – even as part of the bargain with you,' she mused. 'I'm a risk now, aren't I? When we get back to England, I mean: a Party member knowing all this. . . . It doesn't seem logical that he should let me go.'

'I expect,' Leamas replied, 'he is going to use our escape to demonstrate to the Praesidium that there are other Fiedlers in his department who must be hunted down.'

'And other Jews?'

'It gives him a chance to secure his position,' Leamas replied curtly.

'By killing more innocent people? It doesn't seem to worry you much.'

'Of course it worries me. It makes me sick with shame and anger and . . . But I've been brought up differently, Liz; I can't see it in black and white. People who play this game take risks. Fiedler lost and Mundt won. London won – that's the point. It was a foul, foul operation. But it's paid off, and that's the only rule.' As he spoke his voice rose, until finally he was nearly shouting.

'You're trying to convince yourself.' Liz cried. 'They've done a wicked thing. How can you kill Fiedler – he was good, Alec; I know he was. And Mundt . . .'

'What the hell are you complaining about,' Leamas demanded roughly. 'Your Party's always at war, isn't it? Sacrificing the individual to the mass. That's what it says. Socialist reality: fighting night and day – that relentless battle – that's what they say, isn't it? At least you've survived. I never heard that Communists preached the sanctity of human life – perhaps I've got it wrong,' he added sarcastically. 'I agree, yes, I agree, you might have been destroyed. That was on the cards. Mundt's a vicious swine; he saw no point in letting you survive. His promise – I suppose he gave a promise to do his best by you – isn't worth a great deal. So you might have died – today, next year or twenty years on – in a prison in the worker's paradise. And so might I. But I seem to remember the Party is aiming at the destruction of a whole class. Or have I got it wrong?' Extracting a packet of cigarettes from his jacket he handed her two, together with a box of matches. Her fingers trembled as she lit them and passed one back to Leamas.

'You've thought it all out, haven't you?' she asked.

'We happened to fit the mould,' Leamas persisted, 'and I'm sorry. I'm sorry for the others too – the others who fit the mould. But don't complain about the terms, Liz; they're party terms. A small price for a big return. One sacrificed for many. It's not pretty, I know, choosing who it'll be – turning the plan into people.'

She listened in the darkness, for a moment scarcely conscious of anything except the vanishing road before them, and the numb horror in her mind.

'But they let me love you,' she said at last. 'And you let me believe in you and love you.'

'They used us,' Leamas replied pitilessly. 'They cheated us both because it was necessary. It was the only way. Fiedler was bloody nearly home already, don't you see? Mundt would have been caught; can't you understand that?'

'How can you turn the world upside down?' Liz shouted suddenly. 'Fiedler was kind and decent; he was only doing his job, and now you've killed him. Mundt is a spy and a traitor and you protect him. Mundt is a Nazi, do you know that? He hates Jews . . . what side are you on? How can you . . .?'

'There's only one law in this game,' Leamas retorted. 'Mundt is their man; he gives them what they need. That's easy enough to understand, isn't it? Leninism – the expediency of temporary alliances. What do you think spies are: priests, saints and martyrs? They're a squalid procession of vain fools, traitors too, yes; pansies, sadists and drunkards, people who play cowboys and Indians to brighten their rotten lives. Do you think they sit like monks in London balancing the rights and wrongs? I'd have killed Mundt if I could, I hate his guts; but not now. It so happens that they need him. They need him so that the great moronic mass that you admire can sleep soundly in their beds at night. They need him for the safety of ordinary, crummy people like you and me.'

'But what about Fiedler – don't you feel anything for him?'

'This is a war,' Leamas replied. 'It's graphic and unpleasant because it's fought on a tiny scale, at close range; fought with a wastage of innocent life sometimes, I admit. But it's nothing, nothing at all beside other wars – the last or the next.'

'Oh God,' said Liz softly. 'You don't understand. You don't want to. You're trying to persuade yourself. It's far more terrible, what they are doing; to find the humanity in people, in me and whoever else they use, to turn it like a weapon in their hands, and use it to hurt and kill. . . .'

'Christ Almighty!' Leamas cried. 'What else have men done since the world began? I don't believe in anything, don't you see – not even destruction or anarchy. I'm sick, sick of killing but I don't see what else they can do. They don't proselytise; they don't stand in pulpits or on party platforms and tell us to fight for Peace or for God or whatever it is. They're the poor sods who try to keep the preachers from blowing each other sky high.'

'You're wrong,' Liz declared hopelessly; 'they're more wicked than all of us.'

'Because I made love to you when you thought I was a tramp?' Leamas asked savagely.

'Because of their contempt,' Liz replied; 'contempt for what is real and good; contempt for love, contempt for . . .'

'Yes,' Leamas agreed, suddenly weary. 'That is the price they pay; to despise God and Karl Marx in the same sentence. If that is what you mean.'

'It makes you the same,' Liz continued: 'the same as Mundt and all the rest. . . . I should know, I was the one who was kicked about, wasn't I? By them, by you because you don't care. Only Fiedler didn't. . . . But the rest of you . . . you all treated me as if I was . . . nothing . . . just currency to pay with. . . . You're all the same, Alec.'

'Oh, Liz,' he said desperately, 'for God's sake believe me. I hate it, I hate it all; I'm tired. But it's the world, it's mankind that's gone mad. We're a tiny price to pay . . . but everywhere's the same, people cheated and misled, whole lives thrown away, people shot and in prison, whole groups and classes of men written off for nothing. And you, your party – God knows it was built on the bodies of ordinary people. You've never seen men die as I have, Liz. . . .'

As he spoke Liz remembered the drab prison courtyard, and the wardress saying: 'It is a prison for those who slow down the march . . . for those who think they have the right to err.'

Leamas was suddenly tense, peering forward through the windscreen. In the headlights of the car Liz discerned a figure standing in the road. In his hand was a tiny light which he turned on and off as the car approached. 'That's him,' Leamas muttered; switched off the headlights and engine, and coasted silently forward. As they drew up, Leamas leant back and opened the rear door.

Liz did not turn round to look at him as he got in. She was staring stiffly forward, down the street at the falling rain.

'Drive at thirty kilometres,' the man said. His voice was taut, frightened. 'I'll tell you the way. When we reach the place you must get out and run to the wall. The searchlight will be shining at the point where you must climb. Stand in the beam of the searchlight. When the beam moves away begin to climb. You will have ninety seconds to get over. You go first,' he said to Leamas; 'and the girl follows. There are iron rungs in the lower part – after that you must pull yourself up as best you can. You'll have to sit on top and pull the girl up. Do you understand?'

'We understand,' said Leamas. 'How long have we got?'

'If you drive at thirty kilometres we shall be there in about nine minutes. The searchlight will be on the wall at five past one exactly. They can give you ninety seconds. No more.'

'What happens after ninety seconds?' Leamas asked.

'They can only give you ninety seconds,' the man repeated; 'otherwise it is too dangerous. Only one detachment has been briefed. They think you are being infiltrated into West Berlin. They've been told not to make it too easy. Ninety seconds are enough.'

'I bloody well hope so,' said Leamas drily. 'What time do you make it?'

'I checked my watch with the sergeant in charge of the detachment,' the man replied. A light went on and off briefly in the back of the car. 'It is twelve forty-eight. We must leave at five to one. Seven minutes to wait.'

They sat in total silence save for the rain pattering on the roof. The cobble road reached out straight before them, staged by dingy street lights every hundred metres. There was no one about. Above them the sky was lit with the unnatural glow of arclights. Occasionally the beam of a searchlight flickered overhead, and disappeared. Far to the left Leamas caught sight of a fluctuating light just above the sky-line, constantly altering in strength, like the reflection of a fire.

'What's that?' he asked, pointing towards it.

'Information Service,' the man replied. 'A scaffolding of lights. It flashes news headlines into East Berlin.'

'Of course,' Leamas muttered. They were very near the end of the road.

'There is no turning back,' the man continued; 'he told you that? There is no second chance.'

'I know,' Leamas replied.

'If something goes wrong – if you fall or get hurt – don't turn back. They shoot on sight within the area of the wall. You *must* get over.'

'We know,' Leamas repeated; 'he told me.'

'From the moment you get out of the car you are in the area.'

'We know. Now shut up,' Leamas retorted. And then he added: 'are you taking the car back?'

'As soon as you get out of the car I shall drive it away. It is a danger for me, too,' the man replied.

'Too bad,' said Leamas drily.

Again there was silence; then Leamas asked: 'Have you got a gun?'

'Yes,' said the man; 'but I can't give it to you; he said I shouldn't give it to you . . . that you were sure to ask for it.'

Leamas laughed quietly. 'He would,' he said.

Leamas pulled the starter. With a noise that seemed to fill the street the car moved slowly forward.

They had gone about three hundred yards when the man whispered excitedly, 'Go right here, then left.' They swung into a narrow side street. There were empty market stalls on either side so that the car barely passed between them.

'Left here, now!'

They turned again, fast, this time between two tall buildings into what looked like a cul-de-sac. There was washing across the street, and Liz wondered whether they would pass under it. As they approached what seemd to be the dead end the man said: 'Left again – follow the path.' Leamas mounted the curb, crossed the pavement, and they followed a broad footpath bordered by a broken fence to their left, and a tall, windowless building to their right. They heard a shout from somewhere above them, a woman's voice, and Leamas muttered: 'Oh, shut up,' as he steered clumsily round a right-angle bend in the path and came almost immediately upon a major road.

'Which way?' he demanded.

'Straight across – past the chemist – between the chemist and the post office – there!' The man was leaning so far forward that his face was almost level with theirs. He pointed now, reaching past Leamas, the tip of his fingers pressed against the windscreen.

'Get back,' Leamas hissed. 'Get your hand away. How the hell can I see if you wave your hand around like that?' Slamming the car into first gear he drove fast across the wide road. Glancing up to his left he was astonished to glimpse the plump silhouette of the Brandenburg Gate three hundred yards away, and the sinister grouping of military vehicles at the foot of it.

'Where are we going?' asked Leamas suddenly.

'We're nearly there. Go slowly now . . . left, left, go left!' he cried, and Leamas jerked the wheel in the nick of time; they passed under a narrow archway into a courtyard. Half the windows were missing or boarded up; the empty doorways gaped sightlessly at them. At the other end of the yard was an open gateway. 'Through there,' came the whispered command, urgent in the darkness; 'then hard right. You'll see a street lamp on your right. The one beyond it is broken. When you reach the second lamp switch off the engine and coast until you see a fire hydrant. That's the place.'

'Why the hell didn't you drive yourself?'

'He said you should drive; he said it was safer.'

They passed through the gate and turned sharply to the right. They were in a narrow street, pitch dark.

'Lights out!'

Leamas switched off the car lights, drove slowly forwards towards the first street lamp. Ahead, they could just see the second. It was unlit. Switching off the engine they coasted silently past it, until twenty yards ahead of them they discerned the dim outline of the fire hydrant. Leamas braked; the car rolled to a standstill.

'Where are we?' Leamas whispered. 'We crossed the Lenin-allee, didn't we?'

'Griefswalder Strasse. Then we turned north. We're north of Bernauerstrasse.'

'Pankow?'

'Just about. Look,' the man pointed down a side street to the left. At the far end they saw a brief stretch of wall, grey-brown in the weary arclight. Along the top ran a triple strand of barbed wire.

'How will the girl get over the wire?'

'It is already cut where you climb. There is a small gap. You have one minute to reach the wall. Good-bye.'

They got out of the car, all three of them. Leamas took Liz by the arm, and she started from him as if he had hurt her.

'Good-bye,' said the German.

Leamas just whispered: 'Don't start that car till we're over.'

Liz looked at the German for a moment in the pale light. She had a brief impression of a young, anxious face; the face of a boy trying to be brave.

'Good-bye,' said Liz. She disengaged her arm and followed Leamas across the road and into the narrow street that led towards the wall.

As they entered the street they heard the car start up behind them, turn and move quickly away in the direction they had come.

'Pull up the ladder, you bastard,' Leamas muttered, glancing back at the retreating car.

Liz hardly heard him.

CHAPTER 26

IN FROM THE COLD

They walked quickly, Leamas glancing over his shoulder from time to time to make sure she was following. As he reached the end of the alley, he stopped, drew into the shadow of a doorway and looked at his watch.

'Two minutes,' he whispered.

She said nothing. She was staring straight ahead towards the wall, and the black ruins rising behind it.

'Two minutes,' Leamas repeated.

Before them was a strip of thirty yards. It followed the wall in both directions. Perhaps seventy yards to their right was a watch tower; the beam of its searchlight played along the strip. The thin rain hung in the air, so that the light from the arclamps was sallow and chalky, screening the world beyond. There was no one to be seen; not a sound. An empty stage.

The watch tower's searchlight began feeling its way along the wall towards them, hesitant; each time it rested they could see the separate bricks and the careless lines of mortar hastily put on. As they watched the beam stopped immediately in front of them. Leamas looked at his watch.

'Ready?' he asked.

She nodded.

Taking her arm he began walking deliberately across the strip. Liz wanted to run, but he held her so tightly that she could not. They were half-way towards the wall now, the brilliant semi-circle of light drawing them forward, the beam directly above them. Leamas was determined to keep Liz very close to him, as if he were afraid that Mundt would not keep his word and somehow snatch her away at the last moment.

They were almost at the wall when the beam darted to the North leaving them momentarily in total darkness. Still holding Liz's arm, Leamas guided her forward blindly, his left hand reaching ahead of him until suddenly he felt the coarse, sharp contact of the cinder brick. Now he could discern the wall and, looking upwards, the triple strand of wire and the cruel hooks which held it. Metal wedges, like climbers' pitons, had been driven into the brick. Seizing the highest one, Leamas pulled himself quickly upwards until he had reached the top of the wall. He tugged sharply at the lower strand of wire and it came towards him, already cut.

'Come on,' he whispered urgently, 'start climbing.'

Laying himself flat he reached down, grasped her upstretched hand and began drawing her slowly upwards as her foot found the first metal rung.

Suddenly the whole world seemed to break into flame; from everywhere, from above and beside them, massive lights converged, bursting upon them with savage accuracy.

Leamas was blinded, he turned his head away, wrenching wildly at Liz's arm. Now she was swinging free; he thought she had slipped and he called frantically, still drawing her upwards. He could see nothing – only a mad confusion of colour dancing in his eyes.

Then came the hysterical wail of sirens, orders frantically shouted. Half kneeling astride the wall he grasped both her arms in his, and began dragging her to him inch by inch, himself on the verge of falling.

Then they fired – single rounds, three or four and he felt her shudder. Her thin arms slipped from his hands. He heard a voice in English from the Western side of the wall:

'Jump, Alec! Jump, man!'

Now everyone was shouting, English, French and German mixed; he heard Smiley's voice from quite close:

'The girl, where's the girl?'

Shielding his eyes he looked down at the foot of the wall and at last he managed to see her, lying still. For a moment he hesitated, then quite slowly he climbed back down the same rungs, until he was standing beside her. She was dead; her face was turned away, her black hair drawn across her cheek as if to protect her from the rain.

They seemed to hesitate before firing again; someone shouted an order, and still no one fired. Finally they shot him, two or three shots. He stood glaring round him like a blinded bull in the arena. As he fell, Leamas saw a small car smashed between great lorries, and the children waving cheerfully through the window.

The Mask
of Dimitrios

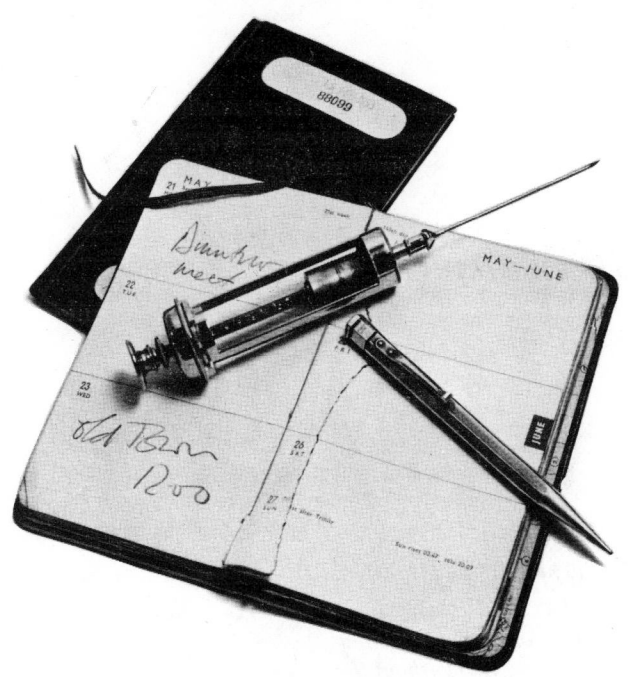

Eric
Ambler

'*But the iniquity of oblivion blindely*
scattereth her poppy, and deals with
the memory of men without distinction
to merit of perpetuity . . . Without the
favour of the everlasting register, the
first man had been as unknown as the
last, and Methuselah's long life had
been his only Chronicle.'
SIR THOMAS BROWNE:
Hydriotaphia

CHAPTER 1

ORIGINS OF AN OBSESSION

A Frenchman named Chamfort, who should have known better, once said that chance was a nickname for Providence.

It is one of those convenient, question-begging aphorisms coined to discredit the unpleasant truth that chance plays an important, if not predominant, part in human affairs. Yet it was not entirely inexcusable. Inevitably, chance does occasionally operate with a sort of fumbling coherence readily mistakable for the workings of a self-conscious Providence.

The story of Dimitrios Makropoulos is an example of this.

The fact that a man like Latimer should so much as learn of the existence of a man like Dimitrios is alone grotesque. That he should actually see the dead body of Dimitrios, that he should spend weeks that he could ill afford probing into the man's shadowy history, and that he should ultimately find himself in the position of owing his life to a criminal's odd taste in interior decoration are breath-taking in their absurdity.

Yet, when these facts are seen side by side with the other facts in the case, it is difficult not to become lost in superstitious awe. Their very absurdity seems to prohibit the use of the words 'chance' and 'coincidence'. For the sceptic there remains only one consolation: if there should be such a thing as a superhuman Law, it is administered with sub-human inefficiency. The choice of Latimer as its instrument could have been made only by an idiot.

During the first fifteen years of his adult life, Charles Latimer became a lecturer in political economy at a minor English university. By the time he was thirty-five he had, in addition, written three books. The first was a study of the influence of Proudhon on nineteenth century Italian political thought. The second was entitled: *The Gotha Programme of 1875*. The third was an assessment of the economic implications of Rosenberg's *Der Mythus des zwanzigsten Jahrhunderts*.

It was soon after he had finished correcting the bulky proofs of the last work, and in the hope of dispelling the black depression which was the aftermath of his temporary association with the philosophy of National Socialism and its prophet, Dr. Rosenberg, that he wrote his first detective story.

A Bloody Shovel was an immediate success. It was followed by '*I,*' said *the Fly* and *Murder's Arms*. From the great army of university professors who write detective stories in their spare time, Latimer soon emerged as one of the shamefaced few who could make money at the sport. It was, perhaps, inevitable that, sooner or later, he would become a professional writer in name as well as in fact. Three things hastened the transition. The first was a disagreement with the university authorities over what he held to be a matter of principle. The second was an illness. The third was the fact that he happened to be unmarried. Not long after the publication of *No Doornail This* and following the illness, which had made inroads on his constitutional reserves, he wrote, with only mild reluctance, a letter of resignation and went abroad to complete his fifth detective story in the sun.

It was the week after he had finished that book's successor that he went to Turkey. He had spent a year in and near Athens and was longing for a change of scene. His health was much improved but the prospect of an English autumn was uninviting. At the suggestion of a Greek friend he took the steamer from the Piræus to Istanbul.

It was in Istanbul and from Colonel Haki that he first heard of Dimitrios.

A letter of introduction is an uneasy document. More often than not, the bearer of it is only casually acquainted with the giver who, in turn, may know the person to whom it is addressed even less well. The chances of its presentation having a satisfactory outcome for all three are slender.

Among the letters of introduction which Latimer carried with him to Istanbul was one to a Madame Chávez, who lived, he had been told, in a villa on the Bosphorus. Three days after he arrived, he wrote to her and received in reply an invitation to join a four day party at the villa. A trifle apprehensively, he accepted.

For Madame Chávez, the road from Buenos Ayres had been as liberally paved with gold as the road to it. A very handsome Turkish woman, she had successfully married and divorced a wealthy Argentine meat broker and, with a fraction of her gains from these transactions, had purchased a small palace which had once housed a minor Turkish royalty. It stood, remote and inconvenient of access, overlooking a bay of fantastic beauty and, apart from the fact that the supplies of fresh water were insufficient to serve even one of its nine bathrooms, was exquisitely appointed. But for the other guests and his hostess's Turkish habit of striking her servants violently in the face when they displeased her (which was often), Latimer, for whom such grandiose discomfort was a novelty, would have enjoyed himself.

The other guests were a very noisy pair of Marseillais, three Italians, two young Turkish naval officers and their 'fiancées' of the moment and an assortment of Istanbul business men with their wives. The greater part of the time they spent in drinking Madame Chávez's seemingly inexhaustible supplies of Dutch gin and dancing to a gramophone attended by a servant who went on steadily playing records whether the guests happened to be dancing at the moment or not. On the pretext of ill-health, Latimer excused himself from much of the drinking and most of the dancing. He was generally ignored.

It was in the late afternoon of his last day there and he was sitting at the end of the vine-covered terrace out of earshot of the gramophone, when he saw a large chauffeur-driven touring car lurching up the long, dusty road to the villa. As it roared into the courtyard below, the occupant of the rear seat flung the door open and vaulted out before the car came to a standstill.

He was a tall man with lean, muscular cheeks whose pale tan contrasted well with a head of grey hair cropped Prussian fashion. A narrow frontal bone, a long beak of a nose and thin lips gave him a somewhat predatory air. He could not be less than fifty, Latimer thought, and studied the waist below the beautifully cut officer's uniform in the hope of detecting the corsets.

He watched the tall officer whip a silk handkerchief from his sleeve, flick some invisible dust from his immaculate patent-leather riding boots, tilt his cap raffishly and stride out of sight. Somewhere in the villa, a bell pealed.

Colonel Haki, for this was the officer's name, was an immediate success with the party. A quarter of an hour after his arrival, Madame Chávez, with an air of shy confusion clearly intended to inform her guests that she regarded herself as hopelessly compromised by the Colonel's unexpected appearance, led him on to the terrace and introduced him. All smiles and gallantry, he clicked heels, kissed hands, bowed, acknowledged the salutes of the naval officers and ogled the businessmen's wives. The performance so fascinated Latimer that, when his turn came to be introduced, the sound of his own name made him jump. The Colonel pump-handled his arm warmly.

'Damned pleased indeed to meet you, old boy,' he said.

'*Monsieur le Colonel parle bien anglais,*' explained Madame Chávez.

'*Quelques mots,*' said Colonel Haki.

Latimer looked amiably into a pair of pale grey eyes. 'How do you do?'

'Cheerio – all – the – best,' replied the Colonel with grave courtesy, and passed on to kiss the hand of, and to run an appraising eye over, a stout girl in a bathing costume.

It was not until late in the evening that Latimer spoke to the Colonel again. The Colonel had injected a good deal of boisterous vitality into the party; cracking jokes, laughing loudly, making humorously brazen advances to the wives and rather more surreptitious ones to the unmarried women. From time to time his eye caught Latimer's and he grinned deprecatingly. 'I've got to play the fool like this – it's expected of me,' said the grin; 'but don't think I like it.' Then, long after dinner, when the guests had begun to take less interest in the dancing and more in the progress of a game of mixed strip poker, the Colonel took him by the arm and walked him on to the terrace.

'You must excuse me, Mr. Latimer,' he said in French, 'but I should very much like to talk with you. Those women – phew!' He slid a cigarette case under Latimer's nose. 'A cigarette?'

'Thank you.'

Colonel Haki glanced over his shoulder. 'The other end of the terrace is more secluded,' he said; and then, as they began to walk: 'you know, I came up here to-day specially to see you. Madame told me you were here and really I could not resist the temptation of talking with the writer whose works I so much admire.'

Latimer murmured a non-committal appreciation of the compliment. He was in a difficulty, for he had no means of knowing whether the Colonel was thinking in terms of political economy or detection. He had once startled and irritated a kindly old don who had professed interest in his 'last book', by asking the old man whether he preferred his corpses shot or bludgeoned. It sounded affected to ask which set of books was under discussion.

Colonel Haki, however, did not wait to be questioned. 'I get all the latest *romans policiers* sent to me from Paris,' he went on. 'I read nothing but *romans policiers*. I would like you to see my collection. Especially I like the English and American ones. All the best of them are translated into French. French writers themselves, I do not find sympathetic. French culture is not such as can produce a *roman policier* of the first order. I have just added your *Une Pelle Ensanglantée* to my library. Formidable! But I cannot quite understand the significance of the title.'

Latimer spent some time trying to explain in French the meaning of 'to call a spade a bloody shovel' and to translate the play on words which had given (to those readers with suitable minds) the essential clue to the murderer's identity in the very title.

Colonel Haki listened intently, nodding his head and saying, 'Yes, I see, I see it clearly now,' before Latimer had reached the point of the explanation.

'Monsieur,' he said when Latimer had given up in despair, 'I wonder whether you would do me the honour of lunching with me one day this week. I think,' he added mysteriously, 'that I may be able to help you.'

Latimer did not see in what way he could be helped by Colonel Haki but said that he would be glad to lunch with him. They arranged to meet at the Pera Palace Hotel three days later.

It was not until the evening before it that Latimer thought very much more about the luncheon appointment. He was sitting in the lounge of his hotel with the manager of his bankers' Istanbul branch.

Collinson, he thought, was a pleasant fellow but a monotonous companion. His conversation consisted almost entirely of gossip about the doings of the English and American colonies in Istanbul. 'Do you know the Fitzwilliams,' he would say. 'No? A pity, you'd like them. Well, the other day . . .' As a source of information about Kemal Ataturk's economic reforms he had proved a failure.

'By the way,' said Latimer after listening to an account of the goings-on of the Turkish-born wife of an American car salesman, 'do you know of a man named Colonel Haki?'

'Haki? What made you think of him?'

'I'm lunching with him to-morrow.'

'Collinson's eyebrows went up. '*Are* you, by Jove!' He scratched his chin. 'Well I know *of* him.' He hesitated. 'Haki's one of those people you hear a lot about in this place but never seem to get a line on. One of the people behind the scenes, if you get me. He's got more influence than a good many of the men who are supposed to be at the top at Ankara. He was one of the Gazi's own particular men in Anatolia in nineteen-nineteen, a deputy in the Provisional Government. I've heard stories about him then. Bloodthirsty devil by all accounts. There was something about torturing prisoners. But then both sides did that and I dare say it was the Sultan's boys that started it. I heard, too, that he can drink a couple of bottles of Scotch at a sitting and stay stone cold sober. Don't believe that though. How did you get on to him?'

Latimer explained. 'What does he do for a living?' he added. 'I don't understand these uniforms.'

Collinson shrugged. 'Well, I've *heard* on good authority that he's the head of the secret police, but that's probably just another story. That's the worst of this place. Can't believe a word they say in the Club. Why, only the other day . . .'

It was with rather more enthusiasm than before that Latimer went to his luncheon appointment the following day. He had judged Colonel Haki to be something of a ruffian and Collinson's vague information had tended to confirm that view.

The Colonel arrived, bursting with apologies, twenty minutes late, and hurried his guest straight into the restaurant. 'We must have a whisky-soda immediately,' he said and called loudly for a bottle of 'Johnnie'.

During most of the meal he talked about the detective stories he had read, his reactions to them, his opinions of the characters and his preference for murderers who shot their victims. At last, with an almost empty bottle of whisky at his elbow and a strawberry ice in front of him, he leaned forward across the table.

'I think, Mr. Latimer,' he said again, 'that I can help you.'

For one wild moment Latimer wondered if he were going to be offered a job in the Turkish secret service; but he said: 'That's very kind of you.'

'It was my ambition,' continued Colonel Haki, 'to write a good *roman policier* of my own. I have often thought that I could do so if I had the time. That is the trouble – the time. I have found that out. But . . .' He paused impressively.

Latimer waited. He was always meeting people who felt that they could write detective stories if they had the time.

'But,' repeated the Colonel, 'I have the plot prepared I would like to make you a present of it.'

Latimer said that it was very good indeed of him.

The Colonel waved away his thanks. 'Your books have given me so much pleasure, Mr. Latimer. I am glad to make you a present of an idea for a new one. I have not the time to use it myself, and, in any case,' he added magnanimously, 'you would make better use of it than I should.'

Latimer mumbled incoherently.

'The scene of the story,' pursued his host, his grey eyes fixed on Latimer's, 'is an English country house belonging to the rich Lord Robinson. There is a party for the English week-end. In the middle of the party, Lord Robinson is discovered in the library sitting at his desk – shot through the temple. The wound is singed. A pool of blood has formed on the desk and it has soaked into a paper. The paper is a new Will which the Lord was about to sign. The old Will divided his money equally between six persons, his relations, who are at the party. The new Will, which he has been prevented from signing by the murderer's bullet, leaves all to one of those relations. Therefore' – he pointed his ice cream spoon accusingly – 'one of the five other relations is the guilty one. That is logical, is it not?'

Latimer opened his mouth, then shut it again and nodded.

Colonel Haki grinned triumphantly. 'That is the trick.

'The trick?'

'The Lord was murdered by none of the suspects, but by the butler, whose wife had been seduced by this Lord! What do you think of that, eh?'

'Very ingenious.'

His host leaned back contentedly and smoothed out his tunic. 'It is only a trick, but I am glad you like it. Of course, I have the whole plot worked out in detail. The *flic* is a High Commissioner of Scotland Yard. He seduces one of the suspects, a very pretty woman, and it is for her sake that he solves the mystery. It is quite artistic. But, as I say, I have the whole thing written out.'

'I should be very interested,' said Latimer with sincerity, 'to read your notes.'

'That is what I hoped you would say. Are you pressed for time?'

'Not a bit.'

'Then let us go back to my office and I will show you what I have done. It is written in French.'

Latimer hesitated only momentarily. He had nothing better to do, and it might be interesting to see Colonel Haki's office.

'I should like to go back with you,' he said.

The Colonel's office was situated at the top of what might once have been a cheap hotel, but which, from the inside, was unmistakably a government building, in Galata. It was a large room at the end of a corridor. When they went in a uniformed clerk was bending over the desk. He straightened his back, clicked his heels and said something in Turkish. The Colonel answered him and nodded a dismissal. Latimer looked round him. Besides the desk there were several small chairs and an American ice-water maker. The walls were bare and the floor was covered with coconut matting. Long green sun lattices hanging outside the windows kept out most of the light. It was very cool after the heat of the car which had brought them.

The Colonel waved him to a chair, gave him a cigarette and began rummaging in a drawer. At last he drew out a sheet or two of typewritten paper and held it out.

'There you are, Mr. Latimer. *The Clue of the Bloodstained Will*, I have called it, but I am not convinced that that is the best title. All the best titles have been used, I find. But I will think of some alternatives. Read it, and do not be afraid to say frankly what you think of it. If there are any details which you think should be altered, I will alter them.'

Latimer took the sheets and read while the Colonel sat on the corner of his desk and swung a long, gleaming leg.

Latimer read through the sheets twice and then put them down. He was feeling ashamed of himself because he had wanted several times to laugh. He should not have come. Now that he *had* come, the best thing he could do was to leave as quickly as possible.

'I cannot suggest any improvements at the moment,' he said slowly; 'of course, it all wants thinking over; it is so easy to make mistakes with problems of this sort. There is so much to be thought of. Questions of British legal procedure, for instance . . .'

'Yes, yes, of course.' Colonel Haki slid off the desk and sat down in his chair. 'But you think you can use it, eh?'

'I am very grateful indeed for your generosity,' said Latimer evasively.

'It is nothing. You shall send me a free copy of the book when it appears.' He swung round in his chair and picked up the telephone. 'I will have a copy made for you to take away.'

Latimer sat back. Well, that was that! It could not take long to make a copy. He listened to the Colonel talking to someone over the telephone and saw him frown. The Colonel put the telephone down and turned to him.

'You will excuse me if I deal with a small matter?'

'Of course.'

The Colonel drew a bulky manila file towards him and began to go through the papers inside it. Then he selected one and glanced down it. As he did so the uniformed clerk rapped on the door and marched in with a thin yellow folder under his arm. The Colonel took the folder and put it on the desk in front of him; then, with a word of instruction, he handed over *The Clue of the Bloodstained Will* to the clerk who clicked his heels and went out. There was silence in the room.

Latimer, affecting preoccupation with his cigarette, glanced across the desk. Colonel Haki was slowly turning the pages inside the folder, and on his face was a look that Latimer had not seen there before. It was the look of the expert attending to the business he understood perfectly. There was a sort of watchful repose in his face that reminded Latimer of a very old and experienced cat contemplating a very young and inexperienced mouse. In that moment he revised his ideas about Colonel Haki. He had been feeling a little sorry for him as one feels sorry for anyone who has unconsciously made a fool of himself. He saw now that the Colonel stood in need of no such consideration. As his long, yellowish fingers turned the pages of the folder, Latimer remembered a sentence of Collinson's: 'There was something about torturing prisoners.' He knew suddenly that he was seeing the real Colonel Haki for the first time. Then the Colonel looked up and his pale eyes rested thoughtfully on Latimer's tie.

For a moment Latimer had an uncomfortable suspicion that although the man across the desk appeared to be looking at his tie, he was actually looking into his mind. Then the Colonel's eyes moved upwards and he grinned slightly in a way that made Latimer feel as if he had been caught stealing something.

He said: 'I wonder if you are interested in *real* murderers, Mr. Latimer.'

CHAPTER 2

THE DOSSIER OF DIMITRIOS

Latimer felt himself redden. From the condescending professional he had been changed suddenly into the ridiculous amateur. It was a little disconcerting.

'Well, yes,' he said slowly. 'I suppose I am.'

Colonel Haki pursed his lips. 'You know, Mr. Latimer,' he said, 'I find the murderer in a *roman policier* much more sympathetic than a real murderer. In a *roman policier* there is a corpse, a number of suspects, a detective and a gallows. That is artistic. The real murderer is not artistic. I, who am a sort of policeman, tell you that squarely.' He tapped the folder on his desk. 'Here is a real murderer. We have known of his existence for nearly twenty years. This is his dossier. We know of one murder he may have committed. There are doubtless others of which we, at any rate, know nothing. This man is typical. A dirty type, common, cowardly, scum. Murder, espionage, drugs – that is the history. There were also two affairs of assassination.'

'Assassination! that argues a certain courage, surely?'

The Colonel laughed unpleasantly. 'My dear friend, Dimitrios would have nothing to do with the actual shooting. No! His kind never risk their skins like that. They stay on the fringe of the plot. They are the professionals, the *entrepreneurs*, the links between the businessmen, the politicians who desire the end but are afraid of the means, and the fanatics, the idealists who are prepared to die for their convictions. The important thing to know about an assassination or an attempted assassination is not who fired the shot, but who paid for the bullet. It is the rats like Dimitrios who can best tell you that. They are always ready to talk to save themselves the inconvenience of a prison cell. Dimitrios would have been the same as any other. Courage!' He laughed again. 'Dimitrios was a little cleverer than some of them. I'll grant you that. As far as I know, no government has ever caught him and there is no photograph in his dossier. But we knew him all right, and so did Sofia and Belgrade and Paris and Athens. He was a great traveller, was Dimitrios.'

'That sounds as though he's dead.'

'Yes, he is dead.' Colonel Haki turned the corners of his thin mouth down contemptuously. 'A fisherman pulled his body out of the Bosphorus last night. It is believed that he had been knifed and thrown overboard from a ship. Like the scum he was, he was floating.'

'At least,' said Latimer, 'he died by violence. That is something very like justice.'

'Ah!' The Colonel leaned forward. 'There is the writer speaking. Everything must be tidy, artistic, like a *roman policier*. Very well!' He pulled the dossier towards him and opened it. 'Just listen, Mr. Latimer, to this. Then you shall tell me if it is artistic.'

He began to read.

'Dimitrios Makropoulos.' He stopped and looked up. 'We have never been able to find out whether that was the surname of the family that adopted him or an alias. He was known usually as Dimitrios.' He turned to the dossier again. 'Dimitrios Makropoulos. Born 1889 in Larissa, Greece. Found abandoned. Parents unknown. Mother believed Roumanian. Registered as Greek subject and adopted by Greek family. Criminal record with Greek authorities. Details unobtainable.' He looked up at Latimer. 'That was before he came to our notice. We first heard of him at Izmir[1] in 1922, a few days after our troops occupied the town. A *deunme*[2] named Sholem was found in his room with his throat cut: He was a money-lender and kept his money under the floorboards. These were ripped up and the money had been taken. There was much violence in Izmir at that time and little notice would have been taken by the military authorities. The thing might have been done by one of our soldiers. Then, another Jew, a relation of Sholem's, drew the attention of the military to a Negro named Dhris Mohammed, who had been spending money in the cafés and boasting that a Jew had lent him the money without interest. Inquiries were made and Dhris was arrested. His replies to the courtmartial were unsatisfactory and he was condemned to death. Then he made a confession. He was a fig-packer, and he said that one of his fellow workmen, whom he called Dimitrios, had told him of Sholem's wealth hidden under the floorboards of his room. They had planned the robbery together and had entered Sholem's room by night.

[1] Smyrna.
[2] Jew turned Muslim.

It had been Dimitrios, he said, who had killed the Jew. He thought that Dimitrios, being registered as a Greek, had escaped and bought a passage on one of the refugee ships that waited at secret places along the coast.'

He shrugged. 'The authorities did not believe his story. We were at war with Greece, and it was the sort of story a guilty man might invent to save his neck. They found that there had been a fig-packer named Dimitrios, that his fellow workmen had disliked him and that he had disappeared.' He grinned. 'Quite a lot of Greeks named Dimitrios disappeared at that time. You could see their bodies in the streets and floating in the harbour. This Negro's story was unprovable. He was hanged.'

He paused. During this recital he had not once referred to the dossier.

'You have a very good memory for facts,' commented Latimer.

The Colonel grinned again. 'I was the president of the courtmartial. It was through that that I was able to mark down Dimitrios later on. I was transferred a year later to the secret police. In 1924 a plot to assassinate the Gazi was discovered. It was the year he abolished the Caliphate and the plot was outwardly the work of a group of religious fanatics. Actually the men behind it were agents of some people in the good graces of a neighbouring friendly government. They had good reasons for wishing the Gazi out of the way. The plot was discovered. The details are unimportant. But one of the agents who escaped was a man known as Dimitrios.' He pushed the cigarettes towards Latimer. 'Please smoke.'

Latimer shook his head. 'Was it the same Dimitrios?'

'It was. Now, tell me frankly. Mr. Latimer. Do you find anything artistic there? Could you make a good *roman policier* out of that? Is there anything there that could be of the slightest interest to a writer?'

'Police work interests me a great deal – naturally. But what happened to Dimitrios? How did the story end?'

Colonel Haki snapped his fingers. 'Ah! I was waiting for you to ask that. I knew you would ask it. And my answer is this: it *didn't* end!'

'Then what happened?'

'I will tell you. The first problem was to identify Dimitrios of Izmir with Dimitrios of Edirné.[1] Accordingly we revived the affair of Sholem, issued a warrant for the arrest of a Greek fig-packer named Dimitrios on a charge of murder and, with that excuse, asked foreign police authorities for assistance. We did not learn much, but what we did learn was sufficient. Dimitrios had been concerned with the attempted assassination of Stambulisky in Bulgaria which had preceded the Macedonian officers' *putsch* in 1923. The Sofia police know very little but that he was

[1] Adrianople

known there to be a Greek from Izmir. A woman with whom he had associated in Sofia was questioned. She stated that she had had a letter from him a short time before. He had given no address, but as she had had very urgent reasons for wishing to get in touch with him she had looked at the postmark. It was from Edirné. The Sofia police obtained a rough description of him that agreed with that given by the Negro in Izmir. The Greek police stated that he had had a criminal record prior to 1922 and gave those particulars of his origin. The warrant is probably still in existence; but we did not find Dimitrios with it.

'It was not until two years later that we heard of him again. We received an inquiry from the Yugoslav Government concerning a Turkish subject named Dimitrios Talat. He was wanted, they said, for robbery; but an agent of ours in Belgrade reported that the robbery was the theft of some secret naval documents and that the charge the Yugoslavs hoped to bring against him was one of espionage on behalf of France. By the first name and the description issued by the Belgrade police we guessed that Talat was probably Dimitrios of Izmir. About the same time our Consul in Switzerland renewed the passport, issued apparently at Ankara, of a man named Talat. It is a common Turkish name; but when it came to entering the record of the renewal it was found from the number that no such passport had been issued. The passport had been forged.' He spread out his heads. 'You see, Mr. Latimer? There is your story. Incomplete. Inartistic. No detection, no suspects, no hidden motives, merely sordid.'

'But interesting, nevertheless,' objected Latimer. 'What happened over the Talat business?'

'Still looking for the end of your story, Mr. Latimer? All right, then. Nothing happened about Talat. It is just a name We never heard it again. If he used the passport we don't know. It does not matter. We have Dimitrios. A corpse, it is true, but we have him. We shall probably never know who killed him. The ordinary police will doubtless make their inquiries and report to us that they have no hope of discovering the murderer. This dossier will go into the archives. It is just one of many similar cases.'

'You said something about drugs.'

Colonel Haki began to look bored. 'Oh, yes. Dimitrios made a lot of money once I should think. Another unfinished story. About three years after the Belgrade affair we heard of him again. Nothing to do with us but the available information was added to the dossier as a routine matter.' He referred to the dossier. 'In 1929, the League of Nations Advisory Committee on the illicit drug traffic received a report from the

French government concerning the seizure of a large quantity of heroin at the Swiss frontier. It was concealed in a mattress in a sleeping car coming from Sofia. One of the car attendants was found to be responsible for the smuggling but all he could or would tell the police was that the drug was to have been collected in Paris by a man who worked at the rail terminus. He did not know the man's name and had never spoken to him; but he described him. The man in question was later arrested. Questioned, he admitted the charge but claimed that he knew nothing of the destination of the drug. He received one consignment a month which was collected by a third man. The police set a trap for this third man and caught him only to find there was a fourth intermediary. They arrested six men in all in connection with that affair and only obtained one real clue. It was that the man at the head of this peddling organization was a man known as Dimitrios. Through the medium of the Committee, the Bulgarian government then revealed that they had found a clandestine heroin laboratory at Radomir and had seized two hundred and thirty kilos of heroin ready for delivery. The consignee's name was Dimitrios. During the next year the French succeeded in discovering one or two other large heroin consignments bound for Dimitrios. But they did not get very much nearer to Dimitrios himself. There were difficulties. The stuff never seemed to come in the same way twice and by the end of the year, 1930, all they had to show in the way of arrests were a number of smugglers and some insignificant pedlars. Judging by the amounts of heroin they did find, Dimitrios must have been making huge sums for himself. Then, quite suddenly, about a year after that, Dimitrios went out of the drug business. The first news the police had of this was an anonymous letter which gave the names of all the principal members of the gang, their life histories and details of how evidence against every one of them might be obtained. The French police had a theory at the time. They said that Dimitrios himself had become a heroin addict. Whether that is true or not, the fact is that by December, the gang was rounded up. One of them, a woman, was already wanted for fraud. Some of them threatened to kill Dimitrios when they were released from prison but the most any of them could tell the police about him was that his surname was Makropoulos and that he had a flat in the seventeenth *arrondissement*. They never found the flat and they never found Dimitrios.'

The clerk had come in and was standing by the desk.

'Ah,' said the Colonel, 'here is your copy.'

Latimer took it and thanked him rather absently.

'And that was the last you heard of Dimitrios?' he added.

'Oh, no. The last we heard of him was about a year later. A Croat attempted to assassinate a Yugoslav politician in Zagreb. In the confession he made to the police, he said that friends had obtained the pistol he used from a man named Dimitrios in Rome. If it was Dimitrios of Izmir he must have returned to his old profession. A dirty type. There are a few more like him who should float in the Bosphorus.'

'You say you never had a photograph of him. How did you identify him?'

'There was a French *carte d'identité* sewn inside the lining of his coat. It was issued about a year ago at Lyons to Dimitrios Makropoulos. It is a visitor's *carte* and he is described as being without occupation. That might mean anything. There was, of course, a photograph in it. We've turned it over to the French. They say that it is quite genuine.' He pushed the dossier aside and stood up. 'There's an inquest to-morrow. I have to go and have a look at the body in the police mortuary. That is a thing you do not have to contend with in books, Mr. Latimer – a list of regulations. A man is found floating in the Bosphorus. A police matter, clearly. But because this man happens to be on my files, my organization has to deal with it also. I have my car waiting. Can I take you anywhere?'

'If my hotel isn't too much out of your way, I should like to be taken there.'

'Of course. You have the plot of your new book safely? Good. Then we are ready.'

In the car, the Colonel elaborated on the virtues of *The Clue of the Bloodstained Will*. Latimer promised to keep in touch with him and let him know how the book progressed. The car pulled up outside his hotel. They had exchanged farewells and Latimer was about to get out when he hesitated and then dropped back into his seat.

'Look here, Colonel,' he said, 'I want to make what will seem to you a rather strange request.'

The Colonel gestured expansively. 'Anything.'

'I have a fancy to see the body of this man Dimitrios. I wonder if it would be possible for you to take me with you.'

The Colonel frowned and then shrugged. 'If you wish to come, by all means do so. But I do not see . . .'

'I have never,' lied Latimer quickly, 'seen either a dead man or a mortuary. I think that every detective story writer should see those things.'

The Colonel's face cleared. 'My dear fellow, of course he should. One cannot write about that which one has never seen.' He signalled the chauffeur on. 'Perhaps,' he added as they drove off again, 'we can in-corporate a scene in a mortuary in your new book. I will think about it.'

The mortuary was a small corrugated iron building in the precincts of a police station near the mosque of Nouri Osmanieh. A police official, collected *en route* by the Colonel, led them across the yard which sepa-rated it from the main building. The afternoon heat had set the air above the concrete quivering and Latimer began to wish that he had not come. It was not the weather for visiting corrugated iron mortuaries.

The official unlocked the door and opened it. A blast of hot, carbolic-laden air came out, as from an oven, to meet them. Latimer took off his hat and followed the Colonel in.

There were no windows and light was supplied by a single high-powered electric lamp in an enamel reflector. On each side of a gangway which ran down the centre, there were four high, wooden trestle tables. All but three were bare. The three were draped with stiff, heavy tar-paulins which bulged slightly above the lever of the other trestles. The heat was overpowering and Latimer felt the sweat begin to soak into his shirt and trickle down his legs.

'It's very hot,' he said.

The Colonel shrugged and nodded towards the trestles. 'They don't complain.'

The official went to the nearest of the three trestles, leaned over it and dragged the tarpaulin back. The Colonel walked over and looked down. Latimer forced himself to follow.

The body lying on the trestle was that of a short, broad-shouldered man of about fifty. From where he stood near the foot of the table, Latimer could see very little of the face, only a section of putty-coloured flesh and a fringe of tousled grey hair. The body was wrapped in a mackintosh sheet. By the feet was a neat pile of crumpled clothing: some underwear, a shirt, socks, a flowered tie and a blue serge suit stained nearly grey by sea water. Beside this pile was a pair of narrow, pointed shoes, the soles of which had warped as they had dried.

Latimer took a step nearer so that he could see the face.

No one had troubled to close the eyes and the whites of them stared upwards at the light. The lower jaw had dropped slightly. It was not quite the face that Latimer had pictured; rather rounder and with thick lips instead of thin, a face that would work and quiver under the stress of emotion. The cheeks were loose and deeply lined. But it was too late now to form any judgment of the mind that had once been behind the face. The mind had gone.

The official had been speaking to the Colonel. Now he stopped.

'Killed by a knife wound in the stomach, according to the doctor,' translated the Colonel. 'Already dead when he got into the water.'

'Where did the clothes come from?'

'Lyons, all except the suit and shoes which are Greek. Poor stuff.'

He renewed his conversation with the official.

Latimer stared at the corpse. So this was Dimitrios. This was the man who had, perhaps, slit the throat of Sholem, the Jew turned Moslem. This was the man who had connived at assassinations, who had spied for France. This was the man who had trafficked in drugs, who had given a gun to a Croat terrorist and who, in the end, had himself died by violence. This putty-coloured bulk was the end of an Odyssey. Dimitrios had returned at last to the country whence he had set out so many years before.

So many years. Europe in labour had through its pain seen for an instant a new glory, and then had collapsed to welter again in the agonies of war and fear. Governments had risen and fallen; men and women had worked, had starved, had made speeches, had fought, had been tortured, had died. Hope had come and gone, a fugitive in the scented bosom of illusion. Men had learned to sniff the heady dreamstuff of the soul and wait impassively while the lathes turned the guns for their destruction. And through those years, Dimitrios had lived and breathed and come to terms with his strange gods. He had been a dangerous man. Now, in the loneliness of death, beside the squalid pile of clothes that was his estate, he was pitiable.

Latimer watched the two men as they discussed the filling-in of a printed form the official had produced. They turned to the clothes and began making an inventory of them.

Yet at some time Dimitrios had made money, much money. What had happened to it? Had he spent it or lost it? 'Easy come, easy go,' they said. But had Dimitrios been the sort of man to let money go easily, howsoever he had acquired it? They knew so little about him! A few odd facts about a few odd incidents in his life, that was all the dossier amounted to. No more. It told you something. It told you that he had been unscrupulous, ruthless and treacherous. It told you that his way of life had been consistently criminal. But it did not tell you anything that enabled you to see the living man who had slit Sholem's throat, who had lived in a flat in Paris 17. And for every one of the crimes recorded in the dossier there must have been others, perhaps even more serious. What had happened in those two- and three-year intervals which the dossier bridged so casually? And what had happened since he had been in Lyons a year ago? By what route had he travelled to keep his appointment with Nemesis?

They were not questions that Colonel Haki would bother even to ask, much less to answer. He was the professional, concerned only with the unfanciful business of disposing of a decomposing body. But there must be people who knew and knew of Dimitrios, his friends (if he had had any), and his enemies, people in Smyrna, people in Sofia, people in Belgrade, in Adrianople, in Paris, in Lyons, people all over Europe, who *could* answer them. If you could find those people and get the answers you would have the material for what would surely be the strangest of biographies.

Latimer's heart missed a beat. It would be an absurd thing to attempt, of course. Unthinkably foolish. If one did it one would begin with, say, Smyrna and try to follow one's man step by step from there, using the dossier as a rough guide. It would be an experiment in detection really. One would, no doubt, fail to discover anything new; but there would be valuable data to be gained even from failure. All the routine inquiries over which one skated so easily in one's novels one would have to make oneself. Not that any man in his senses would dream of going on such a wild goose chase – heavens no! But it was amusing to play with the idea and if one were a little tired of Istanbul . . .

He looked up and caught the Colonel's eye.

The Colonel grimaced a reference to the heat of the place. He had finished his business with the official. 'Have you seen all you wanted to see?'

Latimer nodded.

Colonel Haki turned and looked at the body as if it were a piece of his own handiwork of which he was taking leave. For a moment or two he remained motionless. Then his right arm went out, and, grasping the dead man's hair, he lifted the head so that the sightless eyes stared into his.

'Ugly devil, isn't he,' he said. 'Life is very strange. I've known about him for nearly twenty years and this is the first time I've met him face to face. Those eyes have seen some things I should like to see. It is a pity that the mouth can never speak about them.'

He let the head go and it dropped back with a thud on to the table. Then, he drew out his silk handkerchief and wiped his fingers carefully. 'The sooner he's in a coffin the better,' he added as they walked away.

CHAPTER 3

NINETEEN TWENTY-TWO

In the early hours of an August morning in 1922, the Turkish Nationalist Army under the command of Mustafa Kemal Pasha attacked the centre of the Greek army at Dumlu Punar on the plateau two hundred miles west of Smyrna. By the following morning, the Greek army had broken and was in headlong retreat towards Smyrna and the sea. In the days that followed, the retreat became a rout. Unable to destroy the Turkish army, the Greeks turned with frantic savagery to the business of destroying the Turkish population in the path of their flight. From Alashehr to Smyrna they burnt and slaughtered. Not a village was left standing. Amid the smouldering ruins the pursuing Turks found the bodies of the villagers. Assisted by the few half-crazed Anatolian peasants who had survived, they took their revenge on the Greeks they were able to overtake. To the bodies of the Turkish women and children were added the mutilated carcases of Greek stragglers. But the main Greek army had escaped by sea. Their lust for infidel blood still unsatisfied, the Turks swept on. On the ninth of September, they occupied Smyrna.

For a fortnight, refugees from the oncoming Turks had been pouring into the city to swell the already large Greek and Armenian populations. They had thought that the Greek army would turn and defend Smyrna. But the Greek army had fled. Now they were caught in a trap. The holocaust began.

The register of the Armenian Asia Minor Defence League had been seized by the occupying troops, and, on the night of the tenth, a party of regulars entered the Armenian quarters to find and kill those whose names appeared on the register. The Armenians resisted and the Turks ran amok. The massacre that followed acted like a signal. Encouraged by their officers, the Turkish troops descended next day upon the non-Turkish quarters of the city and began systematically to kill. Dragged from their houses and hiding places, men, women and children were butchered in the streets which soon became littered with mutilated bodies. The wooden walls of the churches, packed with refugees, were drenched with benzine and fired. The occupants who were not burnt alive were bayoneted as they tried to escape. In many parts looted houses had also been set on fire and now the flames began to spread.

At first, attempts were made to isolate the blaze. Then, the wind changed, blowing the fire away from the Turkish quarter, and further outbreaks were started by the troops. Soon, the whole city, with the exception of the Turkish quarter and a few houses near the Kassamba railway station, was burning fiercely. The massacre continued with unabated ferocity. A cordon of troops was drawn round the city to keep the refugees within the burning area. The streams of panic-stricken fugitives were shot down pitilessly or driven back into the inferno. The narrow, gutted streets became so choked with corpses that, even had the would-be rescue parties been able to endure the sickening stench that arose, they could not have passed along them. Smyrna was changed from a city into a charnel-house. Many refugees had tried to reach ships in the inner harbour. Shot, drowned, mangled by propellers, their bodies floated hideously in the blood-tinged water. But the quayside was still crowded with those trying frantically to escape from the blazing waterfront buildings toppling above them a few yards behind. It was said that the screams of these people were heard a mile out at sea. *Giaur Izmir* – infidel Smyrna – had atoned for its sins.

By the time that dawn broke on the fifteenth of September, over one hundred and twenty thousand persons had perished; but somewhere amidst that horror had been Dimitrios, alive.

As, sixteen years later, his train drew into Smyrna, Latimer came to the conclusion that he was being a fool. It was not a conclusion that he had reached hastily or without weighing carefully all the available evidence. It was a conclusion that he disliked exceedingly. Yet there were two hard facts that were inescapable. In the first place, he might have asked Colonel Haki for assistance in gaining access to the records of the courtmartial and confession of Dhris Mohammed and had not been able to think of a reasonable excuse for doing so. In the second place, he knew so little Turkish that, even assuming that he could gain access to the records without Colonel Haki's help, he would be unable to read them. To have set out at all on this fantastic and slightly undignified wild goose chase was bad enough. To have set out without, so to speak, a gun and ammunition with which to make the killing was crass idiocy. Had he not been installed within an hour of his arrival in an excellent hotel, had his room not possessed a very comfortable bed and a view across the gulf to the sun-drenched, khaki hills that lay beyond it, and, above all, had he not been offered a dry Martini by the French proprietor who greeted him, he would have abandoned his experiment in detection and returned forthwith to Istanbul. As it was . . . Dimitrios or no Dimitrios, he might as well see something of Smyrna now that he was in the place. He partly unpacked his suit-cases.

It has been said that Latimer possessed a tenacious mind. Perhaps it would have been more accurate to say that he did not possess the sort of mental air-lock system which enables its fortunate owner to dispose of problems merely by forgetting them. Latimer might banish the problem from his mind but it would soon return to nibble furtively at his consciousness. He would have an uneasy feeling that he had mislaid something without being quite sure what that something was. His thoughts would wander from the business in hand. He would find himself staring blankly into space until, suddenly, there was the problem, back again. Useless to reason that, as he himself had created it, he should, therefore, be able to destroy it. Useless to argue that it was futile and that the solution of it did not matter anyway. It had to be tackled. On his second morning in Smyrna, he shrugged his shoulders irritably, went to the proprietor of his hotel and asked to be put in touch with a good interpreter.

Fedor Muishkin was a self-important little Russian of about sixty with a thick, pendulous underlip which flapped and quivered as he talked. He had an office on the waterfront and earned his living by translating business documents and interpretating for the masters and pursers of foreign cargo vessels using the port. He had been a Menshevik and had fled from Odessa in nineteen-nineteen; but although, as the hotel proprietor pointed out sardonically, he now declared himself in sympathy with the Soviets, he had preferred not to return to Russia. A humbug, mind you, but at the same time a good interpreter. If you wanted an interpreter, Muishkin was the man.

Muishkin himself also said that he was the man. He had a high-pitched, husky voice and scratched himself a great deal. His English was accurate but larded with slang phrases that never seemed quite to fit their contexts. He said: 'If there is anything I can do for you just give me the wire. I'm dirt cheap.'

'I want,' Latimer explained, 'to trace the record of a Greek who left here in September, nineteen twenty-two.'

The other's eyebrows went up. 'Nineteen twenty-two, eh? A Greek who left here?' He chuckled breathlessly. 'A good many of them left here then.' He spat on one forefinger and drew it across his throat. 'Like that! It was damnawful the way those Turks treated those Greeks. Bloody!'

'This man got away on a refugee ship. His name was Dimitrios. He was believed to have conspired with a Negro named Dhris Mohammed to murder a moneylender named Sholem. The Negro was tried by a military court and hanged. Dimitrios got away. I want to inspect, if I can, the records of the evidence taken at the trial, the confession of the Negro and the inquiries concerning Dimitrios.'

Muishkin stared. 'Dimitrios?'

'Yes.'

'Nineteen twenty-two?'

'Yes.' Latimer's heart jumped. 'Why? Did you happen to know him?'

The Russian appeared to be about to say something and then to change his mind. He shook his head. 'No. I was thinking that it was a very common name. Have you permission to examine the police archives?'

'No. I was hoping that you might be able to advise me as to the best way of getting permission. I realise, of course, that your business is only concerned with making translations, but if you could help me in this matter I should be very grateful.'

Muishkin pinched his lower lip thoughtfully. 'Perhaps if you were to approach the British Vice-Consul and request him to secure permission . . .?' He broke off. 'But excuse me,' he said; 'why do you want these records? I ask, not because I cannot mind my own damn business, but that question may be asked by the police. Now,' he went on slowly, 'if it were a *legal* matter and quite above board and Bristol fashion, I have a friend with influence who might arrange the matter quite cheap.'

Latimer felt himself redden. 'As it happens,' he said as casually as he could, 'it *is* a legal matter. I could, of course, go to the Consul, but if you care to arrange this business for me then I shall be saved the trouble.'

'A pleasure. I shall speak to my friend today. The police, you understand, are damnawful and if I go to them myself it will cost plenty. I like to protect my clients.'

'That's very good of you.'

'Don't mention it.' A faraway look came into his eyes. 'I like you British, you know. You understand how to do business. You do not haggle like those damn Greeks. When a man says cash with order you pay cash with order. A deposit? O.K. The British play fair. There is a mutual confidence between all parties. A chap can do his best work under such circumstances. He feels . . .'

'How much?' interrupted Latimer.

'Five hundred piastres?' He said it hesitantly. His eyes were mournful. Here was an artist who had no confidence in himself, a child in business matters, happy only in his work.

Latimer thought for a moment. Five hundred piastres was less than a pound. Cheap enough. Then he detected a gleam in the mournful eyes.

'Two hundred and fifty,' he said firmly.

Muishkin threw up his hands in despair. He had to live. There was his friend, too. He had great influence.

Soon after, having paid over one hundred and fifty piastres on account of a finally agreed price of three hundred (including fifty piastres for the influential friend), Latimer left. It was understood that he would call in the following day to learn the result of the negotiations with the friend. He walked back along the quayside not unpleased with his morning's work. He would have preferred, it was true, to have examined the records himself and to have seen the translation done. He would have felt more like an investigator and less like an inquisitive tourist; but there it was. There was always the chance, of course, that Muishkin might have in mind the pocketing of an easy one hundred and fifty piastres; but somehow he did not think so. He was susceptible to impressions and the Russian had impressed him as being fundamentally, if not superficially, honest. And there could be no question of his being deceived by manufactured documents. Colonal Haki had told him enough about the Dhris Mohammed courtmartial to enable him to detect that sort of fraud. The only thing that could go wrong was that the friend would prove unworthy of his fifty piastres.

Muishkin's office was locked when he called the next day and although he waited for an hour on the filthy wooden landing outside it, the interpreter did not appear. A second call, later in the day, was equally abortive. He shrugged. It hardly seemed worth any man's while to embezzle five shilling worth of Turkish piastres. But he began to lose a little of his confidence.

It was restored by a note that awaited him at the hotel on his return. A page of wild handwriting explained that the writer had been called away from his office to interpret in a dispute between a Roumanian secondmate and the dock police over the death by crowbar of a Greek stevedore, that he could pull out his own finger-nails one by one for causing Mister Latimer inconvenience, that his friend had arranged everything and that he would deliver the translation himself the following evening.

He arrived, sweating profusely, very shortly before the time of the evening meal, and Latimer was drinking an aperitif. Muishkin came towards him waving his arms and rolling his eyes despairingly and, throwing himself into an armchair, emitted a loud gasp of exhaustion.

'What a day! Such heat!' he said.

'Have you got the translation?'

Muishkin nodded wearily, his eyes closed. With what seemed a painful effort he put his hand in his inside pocket and drew out a bundle of papers secured by a wire clip. He thrust them into Latimer's hands – the dying courier delivering his last dispatch.

'Will you have a drink?' said Latimer.

The Russian's eyes flickered open and he looked round like a man regaining consciousness. He said: 'If you like. I will have an absinthe, please. *Avec de la glace.*'

The waiter took the order and Latimer sat back to inspect his purchase.

The translation was handwritten and covered twelve large sheets of paper. Latimer glanced through the first two or three pages. There was no doubt that it was all genuine. He began to read it carefully.

NATIONAL GOVERNMENT OF TURKEY
TRIBUNAL OF INDEPENDENCE

By order of the officer commanding the garrison of Izmir, acting under the Decree Law promulgated at Ankara on the eighteenth day of the sixth month of nineteen twenty-two in the new calendar.

Summary of evidence taken before the Deputy President of the Tribunal, Major-of-Brigade Zia Haki, on the sixth day of the tenth month of nineteen twenty-two in the new calendar.

The Jew, Zakari, complains that the murder of his cousin, Sholem, was the work of Dhris Mohammed, a Negro fig-packer of Buja.

Last week, a patrol belonging to the sixtieth regiment discovered the body of Sholem, a Deunme moneylender, in his room in an unnamed street near the Old Mosque. His throat had been cut. Although this man was neither the son of True Believers nor of good reputation, our vigilant police instituted inquiries and discovered that his money had been taken.

Several days later, the complainant, Zakari, informed the Commandant of Police that he had been in a café and seen the man Dhris showing handfuls of Greek money. He knew Dhris for a poor man and was surprised. Later, when Dhris had become drunk, he heard him boast that the Jew Sholem had lent him money without interest. At that time he knew nothing of the death of Sholem but when his relations told him of it he remembered what he had seen and heard.

Evidence was heard from Abdul Hakk, the owner of the Bar Cristal, who said the Dhris had shown this Greek money, a matter of several hundreds of drachmas, and had boasted that he had had it from the Jew Sholem without interest. He had thought this strange for Sholem was a hard man.

A dock-worker named Ismail also deposed that he had heard this from the prisoner.

Asked to explain how he came into possession of the money, the murderer first denied that he had had the money or that he had ever seen

Sholem and said that as a True Believer, he was hated by the Jew Zakari. He said that Abdul Hakk and Ismail had also lied.

Questioned sternly by the Deputy-President of the Tribunal, he then admitted that he had had the money and that it had been given to him by Sholem for a service he had done. But he could not explain what this service had been and his manner became strange and agitated. He denied killing Sholem and in a blasphemous way called upon the True God to witness his innocence.

The Deputy-President then ordered that the prisoner be hanged, the other members of the Tribunal agreeing that this was right and just.

Latimer had come to the end of a page. He looked at Muishkin. The Russian had swallowed the absinthe and was examining the glass. He caught Latimer's eye. 'Absinthe,' he said, 'is very good indeed. So cooling.'

'Will you have another?'

'If you like.' He smiled and indicated the papers in Latimer's hand. 'That's all right, eh?'

'Oh yes, it looks all right. But they are a little vague about their dates, aren't they? There is no doctor's report either, and no attempt to fix the time of the murder. As for the evidence, it seems fantastically feeble to me. Nothing was proved.'

Muishkin looked surprised. 'But why bother to prove? This Negro was obviously guilty. Best to hang him.'

'I see. Well, if you don't mind, I'll go on glancing through it.'

Muishkin shrugged, stretched himself luxuriously and signalled to the waiter. Latimer turned a page and went on reading.

STATEMENT MADE BY THE MURDERER, DHRIS MOHAMMED, IN THE PRESENCE OF THE GUARD-COMMANDANT OF THE BARRACKS IN IZMIR AND OTHER TRUE WITNESSES

It is said in the book that he shall not prosper who makes lies and I say these things in order to prove my innocence and to save myself from the gallows. I have lied but now I will tell the truth. I am a True Believer. There is no god but God.

I did not kill Sholem. I tell you I did not kill him. Why should I lie now? Yes, I will explain. It was not I but Dimitrios who killed Sholem.

I will tell you about Dimitrios and you will believe me. Dimitrios is a Greek. To Greeks he is a Greek but to True Believers he says that he is also a Believer and that it is only with the authorities that he is a Greek because of some paper signed by his foster-parents.

Dimitrios worked with others of us in the packing sheds and he was hated by many for his violence and for his bitter tongue. But I am a man who loves other men as brothers and I would speak with Dimitrios sometimes as he worked and tell him of the religion of God. And he would listen.

Then, when the Greeks were fleeing before the victorious army of the True God, Dimitrios came to my house and asked me to hide him from the terror of the Greeks. He said that he was a True Believer. So I hid him. Then, our Glorious army came to our aid. But Dimitrios did not go because he was, by reason of this paper signed by his foster-parents a Greek and in fear of his life. So he stayed in my house and when he went out dressed like a Turk. Then, one day, he said certain things to me. There was a Jew, Sholem, he said, who had much money, Greek pieces and some gold, hidden below the floor of his room. It was the time, he said, to take our revenge upon those who had insulted the True God and His Prophet. It was wrong, he said, that a pig of a Jew should have the money rightfully belonging to True Believers. He proposed that we should go secretly to Sholem, bind him and take his money.

At first I was afraid, but he put heart into me, reminding me of the book which says that whosoever fights for the religion of God, whether he be slain or victorious, will surely find a great reward. This is now my reward: to be hanged like a dog.

Yes, I will go on. That night after the curfew we went to the place where Sholem lived and crept up the stairs to his room. The door was bolted. Then Dimitrios knocked and called out that it was a patrol to search the house and Sholem opened the door. He had been in bed and he was grumbling at being woken from his sleep. When he saw us he called upon God and tried to close the door. But Dimitrios seized him and held him while I went in as we had arranged and searched for the loose board which concealed the money. Dimitrios dragged the old man across the bed and kept him down with his knee.

I soon found the loose board and turned round full of joy to tell Dimitrios. He had his back turned towards me and was pressing down on Sholem with the blanket to stifle his cries. He said that he himself would bind Sholem with rope which we had brought. I saw him now draw out his knife. I thought that he was meaning to cut the rope for some purpose and I said nothing. Then, before I could speak, he drove the knife into the old Jew's neck and pulled it across his throat.

I saw the blood bubble and spurt out as if from a fountain and Sholem rolled over. Dimitrios stood away and watched him for a moment then he looked at me. I asked him what he had done and he answered that it was necessary to kill Sholem for fear that he should point us out to the police. Sholem was still moving on the bed and the blood was still-bubbling, but Dimitrios said that he was certainly dead. After that, we took the money.

Then, Dimitrios said that it was better that we should not go together but that each should take his share and go separately. That was agreed. I was afraid then, for Dimitrios had a knife and I had none and I thought he meant to kill me. I wondered why he had told me of the money. He had said that he needed a companion to search for the money while he held Sholem. But I could see that he had meant from the first to kill Sholem. Why then had he brought me? He could have found the money for himself after he had killed the Jew. But we divided the money equally and he smiled and did not try to kill me. We left the place separately. He had told me the day before that there were Greek ships lying off the coast near Smyrna and that he had overheard a man saying that the captains of these ships were taking refugees who could pay. I think that he escaped on one of those ships.

I see now that I was a fool of fools and that he was right to smile at me. He knew that when my purse becomes full my head becomes empty. He knew, God's curses fall upon him, that when I sin by becoming drunk I cannot stop my tongue from wagging. I did not kill Sholem. It was Dimitrios the Greek who killed him. Dimitrios . . . (*here followed a stream of obscenities*). There is no doubt in what I say. As God is God and as Muhammad is His Prophet, I swear that I have said the truth. For the love of God, have mercy.

A note was appended to this, saying that the confession had been signed with a thumb print and witnessed. The record went on:

The murderer was asked for a description of this Dimitrios and said:
He has the look of a Greek but I do not think he is one because he hates his own countrymen. He is shorter than I am and his hair is long and straight. His face is very still and he speaks very little. His eyes are brown and tired-looking. Many men are afraid of him but I do not understand this as he is not strong and I could break him with my two hands.
N.B. The height of this man is 185 centimetres.
Inquiries have been made concerning the man Dimitrios at the packing sheds. He is known and disliked. Nothing has been heard of him for several weeks and he is presumed to have died in the fire. This seems likely.

The murderer was executed on the ninth day of the tenth month of nineteen twenty-two in the new calendar.

Latimer returned to the confession and examined it thoughtfully. It rang true; there was no doubt about that. There was a circumstantial feeling about it. The Negro, Dhris, had obviously been a very stupid man. Could he have invented those details about the scene in Sholem's room? A guilty man inventing a tale would surely have embroidered it differently. And there was his fear that Dimitrios might have been going to kill him. If he himself had been responsible for the killing he would not have thought of that. Colonel Haki had said that it was the sort of story that a man might invent to save his neck. Fear did stimulate even the most sluggish imaginations; but did it stimulate them in quite that sort of way? The authorities obviously had not cared very much whether the story was or was not true. Their inquiries had been pitiably half-hearted; yet even so they had tended to confirm the Negro's story. Dimitrios had been presumed to have died in the fire. There was no evidence offered to support the presumption. It had, no doubt, been easier to hang Dhris Mohammed than to conduct, amidst all the terrible confusion of those October days, a search for a hypothetical Greek named Dimitrios. Dimitrios had, of course, counted on that fact. But for the accident of the Colonel's transfer to the secret police, he would never have been connected with the affair.

Latimer had once seen a zoophysicist friend of his build up the complete skeleton of a prehistoric animal from a fragment of fossilized bone. It had taken the zoophysicist nearly two years and Latimer, the economist, had marvelled at the man's inexhaustible enthusiasm for the task. Now, for the first time, he understood that enthusiasm. He had unearthed a single twisted fragment of the mind of Dimitrios and now he wanted to complete the structure. The fragment was small enough but it was substantial. The wretched Dhris had never had a chance. Dimitrios had used the Negro's dull wits, had played upon his religious fanaticism, his simplicity, his cupidity with a skill that was terrifying. 'We divided the money equally and he smiled and did not try to kill me.' Dimitrios had smiled. And the Negro had been too preoccupied with his fear of the man whom he could have broken with his two hands to wonder about that smile until it was too late. The brown, tired-looking eyes had watched Dhris Mohammed and understood him perfectly.

Latimer folded up the papers, put them in his pocket and turned to Muishkin.

'One hundred and fifty piastres, I owe you.'

'Right,' said Muishkin into his glass. He had ordered and was now finishing his third absinthe. He set down his glass and took the money from Latimer. 'I like you,' he said seriously; 'you have no *snobisme*. Now you will have a drink with me, eh?'

Latimer glanced at his watch. It was getting late and he had had nothing to eat. 'I'd be glad to,' he answered; 'but why not have some dinner with me first?'

'Good!' Muishkin clambered laboriously to his feet. 'Good,' he repeated and Latimer saw that his eyes were unnaturally bright.

At the Russian's suggestion they went out to a restaurant, a place of subdued lights and red plush and gilt and stained mirrors, where French food was served. It was crowded and the atmosphere was thick with cigarette smoke. They sat down in upholstered chairs which exuded wafts of stale scent.

'*Ton*,' said Muishkin looking round. He seized the menu and after some deliberation chose the most expensive dish on it. With their food they drank a syrupy, resinous Smyrna wine. Muishkin began to talk about his life. Odessa, 1918. Stambul, 1919. Smyrna, 1921. Bolsheviks. Wrangel's army. Kiev. A woman they called The Butcher. They used the abattoir as a prison because the prison had become an abattoir. Terrible, damnawful atrocities. Allied army of occupation. The English sporting. American relief. Bed bugs. Typhus. Vickers guns. The Greeks – God, those Greeks! Fortunes waiting to be picked up. Kemalists. His voice droned on while outside, through the cigarette smoke, beyond the red plush and the gilt and the white table-cloths, the amethyst twilight had deepened into night.

Another bottle of syrupy wine arrived. Latimer began to feel sleepy.

'And after so much madness, where are we now?' demanded Muishkin. His English had been steadily deteriorating. Now, his lower lip wet and quivering with emotion, he fixed Latimer with the unwavering stare of the drunk about to become philosophical. 'Where now?' he repeated and thumped the table.

'In Smyrna,' said Latimer and realised suddenly that he had drunk too much of the wine.

Muishkin shook his head irritably. 'We grade rapidly to damnawful hell,' he declared. 'Are you a Marxist?'

'No.'

Muishkin leaned forward confidentially. 'Neither me.' He plucked at Latimer's sleeve. His lip trembled violently. 'I'm a swindler.'

'Are you?'

'Yes.' Tears began to form in his eyes. 'I damn well swindled you.'

'Did you?'

'Yes.' He fumbled in his pocket. 'You are no snob. You must take back fifty piastres.'

'What for?'

'Take them back.' The tears began to course down his cheeks and mingle with the sweat collecting on the point of his chin. 'I swindled you, Mister. There was no damn friend to pay, no permission, nothing.'

'Do you mean that you made up those records yourself?'

Muishkin sat up sharply. '*Je ne suis pas un faussaire*,' he asserted. He wagged a ginger in Latimer's face. 'This type came to me three months ago. By paying large bribes—' the finger stabbed emphatically '—large bribes, he had obtained the permissions to examine the archives for the dossier on the murder of Sholem. The dossier was in the old Arabic script and he brought photographs of the pages to me to translate. He took the photographs back, but I kept the translation on file. You see? I swindled you. You paid fifty piastres too much. Faugh!' He snapped his fingers. 'I could have swindled five hundred piastres, and you would have paid. I am too soft.'

'What did he want with this information?'

Muishkin looked sulky. 'I can mind my own damn nose in the business.'

'What did he look like?'

'He looked like a Frenchman.'

'What sort of a Frenchman?'

But Muishkin's head had sagged forward on to his chest and he did not answer. Then, after a moment or two, he raised his head and stared blankly at Latimer. His face was livid and Latimer guessed that he would very shortly be sick. His lips moved.

'*Je ne suis pas un faussaire*,' he muttered; 'three hundred piastres, dirt cheap!' He stood up suddenly, murmured, '*Excusez-moi*,' and walked rapidly in the direction of the toilet.

Latimer waited for a time then paid the bill and went to investigate. There was another entrance to the toilet and Muishkin had gone. Latimer walked back to his hotel.

From the balcony outside the window of his room, he could see over the bay to the hill beyond. A moon had risen and its reflection gleamed through the tangle of crane jibs along the quay where the steamers berthed. The searchlights of a Turkish cruiser anchored in the roadstead outside the inner port swung round like long white fingers, brushed the summits of the hills and were extinguished. Out in the harbour and on the slopes above the town pinpoints of light twinkled. A slight warm

warm breeze off the sea had begun to stir the leaves of a rubber tree in the garden below him. In another room of the hotel a woman laughed. Somewhere in the distance a gramophone was playing a tango. The turntable was revolving too quickly and the sound was shrill and congested.

Latimer lit a final cigarette and wondered for the hundredth time what the man who looked like a Frenchman had wanted with the dossier of the Sholem murder. At last he pitched his cigarette away and shrugged. One thing was certain: he could not possibly have been interested in Dimitrios.

CHAPTER 4

MR. PETERS

Two days later, Latimer left Smyrna. He did not see Muishkin again.

The situation in which a person, imagining fondly that he is in charge of his own destiny, is, in fact, the sport of circumstances beyond his control, is always fascinating. It is the essential element in most good theatre from the *Œdipus* of Sophocles to *East Lynne*. When, however, that person is oneself and one is examining the situation in retrospect, the fascination becomes a trifle morbid. Thus, when Latimer used afterwards to look back upon those two days in Smyrna, it was not so much his ignorance of the part he was playing but the bliss which accompanied the ignorance that so appalled him. He had gone into the business believing his eyes to be wide open, whereas, actually, they had been tightly shut. That, no doubt, could not have been helped. The galling part was that he had failed for so long to perceive the fact. Of course, he did himself less than justice; but his self-esteem had been punctured; he had been transferred without his knowledge from the role of sophisticated, impersonal weigher of facts to that of active participator in a melodrama.

Of the imminence of that humiliation, however, he had no inkling when, on the morning after his dinner with Muishkin, he sat down with a pencil and a notebook to arrange the material for his experiment in detection.

Some time early in October 1922, Dimitrios had left Smyrna. He had had money and had probably purchased a passage on a Greek steamer.

The next time Colonel Haki had heard of him he had been in Adrianople two years later. In that interim, however, the Bulgarian police had had trouble with him in Sofia in connection with the attempted assassination of Stambulisky. Latimer was a little hazy as to the precise date of that attempt but he began to jot down a rough chronological table

TIME	PLACE	REMARKS	SOURCE OF INFORMATION
1922 (October)	Smyrna	Sholem	Police Archives
1923 (early part)	Sofia	Stambulisky	Colonel Haki
1924 . . .	Adrianople	Kemal attempt	Colonel Haki
1926 . . .	Belgrade	Espionage for France	Colonel Haki
1926 . . .	Switzerland	Talat passport	Colonel Haki
1929–31 (?) .	Paris	Drugs	Colonel Haki
1932 . . .	Zagreb	Croat assassin	Colonel Haki
1937 . . .	Lyons	*Carte d'identité*	Colonel Haki
1938 . . .	Istanbul	Murdered	Colonel Haki

The immediate problem, then, was quite clearcut. In the six months following the murder of Sholem, Dimitrios had escaped from Smyrna, made his way to Sofia and become involved in a plot to assassinate the Bulgarian Prime Minister. Latimer found it a trifle difficult to form any estimate of the time required to become involved in a plot to kill a Prime Minister; but it was fairly certain that Dimitrios must have arrived in Sofia soon after his departure from Smyrna. If he had indeed escaped by Greek steamer he must have gone first to the Piræus and Athens. From Athens he could have reached Sofia overland, via Salonika, or by sea, via the Dardenelles and the Golden Horn to Bourgaz or Varna, Bulgaria's Black Sea Port. Istanbul at that time was in Allied hands. He would have had nothing to fear from the Allies. The question was: what had induced him to go to Sofia?

However, the logical course now was to go to Athens and tackle the job of picking up the trail there. It would not be easy. Even if attempts had been made to record the presence of every refugee among the tens of thousands who had arrived, it was more than probable that what records still existed, if any, were incomplete. There was no point, however, in anticipating failure. He had several valuable friends in Athens and if there was a record in existence it was fairly certain that he would be able to get access to it. He shut up his notebook.

When the weekly boat to the Piræus left Smyrna the following day, Latimer was among the passengers.

During the months following the Turkish occupation of Smyrna, more than eight hundred thousand Greeks returned to their country. They came, boatload after boatload of them, packed on the decks and in the holds. Many of them were naked and starving. Some still carried in their arms the dead children they had had no time to bury. With them came the diseases of typhus, typhoid and smallpox.

War-weary and ruined, gripped by a food shortage and starved of medical supplies, their motherland received them. In the hastily improvised refugee camps they died like flies. Outside Athens, on the Piræus, in Salonika, masses of humanity lay rotting in the cold of a Greek winter. Then, the Fourth Assembly of the League of Nations, in session in Geneva, voted one hundred thousand gold francs to the Nansen relief organization for immediate use in Greece. The work of salvage began. Huge refugee settlements were organized. Food was brought and clothing and medical supplies. The epidemics were stopped. The survivors began to sort themselves into new communities. For the first time in history, large scale disaster had been halted by goodwill and reason. It seemed as if the human animal were at last discovering a conscience, as if it were at last becoming aware of its humanity.

All this and more, Latimer heard from a friend, one Siantos, in Athens. When, however, he came to the point of his inquiries, Siantos pursed his lips.

'A complete register of those who arrived from Smyrna? That is a tall order. If you had seen them come . . . So many and in such a state . . .' And then followed the inevitable question. 'Why are you interested?'

It had occurred to Latimer that this question was going to crop up again and again. He had accordingly prepared his explanation. To have told the truth, to have explained that he was trying, for purely academic reasons, to trace the history of a dead criminal named Dimitrios would have been a long and uneasy business. He was, in any case, not anxious to have a second opinion on his prospects of success. His own was depressing enough. What had seemed a fascinating idea in a Turkish mortuary might well, in the bright, warm light of a Greek autumn, appear merely absurd. Much simpler to avoid the issue altogether.

He answered: 'It is in connection with a new book I am writing. A matter of detail that must be checked. I want to see if it is possible to trace an individual refugee after so long.'

Siantos said that he understood and Latimer grinned ashamedly to himself. The fact that one was a writer could be relied upon to explain away the most curious extravagances.

He had gone to Siantos because he knew that the man had a Government post of some importance in Athens; but now his first disappointment was in store for him. A week went by and, at the end of it, Siantos was able to tell him only that a register was in existence, that it was in the custody of the municipal authorities and that it was not open to inspection by unauthorized persons. Permission would have to be obtained. It took another week, a week of waiting, of sitting in *kafenios*, of being introduced to thirsty men with connections in the municipal offices. At last, however, the permission was forthcoming and the following day Latimer presented himself at the bureau in which the records were housed.

The inquiry office was a bare tiled room with a counter at one end. Behind the counter sat the official in charge. He shrugged over the information Latimer had to give him. A fig-packer named Dimitrios? October 1922? It was impossible. The register had been compiled alphabetically by surname.

Latimer's heart sank. All his trouble, then, was to go for nothing. He had thanked the man and was turning away when he had an idea. There was just a remote chance . . .

He turned back to the official. 'The surname,' he said, 'may have been Makropoulos.'

He was dimly aware, as he said it, that behind him a man had entered the inquiry office through the door leading to the street. The sun was streaming obliquely into the room and for an instant a long, distorted shadow twisted across the tiles as the new-comer passed the window.

'Dimitrios Makropoulos?' repeated the official. 'That is better. If there was a person of that name on the register we will find him. It is a question of patience and organization. Please come this way.'

He raised the flap of the counter for Latimer to go through. As he did so he glanced over Latimer's shoulder.

'Gone!' he exclaimed. 'I have no assistance in my work of organization here. The whole burden falls upon my shoulders. Yet people have no patience. I am engaged for a moment. They cannot wait.' He shrugged. 'That is their affair. I do my duty. If you will follow me, please.'

Latimer followed him down a flight of stone stairs into an extensive basement occupied by row upon row of steel cabinets.

'Organization,' commented the official; 'that is the secret of modern statecraft. Organization will make a greater Greece. A new empire. But patience is necessary.' He led the way to a series of small cabinets in one corner of the basement, pulled open one of the drawers and began with his finger-nail to flick over a series of cards. At last he stopped at a card and examined it carefully before closing the drawer. 'Makropoulos. If there is a record of this man we shall find it in drawer number sixteen. That is organization.'

In drawer number sixteen, however, they drew a blank. The official threw up his hands in despair and searched again without success. Then inspiration came to Latimer.

'Try under the name of Talat,' he said desperately.

'But that is a Turkish name.'

'I know. But try it.'

The official shrugged. There was another reference to the main index. 'Drawer twenty-seven,' announced the official a little impatiently; 'are you sure that this man came to Athens? Many went to Salonika. Why not this fig-packer?'

This was precisely the question that Latimer had been asking himself. He said nothing and watched the official's finger-nail flicking over another series of cards. Suddenly it stopped.

'Have you found it?' said Latimer quickly.

The official pulled out a card. 'Here is one,' he said. 'The man was a fig-packer, but the name is Dimitrios Tala*dis*.'

'Let me see.' Latimer took the card. Dimitrios Taladis! There it was in black and white. He had found out something that Colonel Haki did not know. Dimitrios had used the name Talat before 1926. There could be no doubt that it *was* Dimitrios. He had merely tacked a Greek suffix on to the name. He stared at the card. And there were here some other things that Colonel Haki did not know.

He looked up at the beaming official. 'May I copy this?'

'Of course. Patience and organization, you see. My organization is for use. But I must not let the record out of my sight. That is the regulation.'

Under the now somewhat mystified eyes of the apostle of organization and patience Latimer began to copy the wording on the card into his note-book, translating it as he did so into English. He wrote:

NUMBER T.53462
NATIONAL RELIEF ORGANISATION
Refugee Section: ATHINAI

Sex: Male. *Name:* Dimitrios Taladis. *Born:* Salonika, 1889. *Occupation:* Fig-packer. *Parents:* believed dead. *Identity Papers or Passport:* Identity card lost. Said to have been issued at Smyrna. *Nationality:* Greek. *Arrived:* October 1, 1922. *Coming from:* Smyrna. *On examination:* Able-bodied. No disease. Without money. Assigned to camp at Tabouria. Temporary identity paper issued. *Note:* Left Tabouria on own initiative,

November 29th, 1922: Warrant for arrest on charge of robbery and attempted murder, issued in Athinai, November
30th, 1922. Believed to have escaped by sea.

Yes, that was Dimitrios all right. The date of his birth agreed with
that supplied by the Greek police (and based on information gained
prior to 1922) to Colonel Haki. The place of birth, however, was different. According to the Turkish dossier it had been Larissa. Why had
Dimitrios bothered to change it? If he were giving a false name, he must
have seen that the chances of its falsity being discovered by reference to
the registration records were as great for Salonika as for Larissa.

Salonika 1889! Why Salonika? Then Latimer remembered. Of
course! It was quite simple. In 1889 Salonika had been in Turkish territory, a part of the Ottoman Empire. The registration records of that
period would, in all probability, not be available to the Greek authorities. Dimitrios had certainly been no fool. But why had he picked the
name Taladis? Why had he not chosen a typical Greek name? The
Turkish 'Talat' must have had some special association for him. As for
his identity card issued in Smyrna, that would naturally be 'lost' since,
presumably, it had been issued to him in the name of Makropoulos by
which he was already known to the Greek police.

The date of his arrival fitted in with the vague allusions to time made
in the courtmartial. Unlike the majority of his fellow refugees, he had
been able-bodied and free from disease when he had arrived. Naturally.
Thanks to Sholem's Greek money, he had been able to buy a passage to
the Piræus and travel in comparative comfort instead of being loaded on
to a refugee ship with thousands of others. Dimitrios had known how to
look after himself. The fig-packer had packed enough figs. Dimitrios the
Man had been emerging from his chrysalis. No doubt he had had a
substantial amount of Sholem's money left when he had arrived. Yet to
the relief authorities he had been 'without money'. That had been sensible of him. He might otherwise have been forced to buy food and
clothing for stupid fools who had failed to provide, as he had provided,
for the future. His expenses had been heavy enough as it was; so heavy
that another Sholem had been needed. No doubt he had regretted Dhris
Mohammed's half share.

'Believed to have escaped by sea.' With the proceeds of the second
robbery added to the balance from the first, he had no doubt been able
to pay for his passage to Bourgaz. It would obviously have been too risky
for him to have gone overland. He had only temporary identity papers
and might have been stopped at the frontier, whereas in Bourgaz, the

same papers issued by an international relief commission with considerable prestige would have enabled him to get through.

The official's much-advertised patience was showing signs of wearing thin. Latimer handed over the card, expressed his thanks in a suitable manner and returned thoughtfully to his hotel.

He was feeling pleased with himself. He had discovered some new information about Dimitrios and he had discovered it through his own efforts. It had been, it was true, an obvious piece of routine inquiry; but, in the best Scotland Yard tradition, it had called for patience and persistence. Besides, if he had not thought of trying that Talat name . . . He wished that he could have sent a report of his investigations to Colonel Haki, but that was out of the question. The Colonel would probably fail to understand the spirit in which the experiment in detection was being conducted. In any case, Dimitrios himself would by this time be mouldering below ground, his dossier sealed and forgotten in the archives of the Turkish secret police. The main thing now was to tackle the Sofia affair.

He tried to remember what he knew about postwar Bulgarian politics and speedily came to the conclusion that it was very little. In 1923 Stambulisky had, he knew, been head of a government of liberal tendencies; but of just how liberal those tendencies had been he had no idea. There had been an attempted assassination and later a military *coup d'ètat* carried out at the instigation, if not under the leadership of I.M.R.O., the International Macedonian Revolutionary Organisation. Stambulisky had fled from Sofia, tried to organize a counter-revolution and been killed. That was the gist of the affair, he thought. But of the rights and wrongs of it (if any such distinction were possible), of the nature of the political forces involved, he was quite ignorant. That state of affairs would have to be remedied; and the place in which to remedy it would be Sofia.

That evening he asked Siantos to dinner. Latimer knew him for a vain, generous soul who liked discussing his friends' problems and was flattered when, by making judicious use of his official position, he could help them. After giving thanks for the assistance in the matter of the municipal register, Latimer broached the subject of Sofia.

'I am going to trespass on your kindness still further, my dear Siantos.'

'So much the better.'

'Do you know anyone in Sofia? I want a letter of introduction to an intelligent newspaper man there who could give me some inside information about Bulgarian politics in the 'twenties.'

Siantos smoothed his gleaming white hair and grinned admiringly.

'You writers have bizarre tastes. Something might be done. Do you want a Greek or a Bulgar?'

'Greek for preference. I don't speak Bulgarian.'

Siantos was thoughtful for a moment. 'There is a man in Sofia named Marukakis,' he said at last. 'He is the Sofia correspondent of a French news agency. I do not know him myself, but I might be able to get a letter to him from a friend of mine.' They were sitting in a restaurant, and now Siantos glanced round furtively and lowered his voice. 'There is only one trouble about him from your point of view. I happen to know that he has . . .' The voice sunk still lower in tone. Latimer was prepared for nothing less horrible than leprosy. '. . . Communist tendencies,' concluded Siantos in a whisper.

Latimer raised his eyebrows. 'I don't regard that as a drawback. All the Communists I have ever met have been highly intelligent.'

Siantos looked shocked. 'How can that be? It is dangerous to say such things, my friend. Marxist thought is forbidden in Greece.'

'When can I have that letter?'

Siantos sighed. 'Bizarre!' he remarked. 'I will get it for you to-morrow. You writers . . .!'

Within a week the letter of introduction had been obtained, and Latimer, having secured Greek exit and Bulgarian entry visas, boarded a night train for Sofia.

The train was not crowded and he had hoped to have a sleeping car compartment to himself; but five minutes before the train was due to start, luggage was carried in and deposited above the empty berth. The owner of the luggage followed very soon after it.

'I must apologize for intruding on your privacy,' he said to Latimer in English.

He was a fat, unhealthy-looking man of about fifty-five. He had turned to tip the porter before he spoke, and the first thing about him that impressed Latimer was that the seat of his trousers sagged absurdly, making his walk reminiscent of that of the hind legs of an elephant. Then Latimer saw his face and forgot about the trousers. There was the sort of sallow shapelessness about it that derives from simultaneous over-eating and under-sleeping. From above two heavy satchels of flesh peered a pair of pale-blue, bloodshot eyes that seemed to be permanently weeping. The nose was rubbery and indeterminate. It was the mouth that gave the face expression. The lips were pallid and undefined, seeming thicker than they really were. Pressed together over unnaturally white and regular false teeth, they were set permanently in a saccharine smile. In conjunction with the weeping eyes above it, it created an impression of sweet patience in adversity, quite startling in its intensity. Here, it said, was a man who had suffered, who had been buffeted by fiendishly vindictive Fates as no other man had been buffeted, yet who had retained his humble faith in the essential goodness of Man: here, it said, was a martyr who smiled through the flames – smiled yet who could not but weep for the misery of others as he did so. He reminded Latimer of a high church priest he had known in England who had been unfrocked for embezzling the altar fund.

'The berth was unoccupied,' Latimer pointed out; 'there is no question of your intruding.' He noted with an inward sigh that the man breathed very heavily and noisily through congested nostrils. He would probably snore.

The new-comer sat down on his berth and shook his head slowly. 'How good of you to put it that way! How little kindliness there is in the world these days! How little thought for others!' The bloodshot eyes met Latimer's. 'May I ask how far you are going?'

'Sofia.'

'Sofia. So? A beautiful city, beautiful. I am continuing to Bucaresti. I do hope that we shall have a pleasant journey together.'

Latimer said that he hoped so too. The fat man's English was very accurate, but he spoke it with an atrocious accent which Latimer could not place. It was thick and slightly guttural, as though he were speaking with his mouth full of cake. Occasionally, too, the accurate English would give out in the middle of a difficult sentence, which would be completed in very fluent French or German. Latimer gained the impression that the man had learned his English from books.

The fat man turned and began to unpack a small attaché case containing a pair of woollen pyjamas, some bed socks and a dog-eared paper-backed book. Latimer managed to see the title of the book. It was called *Pearls of Everyday Wisdom* and was in French. The fat man arranged these things carefully on the shelf and then produced a packet of thin Greek cheroots.

'Will you allow me to smoke, please?' he said, extending the packet.

'Please do. But I won't smoke just now myself, thank you.'

The train had begun to gather speed and the attendant came in to make up their beds. When he had gone, Latimer partially undressed and laid down on his bed.

The fat man picked up the book and then put it down again.

'You know,' he said, 'the moment the attendant told me that there was an Englishman on the train, I knew that I should have a pleasant journey.' The smile came into play, sweet and compassionate, a spiritual pat on the head.

'It's very good of you to say so.'

'Oh, no, that is how I feel.' His eyes bleared as smoke irritated them. He dabbed at them with one of the bed socks. 'It is so silly of me to smoke,' he went on ruefully. 'My eyes are a little weak. The Great One in His wisdom has seen fit to give me weak eyes. No doubt He had a purpose. Perhaps it was that I might more keenly appreciate the beauties of His work – Mother Nature in all her exquisite raiment, the trees, the flowers, the clouds, the sky, the snow-capped hills, the wonderful views, the sunset in all its golden magnificence.'

'You ought to wear glasses.'

The fat man shook his head. 'If I needed glasses,' he said solemnly, 'the Great One would guide me to seek them.' He leaned forward earnestly. 'Do you not feel, my friend, that somewhere, above us, about us, within us, there is a Power, a Destiny, that directs us to do the things we do?'

'That's a large question.'

'But only because we are not simple enough, not humble enough, to understand. A man does not need a great education to be a philosopher. Let him only be simple and humble.' He looked at Latimer simply and humbly. 'Live and let live – that is the secret of happiness. Leave the Great One to answer the questions beyond our poor understanding. One cannot fight against one's Destiny. If the Great One wills that we shall do unpleasant things, depend upon it that He has a purpose even though that purpose is not always clear to us. If it is the Great One's will that some should become rich while others should remain poor, then we must accept His will.' He belched slightly and glanced up at the suitcases above Latimer's head. The smile became tenderly whimsical. 'I often think,' he said, 'that there is much food for thought in a train. Don't you? A piece of luggage, for instance. How like a human being! On its journey through Life it will collect many brightly coloured labels. But the labels are only the outward appearances, the face that it puts upon the world. It is what is *inside* that is important. And so often—' he shook his head despondently '—so very often, the suitcase is empty of the Beautiful Things. Don't you agree with me?'

This was nauseating. Latimer emitted a non-committal grunt. 'You speak very good English,' he added.

'English is the most beautiful language, I think. Shakespeare, H. G. Wells – you have some great English writers. But I cannot yet express all my ideas in English. I am, as you will have noticed, more at ease with French.'

'But your own language . . .?'

The fat man spread out large, soft hands on one of which twinkled a rather grubby diamond ring. 'I am a citizen of the world,' he said. 'To me, all countries, all languages are beautiful. If only men could live as brothers, without hatred, seeing only the beautiful things. But no! There are always Communists etcetera. It is, no doubt, the Great One's will.'

Latimer said, 'I think I'll go to sleep now.'

'Sleep!' apostrophized his companion raptly; 'the great mercy vouch-safed to us poor humans. My name,' he added inconsequentially, 'is Mister Peters.'

'It has been very pleasant to have met you, Mr. Peters,' returned Latimer firmly. 'We get into Sofia so early that I shan't trouble to undress.'

He switched off the main light in the compartment leaving only the dark blue emergency light glowing and the small reading lights over the berths. Then he stripped a blanket off his bed and wrapped it round him.

Mr. Peters had watched these preparations in wistful silence. Now, he began to undress, balancing himself dexterously against the lurching of the train as he put on his pyjamas. At last he clambered into his bed and lay still for a moment, the breath whistling through his nostrils. Then he turned over on his side, groped for his book and began to read. Latimer switched off his own reading lamp. A few moments later he was asleep.

The train reached the frontier in the early hours of the morning and he was awakened by the attendant for his papers. Mr. Peters was still reading. His papers had already been examined by the Greek and Bulgarian officials in the corridor outside and Latimer did not have an opportunity of ascertaining the nationality of the citizen of the world. A Bulgarian customs official put his head in the compartment, frowned at their suit-cases and then withdrew. Soon the train moved on over the frontier. Dozing fitfully, Latimer saw the thin strip of sky between the blinds turn blue-black and then grey. The train was due in Sofia at seven. When, at last, he rose to dress and collect his belongings, he saw that Mr. Peters had switched off his reading lamp and had his eyes closed. As the train began to rattle over the network of points outside Sofia, he gently slid the compartment door open.

Mr. Peters stirred and opened his eyes.

'I'm sorry,' said Latimer, 'I tried not to waken you.'

In the semi-darkness of the compartment, the fat man's smile looked like a clown's grimace. 'Please don't trouble yourself about me,' he said. 'I was not asleep. I meant to tell you that the best hotel for you to stay at would be the Slavianska Besseda.'

'That's very kind of you; but I wired a reservation from Athens to the

Grand Palace. It was recommended to me. Do you know it?'
  'Yes. I think it is quite good.' The train began to slow down. 'Good-
bye, Mr. Latimer.'
  'Good-bye.'
  In his eagerness to get to a bath and some breakfast it did not occur to
Latimer to wonder how Mr. Peters had discovered his name.

CHAPTER 5

NINETEEN TWENTY-THREE

Latimer had thought carefully about the problem which awaited him in
Sofia.

  In Smyrna and Athens it had been simply a matter of gaining access
to written records. Any competent private inquiry agents could have
found out as much. Now, however, things were different. Dimitrios had,
to be sure, a police record in Sofia; but, according to Colonel Haki, the
Bulgarian police had known little about him. That they had, indeed,
thought him of little importance was shown by the fact that it was not
until they had received the Colonel's inquiry that they had troubled to
get a description of him from the woman with whom he was known to
have associated. Obviously it was what the police had *not* got in their
records, rather than what they had got, which would be interesting. As
the Colonel had pointed out, the important thing to know about an
assassination was not who had fired the shot but who had paid for the
bullet. What information the ordinary police had would no doubt be
helpful; but their business would have been with shot-firing rather than
bullet-buying. The first thing he had to find out was who had or might
have stood to gain by the death of Stambulisky. Until he had that basic
information it was idle to speculate as to the part Dimitrios had played.
That the information, even if he did obtain it, might turn out to be quite
useless as a basis for anything but a Communist pamphlet, was a con-
tingency that he was not for the moment prepared to consider. He was
beginning to like his experiment and was unwilling to abandon it easily.
If it were to die, he would see that it died hard.

  On the afternoon of his arrival he sought out Marukakis at the office of
the French news agency and presented his letter of introduction.

  The Greek was a dark, lean man of middle age with intelligent, rather bulbous eyes and a way of bringing his lips together at the end of a sentence as though amazed at his own lack of discretion. He greeted Latimer with the watchful courtesy of a negotiator in an armed truce. He spoke in French.

'What information is it that you need, Monsieur?'

'As much as you can give me about the Stambulisky affair of nineteen twenty-three.'

Marukakis raised his eyebrows. 'So long ago? I shall have to refresh my memory. No, it is no trouble, I will gladly help you. Give me an hour.'

'If you could have dinner with me at my hotel this evening, I should be delighted.'

'Where are you staying?'

'The Grand Palace.'

'We can get a better dinner than that at a fraction of the cost. If you like, I will call for you at eight o'clock and take you to the place. Agreed?'

'Certainly.'

'Good. At eight o'clock then. *Au 'voir.*'

He arrived punctually at eight o'clock and led the way in silence across the Boulevard Maria-Louise and up the Rue Alabinska to a small side-street. Half way along it there was a grocer's shop. Marukakis stopped. He looked suddenly self-conscious. 'It does not look very much,' he said doubtfully; 'but the food is sometimes very good. Would you rather go to a better place?'

'Oh no, I'll leave it to you.'

Marukakis looked relieved. 'I thought that I had better ask you,' he said and pushed open the door of the shop.

By some extraordinary means five tables had been arranged. Two of the tables were occupied by a group of men and women noisily eating soup. They sat down at a third. A moustachioed man in shirt sleeves and a green baize apron lounged over and addressed them in Bulgarian.

'I think you had better order,' said Latimer.

Marukakis said something to the waiter who twirled his moustache and lunged away shouting at a dark opening in the wall that looked like the entrance to the cellar. A voice could be heard faintly acknowledging the order. The man returned with a bottle and three glasses.

'I have ordered vodka,' said Marukakis. 'I hope you like it.'

'Very much.'

The waiter filled the three glasses, took one for himself, nodded to Latimer and, throwing back his head, poured the vodka down his throat.

Then he walked away.

'*A votre santé,*' said Marukakis politely. 'Now,' he went on as they set their glasses down, 'that we have drunk together and that we are comrades, I will make a bargain with you. I will give you the information and then you shall tell me why you want it. Does that go?'

'It goes.'

'Very well then.'

Soup was put before them. It was thick and highly spiced and mixed with sour cream. As they ate it Marukakis began to talk.

In a dying civilization, political prestige is the reward not of the shrewdest diagnostician but of the man with the best bedside manner. It is the decoration conferred on mediocrity by ignorance. Yet there remains one sort of political prestige that may still be worn with a certain pathetic dignity; it is that given to the liberal-minded leader of a party of conflicting doctrinaire extremists. His dignity is that of all doomed men: for, whether the two extremes proceed to mutual destruction or whether one of them prevails, doomed he is, either to suffer the hatred of the people or to die a martyr.

Thus it was with Monsieur Stambulisky, leader of the Bulgarian Peasant Agrarian Party, Prime Minister and Minister for Foreign Affairs. The Agrarian Party, faced by organized reaction, was immobilized, rendered powerless by its own internal conflicts. It died without firing a shot in its own defence.

The end began soon after Stambulisky returned to Sofia early in January, from the Lausanne Conference.

On January the twenty-third, the Yugoslav (then Serbian) Government lodged an official protest in Sofia against a series of armed raids carried out by Bulgarian *comitadji* over the Yugoslav frontier. A few days later, on February the fifth, during a performance celebrating the foundation of the National Theatre in Sofia at which the King and Princesses were present, a bomb was thrown into the box in which sat several government ministers. The bomb exploded. Several persons were injured.

Both the authors and objects of these outrages were readily apparent.

From the start, Stambulisky's policy towards the Yugoslav Government had been one of appeasement and conciliation. Relations between the two countries had been improving rapidly. But an objection to this improvement came from the Macedonian Autonomists, represented by the notorious Macedonian Revolutionary Committee, which operated both in Yugoslavia and in Bulgaria. Fearing that friendly relations between the two countries might lead to joint action against them, the Macedonians set to work systematically to poison those relations and to destroy their enemy Stambulisky. The attacks of the *comitadji* and the theatre incident inaugurated a period of organized terrorism.

On March the eighth, Stambulisky played his trump card by announcing that the Narodno Sobranie would be dissolved on the thirteenth and that new elections would be held in April.

This was disaster for the reactionary parties. Bulgaria was prospering under the Agrarian Government. The peasants were solidly behind Stambulisky. An election would have established him even more securely. The funds of the Macedonian Revolutionary Committee increased suddenly.

Almost immediately an attempt was made to assassinate Stambulisky and his Minister of Railways, Atanasoff, at Haskovo on the Thracian frontier. It was frustrated only at the last moment. Several police officials responsible for suppressing the activities of the *comitadji*, including the Prefect of Petrich, were threatened with death. In the face of these menaces, the elections were postponed.

Then, on June the fourth, the Sofia police discovered a plot to assassinate not only Stambulisky but also Muravieff, the War Minister, and Stoyanoff, the Minister of the Interior. A young army officer, believed to have been given the job of killing Stoyanoff, was shot dead by the police in a gun fight. Other young officers, also under the orders of the terrorist Committee, were known to have arrived in Sofia, and a search for them was made. The police were beginning to lose control of the situation.

Now was the time for the Agrarian Party to have acted, to have armed their peasant supporters. But they did not do so. Instead, they played politics among themselves. For them, the enemy was the Macedonian Revolutionary Committee, a terrorist gang, a small organization quite incapable of ousting a government entrenched behind hundreds of thousands of peasant votes. They failed to perceive that the activities of the Committee had been merely the smoke-screen behind which the reactionary parties had been steadily making their preparations for an offensive. They very soon paid for this lack of perception.

At midnight on June the eighth all was calm. By four o'clock on the morning of the ninth, all the members of the Stambulisky Government, with the exception of Stambulisky himself, were in prison and martial law had been declared. The leaders of this *coup d'état* were the the reactionaries Zankoff and Rouseff, neither of whom had ever been connected with the Macedonian Committee.

Too late, Stambulisky tried to rally his peasants to their own defence.

Several weeks later he was surrounded with a few followers in a country house some hundreds of miles from Sofia and captured. Shortly afterwards and in circumstances which are still obscure, he was shot.

It was in this way that, as Marukakis talked, Latimer sorted out the facts in his own mind. The Greek was a fast talker but liable, if he saw the chance, to turn from fact to revolutionary theory. Latimer was drinking his third glass of tea when the recital ended.

For a moment or two he was silent. At last he said: 'Do you know who put up the money for the Committee?'

Marukakis grinned. 'Rumours began to circulate some time after. There were many explanations offered; but, in my opinion, the most reasonable and, incidentally, the only one I was able to find any evidence for, was that the money had been advanced by the bank which held the Committee's funds. It is called the Eurasian Credit Trust.'

'You mean that this bank advanced the money on behalf of a third party?'

'No, I don't. The bank advanced the money on its own behalf. I happened to find out that it had been badly caught owing to the rise in the value of the *Lev* under the Stambulisky administration. In the early part of 1923, before the trouble started in earnest, the *Lev* doubled its value in two months. It was about eight hundred to the pound sterling and it rose to about four hundred. I could look up the actual figures if you are interested. Anyone who had been selling the *Lev* for delivery in three months or more, counting on a fall, would face huge losses. The Eurasian Credit Trust was not, nor is for that matter, the sort of bank to accept a loss like that.'

'What sort of a bank is it?'

'It is registered in Monaco which means not only that it pays no taxes in the countries in which it operates but also that its balance sheet is not published and that it is impossible to find out anything about it. There are lots more like that in Europe. Its head office is in Paris but it operates in the Balkans. Amongst other things it finances the clandestine manufacture of heroin in Bulgaria for illicit export.'

'Do you think that it financed the Zankoff *coup d'état*?'

'Possibly. At any rate it financed the conditions that made the *coup d'état* possible. It was an open secret that the attempt on Stambulisky and Atanassof at Haskovo was the work of foreign gunmen imported and paid by someone specially for the purpose. A lot of people said, too, that although there was a lot of talking and threatening the trouble would have died down if it had not been for foreign *agents provocateurs*.'

This was better than Latimer had hoped.

'Is there any way in which I can get details of the Haskovo affair?'

Marukakis shrugged. 'It is over fifteen years old. The police might tell you something but I doubt it. If I knew what you wanted to know . . .'

Latimer made up his mind. 'Very well, I said I would tell you why I wanted this information and I will.' He went on hurriedly. 'When I was in Stambul some weeks ago I had lunch with a man who happened to be the chief of the Turkish Secret Police. He was interested in detective stories and wanted me to use a plot he had thought of. We were discussing the respective merits of real and fictional murderers when, to illustrate his point, he read me the dossier of a man named Dimitrios Makropoulos or Dimitrios Talat. The man had been a scoundrel and a cut-throat of the worst sort. He had murdered a man in Smyrna and arranged to have another man hanged for it. He had been involved in three attempted assassinations including that of Stambulisky. He had been a French spy and he had organized a gang of drug pedlars in Paris. The day before I heard of him he had been found floating dead in the Bosphorus. He had been knifed in the stomach. For some reason or other I was curious to see him and persuaded this man to take me with him to the mortuary. Dimitrios was there on a table with his clothes piled up beside him.

'It may have been that I had had a good lunch and was feeling stupid but I suddenly had a curious desire to know more about Dimitrios. As you know, I write detective stories. I told myself that if, for once, I tried doing some detecting myself instead of merely writing about other people doing it, I might get some interesting results. My idea was to try to fill in some of the gaps in the dossier. But that was only an excuse. I did not care to admit to myself then that my interest was nothing to do with detection. It is difficult to explain but I see now that my curiosity about Dimitrios was that of the biographer rather than of the detective. There was an emotional element in it, too. I wanted to explain Dimitrios, to account for him, to understand his mind. Merely to label him with disapproval was not enough. I saw him not as a corpse in a mortuary but as a man, not as an isolate, a phenomenon, but as a unit in a disintegrating social system.'

He paused. 'Well, there you are, Marukakis! That is why I am in Sofia, why I am wasting your time with questions about things that happened fifteen years ago. I am gathering material for a biography that will never be written, when I ought to be producing a detective story. It sounds unlikely enough to me. To you it must sound fantastic. But it is my explanation.'

He sat back feeling very foolish. It would have been better to have told a carefully thought out lie.

Marukakis had been staring at his tea. Now he looked up.

'What is your own private explanation of your interest in this Dimitrios?'

'I've just told you.'

'No. I think not. You deceive yourself. You hope *au fond* that by rationalizing Dimitrios, by explaining him, you will also explain that disintegrating social system you spoke about.'

'That is very ingenious; but, if you will forgive my saying so, a little over-simplified. I don't think that I can accept it.'

'It is very good of you to believe me.'

'Why should I not believe you? It is too absurd for disbelief. What do you know of Dimitrios in Bulgaria?'

'Very little. He was, I am told, an intermediary in an attempt to assassinate Stambulisky. That is to say there is no evidence to show that he was going to do any shooting himself. He left Athens, wanted by the police for robbery and attempted murder, towards the end of November 1922. I found that out myself. I also believe that he came to Bulgaria by sea. He was known to the Sofia police. I know that because in 1924 the Turkish secret police made enquiries about him in connection with another matter. The police here questioned a woman with whom he was known to have associated.'

'If she were still here and alive it would be interesting to talk to her.'

'It would. I've traced Dimitrios in Smyrna and in Athens where he called himself Taladis, but so far I have not talked to anyone who ever saw him alive. Unfortunately, I do not even know the woman's name.'

'The police records would contain it. If you like I will make inquiries.'

'I cannot ask you to take the trouble. If I like to waste my time reading police records there is nothing to prevent my doing so, but there is no reason why I should waste your time too.'

'There is plenty to prevent your wasting your time reading police records. In the first place, you cannot read Bulgarian and in the second place, the police would make difficulties. I am, God help me, an accredited journalist working for a French news agency. I have certain privileges. Besides—' he grinned – 'absurd as it is, your detecting intrigues me. The baroque in human affairs is always interesting don't you think?' He looked round. The restaurant had emptired. The waiter was sitting asleep with his feet on one of the tables. Marukakis sighed. 'We shall have to wake the poor devil to pay him.'

On his third day in Sofia, Latimer received a letter from Marukakis.

My dear Mr. Latimer (he wrote in French))
  Here, as I promised, is a précis of all the information about Dimitrios Makropoulos which I have been able to obtain from the police. It is not, as you will see, complete. That is interesting, don't you think! Whether the woman can be found or not, I cannot say until I have made friends with a few more policemen. Perhaps we could meet to-morrow.
  Assuring you of my most distinguished sentiments.
        N. MARUKAKIS.

Attached to this letter was the précis:

POLICE ARCHIVES, SOFIA 1922–4.

Dimitrios Makropoulos. *Citizenship:* Greek. *Place of birth:* Salonika. *Date:* 1889. *Trade:* Described as fig-packer. *Entry:* Varna, December 22nd, 1922, off Italian steamer *Isola Bella. Passport or Identity Card:* Relief Commission Identity Card No. T53462.

At police inspection of papers in Café Spetzi, rue Perotska. Sofia, June 6th 1923, was in company of woman named Irana Preveza, Greek-born Bulgar. D. M. known associate of foreign criminals. Proscribed for deportation, June 7th 1923. Released at request and on assurances of A. Vazoff, June 7th 1923.

In September 1924 request received from Turkish Government for information relating to a fig-packer named 'Dimitrios' wanted on a charge of murder. Above information supplied a month later. Irana Preveza when questioned reported receiving letter from Makropoulos at Adrianople. She gave following description:

Height: 182 centimetres. *Eyes:* brown. *Complexion:* dark, clean-shaven. *Hair:* dark and straight. *Distinguishing marks:* none.

At the foot of this *précis*, Marukakis had added a handwritten note.

  N.B. This is an ordinary police dossier only. Reference is made to a second dossier on the secret file but it is forbidden to inspect this.

Latimer sighed. The second dossier contained no doubt, the details of the part played by Dimitrios in the events of 1923. The Bulgarian authorities had evidently known more about Dimitrios than they had been prepared to confide to the Turkish police. To know that the information was in existence, yet to be unable to get at it was really most irritating.

However, there was much food for thought in what information was available. The most obvious tit-bit was that on board the Italian steamer *Isola Bella* in December 1922, between the Piræus and Varna in the Black Sea, the Relief Commission Identity Card number T.53462 had suffered an alteration. 'Dimitrios Taladis' had become 'Dimitrios Makropoulos'. Either Dimitrios had discovered a talent for forgery or he had met and employed someone with such talent.

Irana Preveza! A real clue that and one that would have to be followed up very carefully. If she were still alive there must surely be some way of finding her. For the moment, however, that task would have to be left to Marukakis. Incidentally, the fact that she was of Greek extraction was suggestive, Dimitrios would probably not have spoken Bulgarian.

'Known associate of foreign criminals,' was distinctly vague. What sort of criminals? Of what foreign nationality? And to what extent had he associated with them? And why had attempts been made to deport him just two days before the Zankoff *coup d'état*? Had Dimitrios been one of the suspected assassins for whom the Sofia police had been searching during that critical week? Colonel Haki had pooh-poohed the idea of his being an assassin at all. 'His kind never risk their skins like that.' But Colonel Haki had not known everything about Dimitrios. And who on earth was the obliging A. Vazoff who had so promptly and effectively intervened on behalf of Dimitrios? The answers to those questions were, no doubt, in that secret second dossier. Most irritating!

As for the description, it might, like most other tabulated descriptions, have fitted tens of thousands of men. With most persons, recognition, even of an initimate, was based on the perception of vague, half-observed quantities which together formed a caricature significant more in its relation to the observer than to the observed. A short man, conscious of his lack of height, would describe a man of medium height as tall. For the ordinary business of hating and loving and getting from the cradle to the deathbed with the least possible discomfort, such caricatures were, no doubt, satisfactory. But he, Latimer, needed more. He needed a portrait of Dimitrios, a portrait by an artist, an arrangement of accented lines infused by some alchemy with the spirit of the sitter. And if that were not available he must make his own portrait of Dimitrios from what crude daubs he could find in police dossiers, superimposing them on one another in the hope that two dimensions might eventually become three.

He had sent a note to Marukakis, and on the following morning received a telephone call from him. They arranged to meet again for dinner that evening.

'Have you got any farther with the police?'

'Yes. I will tell you everything when we meet this evening. Good-bye.'

By the time the evening came, Latimer was feeling very much as he had once used to feel while waiting for examination results: a little excited, a little apprehensive and very much irritated at the decorous delay in publishing information which had been in existence for several days. He smiled rather sourly at Marukakis.

'It is really very good of you to take so much trouble.'

Marukakis flourished a hand. 'Nonsense, my dear friend. I told you I was interested. Shall we go to the grocer's shop again? We can talk there quietly.'

From then until the end of the meal he talked incessantly about the position of the Scandinavian countries in the event of a major European War. Latimer began to feel as baleful as one of his own murderers.

'And now,' said the Greek at last, 'as to this question of your Dimitrios, we are going on a little trip to-night.'

'What do you mean?'

'I said that I would make friends with some policeman and I have done so. As a result I have found out where Irana Preveza is now. It was not very difficult. She turns out to be very well known – to the police.'

Latimer felt his heart begin to beat a little faster. 'Where is she?' he demanded.

'About five minutes' walk away from here. She is the proprietress of a *Nachtlokal* called *La Vierge St. Marie.*'

'*Nachtlokal?*'

He grinned. 'Well, you could call it a night club.'

'I see.'

'She has not always had her own place. For many years she worked either on her own or for other houses. But she grew too old. She had money saved, and so she started her own place. About fifty years of age, but looks younger. The police have quite an affection for her. She does not get up until ten in the evening, so we must wait a little before we try our luck at talking to her. Did you read her description of Dimitrios? No distinguishing marks! That made me laugh.'

'Did it occur to you to wonder how she knew that his height was exactly one hundred and eighty-two centimetres?'

Marukakis frowned. 'Why should it?'

'Very few people know even their own heights exactly.'

'What is your idea?'

'I think that that description came from the second dossier you mentioned, and not from the woman.'

'And so?'

'Just a moment. Do you know who A. Vazoff is?'

'I meant to tell you. I asked the same question. He was a lawyer.'

'Was?'

'He died three years ago. He left much money. It was claimed by a nephew living in Bucaresti. He had no relations living here.' Marukakis paused and then added innocently: 'He used to be on the board of directors of the Eurasian Credit Trust.'

'Vazoff!'

The Greek chuckled. 'I was keeping that as a little surprise for you later, but you may have it now. I found out from the files. Eurasian Credit Trust was not registered in Monaco until 1926. The list of directors prior to that date is still in existence and open to inspection if you know where to find it.'

'But,' spluttered Latimer, 'this is most important. Don't you see what . . .'

Marukakis interrupted him by calling for the bill. Then he glanced at Latimer slyly. 'You know,' he said, 'you English are sublime. You are the only nation in the world that believes that it has a monopoly of ordinary common sense.'

CHAPTER 6

CARTE POSTALE

La Vierge St. Marie was situated, with somewhat dingy logic, in a street of houses behind the church of *Sveta Nedelja*. The street was narrow, sloping and poorly lit. At first it seemed unnaturally silent. But behind the silence there were whispers of music and laughter – whispers that would start out suddenly as a door opened and then be smothered as it closed again. Two men came out of a doorway ahead of them, lit cigarettes and walked quickly away. The footsteps of another pedestrian approached and then stopped as their owner went in to one of the houses.

'Not many people about now,' commented Marukakis; 'too early.'

Most of the doors were panelled with translucent glass and had dim lights showing through them. On some of the panels the number of the house was painted; painted rather more elaborately than was necessary for ordinary purposes. Other doors bore names. There was *Wonderbar*,

O.K., Jymies Bar, Stambul. Torquemada, Vitocha, Le Viol de Lucrece and, higher up the hill, *La Vierge St. Marie.*

For a moment they stood outside it. The door looked less shabby than some of the others. Latimer felt to see if his wallet was safe in his pocket as Marukakis pushed open the door and led the way in. Somewhere in the place an accordion band was playing a *paso-doble.* They were in a narrow passage between walls coated unevenly with red distemper. The floor was carpeted. Facing them at the end of the passage was a small *vestiaire.* When they had entered, it had been empty except for a few hats and coats; but now a pallid man in a white jacket took his place behind the counter, and smiled a welcome. He said: '*Bonsoir, messieurs,*' took their hats and coats and indicated with a flourish a staircase leading down to the right in the direction of the music. It was labelled: BAR-DANCING CABARET.

They found themselves in a low-ceilinged room about thirty feet square. At regular intervals round the pale blue walls were placed oval mirrors supported by *papier-machié* cherubims. The spaces between the mirrors were decorated haphazard with highly stylised pictures, painted on the walls, of monocled men with straw-coloured hair and nude torsoes, and women in riding clothes. In one corner of the room was a minute bar; in the opposite corner the platform on which sat the band – four listless Negroes in white 'Argentine' blouses. Near them was a blue plush curtained doorway. The rest of the wall space was taken up by small cubicles which rose to the shoulder height of those sitting at the tables set inside them. A few more tables encroached on the dance-floor in the centre.

When they came in there were about a dozen persons seated in the cubicles. The band was still playing and two girls who looked as though they might presently form part of the cabaret were dancing solemnly together.

'Too early,' repeated Marukakis; 'but it will be gayer soon.'

A waiter swept them to one of the cubicles and hurried away, to reappear a moment or two later with a bottle of local champagne.

'Have you got plenty of money with you?' murmured Marukakis; 'we shall have to pay at least two hundred leva for this poison.'

Latimer nodded. Two hundred leva was about ten shillings.

The band stopped. The two girls finished their dance, and one of them caught Latimer's eye. They walked over to the cubicle and stood smiling down. Marukakis said something. Still smiling, the two shrugged their shoulders and went away. Marukakis looked doubtfully at Latimer.

'I said that we had business to discuss, but that we would entertain them later. Of course, if you don't want to be bothered with them . . .'

'I don't,' said Latimer and then shuddered as he drank some of the champagne.

Marukakis sighed. 'It seems a pity. We shall have to pay for the wine. Someone may as well drink it.'

'Where is La Preveza?'

'She will be down at any moment now, I should think. Of course,' he added thoughtfully, 'we could go up to her.' He raised his eyes significantly towards the ceiling. 'It is really quite refined, this place. Everything seems to be most discreet.'

'If she will be down here soon there seems to be no point in our going up.' He felt an austere prig and wished that the wine had been drinkable.

'Just so,' said Marukakis gloomily.

But an hour and a half passed by before the proprietress of *La Vierge St. Marie* put in an appearance. During that time things certainly did become gayer. More people arrived, mostly men, although among them were one or two peculiar-looking women. An obvious pimp, who looked very sober, brought in a couple of Germans who looked very drunk and might have been commercial travellers on the spree. A pair of rather sinister young men sat down and ordered Vichy water. There was a certain amount of coming and going through the plush-curtained door. The cubicles were all occupied and extra tables were set up on the dance-floor which soon became a congested mass of swaying sweating couples. Presently, however, the floor was cleared and a number of the girls who had disappeared some minutes before to replace their clothes with a bunch or two of artificial primroses and a great deal of sun-tan powder, did a short dance. They were followed by a youth dressed as a woman who sang songs in German; then they reappeared without their primroses to do another dance. This concluded the cabaret and the audience swarmed back on to the dance-floor. The atmosphere thickened, became hotter and hotter.

Through smarting eyes Latimer was idly watching one of the sinister young men offering the other a pinch of what might have been snuff, but which was not, and wondering whether he should make another attempt to slake his thirst with the wine, when suddenly Marukakis touched his arm.

'That will be her,' he said.

Latimer looked across the room. For a moment a couple on the extreme corner of the dance-floor obstructed the view; then the couple moved an inch or two, and he saw her standing motionless by the curtained door by which she had entered.

She possessed that odd blousy quality that is independent of good clothes and well-dressed hair and skilful maquillage. Her figure was full but good and she held herself well; her dress was probably expensive, her thick, dark hair looked as though it had spent the past two hours in the hands of a hairdresser. Yet she remained, unmistakably and irrevocably, a slattern. There was something temporary, an air of suspended animation, about her. It seemed as if at any moment the hair should begin to straggle, the dress slip down negligently over one soft, creamy shoulder, the hand with the diamond cluster ring which now hung loosely at her side reach up to pluck at pink silk shoulder straps and pat abstractedly at the hair. You saw it in her dark eyes. The mouth was firm and good-humoured in the loose, raddled flesh about it; but the eyes were humid with sleep and the carelessness of sleep. They made you think of things you had forgotten, of clumsy gilt hotel chairs strewn with discarded clothes and of grey dawn light slanting through closed shutters, of attar of roses and of the musty smell of heavy curtains on brass rings, of the sound of the warm, slow breathing of a sleeper against the ticking of a clock in the darkness. Yet now the eyes were open and watchful, moving about while the mouth smiled a greeting here and there. Latimer watched her turn suddenly and go towards the bar.

Marukakis beckoned to the waiter and said something to him. The man hesitated and then nodded. Latimer saw him weave his way towards where Madame Preveza was talking to a fat man with his arm round one of the cabaret girls. The waiter whispered something. Madame Preveza stopped talking and looked at him. He pointed towards Latimer and Marukakis, and for a moment her eyes rested dispassionately on them. Then she turned away, said a word to the waiter and resumed her conversation.

'She'll come in a minute,' said Marukakis.

Soon she left the fat man and went on making her tour of the room, nodding, smiling indulgently. At last she reached their table. Involuntarily, Latimer got to his feet. The eyes studied his face.

'You wished to speak with me, messieurs?' Her voice was husky, a little harsh, and she spoke in strongly accented French.

'We should be honoured if you would sit at our table for a moment,' said Marukakis.

'Of course.' She sat down beside him. Immediately the waiter came up. She waved him away and looked at Latimer. 'I have not seen you before, monsieur. Your friend I have seen, but not in my place.' She looked sideways at Marukakis. 'Are you going to write about me in the

Paris newspapers, monsieur? If so, you must see the rest of my entertainment – you and your friend.'

Marukakis smiled. 'No, madame. We are trespassing on your hospitality to ask for some information.'

'Information?' A blank look had come into the dark eyes. 'I know nothing of any interest to anybody.'

'Your discretion is famous, madame. This, however, concerns a man, now dead and buried, whom you knew over fifteen years ago.'

She laughed shortly and Latimer saw that her teeth were bad. She laughed again, uproariously, so that her body shook. It was an ugly sound that tore away her slumberous dignity, leaving her old. She coughed a little as the laughter died away. 'You pay the most delicate compliments, monsieur,' she gasped. 'Fifteen years! You expect me to remember a man that long? Holy Mother of Christ, I think you shall buy me a drink after all.'

Latimer beckoned to the waiter. 'What will you drink, Madame?'

'Champagne. Not this filth. The waiter will know. Fifteen years!' She was still amused.

'We hardly dared to hope that you would remember,' said Marukakis a trifle coldly. 'But if a name means anything to you, it was Dimitrios – Dimitrios Makropoulos.'

She had been lighting a cigarette. Now she stopped still with the burning match in her fingers. Her eyes were on the end of the cigarette. For several seconds the only movement that Latimer saw in her face was the corners of her mouth turning slowly downward. It seemed to him that the noise about them had receded suddenly, that there was cotton wool in his ears. Then she slowly turned the match between her fingers and dropped it on to the plate in front of her. The eyes did not move. Then, very softly, she said: 'I don't like you here. Get out – both of you!'

'But . . .'

'Get out!' Still she did not raise her voice or move her head.

Marukakis looked across at Latimer, shrugged and stood up. Latimer followed suit. She glared up at them sullenly. 'Sit down,' she snapped; 'do you think I want a scene here?'

They sat down. 'If you will explain, madame,' said Marukakis acidly, 'how we can get out without standing up we should be grateful.'

The fingers of her right hand moved quickly and grasped the stem of a glass. For a moment Latimer thought that she was going to break it in the Greek's face. Then her fingers relaxed and she said something in Greek too rapid for Latimer to understand.

Marukakis shook his head. 'No, he is nothing to do with the police,'

Latimer heard him reply. 'He is a writer of books and he seeks information.'

'Why?'

'He is curious. He saw the dead body of Dimitrios Makropoulos in Stambul a month or two ago, and he is curious about him.'

She turned to Latimer and gripped his sleeve urgently. 'He is dead? You are sure he is dead? You actually saw his body?'

He nodded. Her manner made him feel oddly like the doctor who descends the stairs to announce that all is over. 'He had been stabbed and thrown into the sea,' he added and cursed himself for putting it so clumsily. In her eyes was an emotion he could not quite identify. Perhaps, in her way, she had loved him. A slice of life! Tears should follow.

But there were no tears. She said.

'Had he any money on him?'

Slowly, uncomprehendingly, Latimer shook his head.

'*Merde!*' she said viciously; 'the son of a camel owed me a thousand French francs. Now I shall never see it back. *Salop!* Get out, both of you, before I have you thrown out!

It was nearly half-past three before Latimer and Marukakis left *La Vierge St. Marie.*

The preceding two hours they had spent in Madame Preveza's private office, a be-flowered room filled with furniture: a walnut grand piano draped in a white silk shawl with a fringe and pen-painted birds in the corners of it, small tables loaded with bric-a-brac, many chairs, a browning palm tree in a bamboo stand, a chaise-longue and a large roll-top desk in Spanish oak. They had reached it, under her guidance, via the curtained door, a flight of stairs and a dimly lit corridor with numbered doors on either side of it and a smell that reminded Latimer of an expensive nursing home during visiting hours.

The invitation had been the very last thing that he had expected. It had come close on the heels of her final exhortation to them to get out. She had become plaintive, apologized. A thousand francs was a thousand francs. Now she would never see it. Her eyes had filled with tears. To Latimer she had seemed fantastic. The money had been owing since 1923. She could not seriously have expected its return after fifteen years. Perhaps somewhere in her mind she had kept intact the romantic illusion that one day Dimitrios would walk in and scatter thousand franc notes like leaves about her. The fairy tale gesture! Latimer's news had shattered that illusion and when her first anger had gone she had felt herself in need of sympathy. Forgotten had been their request for information about Dimitrios. The bearers of the bad news must know how bad their news had been. She had been saying farewell to a legend. An audience had been necessary, an audience who would understand what a foolish, generous woman she was. Their drinks she had said, rubbing salt in the wound, were on the house.

They had seated themselves side by side on the chaise-longue while she had rummaged in the roll-top desk. From one of the innumerable pigeon-holes she had produced a small dog-eared notebook. The pages of it had rustled through her fingers. Then:

'February fifteenth, nineteen twenty-three,' she had said suddenly. The notebook had shut with a snap and her eyes had moved upwards calling upon Heaven to testify to the accuracy of the date. 'That was when the money became due to me. A thousand francs and he promised faithfully that he would pay me. It was due to me and he had received it. Sooner than make a big scene – for I detest big scenes – I said that he could borrow it. And he said that he would repay me, that in a matter of weeks he would be getting plenty of money. And he *did* get that money, but he did not pay me my thousand francs. After all I had done for him, too!

'I picked that man up out of the gutter, messieurs. That was in December. Dear Christ, it was cold. In the eastern provinces people were dying quicker than you could have machine-gunned them – and I have seen people machine-gunned. At that time I had no place like this, you understand. Of course, I was a girl then. Often I used to be asked to pose for photographs. There was one that was my favourite. I had on just a simple drape of white chiffon, caught in at the waist with a girdle, and a crown of small white flowers. In my right hand which rested – so – upon a pretty, white column, I held a single red rose. It was used for postcards, *pour les amoureux*, and the photographer coloured the rose and printed a very pretty poem at the bottom of the card.' The dark, moist lids had drooped over her eyes and she had recited softly:

'*Je veux que mon coeur vous serve d'oreiller,*
'*Et à votre bonheur je saurai veiller.*

'Very pretty, don't you think?' The ghost of a smile had tightened her lips. 'I burnt all my photographs several years ago. Sometimes I am sorry for that but I think that I was right. It is not good to be reminded always of the past. That is why, messieurs, I was angry to-night when you spoke of Dimitrios; for he is of the past. One must think of the present and of the future.

'But Dimitrios was not a man who one forgets easily. I have known many men but I have been afraid of only two men in my life. One of them was the man I married and the other was Dimitrios. One deceives oneself you know. One thinks that one wants to be understood when one wants only to be half-understood. If a person really understands you, you fear him. My husband understood me because he loved me and I feared him because of that. But when he grew tired of loving me I could laugh at him and no longer fear him. Dimitrios was different. Dimitrios understood me better than I understood myself; but he did not love me. I do not think he could love anyone. I thought that one day I should be able to laugh at him too, but that day never came. You could not laugh at Dimitrios. I found that out. When he had gone I hated him and told myself that it was because of the thousand francs he owed to me. I wrote it down in my book as proof. But I was lying to myself. He owed me more than a thousand francs. He had always cheated me over the money. It was because I feared him and could not understand him as he understood me that I hated him.

'I was living in a hotel then. A filthy place, full of scum. The *patron* was a dirty bully, but friendly with the police; and while one paid for one's room one was safe, even if one's papers were not in order.

'One afternoon I was resting when I heard the *patron* shouting at someone in the next room. The walls were thin and I could hear everything. At first I paid no attention, for he was always shouting at someone, but after a while I began to listen because they were speaking in Greek and I understand Greek. The *patron* was threatening to call in the police if the room were not paid for. I could not hear what was said in reply for the other man spoke softly; but at last the *patron* went out and there was quiet. I was half-asleep when suddenly I heard the handle of my door being tried. The door was bolted. I watched the handle turn slowly as it was released again. Then there was a knock.

'I asked who was there but there was no answer. I thought that perhaps it was one of my friends and that he had not heard me so I went to the door and unbolted it. Outside was Dimitrios.

'He asked in Greek if he could come in. I asked him what he wanted and he said he wanted to talk to me. I asked him how he knew that I spoke Greek but he did not answer. I knew now that he must be the man in the next room. I had passed him once or twice on the stairs and he had always seemed very polite and nervous as he stood aside for me. But now he was not nervous. I said that I was resting and that he could come to see me later if he wished. But he smiled and pushed the door open and came in and leaned against the wall.

'I told him to get out, that I would call the *patron*; but he only smiled and stayed where he was. He asked me then whether I had heard what the *patron* had said and I replied that I had not heard. I had a pistol in the drawer of my table and I went to it; but he seemed to guess what I was thinking for he moved across the room as if by accident and leaned against the table as if he owned the place. Then he asked me to lend him some money.

'I was never a fool. I had a thousand leva pinned high up in the curtain but only a few coins in my bag. I said that I had no money. He seemed not to take any notice of that and began to tell me that he had not eaten anything since the day before, that he had no money and that he felt ill. But all the time he talked his eyes were moving, looking at the things in the room. I can see him now. His face was smooth and oval and pale and he had very brown, anxious eyes that made you think of a doctor's eyes when he is doing something to you that hurts. He frightened me. I told him again that I had no money but that I had some bread if he wanted it. He said: "Give me the bread."

'I got the bread from the drawer and gave it to him. He ate it slowly, still leaning against the table. When he had finished he asked for a cigarette. I gave him one. Then he said that I needed a protector. I knew then what he was after. I said that I could manage my own affairs. He said that I was a fool and he could prove it. If I would do as he said he would get five thousand leva that day and give me half of it. I asked what he wanted me to do. He told me to write a note that he would dictate. It was addressed to a man whose name I had never heard and simply asked for five thousand leva. I thought he must be mad and to get rid of him I wrote the note and signed it "Irana". He said that he would meet me at a café that evening.

'I did not trouble to keep the appointment. The next morning he came again to my room. This time I would not let him in. He was very angry and said he had two thousand five hundred leva for me. Of course, I did not believe him but he pushed a thousand leva note under the door and said that I should have the rest when I let him in. So I let him in. He gave me immediately another fifteen hundred leva. I asked him where he had got it and he said that he had delivered the note himself to the man who had given him the money immediately.

'I have always been discreet. I am not interested in the real names of my friends. Dimitrios had followed one of them to his home had found out his real name and that he was an important man, and then, with my note in his hand, had threatened to tell his wife and daughters of our friendship unless he paid.

'I was very angry. I said that for the sake of two thousand five hundred leva I had lost one of my good friends. Dimitrios said that he could get me richer friends. He said, too, that he had given the money to me to show that he was serious and that he could have written the note himself and gone to my friend without telling me.

'I saw that this was true. I saw also that he might go to other friends unless I agreed with him. So Dimitrios became my protector and he *did* bring me richer friends. And he bought himself very smart clothes and sometimes went to the best cafés.

'But soon, someone I knew told me that he had become involved in politics and that he often went to certain cafés that the police watched. I told him that he was a fool, but he took no notice. He said that soon he would make a lot of money. And then he became suddenly angry and said that he would not stay behind for anyone, that he was tired of being poor. When I reminded him that it was because of me that he was not starving he turned upon me.

'"You!" he said; "do you think that you make money for me? There are thousands like you. I chose you because although you look soft and sentimental you are cunning and can keep your head. When I came in that day, I guessed that you had money hidden in the curtain because your sort always has money in the curtain. It is an old trick. But it was at your bag that you kept looking so anxiously. I knew then that you were sensible. But you have no imagination. You do not understand money. You can buy anything you fancy and in restaurants they look up to you. It is only those without imagination who stay poor. When you are rich people do not mind what you do. You have the power and that is what is important to a man!" And he went on to tell me about rich men he had seen in Smyrna, men who owned ships and grew figs and had great houses on the hills outside the town.

'Then, for a single moment, because when men become sentimental and tell me their dreams I despise them, I forgot my fear of Dimitrios. Sitting there in his smart clothes with his eyes on mine he appeared to me absurd. I laughed.

'He was always pale but now all the blood left his face and suddenly I was terrified. I thought he meant to kill me. He had a glass in his hand. Slowly he raised it then smashed it on the edge of the table. Then he got up and with the broken half in his hand came towards me. I screamed. He stopped and dropped the glass on the floor. It was stupid, he said, to be angry with me. But I knew why he had stopped. He had remembered that I would be useless to him with my face cut about.

'After that I did not see him much. Often he left Sofia for several days at a time. He did not tell me where he went and I did not ask. But I knew that he had made important friends, for, once, when the police were making difficulties about his papers, he laughed and told me not to worry about the police. They would not dare to touch him, he said.

'But one morning he came to me in great agitation. He looked as if he had been travelling all night and had not shaved for several days. I had never seen him so nervous. He took me by the wrists and said that if anyone asked me I must say that he had been with me for the last three days. I had not seen him for over a week but I had to agree and he went to sleep in my room.

'Nobody asked me about him; but later that day I read in the newspaper that an attempt had been made on Stambulisky at Haskovo and I guessed where Dimitrios had been. I was frightened. An old friend of mine, whom I had known before Dimitrios, wanted to give me an apartment of my own. When Dimitrios had had his sleep and gone, I went to my friend and said that I would take this apartment.

'I was afraid when I had done it, but that night I met Dimitrios and told him. I had expected him to be angry but he was quite calm and said that it would be best for me. Yet I could not tell what he was thinking because he always looked the same, like a doctor when he is doing something to you that hurts. I took courage and reminded him that we had some business to settle. He agreed and said that he would meet me three days later to give me all the money that was due to me.'

She had paused then and looked from Latimer to Marukakis with a faint, taut smile on her lips. There had been something defensive in the smile. She had shrugged her shoulders slightly.

'You think it curious that I should trust Dimitrios. You think that I was a fool. But because Dimitrios frightened me, I would trust him. To distrust him was to remind myself of the fear. All men can be dangerous, as tame animals in a circus can be dangerous when they remember too much. But Dimitrios was different. He had the appearance of being tame; but when you looked into his eyes you saw that he had none of the feelings that make ordinary men soft, that he was always dangerous. I trusted him because there was nothing else for me to do. But I also hated him.

'Three days later I waited for him in the café and he did not come. Several weeks after that I saw him and he said that he had been away but that if I would meet him on the following day, he would pay me the money he owed. The meeting place was a café in the rue Perotska, a low place that I did not like.

'This time he came as he had promised. He said that he was in difficulties about money, that he had a great sum coming to him and that he would pay me within a few weeks.

'I wondered why he had kept the appointment merely to tell me that; but later I understood why. He had come to ask me a favour. He had to have certain letters received by someone he could trust. They were not his letters but those of a friend of his, a Turk named Talat. If this friend could give the address of my apartment, Dimitrios himself would collect the letters when he paid me my money.

'I agreed. I could do nothing else. It meant that if Dimitrios had to collect these letters from me he would have to pay me the money. But I knew in my heart and he knew too that he could have collected the letters and not paid me a sou and I could have done nothing.

'We were sitting there drinking coffee – for Dimitrios was very mean in cafés – when the police came in to inspect papers. It was quite usual at that time, but it was not good to be found in that café because of its reputation. Dimitrios had his papers in order but because he was a foreigner they took his name and mine because I was with him. When they had gone he was very angry; but I think he was angry not because of their taking his name but because they had taken my name as being with him. He was much put out and told me not to trouble about the letters as he would arrange for them with someone else. We left the café and that was the last time I saw him.'

She had had a Mandarine-Curaçao in front of her and now she had drunk it down thirstily. Latimer had cleared his throat.

'And the last you heard of him?'

Suspicion had flickered for an instant in her eyes. Latimer had said: 'Dimitrios is dead, madame. Fifteen years have gone by. Times have changed in Sofia.'

Her queer, taut smile had hovered on her lips.

'"Dimitrios is dead, madame." That sounds very curious to me. It is difficult to think of Dimitrios as dead. How did he look?'

'His hair was grey. He was wearing clothes bought in Greece and in France. Poor stuff.' Unconsciously he had echoed Colonel Haki's phrase.

'Then he did not become rich?'

'He did once become rich, in Paris, but he lost his money.'

She had laughed. 'That must have hurt him.' And then suspicion again: 'You know a lot about Dimitrios, monsieur. If he is dead . . . I don't understand.'

'My friend is a writer,' Marukakis had put in; 'he is naturally interested in human nature.'

'What do you write?'

'Detective stories.'

She had shrugged. 'You do not need to know human nature for that. It is for love stories and romances that one must know human nature. *Romans policiers* are ugly. *Folle Farine* I think is a lovely story. Do you like it?'

'Very much.'

'I have read it seventeen times. It is the best of Ouida's books and I have read them all. One day I shall write my memoirs. I have seen a lot of human nature you know.' The smile had become a trifle arch and she had sighed and fingered a diamond brooch.

'But you wish to know more of Dimitrios. Very well. I heard of Dimitrios again a year later. One day I received a letter from him, from Adrianople. He gave a Poste Restante address. The letter asked me if I had received any letters for this Talat. If I had I was to write saying so but to keep the letters. He said that I was to tell nobody that I had heard from him. He promised again to pay me the money he owed me. I had no letters addressed to Talat and wrote to tell him so. I also said that I needed the money because, now that he had gone away, I had lost all my friends. That was a lie but I thought that by flattering him I would perhaps get the money. I should have known Dimitrios better. He did not even reply.

'A few weeks after that a man came to see me. A type of *fonctionnaire* he was, very severe and businesslike. His clothes looked expensive. He said that the police would probably be coming to question me about Dimitrios.

'I was frightened at that but he said that I had nothing to fear. Only I must be careful what I said to them. He told me what to say: how I must describe Dimitrios so that the police would be satisfied. I showed him the letter from Adrianople and it seemed to amuse him. He said that I could tell the police about the letter coming from Adrianople but that I must say nothing about this name Talat. He said that the letter was a dangerous thing to keep and burnt it. That made me angry but he gave me a thousand leva note and asked me if I liked Dimitrios, if I was a friend. I said that I hated him. Then he said that friendship was a great thing and that he would give me five thousand leva to say what he had told me to the police.'

She had shrugged. 'That is being serious, messieurs. Five thousand leva! When the police came I said what this man had asked me to say and the following day an envelope with five thousand leva in it arrived by post. There was nothing else in the envelope, no letter. That was all

right. But listen! About two years later I saw this man in the street. I
went up to him; but the *salop* pretended that he had not seen me before
and called the police to me. Friendship is a great thing.'

She had picked up the book and put it back in its pigeon hole.

'If you will excuse me, messieurs, it is time I returned to my guests. I
think I have talked too much. You see, I know nothing about Dimitrios
that is of any interest.'

'We have been most interested, madame.'

She had smiled. 'If you are not in a hurry, messieurs, I can show you
more interesting things than Dimitrios. I have two most amusing girls
who . . .'

'We are a little pressed for time, madame. Another night we should be
delighted. Perhaps you would allow us to pay for your drinks.'

She had smiled. 'As you wish, but it has been most agreeable talking
to you. No, no, please! I have a superstition about money being shown in
my own private room. Please arrange it with the waiter at your table.
You will excuse me if I don't come down with you? I have a little
business to attend to. *Au 'voir, Monsieur. Au 'voir, Monsieur. A bientôt.*'

The dark, humid eyes had rested on them affectionately. Latimer had
found himself feeling absurdly distressed at the leave-taking.

It had been a *gérant* who had responded to their request for a bill. He
had had a brisk, cheerful manner.

'Eleven hundred leva, messieurs.'

'What!'

'The price you arranged with madame.'

'You know,' Marukakis remarked as they waited for their change, 'I
think one does wrong to disapprove altogether of Dimitrios. He had his
points.'

'Dimitrios was employed by Vazoff acting on behalf of the Eurasian
Credit Trust to do work in connection with getting rid of Stambulisky. It
would be interesting to know how they recruited him, but that is a thing
we shall never know. However, they must have found him satisfactory
because they employed him to do similar work in Adrianople. He probably used the name Talat there.'

'The Turkish police did not know that. They heard of him simply as
"Dimitrios", put in Latimer. 'What I cannot understand is why Vazoff –
it obviously was Vazoff who visited La Preveza in nineteen twenty-four –
allowed her to tell the police that she had had that letter from
Adrianople.'

'For only one reason, surely. Because Dimitrios was no longer in

Adrianople.' Marukakis stifled a yawn. 'It's been a curious evening.'

They were standing outside Latimer's hotel. The night air was cold. 'I think I'll go in now,' he said.

'You'll be leaving Sofia?'

'For Belgrade. Yes.'

'Then you are still interested in Dimitrios?'

'Oh, yes.' Latimer hesitated. 'I can't tell you how grateful I am to you for your help. It has been a miserable waste of time for you.'

Marukakis laughed and then grinned apologetically. He said: 'I was laughing at myself for envying you your Dimitrios. If you find out any more about him in Belgrade I should like you to write to me. Would you do that?'

'Of course.'

But Latimer was not to reach Belgrade.

He thanked Marukakis again and they shook hands; then he went into the hotel. His room was on the second floor. Key in hand, he climbed the stairs. Along the heavily carpeted corridors his footsteps made no sound. He put the key in the lock, turned it and opened the door.

He had been expecting darkness and the lights in the room were switched on. That startled him a little. The thought flashed through his mind that perhaps he had mistaken the room; but an instant later he saw something which disposed of that notion. That something was chaos.

Strewn about the floor in utter confusion were the contents of his suitcases. Draped carelessly over a chair were the bedclothes. On the mattress, stripped of their binding, were the few English books he had brought with him from Athens. The room looked as if a cageful of chimpanzees had been turned loose in it.

Dazed, Latimer took two steps forward into the room. Then a slight sound to the right of him made him turn his head. The next moment his heart jolted sickeningly.

The door leading to the bathroom was open. Standing just inside it, a disembowelled tube of toothpaste in one hand, a massive pistol held loosely in the other and on his lips a sweet, sad smile, was Mr. Peters.

CHAPTER 7

HALF-A-MILLION FRANCS

Mr. Peters took a firmer grasp of his pistol.

'Would you be so good,' he said gently, 'as to shut the door behind you? I think that if you stretched out your right arm you could do it without moving your feet.' The pistol was now levelled in an unmistakable fashion.

Latimer obeyed. Now, at last, he felt very frightened indeed. He was afraid that he was going to be hurt; he could already feel the doctor probing for the bullet. He was afraid that Mr. Peters was not used to the pistol, that he might fire accidentally. He was afraid of moving his hand too quickly lest the sudden movement should be misinterpreted. The door closed. He began to shake from head to foot and could not decide whether it was anger, fear or shock that made him do so. Suddenly he made up his mind to say something.

'What the hell does this mean?' he demanded harshly and then swore. It was not what he had intended to say and he was a man who very rarely swore. He was sure now that it was anger that was making him tremble. He glowered into Mr. Peters' wet eyes.

The fat man lowered his pistol and sat down on the edge of the mattress.

'This is most awkward,' he said unhappily. 'I did not expect you back so soon. Your *maison close* must have proved disappointing. The inevitable Armenian girls, of course. Appealing enough for a while and then merely dull. I often think that perhaps this great world of ours would be a better, finer place if . . .' He broke off. 'But we can talk about that another time.' Carefully he put the remains of the toothpaste tube on the bedside table. 'I had hoped to get things tidied a little before I left,' he added.

Latimer decided to play for time. 'Including the books, Mr. Peters?'

'Ah, yes, the books!' He shook his head despondently. 'An act of vandalism. A book is a lovely thing, a garden stocked with beautiful flowers, a magic carpet on which to fly away to unknown climes. I am sorry. But it was necessary.'

'What was necessary? What are you talking about?'

Mr. Peters smiled a sad, long-suffering smile. 'A little frankness, Mr. Latimer, *please*. There could be only one reason why your room should be searched and you know it as well as I do. I can see your difficulty, of course. You are wondering exactly where I stand. If it is any consolation to you, however, I may say that my difficulty is in wondering exactly where *you* stand.'

This was fantastic. In his exasperation, Latimer forgot his fears. He took a deep breath.

'Now look here, Mr. Peters, or whatever your name is, I am very tired and I want to go to bed. If I remember correctly, I travelled with you in a train from Athens several days ago. You were, I believe, going to Bucharest. I, on the other hand, got off here in Sofia. I have been out with a friend. I return to my hotel to find my room in a disgusting mess, my books destroyed, and you flourishing a pistol in my face. I conclude that you are either a sneak thief or a drunk. But for your pistol, of which I am, I confess, afraid, I should already have rung for assistance. But it seems to me on reflection that thieves do not ordinarily meet their victims in first class sleeping cars, nor do they tear books to pieces. Again, you do not appear to be drunk. I begin, naturally, to wonder if, after all, you may not be mad. If you are, of course, I can do nothing but humour you and hope for the best. But if you are comparatively sane I must ask you once more for an explanation. I repeat, Mr. Peters – what the hell does this mean?'

Mr. Peters' tear-filled eyes were half-closed. 'Perfect,' he said raptly; 'perfect! No, no, Mr. Latimer, keep away from the bell push, please. That is better. You know, for a moment I was almost convinced of your sincerity. Almost. But, of course, not quite. It really is not kind of you to try to deceive me. Not kind, not considerate and such a waste of time.'

Latimer took a step forward. 'Now listen to me . . .'

The pistol jerked upwards. The smile left Mr. Peters' mouth and his flaccid lips parted slightly. He looked adenoidal and very dangerous. Latimer stepped back quickly. The smile slowly returned.

'Come now, Mr. Latimer. A little frankness, please. I have the best of intentions towards you. I did not seek this interview. But since you have returned so unexpectedly, since I could no longer meet you on a basis of, may I say, disinterested friendship, let us be frank with one another.' He leaned forward a little. 'Why are you so interested in Dimitrios?'

'Dimitrios!'

'Yes, dear Mr. Latimer, Dimitrios. You have come from the Levant. Dimitrios came from there. In Athens you were very energetically seeking his record in the relief commission archives. Here in Sofia you have employed an agent to trace his police record. Why? Wait before you answer. I have no animosity towards you. I bear you no ill-will. Let that

be clear. But, as it happens, I, too, am interested in Dimitrios and because of that I am interested in you. Now, Mr. Latimer, tell me frankly
where you stand. What – forgive the expression, please – is your game?'

Latimer was silent for a moment. He was trying to think quickly and
not succeeding. He was confused. He had come to regard Dimitrios as his
own property, a problem as academic as that of the authorship of an
anonymous sixteenth century lyric. And now, here was the odious Mr.
Peters, with his shabby god and his smiles and his pistol, claiming acquaintance with the problem as though he, Latimer, were the interloper.
There was, of course, no reason why he should be surprised. Dimitrios
must have been known to many persons. Yet he had felt instinctively that
they must all have died with Dimitrios. Absurd, no doubt, but...

'Well, Mr. Latimer.' The fat man's smile had lost none of its sweet-
ness, but there was an edge to his husky voice that made Latimer think of
a small boy pulling the legs off flies.

'I think,' he said slowly, 'that if I am going to answer questions, I
ought to be allowed to ask some. In other words, Mr. Peters, if you will
tell me what *your* game is, I will tell you about mine. I have nothing at all
to hide, but I have a curiosity to satisfy. And it really is no good your
weighing your pistol so ominously. It is no longer an argument. It is of a
large calibre and probably makes a considerable amount of noise when
fired. Besides, you would gain nothing by shooting me. While I thought
that you might fire it to protect yourself from arrest, it no doubt had its
uses. Now, you might just as well put it away in your pocket.'

Mr. Peters smiled on steadily. 'Very neatly and charmingly put, Mr.
Latimer. All the same, I think I shall keep my pistol for the moment.'

'As you please. Do you mind telling me what you hoped to find here –
in the bindings of my books or in the tube of toothpaste?'

'I was looking for an answer to my question, Mr. Latimer. But all I
found was this.' He held up a sheet of paper. It was the chronological
table which Latimer had jotted down in Smyrna. As far as he remembered, he had left it folded in a book he had been reading. 'You see, Mr.
Latimer, I felt that if you hid papers between the leaves of books, you
might also hide more interesting papers in the bindings.'

'It wasn't intended to be hidden.'

But Mr. Peters took no notice. He held up the paper delicately between a finger and thumb – a schoolmaster about to consider a schoolboy essay. He shook his head.

'And is this all you know about Dimitrios, Mr. Latimer?'

'No.'

'Ah!' He gazed pathetically at Latimer's tie. 'Now who, I wonder, is this Colonel Haki, who seems so well informed and so indiscreet? The name is Turkish. And poor Dimitrios was taken from us at Istanbul, was he not? And you have come from Istanbul, haven't you?'

Involuntarily, Latimer nodded and then could have kicked himself, for Mr. Peters' smile broadened.

'Thank you, Mr. Latimer. I can see that you are prepared to be helpful. Now let us see. You were in Istanbul, and so was Dimitrios, and so was Colonel Haki. There was a note here about a passport in the name of Talat. Another Turkish name. And there is Adrianople and the phrase "Kemal attempt". "Attempt" – ah, yes! Now, I wonder if you translated that word literally from the French "*attentat*". You won't tell me? Well, well. I think that perhaps we may take that for granted. You know it almost looks as if you have been reading a Turkish police dossier. Now, doesn't it, eh?'

Latimer had begun to feel rather foolish. He said: 'I don't think you're going to get very far that way. You're forgetting that for every question you ask you're going to have to answer one. For example, I should very much like to know whether you ever actually met Dimitrios?'

Mr. Peters contemplated him for a moment without speaking. Then: 'I don't think that you are very sure of yourself, Mr. Latimer,' he said slowly. 'I have an idea that I could tell you much more than you could tell me.' He dropped the pistol into his overcoat pocket and got to his feet. 'I think I must be going,' he added.

This was not at all what Latimer expected or wanted, but he said 'Good night' calmly enough.

The fat man walked towards the door. But there he stopped. 'Istanbul,' Latimer heard him murmur thoughtfully. 'Istanbul. Smyrna 1922, Athens the same year, Sofia 1923. Adrianople – no, because he comes from Turkey.' he turned round quickly. 'Now, I wonder . . .' He paused, and then seemed to make up his mind. 'I wonder if it would be very stupid of me to imagine that you might be thinking of going to Belgrade in the near future. Would it, Mr. Latimer?'

Latimer was taken by surprise, and, even as he began to say very decidedly that it would be more than stupid of Mr. Peters to imagine any such thing, he knew by the other's triumphant smile that his surprise had been detected and interpreted.

'You will like Belgrade,' Mr. Peters continued happily; 'such a beautiful city. The views from the Terazija and the Kalemegdan! Magnificent!'

Latimer pulled the bedclothes off the chair and sat down facing him.

'Mr. Peters,' he said, 'in Smyrna I had occasion to examine certain fifteen-year-old police records. I afterwards found out that those same records had been examined three months previously by someone else. I wonder if you would like to tell me if that someone else was you.'

But the fat man's watery eyes were staring into vacancy. A slight frown gathered on his forehead. He said, as though he were listening to Latimer's voice for mistakes in intonation: 'Would you mind repeating that question?'

Latimer repeated the question.

There was another pause. Then Mr. Peters shook his head decidedly. 'No, Mr. Latimer, it was not I.'

'But you were yourself making inquiries about Dimitrios in Athens, weren't you, Mr. Peters? You were the person who came into the bureau while I was asking about Dimitrios, weren't you? You made a rather hurried exit, I seem to remember. Unfortunately I did not see it, but the official there commented on it. And it was design, not accident, that brought you to Sofia on the train by which I was travelling, wasn't it? You also took care to find out from me – very neatly, I admit – at which hotel I was staying, before I got off the train. That's right, isn't it?'

Mr. Peters was smiling sunnily again. He nodded. 'Yes, Mr. Latimer, all quite right. I know everything that you have done since you left the record bureau in Athens. I have already told you that I am interested in anyone who is interested in Dimitrios. Of course, you found out all about this man who had been before you in Smyrna?'

The last sentence was put in a little too casually. Latimer said: 'No, Mr. Peters, I did not.'

'But surely you were interested?'

'Not very.'

The fat man sighed. 'I do not think that you are being frank with me. How much better if . . .'

'Listen!' Latimer interrupted rudely. 'I'm going to be frank. You are doing your level best to pump me. I'm not going to be pumped. Let that be clear. I made you an offer. You answer my questions and I'll answer yours. The only questions you've answered so far have been questions to which I had already guessed the answers. I still want to know why you are interested in this dead man Dimitrios. You said that you could tell me more than I could tell you. That may be so. But *I* have an idea, Mr. Peters, that it is more important for you to have my answers than it is for me to have your answers. Breaking into hotel rooms and making this sort of mess isn't the sort of thing any man does in a spirit of idle inquiry. To be honest, I cannot for the life of me conceive of any reason for your interest in Dimitrios. It did occur to me that perhaps Dimitrios had kept some of that money he earned in Paris. . . . You know about that, I expect?' And in response to a faint nod from Mr. Peters: 'Yes, I thought you might. But, as I say, it did occur to me that Dimitrios might have hidden his treasure and that you were interested in finding out where. Unfortunately my own information disposes of that possibility. His belongings were on the mortuary table beside him, and there wasn't a penny piece there. Just a bundle of cheap clothes. And as for . . .'

But Mr. Peters had stepped forward and was staring down at him with a peculiar expression on his face. Latimer allowed the sentence he had begun to trail off lamely into silence. 'What is the matter?' he added.

'Did I understand you to say,' said the fat man slowly, 'that you actually saw the body of Dimitrios in the mortuary?'

'Yes; what of it? Have I carelessly let slip another useful piece of information?'

But Mr. Peters did not answer. He had produced one of his thin cheroots and was lighting it carefully. Suddenly he blew out a jet of smoke and started to waddle slowly up and down the room, his eyes screwed up as if he were in great pain. He began to talk.

'Mr. Latimer, we must reach an understanding. We must stop this quarrelling.' He halted in his tracks and looked down at Latimer again. 'It is absolutely essential, Mr. Latimer,' he said, 'that I know what you are after. No, no, please! Don't interrupt me. I admit that I probably need your answers more than you need mine. But I cannot give you mine at present. Yes, yes, I heard what you said. But I am talking seriously. Listen, please.

'You are interested in the history of Dimitrios. You are thinking of going to Belgrade to find out more about him. You cannot deny that. Now, both of us know that Dimitrios was in Belgrade in 1926. Also, I can tell you that he was never there after 1926. Why are you interested? You will not tell me. Very well, I will tell you something more. If you go to Belgrade you will not discover a single trace of Dimitrios. Furthermore, you may find yourself in trouble with the authorities if you pursue the matter. There is only one man who could and would, under certain circumstances, tell you what you want to know. He is a Pole, and he lives near Geneva.

'Now then! I will give you his name and I will give you a letter to him. I will do that for you. But first I must know why you want this information. I thought at first that you might perhaps be connected with the Turkish police – there are so many Englishmen in the Near Eastern police departments these days – but that possibility I no longer consider. Your passport describes you as a writer, but that is a very elastic term. Who are you, Mr. Latimer, and what is your game?'

He paused expectantly. Latimer stared back at him with what he hoped was an inscrutable expression. Mr. Peters, unabashed, went on:

'Naturally, when I ask what your name is, I use the phrase in a specific sense. Your game is, of course, to get money. But that is not the answer I need. Are you a rich man, Mr. Latimer? No? Then what I have to say may be simplified. I am proposing an alliance, Mr. Latimer, a pooling of resources. I am aware of certain facts which I cannot tell you about at the moment. You, on the other hand, possess an important piece of information. You may not know that it is important, but nevertheless it *is*. Now, my facts alone are not worth a great deal. Your piece of information is quite valueless without my facts. The two together, however, are worth at the very least' – he stroked his chin – 'at the very least five thousand English pounds, a million French francs.' He smiled triumphantly. 'What do you say to that?'

'You will forgive me,' replied Latimer coldly, 'if I say that I cannot understand what you're talking about, won't you? Not that it makes any difference whether you do or don't. I am *tired*, Mr. Peters, *very* tired. I want badly to go to bed.' He got to his feet and, pulling the bedclothes on to the bed, began to remake it. 'There is, I suppose, no reason why you should not know why I am interested in Dimitrios,' he went on as he dragged a sheet into position. 'The reason is certainly nothing to do with money. I write detective stories for a living. In Stambul I heard from a Colonel Haki, who is something to do with the police there, about a criminal named Dimitrios, who had been found dead in the Bosphorus. Partly for amusement – the sort of amusement that one derives from cross-word puzzles – partly from a desire to try my hand at practical detection, I set out to trace the man's history. That is all. I don't expect you to understand it. You are probably wondering at the moment why I couldn't think of a more convincing story. I am sorry. If you don't like the truth, you can lump it.'

Mr. Peters had listened in silence. Now he waddled to the window, pitched out his cheroot and faced Latimer across the bed.

'Detective stories! Now, that is most interesting to me, Mr. Latimer. I am so fond of them. I wonder if you would tell me the names of some of your books.'

Latimer gave him several titles.

'And your publisher?'

'English, American, French, Swedish, Norwegian, Dutch or Hungarian?'

'Hungarian, please.'

Latimer told him.

Mr. Peters nodded slowly. 'A good firm, I believe.' He seemed to reach a decision. 'Have you a pen and paper, Mr. Latimer?'

Latimer nodded wearily towards the writing-table. The other went to it and sat down. As he finished making the bed and began to collect his belongings from the floor, Latimer heard the hotel pen scratching over a piece of the hotel paper. Mr. Peters was keeping his word.

At last he finished and the chair creaked as he got up. Latimer, who was replacing some shoe trees, straightened his back. Mr. Peters had recovered his smile. Goodwill oozed from him like sweat.

'Here, Mr. Latimer,' he announced, 'are three pieces of paper. On the first one is written the name of the man of whom I spoke to you. His name is Grodek – Wladyslaw Grodek. He lives just outside Geneva. The second is a letter to him. If you present that letter he will know that you are a friend of mine and that he can be frank with you. He is retired now, so I think I may safely tell you that he was at one time the most successful professional agent in Europe. More secret naval and military information has passed through his hands than through those of any other one man. It was always accurate, what is more. He dealt with quite a number of governments. His headquarters were in Brussels. To an author I should think he would be very interesting. You will like him, I think. He is a great lover of animals. A beautiful character *au fond*. Incidentally, it was he who employed Dimitrios in 1926.

'I see. Thank you very much. What about the third piece of paper?'

Mr. Peters hesitated. His smile became a little smug. 'I think you said that you were not rich.'

'No, I am not rich.'

'Half a million francs, two thousand five hundred English pounds, would be useful to you?'

'Undoubtedly.'

'Well, then, Mr. Latimer, when you have tired of Geneva I want you to – how do you say? – to kill two birds with one stone.' He pulled Latimer's chronological table from his pocket. 'On this list of yours you have other dates besides 1926 still to be accounted for if you are to know what there is to know about Dimitrios. The place to account for them is Paris. That is the first thing. The second is that, if you will come to Paris, if you will put yourself in touch with me there, if you will consider, then, the pooling of resources, the alliance that I have already proposed to you, I can definitely guarantee that in a very few days you will have at least two thousand five hundred English pounds to pay into your account – half a million French francs!'

'I do wish,' retorted Latimer irritably, 'that you would be a little more explicit. Half a million francs for doing what? Who is going to pay this money? You are far too mysterious, Mr. Peters – far too mysterious to be true.'

Mr. Peters' smile tightened. Here was a Christian, reviled but unembittered, waiting steadfastly for the lions to be admitted into the arena.

'Mr. Latimer,' he said gently, 'I know that you do not trust me. That is the reason why I have given you Grodek's address and that letter to him. I want to give you concrete evidence of my goodwill towards you, to prove that my word is to be trusted. And I want to show that I trust you, that I believe what you have told me. At the moment I cannot say more. But if you will believe in and trust me, if you will come to Paris, then here, on this piece of paper, is an address. When you arrive send a *pneumatique* to me. Do not call, for it is the address of a friend. If you will simply send a *pneumatique* giving me your address, I will be able to explain everything. It is perfectly simple.'

It was time, Latimer decided, to get rid of Mr. Peters.

'Well,' he said, 'this is all very confusing. You seem to me to have jumped to a lot of conclusions. I had not definitely arranged to go to Belgrade. It is not certain that I shall have time to go to Geneva. As for going on to Paris, that is a thing which I could not possibly consider at the moment. I have a great deal of work to do, of course, and . . .'

Mr. Peters buttoned up his overcoat. 'Of course.' And then, with a curious urgency in his tone: 'But if you *should* find time to come to Paris, do please send me that *pneumatique*. I have put you to so much trouble, I should like to make restitution in a practical way. Half a million francs is worth considering, eh? And I would guarantee it. But we must trust one another. That is most important.' He shook his head despondently. 'One goes through life like a flower with its face turned to the sun, ever seeking, ever hoping, wanting to trust others, but afraid to do so. How much better if we trusted one another, if we saw only the good things, the finer things in our fellow creatures! How much better if we were *frank* and *open*, if we went on our ways without the cloak of hypocrisy and lies that we wear now! It only causes trouble, and trouble is bad for business. Besides, life is so short. We are here on this globe for a short time only before the Great One recalls us.' He heaved a very noisy sigh. 'But you are a writer, Mr. Latimer, and sensitive to these things. You could express them so much better than I could.' He held out his hand. 'Good night, Mr. Latimer. I won't say "goodbye."'

Latime took the hand. It was dry and very soft.

'Good night.'

At the door he half turned. 'Half a million francs, Mr. Latimer, will buy a lot of good things. I do hope that we shall meet in Paris. Good night.'

'I hope so, too. Good night.'

The door closed and Mr. Peters was gone; but to Latimer's overwrought imagination is seemed as if his smile, like the Cheshire cat's, remained behind him, floating in the air. He leaned against the door and surveyed for an instant the upturned suit-cases. Outside it was beginning to get light. He looked at his watch. Five o'clock. The business of clearing up the room could wait. He undressed and got into bed.

CHAPTER 8

GRODEK

It was eleven o'clock when Latimer, having been awake for about a quarter of an hour, finally opened his eyes. There, on the bedside table, were Mr. Peters' three pieces of paper. They were an unpleasant reminder that he had some thinking to do and some decisions to make. But for their presence and the fact that in the morning light his room looked like a rag-picker's workshop, he might have dismissed his recollections of the visitation as being no more than part of the bad dreams which had troubled his sleep. He would have liked so to dismiss them. But Mr. Peters, with his mystery, his absurd references to half millions of francs, his threats and his hintings, was not so easily disposed of. He . . .

Latimer sat up in bed and reached for the three pieces of paper.

The first, as Peters had said, contained the Geneva address:

Wladyslaw Grodek,
Villa Acacias,
Chambésy.
(At 7 km. from Geneva.)

The writing was scratchy, florid and difficult to read. The figure seven was made with a stroke across the middle in the French way.

He turned hopefully to the letter. It consisted of only six lines and was written in a language and with an alphabet which he did not recognize, but which he concluded was probably Polish. It began, as far as he could see, without any preliminary 'Dear Grodek', and ended with an indecipherable initial. In the middle of the second line he made out his own name spelt with what looked like a 'Y' instead of an 'I'. He sighed. He could, of course, take the thing to a bureau and have it translated, but Mr. Peters would no doubt have thought of that, and it was unlikely that the result would supply any sort of answer to the questions that he, Latimer, badly wanted answered: the questions of who and what was Mr. Peters.

He turned to the second address:

> Mr. Peters,
> aux soins de Caillé,
> 3, Impasse des Huit Anges,
> Paris 7.

And that brought his thoughts back to their starting point. Why, in the name of all that was reasonable, should Mr. Peters want him to go to Paris? What was this information that was worth so much money? Who was going to pay for it?

He tried to remember at exactly what point in their encounter Mr. Peters had changed his tactics so abruptly. He had an idea that it had been when he had said something about having seen Dimitrios in the mortuary. But there could surely be nothing in that. Could it have been his reference to the 'treasure' of Dimitrios that had . . .

He snapped his fingers. Of course! What a fool not to think of it before! He had been ignoring an important fact. Dimitrios had not died a natural death. *Dimitrios had been murdered.*

Colonel Haki's doubts of the possibility of tracing the murderer and his own preoccupation with the past had caused him to lose sight of the fact or, at any rate, to see in it no more than a logical ending to an ugly story. He had failed to take into account the two consequent facts; that the murderer was still at large (and probably alive) and that there must have been a motive for the murder.

A murderer and a motive. The motive would be monetary gain. What money? Naturally, the money that had been made out of the drug-peddling business in Paris, the money that had so unaccountably disappeared. Mr. Peters' references to half millions of francs did not seem quite as fantastic when you looked at the problem from that point of view. As for the murderer – why not Peters? It was not difficult to see him in the part. What was it he had said in the train? 'If the Great One wills that we shall do unpleasant things, depend upon it that He has a purpose even though that purpose is not always clear to us.' It was tantamount to

a licence to murder. How odd if it had been his apology for the murder of
Dimitrios! You could see his soft lips moving over the words as he pulled
the trigger.

But at that Latimer frowned. No trigger had been pulled. Dimitrios
had been stabbed. He began to reconstruct the picture in his mind, to see
Peters stabbing someone. Yet the picture seemed wrong. It was difficult
to see Peters wielding a stabbing knife. The difficulty made him begin to
think again. There really was no reason at all even to suspect Peters of
the murder. And even if there had been a reason, the fact of Peters'
murdering Dimitrios for his money still did not explain the connection
(if a connection existed) between that money and the half million francs
(if they existed). And, anyway, what was this mysterious piece of information he was supposed to possess? It was all very like being faced by an
algebraic problem containing many unknown quantities and having
only one biquadratic equation with which to solve it. If he *were* to solve it
. . .

Now why should Peters be so anxious for him to go to Paris? Surely it
would have been just as simple to have pooled their resources (whatever
that might mean) in Sofia. Confound Mr. Peters! Latimer got out of bed
and turned on his bath. Sitting in the hot, slightly rusty water he reduced his predicament to its essentials.

He had a choice of two courses of action.

He could go back to Athens, work on his new book and put Dimitrios
and Marukakis and Mr. Peters and this Grodek out of his mind. Or, he
could go to Geneva, see Grodek (if there were such a person) and post-
pone making any decision about Mr. Peters' proposals.

The first course was obviously the sensible one. After all, the justification of his researches into the past life of Dimitrios had been that he
was making an impersonal experiment in detection. The experiment
must not be allowed to become an obsession. He had found out some
interesting things about the man. Honour should be satisfied. And it was
high time he got on with the book. He had his living to earn and no
amount of information about Dimitrios and Mr. Peters or anyone else
would compensate for a lean bank balance six months hence. As for the
half million francs, that could not be taken seriously. Yes, he would
return to Athens at once.

He got out of the bath and began to dry himself.

On the other hand there was the matter of Mr. Peters to be cleared up.
He could not reasonably be expected to leave these things as they were
and hurry off to write a detective story. It was too much to ask of any
man. Besides, here was *real* murder: not neat, tidy book-murder with

corpse and clues and suspects and hangman, but murder over which a chief of police shrugged his shoulders, wiped his hands and consigned the stinking victim to a coffin. Yes, that was it. It was real. Dimitrios was or had been real. Here were no strutting paper figures, but tangible evocative men and women, as real as Proudhon, Montesquieu and Rosa Luxemburg.

Aloud Latimer murmured: 'Comfortable, very comfortable! You want to go to Geneva. You don't want to work. You're feeling lazy and your curiosity has been aroused. In any case, the detective story-writer has no business with reality except in so far as it concerns the technicalities of such things as ballistics, medicine, the laws of evidence and police procedure. Let that be quite clear. Now then! no more of this nonsense.'

He shaved, dressed, collected his belongings, packed and went downstairs to inquire about the trains to Athens. The reception clerk brought him a time-table and found the Athens page.

Latimer stared at it in silence for a moment. Then:

'Supposing,' he said slowly, 'that I wanted to go to Geneva from here.'

On his second evening in Geneva, Latimer received a letter bearing the Chambésy postmark. It was from Wladyslaw Grodek and was in answer to a letter Latimer had sent enclosing Mr. Peters' note.

Herr Grodek wrote briefly and in French:

> Villa Acacias,
> Chambésy.
> Friday.

My dear Mr Latimer,
> *I should be pleased if you could come to the Villa Acacias for luncheon to-morrow. Unless I hear that you cannot come, my chauffeur will call at your hotel at eleven-thirty.*
> *Please accept the expression of my most distinguished sentiments.*
>   GRODEK.

The chauffeur arrived punctually, saluted, ushered Latimer ceremoniously into a huge chocolate-coloured *coupé de ville*, and drove off through the rain as if he were escaping from the scene of a crime.

Idly, Latimer surveyed the interior of the car. Everything about it from the inland wood panelling and ivory fittings to the too-comfortable upholstery suggested money, a great deal of money. Money, he reflected, that, if Peters were to be believed, had been made out of espionage.

Unreasonably he found it odd that there should be no evidence in the car of the sinister origin of its purchase price. He wondered what Herr Grodek would look like. He might possibly have a pointed white beard. Peters had said that he was a Polish national, a great lover of animals and a beautiful character *au fond*. Did that mean that superficially he was an ugly character? As for his alleged love of animals, that meant nothing. Great animal lovers were sometimes pathetic in their hatred of humanity. Would a professional spy, uninspired by any patriotic motives, hate the world he worked in? A stupid question.

For a time they travelled along the road which ran by the northerly shore of the lake; but at Pregny they turned to the left and began to climb a long hill. About a kilometre farther on, the car swung off into a narrow lane through a pine forest. They stopped before a pair of iron gates which the chauffeur got out to open. Then they drove on up a steep drive with a right-angle turn in the middle to stop at last before a large, ugly *chalet*.

The chauffeur opened the door and he got out and walked towards the door of the house. As he did so it was opened by a stout, cheerful-looking woman who looked as though she might be the housekeeper. He went in.

He found himself in a small lobby no more than six feet wide. On one wall was a row of clothes pegs draped carelessly with hats and coats, a woman's and a man's, a climbing rope and an odd ski-stick. Against the opposite wall were stacked three pairs of well-greased skis.

The housekeeper took his coat and hat and he walked through the lobby into a large room.

It was built rather like an inn with stairs leading to a gallery which ran along two sides of the room, and a vast cowled fireplace. A wood fire roared in the grate and the pinewood floor was covered with thick rugs. It was very warm and clean.

With a smiling assurance that Herr Grodek would be down immediately, the housekeeper withdrew. There were arm chairs in front of the fire and Latimer walked towards them. As he did so there was quick rustle and a Siamese cat leaped on to the back of the nearest chair and stared at him with hostile blue eyes. It was joined by another. Latimer moved towards them and they drew back arching their backs. Giving them a wide berth, Latimer made his way to the fire. The cats watched him narrowly. The logs shifted restlessly in the grate. There was a moment's silence; then Herr Grodek came down the stairs.

The first thing that drew Latimer's attention to the fact was that the cats lifted their heads suddenly, stared over his shoulder and then jumped lightly to the floor. He looked round. The man had reached the foot of the stairs. Now he turned and walked towards Latimer with his hand outstretched and words of apology on his lips.

He was a tall, broad-shouldered man of about sixty with thinning grey hair still tinged with the original straw colour which had matched the fair, clean-shaven cheeks and blue-grey eyes. His face was pear-shaped, tapering from a broad forehead, past a small tight mouth to a shin which receded almost into the neck. You might have put him down as an Englishman or a Dane of more than average intelligence; a retired consulting engineer, perhaps. In his slippers and his thick baggy tweeds and with his vigorous, decisive movements he looked like a man enjoying the well-earned fruits of a blameless and worthy career.

He said: 'Excuse me, please, monsieur. I did not hear the car arrive.'

His French, though curiously accented, was very ready, and Latimer found the fact incongruous. The small mouth would have been more at home with English.

'It is very kind of you to receive me so hospitably, Monsieur Grodek. I don't know what Peters said in his letter, because . . .'

'Because,' interrupted the tall man heartily, 'you very wisely have never troubled to learn Polish. I can sympathize with you. It is a horrible tongue. You have introduced yourself to Anton and Simone here.' He indicated the cats. 'I am convinced that they resent the fact that I do not speak Siamese. Do you like cats? Anton and Simone have critical intelligence, I am sure of it. They are not like ordinary cats, are you, *mes enfants?*' He seized one of them and held it up for Latimer's inspection. '*Ah, Simone cherie, comme tu es mignonne! Comme tu es bête!*' He released it so that it stood on the palms of his hands. '*Allez vite! Va promener avec ton vrai amant, ton cher Anton!*' The cat jumped to the floor and stalked indignantly away. Grodek dusted his hands lightly together. 'Beautiful, aren't they! And so human. They become ill-tempered when the weather is bad. I wish so much that we could have had a fine day for your visit, Monsieur. When the sun is shining the view from here is very pretty.'

Latimer said that he had guessed from what he had seen that it would be. He was puzzled. Both his host and his reception were totally unlike those he had expected. Grodek might look like a retired consulting engineer, but he had a quality which seemed to render the simile absurd. It was a quality that derived somehow from the contrast between his appearance and his quick, neat gestures, the urgency of his small lips. You could picture him without effort in the role of lover; which was a thing, Latimer reflected, that you could say of few men of sixty and few of under sixty. He wondered about the woman whose belongings he had seen in the entrance lobby. He added lamely: 'It must be agreeable here in the summer.'

Grodek nodded. He had opened a cupboard by the fireplace. 'Agreeable enough. What will you drink? English whisky?'

'Thank you.'

'Good. I, too, prefer it as an aperitif.'

He began to splash whisky into two tumblers. 'In the summer I work outside. That is very good for me but not good for my work, I think. Do you find that you can work out of doors?'

'No, I don't. The flies. . . .'

'Exactly! the flies. I am writing a book, you know.'

'Indeed. Your memoirs?'

Grodek looked up from the bottle of soda water he was opening and Latimer saw a glint of amusement in his eyes as he shook his head. 'No, monsieur. A life of St. Francis. I confidently expect to be dead before it is finished.'

'It must be a very exhaustive study.'

'Oh yes.' He handed Latimer a drink. 'You see, the advantage of St. Francis from my point of view is that he has been written about so extensively that I need not go to original sources for my material. There is no serious research for me to do. The work therefore serves its purpose in permitting me to live here in almost absolute idleness with an easy conscience.' He raised his glass. '*A votre santé.*'

'*A la vôtre.*' Latimer was beginning to wonder if his host were, after all, no more than an affected ass. He drank a little of his whisky. 'I wonder,' he said, 'if Peters mentioned the purpose of my visit to you in the letter I brought with me from Sofia.'

'No, he did not. But I received a letter from him yesterday which did mention it.' He was putting down his glass and he gave Latimer a sidelong look as he added: 'It interested me very much.' And then: 'Have you known Peters long?'

There was an unmistakable hesitation at the name. Latimer guessed that the other's lips had been framing a word of a different shape.

'I have met him once or twice. Once in a train, once in my hotel. And you, monsieur? You must know him very well.'

Grodek raised his eyebrows. 'And what makes you so sure of that?'

Latimer smiled easily because he felt uneasy. He had, he felt, committed some sort of indiscretion. 'If he had not known you very well he would surely not have given me an introduction to you or asked you to give me information of so confidential a character.' He felt pleased with that speech.

Grodek regarded him thoughtfully and Latimer found himself wondering how on earth he could have been as foolish as to liken the man to a retired consulting engineer. For no reason that he could fathom, he wished suddenly that he had Mr. Peters' pistol in his hand. It was not that there was anything menacing in the other's attitude. It was just that...

'Monsieur,' said Herr Grodek; 'I wonder what your attitude would be if I were to ask an impertinent question; if I were, for instance, to ask you to tell me seriously if a literary interest in human frailty were your only reason for approaching me.'

Latimer felt himself redden. 'I can assure you...' he began.

'I am quite certain that you can,' Grodek interrupted smoothly. 'But – forgive me – what are your assurances worth?'

'I can only give you my word, Monsieur, to treat any information you may give me as confidential,' retorted Latimer stiffly.

The other sighed. 'I don't think I have made myself quite clear,' he said carefully. 'The information itself is nothing. What happened in Belgrade in 1926 is of little importance now. It is my own position of which I am thinking. To be frank, our friend Peters has been a little indiscreet in sending you to me. He admits it but craves my indulgence and asks me as a favour – he recalls that I am under a slight obligation to him – to give you the information you need about Dimitrios Talat. He explains that you are a writer and that your interest is merely that of a writer. Very well! There is one thing, however, which I find inexplicable.' He paused, picked up his glass and drained it. 'As a student of human behaviour, Monsieur,' he went on, 'you must have noticed that most persons have behind their actions one stimulus which tends to dominate all others. With some of us it is vanity, with others the gratification of the senses, with still others the desire for money, and so on. Er – Peters happens to be one of those with the money stimulus very highly developed. Without being unkind to him, I think I may tell you that he has the miser's love of money for its own sake. Do not misunderstand me, please. I do not say that he will act only under that money stimulus. What I mean is that I cannot from my knowledge of Peters imagine him going to the trouble of sending you here to me and writing to me in the way he has written, in the interests of the English detective story. You see my point? I am a little suspicious. I still have enemies in this world. Supposing, therefore, that you will tell me just what your relations with our friend Peters are. Would you like to do that?'

'I should be delighted to do so. Unfortunately I can't. And for a simple reason. I don't know what those relations are myself.'

Grodek's eyes hardened. 'I was not joking.'

'Nor was I. I have been investigating the history of this man Dimitrios. While doing so I have met Peters. For some reason that I do not know of, he, too, is interested in Dimitrios. He overheard me making inquiries in the relief commission archives in Athens. He then followed me to Sofia and approached me there – behind a pistol, I may add – for an explanation of my interest in this man, who, by the way, was murdered before I ever heard of him. He followed this up with an offer. He said that if I would meet him in Paris and collaborate with him in some scheme he had in mind we should each profit to the tune of half a million francs. He said that I possessed a piece of information which, though valueless by itself, would, when used in conjunction with information in his possession, be of great value. I did not believe him and refused to have anything to do with his scheme. Accordingly, as an inducement to me and as evidence of his goodwill, he gave me the note to you. I had told him, you see, that my interest was that of a writer and admitted that I was about to go to Belgrade to collect more information there if I could. He told me that you were the only person who could supply it.'

Grodek's eyebrows went up. 'I don't want to seem too inquisitive, but I should like to know how you knew that Dimitrios Talat was in Belgrade in 1926.'

'I was told by a Turkish official with whom I became friendly in Istanbul. He described the man's history to me; his history, that is, as far as it was known in Istanbul.'

'I see. And what, may I ask, is this so valuable piece of information in your possession?'

'I don't know.'

Grodek frowned. 'Come now, monsieur. You ask for my confidences. The least you can do is to give me yours.'

'I am telling you the truth. I don't know. I talked fairly freely to Peters. Then, at one point in the conversation, he became excited.'

'At what point?'

'I was explaining, I think, how I knew that Dimitrios had no money when he died. It was after that he started talking about this million francs.'

'And how *did* you know?'

'Because when I saw the body everything taken from it was on the mortuary table. Everything, that is, except his *carte d'identité* which had been removed from the lining of his coat and forwarded to the French authorities. There was no money. Not a penny.'

For several seconds Grodek stared at him. Then he walked over to the cupboard where the drinks were kept. 'Another drink?'

He poured the drinks out in silence, handed Latimer his and raised his glass solemnly. 'A toast, monsieur. To the English detective story!'

Amused, Latimer raised his glass to his lips. His host had done the same. Suddenly, however, he choked and, dragging a handkerchief from his pocket, set his glass down again. To his surprise, Latimer saw that the man was laughing.

'Forgive me,' he gasped; 'a thought crossed my mind that made me laugh. It was' – he hesitated a fraction of a second – 'it was the thought of our friend Peters confronting you with a pistol. He is quite terrified of firearms.'

'He seemed to keep his fears to himself quite successfully.' Latimer spoke a trifle irritably. He had a suspicion that there was another joke somewhere, the point of which he had missed.

'A clever man, Peters.' Grodek chuckled and patted Latimer on the shoulder. He seemed suddenly in excellent spirits. 'My dear chap, please don't say that I have offended you. Look, we will have luncheon now. I hope you will like it. Are you hungry? Greta is really a splendid cook and there is nothing Swiss about my wines. Afterwards, I will tell you about Dimitrios and the trouble he caused me, and Belgrade and 1926. Does that please you?'

'It's very good of you to put yourself out like this.'

He thought that Grodek was about to laugh again, but the Pole seemed to change his mind. He became instead very solemn. 'It is a pleasure, monsieur. Peters is a very good friend of mine. Besides, I like you personally, and we have so few visitors here.' He hesitated. 'May I be permitted as a friend to give you a word of advice?'

'Please do.'

'Then, if I were in your place, I should be inclined to take our friend Peters at his word and go to Paris.'

Latimer was perplexed. 'I don't know . . .' he began slowly.

But the housekeeper, Greta, had come into the room.

'Luncheon!' exclaimed Grodek with satisfaction.

Later, when he had an opportunity of asking Grodek to explain his 'word of advice', Latimer forgot to do so. By that time he had other things to think about.

CHAPTER 9

BELGRADE, 1926

Men have learned to distrust their imaginations. It is therefore, strange to them when they chance to discover that a world conceived in the imagination, outside experience, does exist in fact. The afternoon which Latimer spent at the Villa Acacias, listening to Wladyslaw Grodek, he recalls as, in that sense, one of the strangest of his life. In a letter (written in French) to the Greek, Marukakis, which he began that evening, while the whole thing was still fresh in his mind, and finished on the following day, the Sunday, he placed it on record.

> Geneva.
> Saturday.

My dear Marukakis,

> I remember that I promised to write to you to let you know if I discovered anything more about Dimitrios. I wonder if you will be as surprised as I am that I have actually done so. Discovered something, I mean; for I intended to write to you in any case to thank you again for the help you gave me in Sofia.
>
> When I left you there, I was bound, you may remember, for Belgrade. Why, then, am I writing from Geneva?
>
> I was afraid that you would ask that question.
>
> My dear fellow, I wish that I knew the answer. I know part of it. The man, the professional spy, who employed Dimitrios in Belgrade in 1926, lives just outside Geneva. I saw him to-day and talked with him about Dimitrios. I can even explain how I got into touch with him. I was introduced. But just why I was introduced and just what the man who introduced us hopes to get out of it I cannot imagine. I shall, I hope, discover those things eventually. Meanwhile, let me say that if you find this mystery irritating, I find it no less so. Let me tell you about Dimitrios.
>
> Did you ever believe in the existence of the 'master' spy? Until to-day I most certainly did not. Now I do. The reason for this is that I have spent the greater part of to-day talking to one. I cannot tell you his name, so I shall call him, in the

best spy-story tradition, 'G'.

G. was a 'master' spy (he has retired now) in the same sense that the printer my publisher uses is a 'master' printer. He was an employer of spy labour. His work was mainly (though not entirely) administrative in character.

Now I know that a lot of nonsense is talked and written about spies and espionage, but let me try to put the question to you as G. put it to me.

He began by quoting Napoleon as saying that in war the basic element of all successful strategy was surprise.

G. is, I should say, a confirmed Napoleon-quoter. No doubt Napoleon did say that or something like it. I am quite sure he wasn't the first military leader to do so. Alexander, Cæsar, Genghis Khan and Frederick of Prussia all had the same idea. In nineteen eighteen Foch thought of it, too. But to return to G.

G. says that 'the experiences of the 1914–18 conflict' showed that in a future war (that sounds so beautifully distant, doesn't it?) the mobility and striking power of modern armies and navies and the existence of air forces would render the element of surprise more important than ever; so important, in fact, that it was possible that the people who got in with a surprise attack first might win the war. It was more than ever necessary to guard against surprise, to guard against it, moreover, *before* the war had started.

Now, there are roughly twenty-seven independent states in Europe. Each has an army and an air force and most have some sort of navy as well. For its own security, each of those armies, air forces and navies must know what each corresponding force in each of the other twenty-six countries is doing – what its strength is, what its efficiency is, what secret preparations it is making. That means spies – armies of them.

In 1926 G. was employed by Italy; and in the spring of that year he set up house in Belgrade.

Relations between Yugoslavia and Italy were strained at the time. The Italian seizure of Fiume was still as fresh in Yugoslav minds as the bombardment of Corfu; there were rumours, too (not unfounded as it was learned later in the year) that Mussolini contemplated occupying Albania.

Italy, on her side, was suspicious of Yugoslavia. Fiume was held under Yugoslav guns. A Yugoslav Albania alongside the

Straits of Otranto was an unthinkable proposition. An independent Albania was tolerable only as long as it was under a predominantly Italian influence. It might be desirable to make certain of things. But the Yugoslavs might put up a fight. Reports from Italian agents in Belgrade indicated that in the event of war Yugoslavia intended to protect her seaboard by bottling herself up in the Adriatic with minefields laid just north of the Straits of Otranto.

I don't know much about these things, but apparently one does not have to lay a couple of hundred miles' worth of mines to make a two-hundred-miles wide corridor of sea impassable. One just lays one or two small fields without letting one's enemy know just where. It is necessary, then, for them to find out the positions of those minefields.

That, then, was G.'s job in Belgrade. Italian agents found out about the minefields. G., the expert spy, was commissioned to do the real work of discovering where they were to be laid, without – a most important point this – without letting the Yugoslavs find out that he had done so. If they did find out, of course, they would promptly change the positions.

In that last part of his task G. failed. The reason for his failure was Dimitrios.

It has always seemed to me that a spy's job must be an extraordinarily difficult one. What I mean is this. If I were sent to Belgrade by the British Government with orders to get hold of the details of a secret mine-laying project for the Straits of Otranto, I should not even know where to start. Supposing I knew, as G. knew, that the details were recorded by means of marking on a navigational chart of the Straits. Very well. How many copies of the chart are kept? I would not know. Where are they kept? I would not know. I might reasonably suppose that at least one copy would be kept somewhere in the Ministry of Marine; but the Ministry of Marine is a large place. Moreover, the chart will almost certainly be under lock and key. And even if, as seems unlikely, I were able to find in which room it is kept and how to get to it, how should I set about obtaining a copy of it without letting the Yugoslavs know that I had done so?'

When I tell you that within a month of his arrival in Belgrade, G. had not only found out where a copy of the chart was kept, but had also made up his mind how he was

going to copy that copy *without the Yugoslavs knowing*, you will
see that he is entitled to describe himself as competent.

How did he do it? What ingenious manœuvre, what subtle
trick made it possible? I shall try to break the news gently.

Posing as a German, the representative of an optical
instrument-maker in Dresden, he struck up an acquaintance
with a clerk in the Submarine Defence Department (which
dealt with submarine nets, booms, mine-laying and mine-
sweeping) of the Ministry of Marine!

Pitiful, wasn't it! The amazing thing is that he himself regards it as a very astute move. His sense of humour is quite
paralysed. When I asked him if he ever read spy stories, he
said that he did not, as they always seemed to him very naïve.
But there is worse to come.

He struck up this acquaintance by going to the Ministry
and asking the door-keeper to direct him to the Department
of Supply, a perfectly normal request for an outsider to make.
Having got past the door-keeper, he stopped someone in a
corridor, said that he had been directed to the Submarine
Defence Department and had got lost and asked to be re-
directed. Having got to the S.D. Department, he marched in
and asked if it was the Department of Supply. They said that
it was not, and out he went. He was in there not more than a
minute, but in that time he had cast a quick eye over the
personnel of the department, or, at all events, those of them he
could see. He marked down three. That evening he waited
outside the Ministry until the first of them came out. This
man he followed home. Having found out his name and as
much as he could about him, he repeated the process on succeeding evenings with the other two. Then he made his
choice. It fell on a man named Bulić.

Now, G.'s initial tactics may have lacked subtlety; but
there was considerable subtlety in the way he developed
them. He himself is quite oblivious of any distinction here. He
is not the first successful man to misunderstand the reasons for
his own success.

G.'s first piece of subtlety lay in his choice of Bulić as a tool.

Bulić was a disagreeable, conceited man of between forty
and fifty, older than most of his fellow clerks and disliked by
them. His wife was ten years younger than he, dissatisfied and
pretty. He suffered from catarrh. He was in the habit of going

to a café for a drink when he left the Ministry for the day, and it was in this café that G. made his acquaintance by the simple process of asking him for a match, offering him a cigar and, finally, buying him a drink.

You may imagine that a clerk in a government department dealing with highly confidentail matters would naturally tend to be suspicious of café acquaintances who tried to pump him about his work. G. was ready to deal with those suspicions long before they entered Bulić's head.

The acquaintance ripened. G. would be in the café every evening when Bulić entered. They would carry on a desultory conversation. G., as a stranger to Belgrade, would ask Bulić's advice about this and that. He would pay for Bulić's drinks. He let Bulić condescend to him. Sometimes they would play a game of chess. Bulić would win. At other times they would play four-pack *bezique* with other frequenters of the café. Then, one evening, G. told Bulić a story.

He had been told by a mutual acquaintance, he said, that he, Bulić, held an important post in the Ministry of Marine.

For Bulić the 'mutual acquaintance' could have been one of several men with whom they played cards and exchanged opinions and who were vaguely aware that he worked in the Ministry. He frowned and opened his mouth. He was probably about to enter a mock-modest qualification of the adjective 'important', but G. swept on. As chief salesman for a highly respectable firm of optical instrument makers, he was deputed to obtain an order due to be placed by the Ministry of Marine for binoculars. He had submitted his quotation and had hopes of securing the order but, as Bulić would know, there was nothing like a friend at court in these affairs. If, therefore, the good and influential Bulić would bring pressure to bear to see that the Dresden company secured the order, Bulić would be in pocket to the tune of twenty thousand dinar.

Consider that proposition from Bulić's point of view. Here was he, an insignificant clerk, being flattered by the representative of a great German company and promised twenty thousand dinar, as much as he ordinarily earned in six months, for doing precisely nothing. If the quotation were already submitted, there was nothing to be done there. It would stand its chance with the other quotations. If the Dresden company secured the order he would be twenty thousand dinar in pocket without having compromised himself in any way. If they lost it *he* would lose nothing except the respect of this stupid and misinformed German.

G. admits that Bulić did make a half-hearted effort to be honest. He mumbled something about his not being sure that his influence could help. This, G. chose to treat as an attempt to increase the bribe. Bulić protested that no such thought had been in his mind. He was lost. Within five minutes he had agreed.

In the days that followed, Bulić and G. became close friends. G. ran no risk. Bulić could not know that no quotation had been submitted by the Dresden company as all quotations received by the Department of Supply were confidential until the order was placed. If he were inquisitive enough to make inquiries, he would find, as G. had found by previous reference to the *Official Gazette*, that quotations for binoculars had actually been asked for by the Department of Supply.

G. now got to work.

Bulić, remember, had to play the part assigned to him by G., the part of influential official. G., furthermore, began to make himself very amiable by entertaining Bulić and the pretty but stupid Madame Bulić at expensive restaurants and night clubs. The pair responded like thirsty plants to rain. Could Bulić be cautious when, having had the best part of a bottle of sweet champagne, he found himself involved in an argument about Italy's overwhelming naval strength and her threat to Yugoslavia's seaboard? It was unlikely. He was a little drunk. His wife was present. For the first time in his dreary life, his judgment was being treated with the deference due to it. Besides, he had his part to play. It would not do to seem to be ignorant of what was going on behind the scenes. He began to brag. He himself had seen the very plans that in operation would immobilize Italy's fleet in the Adriatic. Naturally, he had to be discreet, but . . .

By the end of that evening G. knew that Bulić had access to a copy of the chart. He had also made up his mind that Bulić was going to get that copy for him.

He made his plans carefully. Then he looked round for a suitable man to carry them out. He needed a go-between. He found Dimitrios.

Just how G. came to hear of Dimitrios is not clear. I fancy that he was anxious not to compromise any of his old associates. One can conceive that his reticence might be understandable. Anyway, Dimitrios was recommended to him. I asked in what business the recommender was engaged. I hoped, I admit to be able to find some link with the Eurasian Credit Trust episode. But G. became vague. It was so very long ago. But he remembered the verbal testimonial which accompanied the recommendation.

Dimitrios Talat was a Greek-speaking Turk with an 'effective' passport and a reputation for being 'useful' and at the same time discreet. He was also said to have had experience in 'financial work of a confidential nature'.

If one did not happen to know just what he was useful for and the nature of the financial work he had done, one might have supposed that the man under discussion was some sort of accountant. But there is, it seems, a jargon in these affairs. G. understood it and decided that Dimitrios was the man for the job in hand. He wrote to Dimitrios – he gave me the address as though it were a sort of American Express poste restante – care of the Eurasian Credit Trust in Bucharest!

Dimitrios arrived in Belgrade five days later and presented himself at G.'s house just off the Knez Miletina.

G. remembers the occasion very well. Dimitrios, he says, was a man of medium height who might have been almost any age between thirty-five and fifty – he was actually thirty-seven. He was smartly dressed and . . . But I had better quote G.'s own words:

'He was chic in an expensive way, and his hair was becoming grey at the sides of his head. He had a sleek, satisfied, confident air and something about the eyes that I recognized immediately. The man was a pimp. I can always recognize it. Do not ask me how. I have a woman's instinct for these things.'

So there you have it. Dimitrios had prospered. Had there been any more Madame Preveza's? We shall never know. At all events, G. detected the pimp in Dimitrios and was not displeased. A pimp, he reasoned, could be relied upon not to fool about with women to the detriment of the business in hand. Also Dimitrios was of pleasing address. I think that I had better quote G. again:

'He could wear his clothes gracefully. Also he looked intelligent. I was pleased by this because I did not care to employ riff-raff from the gutters. Sometimes it was necessary but
I never liked it. They did not always understand my curious
temperament.'

G., you see, was fussy.

Dimitrios had not wasted his time. He could now speak
both German and French with reasonable accuracy. He said:

'I came as soon as I received your letter. I was busy in
Bucharest but I was glad to get your letter as I had heard of you.'

G. explained carefully and with circumspection (it did not
do to give too much away to a prospective employee) what he
wanted done. Dimitrios listened unemotionally. When G.
had finished, he asked how much he was to be paid.

'Thirty thousand dinar,' said G.

'Fifty thousand,' said Dimitrios, 'and I would prefer to
have it in Swiss francs.'

They compromised on forty thousand to be paid in Swiss
francs. Dimitrios smiled and shrugged his agreement.

It was the man's eyes when he smiled, says G., that first
made him distrust his new employee.

I found that odd. Could it be that there was honour among
scoundrels, that G., being the man he was and knowing (up to
a point) the sort of man Dimitrios was, would yet need a smile
to awaken distrust? Incredible. But there was no doubt that
he remembered those eyes very vividly. Preveza remembered
them, too, didn't she? 'Brown, anxious eyes that made you
think of a doctor's eyes when he is doing something to you
that hurts.' That was it, wasn't it? My theory is that it was not
until Dimitrios smiled that G. realized the quality of the man
whose services he had bought. 'He had the appearance of
being tame; but when you looked into his eyes you saw that he
had none of the feelings that make ordinary men soft, that he
was always dangerous.' Preveza again. Did G. sense the same
thing? He may not have explained it to himself in that way –
he is not the sort of man to set much store by feelings – but I
think he may have wondered if he had made a mistake in
employing Dimitrios. Their two minds were not so very dissi-
milar and that sort of wolf prefers to hunt alone. At all events,
G. decided to keep a wary eye on Dimitrios.

Meanwhile, Bulić was finding life more pleasant than it

had ever been before. He was being entertained at rich places. His wife, warmed by unfamiliar luxury, no longer looked at him with contempt and distaste in her eyes. With the money they saved on the meals provided by the stupid German she could drink her favourite cognac; and when she drank she became friendly and agreeable. In a week's time, moreover, he might become the possessor of twenty thousand dinar. There was a chance. He felt very well, he said one night, and added that cheap food was bad for his catarrh. That was the nearest he came to forgetting to play his part.

The order for the binoculars was given to a Czech firm. The *Official Gazette*, in which the fact was announced, was published at noon. At one minute past noon, G. had a copy and was on his way to an engraver on whose bench lay a half-finished copper die. By six o'clock he was waiting opposite the entrance to the Ministry. Soon after six, Bulić appeared. He had seen the *Official Gazette*. A copy was under his arm. His dejection was visible from where G. stood. G. began to follow him.

Ordinarily, Bulić would have crossed the road before many minutes had passed, to get to his café. To-night he hesitated and then walked straight on. He was not anxious to meet the man from Dresden.

G. turned down a side street and hailed a taxi. Within two minutes his taxi had made a detour and was approaching Bulić. Suddenly, he signalled to the driver to stop, bounded out on to the pavement and embraced Bulić delightedly. Before the bewildered clerk could protest, he was bundled into the taxi and G. was pouring congratulations and thanks into his ear and pressing a cheque for twenty thousand dinar into his hand.

'But I thought you'd lost the order,' mumbles Bulić at last.

G. laughs as if at a huge joke. 'Lost it!' And then he 'understands'. 'Of course! I forgot to tell you. The quotation was submitted through a Czech subsidiary of ours. Look, does this explain it?' He thrusts one of the newly printed cards into Bulić's hand. 'I don't use this card often. Most people know that these Czechs are owned by our company in Dresden.' He brushes the matter aside. 'But we must have a drink immediately. Driver!'

That night they celebrated. His first bewilderment over,

Bulić took full advantage of the situation. He became drunk. He began to brag of the potency of his influence in the Ministry until even G., who had every reason for satisfaction, was hard put to it to remain civil.

But towards the end of the evening, he drew Bulić aside. Estimates, he said, had been invited for rangefinders. Could he, Bulić assist? Of course he could. And now Bulić became cunning. Now that the value of his co-operation had been established, he had a right to expect something on account.

G. had not anticipated this, but, secretly amused, he agreed at once. Bulić received another cheque; this time it was for ten thousand dinar. The understanding was that he should be paid a further ten thousand when the order was placed with G.'s 'employers'.

Bulić was now wealthier than ever before. He had thirty thousand dinar. Two evenings later, in the supper room of a fashionable hotel, G. introduced him to a Freiherr von Kiessling. The Freiherr von Kiessling's other name was, needless to say, Dimitrios.

'You would have thought,' says G., 'that he had been living in such places all his life. For all I know, he may have been doing so. His manner was perfect. When I introduced Bulić as an important official in the Ministry of Marine, he condescended magnificently. With Madame Bulić he was superb. He might have been greeting a princess. But I saw the way his fingers moved across the palm of her hand as he bent to kiss the back of it.'

Dimitrios had displayed himself in the supper room before G. had affected to claim acquaintance with him in order to give G. time to prepare the ground. The 'Freiherr', G. told the Bulićs after he had drawn their attention to Dimitrios, was a very important man. Something of a mystery, perhaps; but a very important factor in international big business. He was enormously rich and was believed to control as many as twenty-seven companies. He might be a useful man to know.

The Bulićs were enchanted to be presented to him. When the 'Freiherr' agreed to drink a glass of champagne at their table, they felt themselves honoured indeed. In their halting German they strove to make themselves agreeable. This, Bulić must have felt, was what he had been waiting for all his life: at last he was in touch with the people who counted, the real people, the people who made men and broke them, the people who might make him. Perhaps he saw himself a director of one of the 'Freiherr's' companies, with a fine house and others dependent on him, loyal servants who would respect him as a man as well as a master. When, the next morning, he went to his stool in the Ministry, there must have been joy in his heart, joy made all the sweeter by the faint misgivings, the slight prickings of conscience which could so easily be stilled. After all, G. had had his money's worth. He, Bulić, had nothing to lose. Besides, you never knew what might come of it all. Men had taken stranger paths to fortune.

The 'Freiherr' had been good enough to say that he would have supper with Herr G. and his two charming friends two evenings later.

I questioned G. about this. Would it not have been better to have struck while the iron was hot. Two days gave the Bulićs time to think. 'Precisely,' was G.'s reply; 'time to think of the good things to come, to prepare themselves for the feast, to dream.' He became preternaturally solemn at the thought and then, grinning, suddenly quoted Goethe at me. *Ach! warum, ihr Götter, ist unendlich, alles, alles, endlich unser Glück nur?* G., you see, lays claim to a sense of humour.

That supper was the critical moment for him. Dimitrios got to work on madame. It was such a pleasure to meet such pleasant people as madame – and of course, her husband. She – and her husband, naturally – must certainly come and stay with him in Bavaria next month. He preferred it to his Paris house and Cannes was sometimes chilly in the spring. Madame would enjoy Bavaria; and so, no doubt, would her husband. That was, if he could tear himself away from the Ministry.

Crude, simple stuff, no doubt; but the Bulićs were crude, simple people. Madame lapped it up with her sweet champagne while Bulić became sulky. Then the great moment arrived.

The flower girl stopped by the table with her tray of orchids. Dimitrios turned round and, selecting the largest and most expensive bloom, handed it with a little flourish to Madame Bulić with a request that she accept it as a token of his esteem. Madame would accept it. Dimitrios drew out his wallet to pay. The next moment a thick wad of thousand dinar notes fell from his breast pocket on to the table.

With a word of apology Dimitrios put the money back in his pocket. G., taking his cue, remarked that it was rather a lot of money to carry in one's pocket and asked if the 'Freiherr' always carried as much. No, he did not. He had won the money at Alessandro's earlier in the evening and had forgotten to leave it upstairs in his room. Did madame know Alessandro's? She did not. Both the Bulićs were silent as the 'Freiherr' talked on: they had never seen so much money before. In the 'Freiherr's' opinion Alessandro's was the most reliable gambling place in Belgrade. It was your own luck not the croupier's skill that mattered at Alessandro's. Personally he was having a run of luck that evening – this with velvety eyes on madame – and had won a little more than usual. He hesitated at that point. And then: 'As you have never been in the place, I should be delighted if you would accompany me as my guests later.'

Of course, they went; and, of course, they were expected and preparations had been made. Dimitrios had arranged everything. No roulette – it is difficult to cheat a man at roulette – but there was *trente et quarante*. The minimum stake was two hundred and fifty dinar.

They had drinks and watched the play for a time. Then G. decided that he would play a little. They watched him win twice. Then the 'Freiherr' asked madame if she would like to play. She looked at her husband. He said, apologetically, that he had very little money with him. But Dimitrios was ready for that. No trouble at all, Herr Bulić! He personally was well known to Alessandro. Any friend of his could be accommodated. If he should happen to lose a few dinar, Alessandro would take a cheque or a note.

The farce went on. Alessandro was summoned and introduced. The situation was explained to him. He raised protesting hands. Any friend of the 'Freiherr' need not even ask such a thing. Besides, he had not yet played. Time to talk of such things if he had a little bad luck.

G. thinks that if Dimitrios had allowed the two to talk to one another for even a moment, they would not have played. Two hundred and fifty dinar was the minimum stake, and not even the possession of thirty thousand could overcome their consciousness of the value in terms of food and rent of two hundred and fifty. But Dimitrios did not give them a chance to exchange misgivings. Instead, as they were waiting at the table behind G.'s chair, he murmured to Bulić that if he, Bulić, had time, he, the 'Freiherr', would like to talk business with him over luncheon one day that week.

It was beautifully timed. It could, I feel, have meant only one thing to Bulić: 'My dear Bulić, there really is no need for you to concern yourself over a paltry few hundred dinar. I am interested in you, and that means that your fortune is made. Please do not disappoint me by showing yourself less important than you seem now.'

Madame Bulić began to play.

Her first two hundred and fifty she lost on *couleur*. The second won on *inverse*. Then, Dimitrios, advising greater caution, suggested that she play *à cheval*. There was a *refait* and then a second *refait*. Ultimately she lost again.

At the end of an hour the five thousand dinar's worth of chips she had been given had gone. Dimitrios, sympathizing with her for her 'bad luck', pushed across some five hundred dinar chips from a pile in front of him and begged that she would play with them 'for luck'.

The tortured Bulić may have had the idea that these were a gift, for he made only the faintest sound of protest. That they had not been a gift he was presently to discover. Madame Bulić, thoroughly miserable now and becoming a little untidy, played on. She won a little; she lost more. At half-past two Bulić signed a promissory note to Alessandro for twelve thousand dinar. G. bought them a drink.

It is easy to picture the scene between the Bulićs when at last they were alone – the recriminations, the tears, the interminable arguments – only too easy. Yet, bad as things were, the gloom was not unrelieved; for Bulić was to lunch the following day with the 'Freiherr'. And they were to talk business.

They did talk business. Dimitrios had been told to be encouraging. No doubt he was. Hints of big deals afoot, of opportunities for making fabulous sums for those who were in the know, talk of castles in Bavaria – it would all be there. Bulić had only to listen and let his heart beat faster. What did twelve thousand dinar matter? You had to think in millions.

All the same, it was Dimitrios who raised the subject of his guest's debt to Alessandro. He supposed that Bulić would be going along that very night to settle it. He personally would be playing again. One could not, after all, win so much without giving Alessandro a chance to lose some more. Supposing that they went along together – just the two of them. Women were bad gamblers.

When they met that night Bulić had nearly thirty-five thousand dinar in his pocket. He must have added his savings to G.'s thirty thousand. When Dimitrios reported to G. – in the early hours of the following morning – he said that Bulić had, in spite of Alessandro's protests, insisted on redeeming his promissory note before he started to play. 'I pay my debts,' he told Dimitrios proudly. The balance of the money he spent, with a flourish, on five hundred dinar chips. To-night he was going to make a killing. He refused a drink. He meant to keep a cool head.

G. grinned at this and perhaps he was wise to do so. Pity is sometimes too uncomfortable; and I do find Bulić pitiable. You may say that he was a weak fool. So he was. But Providence is never quite as calculating as were G. and Dimitrios. It may bludgeon away at a man, but it never feels between his ribs with a knife. Bulić had no chance. They understood him and used their understanding with skill. With the cards as neatly stacked against me as they were against him, I should perhaps be no less weak, no less foolish. It is a comfort to believe that the occasion is unlikely to arise.

Inevitably he lost. He began to play with just over forty chips. It took him two hours of winning and losing to get rid of them. Then, quite calmly, he took another twenty on credit. He said that his luck must change. The poor wretch did not even suspect that he was being cheated. Why should he suspect? The 'Freiherr' was losing even more than he was. He doubled his stakes and survived for forty minutes. He borrowed again and lost again. He had lost thirty-eight thousand dinar more than he had in the world when, white and sweating, he decided to stop.

After that it was plain sailing for Dimitrios. The following night Bulić returned. They let him win thirty thousand back. The third night he lost another fourteen thousand. On the fourth night, when he was about twenty-five thousand in debt, Alessandro asked for his money. Bulić promised to redeem his notes within a week. The first person to whom he went for help was G.

G. was sympathetic. Twenty-five thousand was a lot of money, wasn't it? Of course, any money he used in connection with orders received was his employers', and he was not empowered to do what he liked with it. But he himself could spare two hundred and fifty for a few days if it were any help. He would have liked to do more, but . . . Bulić took the two hundred and fifty.

With it G. gave him a word of advice. The 'Freiherr' was the man to get him out of his difficulty. He never lent money – with him it was a question of principle, he believed – but he had a reputation for helping his friends by putting them in the way of earning quite substantial sums. Why not have a talk with him?

The 'talk' between Bulić and Dimitrios took place after a dinner in the 'Freiherr's' hotel sitting-room. G. was out of sight in the adjoining bedroom.

When Bulić at last got to the point, he asked about Alessandro. Would he insist on his money? What would happen if he were not paid?

Dimitrios affected surprise. There was no question, he hoped, of Alessandro's not being paid. After all, it was on his personal recommendation that Alessandro had given credit in the first place. He would not like there to be any unpleasantness. What sort of unpleasantness? Well, Alessandro held the promissory notes and could take the matter to the police. He hoped sincerely that that would not happen.

Bulić was hoping so, too. Now, he had everything to lose, including his post at the Ministry. It might even come out that he had taken money from G. That might even mean prison. Would they believe that he had done nothing in return for those thirty thousand dinar? It was madness to expect them to do so. His only chance was to get the money from the 'Freiherr' – somehow.

To his pleas for a loan Dimitrios shook his head. No. That would simply make matters worse, for then he would owe the money to a friend instead of to an enemy; besides, it was a matter of principle with him. At the same time, he wanted to help. There was just one way; but would Herr Bulić feel disposed to take it? That was the question. He scarcely liked to mention the matter; but, since Herr Bulić pressed him, he knew of certain persons who were interested in obtaining some information from the Ministry of Marine that could not be obtained through the usual channels. They could probably be persuaded to pay as much as fifty thousand dinar for this information if they could rely upon its being accurate.

G. said that he attributed quite a lot of the success of his plan (he deems it successful in the same way that a surgeon deems an operation successful when the patient leaves the operating theatre alive) to his careful use of figures. Every sum from the original twenty thousand dinar to the amounts of the successive debts to Alessandro (who was an Italian agent) and the final amount offered by Dimitrios was carefully calculated with an eye to its psychological value. That final fifty thousand, for example. Its appeal to Bulić was twofold. It would pay off his debt and still leave him with nearly as much as he had had before he met the 'Freiherr'. To the incentive of fear they added that of greed.

But Bulić did not give in immediately. When he heard exactly what the information was, he became frightened and angry. The anger was dealt with very efficiently by Dimitrios. If Bulić had begun to entertain doubts about the *bona fides* of the 'Freiherr' those doubts were now made certainties; for when he shouted 'dirty spy', the 'Freiherr's' easy charm deserted him. Bulić was kicked in the stomach and then, as he bent forward retching, in the face. Gasping for breath and with pain and bleeding from the mouth, he was flung into a chair while Dimitrios explained coldly that the only risk he ran was in not doing as he was told.

His instructions were simple. Bulić was to get a copy of the chart and bring it to the hotel when he left the Ministry the following evening. An hour later the chart would be returned to him to replace in the morning. That was all. He would be paid when he brought the chart. He was warned of the consequences to himself if he should decide to go to the authorities with his story, reminded of the fifty thousand that awaited him and dismissed.

He duly returned the following night with the chart folded in four under his coat. Dimitrios took the chart into G. and returned to keep watch on Bulić while it was photographed and the negative developed. Apparently Bulić had nothing to say. When G. had finished he took the money and the chart from Dimitrios and went without a word.

G. says that in the bedroom at that moment, when he heard the door close behind Bulić and as he held the negative up to the light, he was feeling very pleased with himself. Expenses had been low; there had been no wasted effort; there had been no tiresome delays; everybody, even Bulić, had done well out of the business. It only remained to hope that Bulić would return the chart safely. There was really no reason why he should not do so. A very satisfactory affair from every point of view.

And then Dimitrios came into the room.

It was at that moment that G. realized that he had made one mistake.

'My wages,' said Dimitrios, and held out his hand.

G. met his employee's eyes and nodded. He needed a gun and he had not got one. 'We'll go to my house now,' he said and started towards the door.

Dimitrios shook his head deliberately. 'My wages are in your pocket.'

'Not your wages. Only mine.'

Dimitrios produced a revolver. A smile played about his lips. 'What I want is in your pocket, *mein Herr*. Put your hands behind your head.'

G. obeyed. Dimitrios walked towards him. G., looking steadily into those brown anxious eyes, saw that he was in danger. Two feet in front of him Dimitrios stopped. 'Please be careful, *mein Herr*.'

The smile disappeared. Dimitrios stepped forward suddenly and, jamming his revolver into G.'s stomach, snatched the negative from G.'s pocket with his free hand. Then, as suddenly, he stood back. 'You may go,' he said.

G. went. Dimitrios, in turn, had made *his* mistake.

All that night men, hastily recruited from the criminal cafés, scoured Belgrade for Dimitrios. But Dimitrios had disappeared. G. never saw him again.

What happened to the negative? Let me give you G.'s own words:

'When the morning came and my men had failed to find him, I knew what I must do. I felt very bitter. After all my careful work it was most disappointing. But there was nothing

else for it. I had known for a week that Dimitrios had been
into touch with a French agent. The negative would be in
that agent's hands by now. I really had no choice. A friend of
mine in the German Embassy was able to oblige me. The
Germans were anxious to please Belgrade at the time. What
more natural than that they should pass on an item of information interesting to the Yugoslav government?'

'Do you mean,' I said, 'that you deliberately arranged for
the Yugoslav authorities to be informed of the removal of the
chart and of the fact that it had been photographed?'

'Unfortunately, it was the only thing I could do. You see, I
had to render the chart worthless. It was really very foolish of
Dimitrios to let me go; but he was inexperienced. He probably thought that I should blackmail Bulić into bringing the
chart out again. But I realized that I should not be paid much
for bringing in information already in the possession of the
French. Besides, my reputation would have suffered. I was
very bitter about the whole affair. The only amusing aspect of
it was that the French had paid over to Dimitrios half the
agreed price for the chart before they discovered that the
information on it had been rendered obsolete by my little
démarche.'

'What about Bulić?'

G. pulled a face. 'Yes, I was sorry about that. I always have
felt a certain responsibility towards those who work for me.
He was arrested almost at once. There was no doubt as to
which of the Ministry copies had been used. They were kept
rolled in metal cylinders. Bulić had folded this one to bring it
out of the Ministry. It was the only one with creases in it. His
finger-prints did the rest. Very wisely he told the authorities
all he knew about Dimitrios. As a result they sent him to
prison for life instead of shooting him. I quite expected him to
implicate me, but he didn't. I was a little surprised. After all it
was I who introduced him to Dimitrios. I wondered at the
time whether it was because he was unwilling to face an additional charge of accepting bribes or because he felt grateful
to me for lending him that two hundred and fifty dinar.
Probably he did not connect me with the business of the
chart at all. In any case, I was pleased. I still had work to
do in Belgrade, and being wanted by the police, even under
another name, might have complicated my life. I have

never been able to bring myself to wear disguises.'

I asked him one more question. Here is his answer:

'Oh, yes, I obtained the new charts as soon as they had been made. In quite a different way, of course. With so much of my money invested in the enterprise I could not return empty handed. It is always the same: for one reason or another there are always these delays, these wastages of effort and money. You may say that I was careless in my handling of Dimitrios. That would be unjust. It was a small error of judgment on my part, that is all. I counted on his being like all the other fools in the world, on his being too greedy; I thought he would wait until he had from me the forty thousand dinar due to him before he tried to take the photograph as well. He took me by surprise. That error of judgment cost me a lot of money.'

'It cost Bulić his liberty.' I am afraid I said it a trifle grimly, for he frowned.

'My dear Monsieur Latimer,' he retorted stiffly, 'Bulić, was a traitor and he was rewarded according to his deserts. One cannot sentimentalize over him. In war there are always casualties. Bulić was very lucky. I should certainly have used him again, and he might ultimately have been shot. As it was, he went to prison. For all I know he is still in prison. I do not wish to seem callous, but I must say that he is better off there. His liberty? Rubbish! He had none to lose. As for his wife, I have no doubt that she has done better for herself. She always gave me the impression of wanting to do so. I do not blame her. He was an objectionable man. I seem to remember that he tended to dribble as he ate. What is more, he was a nuisance. You would have thought, would you not, that on leaving Dimitrios that evening he would have gone there and then to Alessandro to pay his debt? He did not do so. When he was arrested late the following day he still had the fifty thousand dinar in his pocket. More waste. It is at times like those, my friend, that one needs one's sense of humour.'

Well, my dear Marukakis, that is all. It is, I think, more than enough. For me, wandering among the ghosts of old lies, there is comfort in the thought that you might write to me and tell me that all this was worth finding out. You might. For myself, I begin to wonder. It is such a poor story, isn't it? There is no hero, no heroine; there are only knaves and fools.

Or do I mean only fools?

But it really is too early in the afternoon to pose such questions. Besides, I have packing to do. In a few days I shall send you a post card with my name and new address on it in the hope that you will have time to write. In any case, we shall, I hope, meet again very soon. *Croyez en mes meilleurs souvenirs.*

Charles Latimer.

CHAPTER 10

THE EIGHT ANGELS

It was on a slate-grey November day that Latimer arrived in Paris.

As the taxi crossed the bridge to the Ile de la Cité, he saw for a moment a panorama of low, black clouds moving quickly in the chill, dusty wind. The long façade of the houses on the Quai de Corse were still and secretive. It was as if each window concealed a watcher. There seemed to be few people about. Paris, in that late autumn afternoon, had the macabre formality of a steel engraving.

It depressed him, and as he climbed the stairs of his hotel on the Quai Voltaire he wished fervently that he had gone back to Athens.

His room was cold. It was too early for an aperitif. He had been able to eat enough of his meal on the train to render an early dinner unnecessary. He decided to inspect the outside of number three, Impasse des Huit Anges. With some difficulty he found the Impasse tucked away in a side street off the Rue de Rennes.

It was a wide, cobbled passage shaped like an L and flanked at the entrance by a pair of tall iron gates. They were fastened back, against the walls that supported them, with heavy staples, and had evidently not been shut for years. A row of spiked railings separated one side of the Impasse from the blank side-wall of the adjoining block of houses. Another blank cement wall, unguarded by railings but protected by the words 'DEFENSE D'AFFICHER, LOI DU 10 AVRIL 1929' in weatherbeaten black paint, faced it.

There were only three houses in the Impasse. They were grouped out of sight of the road, in the foot of the L, and looked out through the narrow gap between the building on which bill-posting was forbidden and the back of a hotel over which drainpipes writhed like snakes, on to yet another sightless expanse of cement. Life in the Impasse des Huit Anges would, Latimer thought, be rather like a rehearsal for Eternity. That others before him had found it so was suggested by the fact that, of the three houses, two were shuttered and obviously quite empty, while the third, number three, was occupied on the fourth and top floors only.

Feeling as if he was trespassing, Latimer walked slowly across the irregular cobbles to the entrance of number three.

The door was open and he could see along a tiled corridor to a small, dank yard at the back. The concierge's room, to the right of the door, was empty and showed no signs of having been used recently. Beside it, on the wall, was nailed a dusty board with four brass name slots screwed to it. Three of the slots were empty. In the fourth was a grimy piece of paper with the name 'CAILLE' clumsily printed on it in violet ink.

There was nothing to be learned from this but the fact, which Latimer had not doubted, that Mr. Peters' accommodation address existed. He turned and walked back to the street. In the Rue de Rennes he found a post office where he bought a *pneumatique* letter-card, wrote in it his name and that of his hotel, addressed it to Mr. Peters and dropped it down the chute. He also sent a postcard to Marukakis. What happened now depended to a great extent on Mr. Peters. But there was something he could and should do: that was to find out what, if anything, the Paris newspapers had had to say about the breaking up in December 1931 of a drug-peddling gang.

At nine o'clock the following morning, being without word from Peters, he decided to spend the morning with newspaper files.

The paper he finally selected for detailed reading had made a number of references to the case. The first was dated November 29, 1931. It was headed: 'DRUG TRAFFICKERS ARRESTED,' and went on:

'A man and a woman engaged in the distribution of drugs to addicts were arrested yesterday in the Alésia quarter. They are said to be members of a notorious foreign gang. The police expect to make further arrests within a few days.'

That was all. It read curiously, Latimer thought. Those three bald sentences looked as if they had been lifted out of a longer report. The absence of names, too, was odd. Police censorship, perhaps.

The next reference appeared on December the fourth under the heading: 'DRUG GANG, THREE MORE ARRESTS.'

'Three members of a criminal drug distributing organization were arrested late last night in a café near the Porte d'Orleans. Police entering the café to make the arrests were compelled to fire on one of the men who was armed and who made a desperate attempt to escape. He was slightly wounded. The other two, one of whom was a foreigner, did not resist.

'This brings the number of drug gang arrests to five, for it is believed that the three men arrested last night belonged to the same gang as the man and woman arrested a week ago in the Alésia quarter.

'The police state that still more arrests are likely to be made, as the Bureau Général des Stupéfiants has in its possession evidence implicating the actual organizers of the gang.

'Monsier Auguste Lafon, director of the Bureau, said: "We have known of this gang for some time and have conducted painstaking investigations into their activities. We could have made arrests but we held our hands. It was the leaders, the big criminals whom we wanted. Without leaders, with their sources of supply cut off, the army of drug pedlars that infests Paris will be powerless to carry on their nefarious trade. We intend to smash this gang and others like it."'

Then, on December the eleventh, the newspaper reported:

'DRUG GANG SMASHED,
NEW ARRESTS.'
'Now we have them all,' says Lafon.
'THE COUNCIL OF SEVEN.'

'Six men and one woman are now under arrest as a result of the attack launched by Monsieur Lafon, director of the Bureau Général des Stupéfiants, on a notorious gang of foreign drug traffickers operating in Paris and Marseilles.

'The attack began with the arrest two weeks ago of a woman and her male accomplice in the Alésia quarter. It reached its climax yesterday with the arrest in Marseilles of two men believed to be the remaining members of the gang's "Council of Seven", which was responsible for the organization of this criminal enterprise.

'At the request of the police we have hitherto remained silent as to the names of those arrested as it was desired not to put the others on their guard. Now that restriction has been lifted.

'The woman, Lydia Prokofievna, is a Russian who is believed to have come to France from Turkey with a Nansen passport in 1924. She is known in criminal circles as "The Grand Duchess". The man arrested with her was a Dutchman named Manus Visser who, through his association with Prokofievna, was sometimes referred to as "Monsieur le Duc".

'The names of the other five under arrest are; Luis Galindo, a naturalized Frenchman of Mexican origin, who now lies in hospital with a bullet wound in the thigh, Jean-Baptiste Lenôtre, a Frenchman from Bordeaux, and Jacob Werner, a Belgian, who were arrested with Galindo, Pierre Lamare or "Jo-jo", a Niçois, and Frederik Petersen, a Dane, who were arrested in Marseilles.

'In a statement to the press last night, Monsieur Lafon said: "Now we have them all. The gang is smashed. We have cut off the head and with it the brains. The body will now die a speedy death. It is finished."

'Lamare and Petersen are to be questioned by the examining magistrate to-day. It is expected that there will be a mass-trial of the prisoners.

'See the special article, SECRETS OF THE DRUG GANGS, on page 3.'

In England, Latimer reflected, Monsieur Lafon would have found himself in serious trouble. It hardly seemed worthwhile trying the accused after he and the press between them had already pronounced the verdict. But then, the accused was always guilty in a French trial. To give him a trial at all was, practically speaking, merely to ask him whether he had anything to say before he was sentenced.

He turned to the special article on page three.

The author, who called himself '*Veilleur*', revealed that the stuff known as morphine was an opium derivative with the formula $C_{17}H_{19}O_3H$ and that its usual medical form was morphine hydrochloride, that heroin (diacetylmorphine), another opium derived alkaloid, was preferred to morphine by addicts because it acted more speedily and powerfully and was easier to take, that cocaine was made from the leaves of the coco bush and served up in the form of cocaine hydrochloride (formula $C_{17}H_{21}O_4N, HCl$) and that the effects of all three drugs were approximately the same, namely: that they were aphrodisiac, that they produced states of mental and physical exhilaration in the early stages and that eventually the addict suffered physical and moral degeneration and mental tortures of the most appalling kind. The traffic in these drugs, declared '*Veilleur*', was carried on on a gigantic scale and it was possible for anyone to obtain them in Paris and Marseilles. There were illicit factories in every country in Europe. World production of these drugs exceeded legitimate medical consumption many times over. There were millions of addicts in Western Europe. Drug smuggling was a vast well-organized business. There followed a list of recent seizures of illicit drugs: sixteen kilos of heroin found in each of six cases of machinery consigned from Amsterdam to Paris, twenty-five kilos of cocaine found between the false sides of a drum of oil consigned from New York to Cherbourg, ten kilos of morphine found in the false bottom of a cabin trunk landed at Marseilles, two hundred kilos of heroin found in an illicit factory in a garage near Lyons. The gangs that peddled these drugs were controlled by rich and outwardly respectable men. The police were bribed by these vermin. There were bars and dances in Paris where the drugs were distributed under the very eyes of the police who were laughed at by the pedlars. '*Veilleur*' choked with indignation. Had he been writing three years later he would certainly have implicated Stavisky and half the Chamber of Deputies. But for once, he went on, the police had taken action. It was to be hoped that they would do so again. Meanwhile, however, there were thousands of Frenchmen – yes, *and* Frenchwomen! – suffering the tortures of the damned through this diabolical traffic which was sapping the virility of the nation. All of which suggested that, although '*Veilleur's*' heart was in the right place, he knew none of the secrets of the drug gangs.

With the arrest of the 'Council of Seven', interest in the case seemed to wane. The fact that 'The Grand Duchess' had been transferred to Nice to stand trial there for a fraud committed three years previously may have been responsible for this. The trial of the men was dealt with briefly. All were sentenced: Galindo, Lenôtre and Werner to fines of five thousand francs and three months' imprisonment, Lamare, Petersen and Visser to fines of two thousand francs and one month's imprisonment.

Latimer was amazed by the lightness of the sentences. '*Veilleur*', who bobbed up again to comment on the affair, was outraged but not amazed. But for the existence of a set of obsolete and wholly ridiculous laws, he thundered, the whole six would have been imprisoned for life. And which of them was the leader of the gang? Ah! Did the police suppose that these alley rats had financed an organization which, on the evidence given in court, had in one month taken delivery of and distributed heroin and morphine to the value of two and a half million francs? It was absurd. The police . . .

It was the nearest the newspaper got to the fact that the police had failed to find Dimitrios. That was not surprising. The police were not going to tell the press that the arrests were made possible only by a dossier obligingly supplied by some anonymous well-wisher whom they suspected of being the leader of the gang. All the same, it was irritating to find that he knew more than the newspaper he had relied upon to clarify the affair for him.

He was about to shut the file in disgust when his attention was caught by an illustration. It was a smudgy reproduction of a photograph of three of the prisoners being led from the court by detectives to whom they were handcuffed. All three had turned their faces away from the camera but the fact of their being handcuffed had prevented them from concealing themselves effectively.

Latimer left the newspaper office in better spirits than those in which he had entered it.

At his hotel a message awaited him. Unless he sent a *pneumatique* making other arrangements, Mr. Peters would call upon him at six o'clock that evening.

Mr. Peters arrived soon after half-past five. He greeted Latimer effusively.

'My *dear* Mr. Latimer! I cannot tell you how pleased I am to see you. Our last meeting took place under such inauspicious circumstances that I hardly dared hope. . . . But let us talk of pleasanter things. Welcome to Paris! Have you had a good journey? You are looking well. Tell me, what did you think of Grodek? He wrote telling me how charming and sympathetic you were. A good fellow, isn't he? Those cats of his! He worships them.'

'He was very helpful. Do, please, sit down.'

'I knew he would be.'

For Latimer, Mr. Peters' sweet smile was like the greeting of an old and detested acquaintance. 'He was also mysterious. He urged me to come to Paris to see you.'

'Did he?' Mr. Peters did not seem pleased. His smile faded a little. 'And what else did he say, Mr. Latimer?'

'He said that you were a clever man. He seemed to find something I said about you amusing.'

Mr. Peters sat down carefully on the bed. His smile had quite gone. 'And what was it you said?'

'He insisted upon knowing what business I had with you. I told him all I could. As I knew nothing,' went on Latimer spitefully, 'I felt that I could safely confide in him. If you do not like that, I am sorry. You must remember that I am still in complete ignorance concerning this precious scheme of yours.'

'Grodek did not tell you?'

'No. Could he have done so?'

The smile once more tightened his soft lips. It was as if some obscene plant had turned its face to the sun. 'Yes, Mr. Latimer, he could have done so. What you have told me explains the flippant tone of his letter to me. I am glad you satisfied his curiosity. The rich are so often covetous of others' goods in this world of ours. Grodek is a dear friend of mine but it is just as well that he knows that we stand in no need of assistance. He might otherwise be tempted by the prospect of gain.'

Latimer regarded him thoughtfully for a moment. Then: 'Have you got your pistol with you, Mr. Peters?'

The fat man looked horrified. 'Dear me no, Mr. Latimer. Why should I bring such a thing on a friendly visit to you?'

'Good,' said Latimer curtly. He backed towards the door and turned the key in the lock. The key he put in his pocket. 'Now then,' he went on grimly, 'I don't want to seem a bad host but there are limits to my patience. I have come a long way to see you and I still don't know why. I want to know why.'

'And so you shall.'

'I've heard that before,' answered Latimer rudely. 'Now before you start beating about the bush again there are one or two things *you* should know. I am not a violent man, Mr. Peters. To be honest with you, I dread violence. But there are times when the most peace-loving among us must use it. This may be one of them. I am younger than you and, I should say, in better condition. If you persist in being mysterious I shall attack you. That is the first thing.

'The second is that I know who you are. Your name is not Peters but Petersen, Frederik Petersen. You were a member of the drug-peddling gang organized by Dimitrios and you were arrested in December 1931, fined two thousand francs and sentenced to one month's imprisonment.'

Mr. Peters' smile was tortured. 'Did Grodek tell you this?' He asked the question gently and sorrowfully. The word 'Grodek' might have been another way of saying 'Judas'.

'No. I saw a picture of you this morning in a newspaper file.'

'A newspaper. Ah, yes! I could not believe that my friend Grodek . . .'

'You don't deny it?'

'Oh, no. It is the truth.'

'Well then, Mr. Petersen . . .'

'Peters, Mr. Latimer. I decided to change the name.'

'All right then – Peters. We come to my third point. When I was in Istanbul I heard some interesting things about the end of that gang. It was said that Dimitrios betrayed the lot of you by sending to the police, anonymously, a dossier convicting the seven of you. Is that true?'

'Dimitrios behaved very badly to us all,' said Mr. Peters huskily.

'It was also said that Dimitrios had become an addict himself. Is that true?'

'Unhappily, it is. Otherwise I do not think he would have betrayed us. We were making so much money for him.'

'I was also told there was talk of vengeance, that you all threatened to kill Dimitrios as soon as you were free.'

'*I* did not threaten,' Mr. Peters corrected him. 'Some of the others did so. Galindo, for example, was always a hothead.'

'I see. You did not threaten; you preferred to act.'

'I don't understand you, Mr. Latimer.' And he looked as if he really did not understand.

'No? Let me put it to you this way. Dimitrios was murdered near Istanbul roughly two months ago. Very shortly after the time when the murder could have taken place, you were in Athens. That is not very far from Istanbul, is it? Dimitrios, it is said, died a poor man. Now, is that likely? As you have just pointed out, his gang made a lot of money for him in 1931. From what I have heard of him, he was not the man to lose money he had made. Do you know what is in my mind, Mr. Peters? I am wondering whether it would not be reasonable to suppose that you killed Dimitrios for his money. What have you to say to that?'

Mr. Peters did not answer for a moment but contemplated Latimer unhappily in the manner of a good shepherd about to admonish an erring lamb.

Then he said: 'Mr. Latimer, I think that you are very indiscreet.'

'Do you?'

'And also very fortunate. Just suppose that I had, as you suggested, killed Dimitrios. Think what I should be forced to do. I should be forced to kill you also, now shouldn't I?' He put his hand in his breast pocket. It emerged holding the pistol. 'You see, I lied to you just now. I admit it. I was so curious to know what you were going to do if you thought I was unarmed. Besides, it seemed so impolite to come here carrying a pistol. So I lied. Do you understand my feelings a little? I am so anxious to have your confidence.'

'All of which is as skilful a reply to an accusation of murder as one could wish for.'

Mr. Peters put away his pistol wearily. 'Mr. Latimer, this is not a detective story. There is no *need* to be so stupid. Even if you cannot be discreet, at least use your imagination. Is it likely that Dimitrios would make a Will in my favour? No. Then how do you suppose that I could kill him for his money? People in these days do not keep their wealth in treasure chests. Come now, Mr. Latimer, let us please be sensible. Let us eat dinner together and then talk business. I suggest that after dinner we drink coffee in my apartment – it is a little more comfortable than this room – though if you would prefer to go to a café I shall understand. You probably disapprove of me. I really cannot blame you. But at least let us cultivate the illusion of friendship.'

For a moment Latimer felt himself warming to Mr. Peters. True, the last part of his appeal had been accompanied by an almost visible accretion of self-pity; but he had not smiled. Besides, the man had already made him feel a fool: it would be too much if he made him feel a pompous ass as well. At the same time . . .

'I am as hungry as you,' he said; 'and I can see no reason why I should prefer a café to your apartment. At the same time, Mr. Peters, anxious though I am to be friendly, I feel that I should warn you now that unless I have, this evening, a satisfactory explanation of your asking me to meet you here in Paris, I shall – half a million francs or no half a million francs – leave by the first available train. Is that clear?'

Mr. Peters' smile returned. 'It could not be clearer, Mr. Latimer. And may I say how much I appreciate your frankness?' The smile became rancid. 'How much better if we could always be so frank, if we could always open our hearts to our fellow men without fear, fear of being misunderstood, Misinterpreted! How much easier this life of ours would be! But we are so blind, so very blind. If the Great One chooses that we should do things of which the world may disapprove, let us not be ashamed of those things. For we are, after all, merely doing his Will and how can we understand His purposes? How?'

'I don't know.'

'Ah! none of us knows, Mr. Latimer. None of us knows – until he reaches The Other Side.'

'Quite so. Where shall we dine? There is a Danish place near here, isn't there?'

Mr. Peters struggled into his overcoat. 'No, Mr. Latimer, as you are doubtless well aware, there is not.' He sighed unhappily. 'It is unkind of you to make fun of me. And in any case I prefer French cooking.'

At his suggestion and expense they ate in a cheap restaurant in the Rue Jacob. Afterwards they went to the Impasse des Huit Anges.

'What about Caillé?' said Latimer as they climbed the dusty stairs.

'He is away. At the moment I am in sole possession.'

'I see.'

Mr. Peters, who was breathing heavily by the time they had reached the second landing, paused for a moment. 'You have concluded, I suppose, that I am Caillé.'

'Yes.'

Mr. Peters began to climb again. The stairs creaked under his weight. Latimer, following two or three stairs behind, was reminded of a circus elephant picking its way unwilling up a pyramid of coloured blocks to perform a balancing trick. They reached the fourth floor. Mr. Peters stopped and, standing panting before a battered door, hauled out a bunch of keys. A moment later he pushed open the door, pressed a switch and waved Latimer in.

The room ran from front to back of the house and was divided into two by a curtain to the left of the door. The half beyond the curtain was of a different shape from that which contained the door as it included the space between the end of the landing, the rear wall and the next house. The space formed an alcove. At each end of the room was a tall French window.

But if it was, architecturally speaking, the sort of room that one would expect to find in a French house of that type and age, it was in every other respect fantastic.

The first thing that Latimer saw was the dividing curtain. It was of imitation cloth of gold. The walls and ceiling were distempered an angry blue and bespattered with gold five-pointed stars. Scattered all over the floor, so that not a square inch of it showed, were cheap Moroccan rugs. They overlapped a good deal so that in places there were humps of three and even four thicknesses of rug. There were three huge divans piled high with cushions, some tooled leather ottoman seats and Moroccan table with a brass tray upon it. In one corner stood an enormous brass gong. The light came from fretted oak lanterns. In the centre of it all stood a small chromium-plated electric radiator. There was a choking smell of upholstery dust.

'Home!' said Mr. Peters. 'Take your things off, Mr. Latimer; would you like to see the rest of the place?'

'Very much.'

'Outwardly, just another uncomfortable French house,' commented Mr. Peters as he toiled up the stairs again; 'actually an oasis in a desert of discomfort. This is my bedroom.'

Latimer had another glimpse of French Morocco. This time it was adorned by a pair of crumpled flannel pyjamas.

'And the toilet.'

Latimer looked at the toilet and learned that his host had a spare set of false teeth.

'Now,' said Mr. Peters, 'I will show you something curious.'

He led the way out on to the landing. Facing them was a large clothes cupboard. He opened the door and struck a match. Along the back of the cupboard was a row of metal clothes pegs. Grasping the centre one, he turned it like a latch and pulled. The back of the cupboard swung towards them and Latimer felt the night air on his face and heard the noises of the city.

'There is a narrow iron platform running along the outside wall to the next house,' explained Mr. Peters. 'There is another cupboard there like this one. You can see nothing because there are only blank walls facing us. Equally, no one could see us should we choose to leave that way. It was Dimitrios who had this done.'

'Dimitrios!'

'Dimitrios owned all three of these houses. They were kept empty for reasons of privacy. Sometimes, they were used as stores. These two floors were used for meetings. Morally, no doubt, the houses still belong to Dimitrios. Fortunately for me, he took the precaution of buying them in my name. I also conducted the negotiations. The police never found out about them. I was able, therefore, to move in when I came out of prison. In case Dimitrios should ever wonder what had happened to his property, *I* took the precaution of buying them from myself in the name of Caillé. Do you like Algerian coffee?'

'Yes.'

'It takes a little longer to prepare than French but I prefer it. Shall we go downstairs again?'

They went downstairs. Having seen Latimer uncomfortably ensconced amid a sea of cushions, Mr. Peters disappeared into the alcove.

Latimer got rid of some of the cushions and looked about him. It was odd to feel that the house had once belonged to Dimitrios. Yet the evidence around him of the tenancy of the preposterous Mr. Peters was a good deal odder. There was a small (fretted) shelf above his head. On it were paperbound books. There was *Pearls of Everyday Wisdom*. That was the one he had been reading in the train from Athens. There was, besides, Plato's Symposium, in French and uncut, an anthology called *Poèmes Erotiques*, which had no author's name on it and *had* been cut, Æsop's *Fables* in English, Mrs. Humphry Ward's *Robert Elsmere* in French, a German gazetteer, and several books by Dr. Frank Crane in a language which Latimer took to be Danish.

Mr. Peters came back carrying a Moroccan tray on which were a curious looking coffee percolator, a spirit lamp, two cups and a Moroccan cigarette box. The spirit lamp he lighted and put under the percolator. The cigarettes he placed beside Latimer on the divan. Then he reached up above Latimer's head, brought down one of the Danish books and flicked over one or two of the pages. A small photograph fluttered to the floor. He picked it up and handed it to Latimer.

'Do you recognize him, Mr. Latimer?'

It was a faded head and shoulders photograph of a middle aged man with . . .

Latimer looked up. 'It's Dimitrios!' he exclaimed. 'Where did you get it?'

Mr. Peters took the photograph from Latimer's fingers. 'You recognize it? Good.' He sat down on one of the ottoman seats and adjusted the spirit lamp. Then he looked up. If it had been possible for Mr. Peters' set, lustreless eyes to gleam, Latimer would have said that they were gleaming with pleasure.

'Help yourself to cigarettes, Mr. Latimer,' he said. 'I am going to tell you a story.'

CHAPTER 11

PARIS, 1928–1931

'Often, when the day's work is done,' said Mr. Peters reminiscently, 'I sit by the fire, like this, and wonder if my life has been as successful as it might have been. True, I have made money – a little property, some *rentes*, a few shares here and there – but it is not of money that I think. Money is not everything. What have I done with my life in this world of ours? I think sometimes that it would have been better if I had married and brought up a family; but I have always been too restless, too interested in this world of ours as a whole. Perhaps it is that I have never known what I have wanted of life. So many of us poor human creatures are like that. We go on year after year, ever seeking, ever hoping – for what? We do not know. Money? Only when we have little. I sometimes think that he who has only a crust is happier than many millionaires. For the man with a crust knows what he wants – two crusts. His life is not complicated by possessions. I only know that there *is* something that I want above all else. Yet, how shall I know what it is? I have' – he waved a hand towards the bookshelf – 'sought consolation in philosophy and the arts. Plato, H. G. Wells; yes, I have read widely. These things comfort, yet they do not satisfy.' He smiled bravely, the victim of an almost unbearable *Weltschmerz*. 'We must all just wait until the Great One summons us.'

Waiting for him to go on, Latimer thought how difficult it was to dislike a man when he was making coffee for you. The stubby fingers gave the percolator lid a gentle, congratulatory pat. Mr. Peters straightened his back and emitted a sigh of satisfaction.

'Yes, Mr. Latimer, most of us go through life without knowing what we want of it. But Dimitrios, you know, was not like that. Dimitrios knew exactly what he wanted. He wanted money and he wanted power. Just those two things; as much of them as he could get. The curious thing is that I helped him to get them.

'It was in 1928 that I first set eyes on Dimitrios. It was here in Paris. I was, at the time, the part-owner, with a man named Giraud, of a *boîte* in the rue Blanche. We called it *Le Kasbah Parisien* and it was a very gay and cosy place with divans and amber lights and rugs. I had met Giraud in Marrakesh and we decided that everything should be just like a place we knew there. Everything was Moroccan; everything, that is, except the band for dancing which was South American.

'We opened it in 1926 which was a good year in Paris. The Americans and English, but especially the Americans, had money to spend on champagne and the French used to come, too. Most Frenchmen are sentimental about Morocco unless they have done their military service there. And the *Kasbah was* Morocco. We had Arab and Senegalese waiters and the champagne actually came from Meknes. It was a little sweet for the Americans but very nice all the same and quite cheap.

'For two years we made money and then, as is the way with such places, the clientèle began to change in character. We had more French and fewer Americans, more *maquereaux* and fewer gentlemen, more *poules* and fewer *chic* ladies. We still made a profit but it was not as great and we had to do more for it. I began to think that it was time to move on.

'It was Giraud who brought Dimitrios to *Le Kasbah*.

'I had met Giraud when I was in Marrakesh. He was a half-caste, his mother being an Arab and his father a French soldier. He was born in Algiers and had a French passport.

'Mostly you would not have known that he had Arab blood. It was only when you saw him with Arabs that you knew. He never really liked Arabs. I never really liked him. It was not that he did not trust me – that was no more than hurtful to me – but that I could not trust him. If I had had enough money to open *Le Kasbah* by myself I would not have taken him as a partner. He would try to trick me over the accounts and though he never succeeded I did not like it. I cannot stand dishonesty. By the spring of 1928 I was very weary of Giraud.

'I do not know exactly how he met Dimitrios. I think that it was at some *boîte* higher up the rue Blanche; for we did not open until eleven o'clock and Giraud liked to dance at other places beforehand. But, one evening, he brought Dimitrios into *Le Kasbah* and then took me aside. He remarked that profits had been getting smaller and said that we could make some money for ourselves if we did business with this friend of his, Dimitrios Makropoulos.

'The first time I saw Dimitrios I was not impressed by him. He was, I thought, just such a type of *maquereau* as I had seen before. His clothes fitted tightly and he had greying hair and polished fingernails and he looked at women in a way that those who came to *Le Kasbah* would not like. But I went over to his table with Giraud and we shook hands. Then he pointed to the chair beside him and told me to sit down. One would have thought that I was a waiter instead of the *patron*.'

He turned his watery eyes to Latimer. 'You may think, Mr. Latimer, that, for one who was not impressed, I remember the occasion very clearly. That is true. I do remember it clearly. You understand, I did not then know Dimitrios as I came to know him later. He made his impression without seeming to do so. At the time he irritated me. Without sitting down, I asked him what he wanted.

'For a moment he looked at me. He had very soft, brown eyes, you know. Then he said: 'I want champagne, my friend. Have you any objection? I can pay for it, you know. Are you going to be polite to me or shall I take my business proposals to more intelligent people?'

'I am an even-tempered man. I do not like trouble. I often think how much pleasanter a place this world of ours would be if people were polite and softly spoken with one another. But there are times when it is difficult. I told Dimitrios that nothing would induce me to be polite to him and that he could go when he pleased.

'But for Giraud he would have gone and I should not be sitting here talking to you. Giraud sat down at the table with him, apologizing for me. Dimitrios was watching me while Giraud was speaking, and I could see that he was wondering about me.

'I was now quite sure that I did not want to do business of any kind with this Dimitrios; but because of Giraud I agreed to listen, and we sat down together while Dimitrios told us what his proposal was. He talked very convincingly, and at last I agreed to do what he wanted. We had been in association with Dimitrios for several months, when one day . . .'

'Just a moment,' interrupted Latimer; 'what was this association? Was this the beginning of the drug peddling?'

Mr. Peters hesitated and frowned. 'No, Mr. Latimer, it was not.' He hesitated again and then broke suddenly into French. 'I will tell you what our business together was if you insist; but it is so difficult to explain these things to a person who does not understand the *milieu*, who is not sympathetic. It involves matters so much outside your experience.'

Latimer's 'Indeed?' was a trifle acid.

'You see, Mr. Latimer, I have read one of your books. It terrified me. There was about it an atmosphere of intolerance, of prejudice, of ferocious moral rectitude that I found quite unnerving. Please do not misunderstand me, Mr. Latimer. I do not fear your moral censure, but I resent, quite definitely, your being shocked.'

'As you have not yet told me what I am expected to be shocked at,' Latimer pointed out irritably, 'it is a little difficult for me to answer you.'

'Yes, yes, of course. But, forgive me, does not your interest in Dimitrios arise largely from the fact that you are shocked by him?'

Latimer thought for a moment. 'I think that that may be true. But it is just because I am shocked by him that I am trying to understand, to explain him. I do not believe in the inhuman, professional devil that one reads about in crime stories; and yet everything that I have heard about Dimitrios suggests that he consistently acted with quite revolting inhumanity – not just once or twice, but consistently.'

'Are the desires for money and power inhuman? With money and power a vain man can do so much to give himself pleasure. His vanity was one of the first things that I noticed about Dimitrios. It was that quiet, profound vanity that makes the man who has it so much more dangerous than ordinary people with their peacock antics. Come now, Mr. Latimer, be reasonable! The difference between Dimitrios and the more respectable type of successful business man is only a difference of method – legal method or illegal method. Both are in their respective ways equally ruthless.'

'Rubbish!'

'No doubt. It is interesting, though, is it not, to note that I am now attempting to defend Dimitrios against attack from the forces of moral rectitude. He would not, I feel sure, be at all grateful to me for doing so. Dimitrios was, for all his apparent *savoir faire*, hopelessly uneducated. The words "moral rectitude" would mean nothing to him. Ah! the coffee is ready.'

He poured it out in silence, raised his own cup to his nose and sampled the aroma. Then he put the cup down.

'Dimitrios,' he said, 'was connected at the time with what I believe you call the white slave traffic. It is such an interesting phrase to me. "Traffic" – a word full of horrible significance. "White slave" – consider the implications of the adjective. Does anyone talk nowadays about the *coloured* slave traffic? I think not. Yet the majority of the women involved are coloured. I fail to see why the consequences of the traffic should be any more disagreeable to a white girl from a Bucharest slum than to a negro girl from Dakar or a Chinese girl from Harbin. The League of Nations Committee is unprejudiced enough to appreciate that aspect of the question. They are intelligent enough, too, to mistrust the world "slave". They refer to the "traffic in women".

'I have never liked the business. It is impossible to treat human beings as one would treat ordinary inanimate merchandise. There is always trouble. Besides, the overhead expenses of a trafficker in what is considered a fair way of business are enormous. There are always false birth, marriage and death certificates to be obtained and travelling expenses and bribes to pay quite apart from the cost of maintaining several identities. You have no idea of the cost of forged documents, Mr. Latimer. There used to be three recognized sources of supply: one in Zürich, one in Amsterdam and one in Brussels. All neutrals! Odd, isn't it? You used to be able to get a false-real Danish passport – that is, a real Danish passport treated chemically to remove the original entries and photograph and then filled in with new ones – for, let me see, about two thousand francs at the present rate of exchange. A real-false – manufactured from start to finish by the agent – would have cost you a little less, say fifteen hundred. Nowadays you would have to pay twice as much. Most of the business is done here in Paris now. It is the refugees, of course. The point is that a trafficker needs plenty of capital. If he is known, there are always plenty of people willing to provide it, but they expect fantastic dividends. It is better to have one's own capital.

'Dimitrios had his own capital; but he also had access to capital which was not his own. He represented certain very rich men. He was never at a loss for money. When he came to Giraud and me he was in a different sort of difficulty. Owing to League of Nations activities, the laws in quite a number of countries had been altered and tightened up in such a way that it was sometimes very difficult indeed to get women from one place to another. All very praiseworthy, but a great nuisance to men like Dimitrios. It was not that it made it impossible for them to do their business. It didn't. But it made things more complicated and expensive for them.

'Before Dimitrios came to us he had had a very simple technique. He knew people in Alexandria who would advise him about their requirements. Then he would go to, say, Poland, recruit the women, take them to France on their own passports and then ship them from Marseilles. That was all. It was enough to say that the girls were going to fulfil a theatrical engagement. When the regulations were tightened up, however, it was no longer as simple. The night he came to *Le Kasbah* he told us that he had just encountered his first trouble. He had recruited twelve women from a *Madame* in Vilna, but the Poles would not let him bring them out without guarantees as to their destination and the respectability of their future employment. Respectability! But that was the law.

'Naturally, Dimitrios had told the Polish authorities that he would provide the guarantees. It would have been fatal for him not to have done so, for then he would have been suspect. Somehow he had to obtain the guarantees. That was where Giraud and I came in. We were to say that we were employing the girls as cabaret dancers and deal with any inquiries that might be made by the Polish Consular authorities. As long as they stayed in Paris for a week or so, we were perfectly safe. If inquiries were made after that we knew nothing. They had completed their engagement and gone. Where they had gone to was no business of ours.

'That was the way Dimitrios put it to us. He said that for our part of the affair he would pay us five thousand francs. It was money easily earned, but I was doubtful; and it was Giraud who finally persuaded me to agree. But I told Dimitrios that my agreement only applied to this particular case and that I could not consider myself committed to helping him again. Giraud grumbled, but agreed to accept the condition.

'A month later Dimitrios came to see us again, paid us the balance of the five thousand francs and said that he had another job for us. I objected; but, as Giraud immediately pointed out, we had had no trouble on the first occasion and my objection was not very firm. The money was useful. It paid the South Americans for a week.

'I believe now that Dimitrios lied to us about that first five thousand francs. I do not think that we earned it. I think he gave it to us simply to gain our confidence. It was like him to do a thing like that. Another man might try to trick you into serving his ends; but Dimitrios bought you. Yet he bought you cheaply. He set one's common sense fighting against one's instinctive suspicions of him.

'I have said that we earned that first five thousand francs without trouble. The second caused us a lot of trouble. The Polish authorities made some *chi-chi* and we had the police visiting us and asking questions. Worse, we had to have these women in *Le Kasbah* to prove that we were employing them. They could not dance a step and were a great inconvenience to us, as we had to be amiable to them in case one should go to the police and tell the truth. They drank champagne all the time, and if Dimitrios had not agreed to pay for it we should have lost money.

'He was, of course, very apologetic and said that there had been a mistake. He paid us ten thousand francs for our trouble and promised that if we would continue to help him there would be no more Polish girls and no more *chi-chi*. After some argument we agreed, and for several months we were paid our ten thousand francs. We had during that time only occasional visits from the police, and there was no unpleasantness.

But at last we had trouble again. This time it was because of the Italian authorities. Both Giraud and I were questioned by the examining magistrate for the district and kept for a day at the Commissariat. The day after that I quarrelled with Giraud.

'I say that I quarrelled. It would be more correct to say that our quarrel became open. I have told you that I did not like Giraud. He was crude and stupid and, as I have said, he sometimes tried to cheat me. He was suspicious, too; suspicious in a loud, stupid way like an animal; and he encouraged the wrong sort of clientèle. His friends were detestable: *maquereaux*, all of them. He used to call people *"mon gar"*. He would have been better as the *patron* of a *bistro*. For all I know he may be one now; but I think it more likely that he is in a prison. He often became violent when he was angry and sometimes injured people badly.

'That day after our unpleasantness with the police I said that we should have no more to do with this business of the women. That made him angry. He said that we should be fools to give up ten thousand francs a month because of a few police and that I was too nervous for his taste. I understood his point of view. He had had much to do with the police both in Marrakesh and Algiers, and he had a contempt for them. As long as he could keep out of prison and make money he was satisfied. I have never thought that way. I do not like the police to be interested in me, even though they cannot arrest me. Giraud was right. I was nervous. But although I understood his point of view I could not agree with it, and I said so. I also said that, if he wished, he could buy my share in *Le Kasbah Parisien* for the amount of money I had originally invested.

'It was a sacrifice on my part, you know, but I was tired of Giraud and wanted to be rid of him. I did get rid of him. He agreed immediately. That night we saw Dimitrios and explained the situation to him. Giraud was delighted with his bargain and enjoyed himself very much cracking clumsy jokes at my expense. Dimitrios smiled at these jokes; but when Giraud left us alone for a moment, he asked me to leave soon after he did and meet him at a café as he had something to say to me.

'I very nearly did not go. On the whole, I think that it was as well that I did go. I profited by my association with Dimitrios. There are, I think, very few associates of Dimitrios who could say as much; but I was lucky. Besides, I think that he had a respect for my intelligence. Generally he could bluff me, but not always.

'He was waiting in the café for me, and I sat down beside him and asked him what he wanted. I was never polite to him.

'He said: "I think you are wise to leave Giraud. The business with the women has become too dangerous. It was always difficult. Now I have finished with it."

'I asked him if he proposed to tell Giraud that and he smiled.

'"Not yet," he said; "not until you have your money from him."

'I said suspiciously that he was very kind, but he shook his head impatiently. "Giraud is a fool," he said. "If you had not been there with him, I should have made other arrangements about the women. Now, I am offering you a chance to work with me. I should be a fool if I made you angry with me to begin with by costing you your investment in *Le Kasbah*."

'Then he asked me if I knew anything about the heroin business. I did know a little about it. He then told me that he had sufficient capital to buy twenty kilogrammes a month and finance its distribution in Paris and asked me if I were interested in working for him.

'Now, twenty kilogrammes of heroin is a serious thing, Mr. Latimer. It is worth a lot of money. I asked him how he proposed to distribute so much. He said that, for the moment, that would be his affair. What he wanted me to do was to negotiate the purchases abroad and find ways of bringing it into the country. If I agreed to his proposal I was to begin by going to Bulgaria as his representative, dealing with suppliers there of whom he already knew and arranging for the transport of the stuff to Paris. He offered me ten percent of the value of every kilo I supplied him with.

'I said that I would think it over, but my mind was already made up. With the price of heroin as it was then, I knew that I would make nearly twenty thousand francs a month. I also knew that he was going to make a great deal more than that for himself. Even if, with my commission and expenses, he had to pay in effect fifteen thousand francs a kilo for the stuff, it would be good business for him. Selling heroin by the gramme in Paris, one can get nearly one hundred thousand francs a kilo for it. With the commissions to the actual pedlars and others, he would make not less than thirty thousand francs on each kilo. That meant over half a million francs a month for him. Capital is a wonderful thing if one knows just what to do with it and does not mind a little risk.

'In the September of 1928 I went to Bulgaria for Dimitrios with instructions from him to get the first twenty kilos to him by November. He had already begun to make arrangements with agents and pedlars. The sooner I could get the stuff the better.

'Dimitrios had given me the name of a man in Sofia who would put me in touch with the suppliers. This man did so. He also arranged for the credits with which I was to make the purchases. He . . .'

Latimer had an idea. He said suddenly: 'What was this man's name?'

Mr. Peters frowned at the interruption. 'I do not think that you ought to ask me that, Mr. Latimer.'

'Was it Vazoff?'

Mr. Peters' eyes watered at him. 'Yes, it was.'

'And were the credits arranged through the Eurasian Credit Trust?'

'You evidently know a great deal more than I had thought.' Mr. Peters was obviously not pleased by the fact. 'May I ask . . .?'

'I was guessing. But you need not have worried about compromising Vazoff. He died three years ago.'

'I am aware of it. Did you guess that Vazoff was dead? And how much more guessing have you done, Mr. Latimer?'

'That is all. Please continue.'

'Frankness . . .' began Mr. Peters and then stopped and drank his coffee. 'We will return to the subject,' he said at last. 'Yes, Mr. Latimer, I admit that you are right. Through Vazoff, I purchased the supplies Dimitrios needed and paid for them with drafts on Eurasian Credit Trust of Sofia. There was no difficulty about that. My real task was to transport the stuff to France. I decided to send it by rail to Salonika and ship it from there to Marseilles.'

'As heroin?'

'Obviously not. But I must confess it was difficult to know how to disguise it. The only goods which come into France from Bulgaria regularly, and which would not, therefore, be subject to special examination by the French Customs, were things like grain and tobacco and attar of roses. Dimitrios was pressing for delivery and I was at my wits' end.' He paused dramatically.

'Well, how *did* you smuggle it?'

'In a coffin, Mr. Latimer. The French, I reflected, are a race with a great respect for the solemnity of death. Have you ever attended a French funeral? *Pompe funèbre*, you know. It is most impressive. No Customs official, I felt certain, would care to play the ghoul. I purchased the coffin in Sofia. It was a beautiful thing with very fine carving on it. I also purchased a suit of mourning clothes and accompanied the coffin myself. I am a man who responds very readily to emotion and really I was most moved by the marks of simple respect for my grief shown by the stevedores who handled the coffin at the dock. Not even my own personal luggage was examined at the Customs.

'I had warned Dimitrios and a hearse was waiting for me and the coffin. I was pleased by my success, but Dimitrios, when I saw him, shrugged. I could not, he said very reasonably, arrive in France with a coffin every month. I think he thought the whole affair a little unbusinesslike. He was right, of course. He had, however, a suggestion.

There was an Italian shipping line which ran one cargo steamer a month from Varna to Genoa. The stuff could be shipped to Genoa in small cases and manifested as special tobacco consigned to France. That would prevent the Italian Customs examining it. There was a man in Nice who could arrange for the transport of the stuff from Genoa by bribing the warehouse people to release it from bond and then smuggling it through by road. I wished to know how that would affect my financial interest in the supplies. He said that I should lose nothing as there was other work for me to do.

'It was curious how we all accepted his leadership almost without question. Yes, he had the money; but there was more than that to it. He dominated us because he knew precisely what he wanted and precisely how to get it with the least possible trouble and at the lowest possible cost. He knew how to find the people to work for him, too; and, when he had found them, he knew how to handle them.

'There were seven of us who took our instructions directly from Dimitrios and not one was the sort of person to take instructions easily. For instance, Visser, the Dutchman, had sold German machine guns to the Chinese, spied for the Japanese and served a term of imprisonment for killing a coolie in Batavia. He was not an easy man to handle. It was he who made the arrangements with the clubs and bars through which we reached the addicts.

'You see, the system of distribution was very carefully organized. Both Lenôtre and Galindo had for several years been peddling drugs which they bought from a man in the employ of a big French wholesale drug manufacturer. That sort of thing used to be quite easy before the 1931 regulations. Both those men knew well those who needed the stuff and where to find them. Before Dimitrios came on the scene they had been dealing mostly in morphine and cocaine and always they had been handicapped by limited supplies. When Dimitrios offered them un-limited supplies of heroin they were quite ready to abandon the wholesale chemist and sell their clients heroin.

'But that was only one part of the business. Drug addicts, you know, are always very eager to get other people to take drugs too. Con-sequently, your circle of consumers is ever widening. It is most important, as you may imagine, to see that when you are approached by new customers they are not representatives of the *Brigade des Stupéfiants* or similar undesirables. That was where Visser's work came in. The would-be buyer would come to, say, Lenôtre in the first place on the recommendation of a regular customer known to Lenôtre. But, on being asked for drugs, Lenôtre would pretend to be astonished. Drugs? He knew nothing of such things. Personally, he never used them. But, if one did use them, he had heard that the place to go to was the So-and-So Bar. At the So-and-So Bar which would be on Visser's list, the prospective customer would receive much the same sort of answer. Drugs? No. Nothing of that kind at the So-and-So Bar but if it should be possible to call in again the following night, there might possibly be someone who could help. The following night, the Grand Duchess would be there.

'She was a curious woman. She had been brought into the business by Visser and was, I think, the only one of us Dimitrios had not found for himself. She was very clever. Her capacity for weighing up complete strangers was extraordinary. She could, I think, tell the most convincingly disguised detective just by looking at him across a room. It was her business to examine the person who wanted to buy and decide whether he or she should be supplied or not and how much was to be charged. She was very valuable to us.

'The other man was the Belgian, Werner. It was he who dealt with the small pedlars. He had been a chemist at one time and he used to dilute the heroin. Dimitrios never mentioned that part of the business.

'Some dilution very soon became necessary. Within six months of our beginning, I had had to increase the monthly heroin supply to fifty kilos. And I had other work to do. Lenôtre and Galindo had reported in the early stages that, if they were to get all the business they knew of, they would have to have morphine and cocaine to sell as well as heroin. Morphine addicts did not always like heroin and cocaine addicts would sometimes refuse it if they could get cocaine elsewhere. I had then to arrange for supplies of morphine and cocaine. The morphine problem was a simple one as it could be supplied at the same time and by the same people as the heroin; but the cocaine was a different matter. For that, it was necessary to go to Germany. I had plenty to do.

'We had our troubles, of course. They usually came to my part of the business. By the time we had been operating for a year, I had made several alternative arrangements for bringing in our supplies. In addition to the Genoa route for heroin and morphine which Lamare handled, I had come to terms with a sleeping car attendant on the Orient Express. He used to take the stuff aboard at Sofia and deliver it when the train was shunted into the siding in Paris. It was not a very safe route and I had to take elaborate precautions to protect myself in case of trouble, but it was rapid. Cocaine used to come in in cases of machinery from Germany. We had also begun to receive consignments of heroin from an Istanbul factory. These were brought by a cargo boat which left them floating outside the port of Marseilles in anchored containers for Lamare to collect at night.

'There was one week of disaster. In the last week of the June of 1929, fifteen kilos of heroin were seized on the Orient Express and the police arrested six of my men including the sleeping car attendant. That would have been bad enough; but during the same week Lamare had to abandon a consignment of forty kilos of heroin and morphine near Sospel. He himself escaped but we were in a serious difficulty, for the loss of those fifty-five kilos meant that we were left with only eight kilos to meet commitments for over fifty. None was due on the Istanbul boat for several days. We were in despair. Lenôtre and Galindo and Werner had a terrible time. Two of Galindo's clientèle committed suicide and in one of the bars there was a *fracas* in which Werner had his head cut.

'I did the best I could. I went to Sofia myself and brought back ten kilos in a trunk; but that was not enough. Dimitrios did not, I must say, blame me. It would have been unfair to have done so. But he was angry. He decided that, in future, reserve stocks must be held. It was soon after that week that he bought these houses. Until then we had always met him in a room over a café near the Porte d'Orleans. Now he said that these houses should be our headquarters. We never knew where he lived and could never get in touch with him until he chose to telephone one or other of us. We were to discover later that this ignorance of his address put us at a disastrous disadvantage. But other things happened before we made that discovery.

'The task of creating stocks was left to me. It was by no means easy. If we were both to create stocks and to maintain existing supplies we had to increase the size of the consignments. That means that there was a greater risk of seizure. It also meant that we had to find more new methods of bringing the stuff in. Things were complicated, too, by the Bulgarian Government's closing down the factory at Radomir from which we drew the bulk of our supplies. It soon opened again in a different part of the country; but inevitably there were delays. We were forced to rely more and more upon Istanbul.

'It was a trying time. In two months we lost by seizure no less than ninety kilos of heroin, twenty of morphine and five of cocaine. But, in spite of ups and downs, the stock increased steadily. By the end of 1930, we had, beneath the floorboards of those houses next door, two hundred and fifty kilos of heroin, two hundred odd kilos of morphine, ninety kilos of cocaine and a small quantity of prepared Turkish opium.'

Mr. Peters poured out the remainder of the coffee and extinguished the spirit lamp. Then he took a cigarette, wetted the end of it with his tongue and lit it.

'Have you ever known a drug addict, Mr. Latimer?' he asked
suddenly.

'I don't think so.'

'Ah, you don't *think* so. You do not know for certain. Yes, it is possible
for a drug taker to conceal his little weakness for quite a time. But he –
especially *she* – cannot conceal it indefinitely, you know. The process is
always roughly the same. It begins as an experiment. It may make you
feel sick the first time; but you will try again and the next time it will be
as it should be. A delicious sensation, warm, brilliant. Time stands still;
but the mind moves at a tremendous pace and, it seems to you, with
incredible efficiency. You were stupid; you become highly intelligent.
You were unhappy; you become carefree. What you do not like you
forget; and what you do like you experience with an intensity of pleasure
undreamed of. Three hours of Paradise. And afterwards it is not too bad;
not nearly as bad as it was when you had too much champagne. You
want to be quiet; you feel a little ill at ease; that is all. Soon you are
yourself again. Nothing has happened to you except that you have
enjoyed yourself amazingly. If you do not wish to take the drug again,
you tell yourself you need not do so. As an intelligent person you are
superior to the stuff. Then, therefore, there is no logical reason why you
should not enjoy yourself again, is there? Of course there isn't! And so
you do. But this time it is a little disappointing. Your half a gramme was
not quite enough. Disappointment must be dealt with. You must
wander in Paradise just once more before you decide not to take the stuff
again. A trifle more; nearly a gramme perhaps. Paradise again and still
you don't feel any the worse for it. And since you don't feel any the worse
for it, why not continue? Everybody knows that the stuff does ultimately
have a bad effect on you; but the moment you detect any bad effects *you*
will stop. Only fools become addicts. One and a half grammes. It really
is something to look forward to in life. Only three months ago everything
was so dreary; but now . . . Two grammes. Naturally, as you are taking a
little more it is only reasonable to expect to feel a little ill and depressed
afterwards. It's four months now. You must stop soon. Two and a half
grammes. Your nose and throat get so dry these days. Other people seem
to get on your nerves, too. Perhaps it is because you are sleeping so
badly. They make too much noise. They talk so loudly. And what are
they saying? Yes, *what*? Things about *you*, vicious lies. You can see it in
their faces. Three grammes. And there are other things to be considered;
other dangers. You have to be careful. Food tastes horrible. You cannot
remember things that you have to do; important things. Even if you
should happen to remember them, there are so many other things to

worry you apart from this beastliness of having to live. For instance, your nose keeps running: that is, it is not really running but you think it must be, so you have to keep touching it to make sure. Another thing: there is always a fly annoying you. This terrible fly *will* never leave you alone and in peace. It is on your face, on your hand, on your neck. You must pull yourself together. Three and a half grammes. You see the idea, Mr. Latimer?'

'You don't seem to approve of drug-taking.'

'Approve!' Mr. Peters stared, aghast. 'It is terrible, *terrible*! Lives are ruined. They lose the power to work yet they must find money to pay for their special stuff. Under such circumstances people become desperate and may even do something criminal to get it. I see what is in your mind, Mr. Latimer. You feel that it is strange that I should have been connected with, that I should have made money out of, a thing of which I disapprove so sternly. But consider. If *I* had not made the money, someone else would have done so. Not one of those unfortunate creatures would have been any better off and I should have lost money.'

'What about this ever-increasing clientèle of yours? You cannot pretend that all of those your organization supplied were habitual drug-takers before you went to work.'

'Of course they were not. But that side of the business was nothing to do with *me*. That was Lenôtre and Galindo. And I may tell you that Lenôtre and Galindo and Werner, too, were themselves addicts. They used cocaine. It is harder on the constitution but, whereas one can become a dangerous heroin addict in a few months, one can spend several years killing oneself with cocaine.'

'What did Dimitrios take?'

'Heroin. It was a great surprise to us the first time we noticed it. We would meet him in this room as a rule at about six o'clock in the evening. It was on one of those evenings in the spring of 1931 when we had our surprise.'

'Dimitrios arrived late. That in itself was unusual; but we took little notice of it. As a rule, at these meetings, he would sit very quietly with his eyes half-closed, looking a little troubled as though he had a headache, so that even when one became used to him one constantly wished to ask if all was well with him. Watching him sometimes I used to be amazed at myself for allowing myself to be led by him. Then I would see his face change as he turned to meet some objection from Visser – it was always Visser who objected – and I would understand. Visser was a violent man and quick and cunning as well; but he seemed a child beside Dimitrios. Once when Dimitrios had been making a fool of him, Visser pulled out a pistol. He was white with rage. I could see his finger squeezing the trigger. If I had been Dimitrios, I should have prayed. But Dimitrios only smiled in the insolent way he had and, turning his back on Visser, began to talk to me about some business matter. Dimitrios was always quiet like that, even when he was angry.

'That was why we were so surprised that evening. He came in late and he stood inside the door looking at us for nearly a minute. Then he walked over to his place and sat down. Visser had been saying something about the *patron* of a café who had been making trouble and now he went on. There was nothing remarkable about what he was saying. I think he was telling Galindo that he must stop using the café as it was unsafe.

'Suddenly, Dimitrios leaned across the table, shouted "*Imbecile!*" and spat in Visser's face.

'Visser was as surprised as the rest of us. He opened his mouth to speak but Dimitrios did not give him time to say anything. Before we could grasp what was happening, he was accusing Visser of the most fantastic things. The words poured out and he spat again like a guttersnipe.

'Visser went white and got to his feet with his hand in the pocket where he kept his pistol; but Lenôtre, who was beside him, got up, too, and whispered something to him which made Visser take his hand from his pocket. Lenôtre was used to people who had been taking drugs and he and Galindo and Werner had recognized the signs as soon as Dimitrios had entered the room. But Dimitrios had seen Lenôtre whisper and turned to him. From Lenôtre he came to the rest of us. We were fools, he told us, if we thought that he did not know that we were plotting against him. He called us a lot of very unpleasant names in French and Greek. Then he began to boast that he was cleverer than the rest of us together, that but for him we should be starving, that he alone was responsible for our success (which was true although we did not like to be told it) and that he could do with us as he wished. He went on for half an hour, abusing us and boasting alternately. None of us said a word. Then, as suddenly as he had started, he stopped, stood up and walked out of the room.

'I suppose that we should have been prepared for treachery after that. Heroin addicts have a reputation for it. Yet we were not prepared. I think it may have been that we were so conscious of the amount of money he was making. I only know that, when he had gone, Lenôtre and Galindo laughed and asked Werner if the boss were paying for the stuff he used. Even Visser grinned. A joke was made of it, you see.

'Next time we saw Dimitrios he was quite normal and no reference was made to his outburst. But as the months went by, although we had no more outbursts, he became bad-tempered and little difficulties would make him angry. His appearance was changing, too. He looked thin and ill and his eyes were dull. He did not always come to the meetings.

'Then, we had our second warning.

'Early in September, he announced suddenly that he proposed to reduce the consignments for the next three months and use our stock. This startled us and there were many objections. I was one of the objectors. I had had a great deal of trouble building up the stock and did not want to see it distributed without reason. The others reminded him of the trouble they had had when supplies ran out before. But Dimitrios would not listen. He had been warned, he said, that there was to be a new drive by the police. Not only, he said, would so large a stock compromise us seriously if it were discovered; but its seizure would be a serious financial loss. He, too, was sorry to see it go but it was best to play for safety.

'I do not think that the notion that he might be liquidating his assets before he got out occurred to any of us; and you may say that for people of experience we were very trusting. You would be right to say that. With the exception of Visser we seemed always to be on the defensive in our dealings with Dimitrios. Even Lydia, who understood so much about people, was defeated by him. As for Visser, he was too paralysed by his own conceit to believe that anyone, even a drug-addict, could betray him. Besides, why should we suspect him? We were making money, but he was making more, much more. What logical reason was there for suspecting him? Who could possibly have foreseen that he would become so unstable and behave like a madman?'

He shrugged. 'You know the rest. He turned informer. We were all arrested. I was in Marseilles with Lamare when we were caught. The police were quite clever. They watched us for a week before they took us. They hoped, I think, to catch us with some of the stuff. Luckily, we noticed them the day before we were due to take delivery of a big consignment from Istanbul. Lenôtre and Galindo and Werner were not so lucky. They had some of the stuff in their pockets. The police tried of course, to make me tell them about Dimitrios and showed me the dossier he had sent them. They might as well have asked me for the moon. Visser, I found out later, knew more than the rest of us but he did not tell the police what it was. He had other ideas. He told the police that Dimitrios had had an apartment in the seventeenth arrondissement. That was a lie. Visser wanted to get a lighter sentence than the rest of us. He did not. He died not long ago, poor fellow.' Mr. Peters heaved a sigh and produced one of his cheroots.

Latimer touched his second cup of coffee. It was quite cold. He took a cigarette and accepted a light from his host's match.

'Well?' he said when he saw that the cheroot was slight. 'What then? I am still waiting to hear how I am to earn a half a million francs.'

Mr. Peters smiled as if he were presiding at a Sunday School treat and Latimer had asked for a second currant bun. 'That, Mr. Latimer, is part of another story.'

'What story?'

'The story of what happened to Dimitrios after he disappeared from view.'

'Well, what *did* happen to him?' Latimer demanded testily.

Without replying, Mr. Peters picked up the photograph that lay on the table and handed it to him again.

Latimer looked at it and frowned. 'Yes, I've seen this. It's Dimitrios all right. What about it?'

Mr. Peters smiled very sweetly and gently. 'That, Mr. Latimer, is a photograph of Manus Visser.'

'What on earth do you mean?'

'I told you that Visser had other ideas about using the knowledge he had been clever enough to acquire about Dimitrios. What you saw on the mortuary table in Istanbul, Mr. Latimer, was Visser after he had tried to put those ideas into practice.'

'But it was Dimitrios. I saw . . .'

'You saw the body of Visser, Mr. Latimer, after Dimitrios had killed him. Dimitrios himself, I am glad to say, is alive and in good health.'

CHAPTER 12

MONSIEUR C. K.

Latimer stared. His jaw had dropped and he knew that he looked ridiculous and that there was nothing to be done about the fact. Dimitrios was alive. It did not even occur to him to question the statement seriously. He knew instinctively that it was true. It was as if a doctor had warned him that he was suffering from a dangerous disease of the symptoms of which he had been only vaguely aware. He was surprised beyond words, resentful, curious and a little frightened; while his mind began to work feverishly to meet and deal with a new and strange set of conditions. He shut his mouth, then opened it again to say, feebly: 'I can't believe it.'

Mr. Peters was clearly gratified by the effect of his announcement.

'I scarcely hoped,' he said, 'that you would have had no suspicions of the truth. Grodek, of course, understood. He had been puzzled by certain questions I asked him some time ago. When you came he was even more curious. That was why he wanted to know so much. But as soon as you told him that you had seen the body in Istanbul, he understood. He saw at once that the one thing that rendered you unique from my point of view was the fact of your having seen the face of the man buried as Dimitrios. It was obvious. Not to you, perhaps. I suppose that when one sees a perfect stranger on a mortuary slab and a policeman tells one that his name is Dimitrios Makropoulos, one assumes, if one has your respect for the police, that one has the truth of the matter. I *knew* that it was not Dimitrios you saw. But – I could not prove it. You, on the other hand, can. *You* can identify Manus Visser.' He paused significantly and then, as Latimer made no comment, added: 'How did they identify him as Dimitrios?'

'There was a French *carte d'identité*, issued in Lyons a year ago to Dimitrios Makropoulos, sewn inside the lining of his coat.' Latimer spoke mechanically. He was thinking of Grodek's toast to the English detective story and of Grodek's inability to stop himself laughing at his own joke. Heavens! what a fool the man must have thought him!

'A French *carte d'identité*!' echoed Mr. Peters. 'That I find amusing. Very amusing.'

'It had been pronounced genuine by the French authorities and it had a photograph in it.'

Mr. Peters smiled tolerantly. 'I could get you a dozen genuine French *cartes d'identité*, Mr. Latimer, each in the name of Dimitrios Makropoulos and each with a different photograph. Look!' He drew a green *permis de séjour* from his pocket, opened it and, with his fingers over the space taken up by the identifying particulars, displayed the photograph in it. 'Does that look very much like me, Mr. Latimer?'

Latimer shook his head.

'And yet,' declared Mr. Peters, 'it *is* a genuine photograph of me taken three years ago. I made no effort to deceive. It is simply that I am not *photogénique*, that is all. Very few men are. The camera is a consistent liar. Dimitrios could have used photographs of anyone with the same type of face as Visser. That photograph I showed you a few moments ago is of someone like Visser.'

'If Dimitrios is still alive, where is he?'

'Here in Paris.' Mr. Peters leaned forward and patted Latimer's knee. 'You have been very reasonable, Mr. Latimer,' he said kindly. 'I shall tell you everything.'

'It's very good of you,' said Latimer bitterly.

'No! no! You have a *right* to know,' said Mr. Peters. He pursed his lips with the air of one who knows justice when he sees it. 'I shall tell you everything,' he said again and relit his cheroot.

'As you may imagine,' he went on, 'we were all very angry with Dimitrios. Some of us threatened revenge. But, Mr. Latimer, I have never been one to beat my head against a wall. Dimitrios had disappeared and there was no way of finding him. The indignities of prison life a memory, I purged my heart of malice and went abroad to regain my sense of proportion. I became a wanderer, Mr. Latimer. A little business here, a little business there, travel and meditation – that was my life. I could afford to sit, when I wished, in a café and see this world of ours go by and try to understand my fellow men. How little true understanding there is! As I go through this life of ours, Mr. Latimer, I sometimes wonder if perhaps it is not all a dream and if one day we shall not wake up to find that we have only been asleep like children in a cradle rocked by the Great One. That will be a great day. I have, I know, done things of which I have been ashamed; but the Great One will understand. That is how I think of the Great One: as someone who understands that it is sometimes necessary, for business reasons, to do unpleasant things; someone who understands not as a judge in a courtroom,' he added a trifle vindictively, 'but as a *friend*.'

He wiped the corners of his mouth. 'You will think, Mr. Latimer, that I am something of a mystic. Perhaps I am. I do not believe in coincidence. If the Great One wills that one shall meet a person, then one meets him. There is nothing strange about it. That was why, when I met Visser, I was not surprised. It was a little under two years ago that I met him, and in Rome.

'I had not, of course, seen him for five years. Poor fellow! he had had a bad time. A few months after his release from prison he was pressed for money and forged a cheque. They sent him back to prison for three years and then, when he came out, deported him. He was almost penniless and he could not work in France where he knew useful people. I could not blame him for feeling bitter.

'He asked me to lend him money. We had met in a café and he told me that he had to go to Zürich to buy a new passport but that he had no money. His Dutch passport was useless because it was in his real name. I would have liked to have helped him; for, although I had never liked him very much, I felt sorry for him. But I hesitated. So often one's generous instincts run away with one. I should have been wiser to have said at once that I had no money to lend; but as I hesitated he knew that I had money. It was a foolish mistake on my part I thought at the time. It is only since that I have learned that my generous instinct was working for my own good.

'He became very pressing and swore that he would pay me back. This life of ours is so difficult sometimes, is it not? A person swears that he will repay money and you know that he is sincere. Yet you know also that he may to-morrow tell himself with equal sincerity that your money is his by right of need, that you can afford to lose so insignificant a sum and that you must in any case pay for your magnanimity. And then he grows to dislike you and you have lost a friend as well as your money. I decided to refuse Visser.

'At my refusal he became angry and accused me of not trusting him to pay a debt of honour, which was a foolish way for him to talk. Then he pleaded with me. He could prove, he said, that he would be able to repay the money and began to tell me some interesting things.

'I have said that Visser had known a little more about Dimitrios than the rest of us. That was true. He had taken a lot of trouble finding it out. It was just after that evening when he had pulled out a pistol to threaten Dimitrios and Dimitrios had turned his back upon him. Nobody had treated him like that before and he wished to know more about the man who had humiliated him: that, at least, is what I believe. He himself said that he had suspected that Dimitrios would betray us; but that, I knew, was nonsense. Whatever his reason, however, he decided to follow Dimitrios when he left the Impasse.

'The first night that he tried he was unsuccessful. There was a large closed car waiting at the entrance to the Impasse and Dimitrios was driven off in it before Visser could find a taxi in which to follow. The second night he had a hired car ready. He did not come to the meeting but waited for Dimitrios in the Rue de Rennes. When the closed car appeared, Visser drove off after it. Dimitrios stopped outside a big apartment house in the Avenue de Wagram and went inside while the big car drove away. Visser noted the address and about a week later, at a time when he knew that Dimitrios would be here in this room, he called at the apartment house and asked for Monsieur Makropoulos. Naturally, the concièrge knew of no one of that name but Visser gave him money and described Dimitrios and found that he had an apartment there in the name of Rougemont.

'Now Visser, for all his conceit, was no fool. He knew that Dimitrios would have foreseen that he might be followed and guessed that the Rougemont apartment was not his only place. Accordingly he set himself to watch Monsieur Rougemont's comings and goings. It was not long before he discovered that there was another way out of the apartment house at the rear and that Dimitrios used to leave that way.

'One night when Dimitrios left by the back entrance Visser followed him. He did not have far to go. He found that Dimitrios lived in a big house just off the Avenue Hoche. It belonged, he found, to a titled and very *chic* woman. I shall call her Madame la Comtesse. Later Visser saw Dimitrios leave with her for the opera. Dimitrios was *en grande tenue* and they had a large Hispano to take them there.

'At that point Visser lost interest. He knew where Dimitrios lived. No doubt he felt that he had in some way obtained his revenge by discovering that much. He must, too, have been tired of waiting about in the streets. His curiosity was satisfied. What he had discovered was, after all, very much what he might have expected to discover. Dimitrios was a man with a large income. He was spending it in the same way as other men with large incomes.

'They told me that, when Visser was arrested in Paris, he said very little about Dimitrios. Yet he must have had ugly thoughts, for he was by nature a violent man and very conceited. It would have been useless, in any case, for him to have tried to have Dimitrios arrested, for he could only have sent them to the apartment in the Avenue de Wagram and the house of Madame la Comtesse off the Avenue Hoche, and he knew that Dimitrios would have gone away. He had, as I said, other ideas about his knowledge.

'I think that, to begin with, he had intended to kill Dimitrios when he found him; but as he began to get short of money his hatred of Dimitrios became more reasonable. He probably remembered the Hispano and the luxury of the house of Madame la Comtesse. She would perhaps be worried to hear that her friend made his money by selling heroin and Dimitrios might be ready to pay good money to save her that worry. But it was easier to think about Dimitrios and his money than it was to find them. For several months after he was released from prison early in 1932, Visser looked for Dimitrios. The apartment in the Avenue de Wagram was no longer occupied. The house of Madame la Comtesse was shut up and the concièrge said that she was in Biarritz. Visser went to Biarritz and found that she was staying with friends. Dimitrios was not with her. Visser returned to Paris. Then he had what I think was quite a good idea. He himself was pleased with it. Unfortunately for him, it came a little too late. He remembered one day that Dimitrios had been a drug addict, and it occurred to him that Dimitrios might have done what many other wealthy addicts do when their addiction reaches an advanced stage. He might have entered a clinic to be cured.

'There are five private clinics near Paris which specialize in such cures. On the pretext of making inquiries as to terms on behalf of an imaginary brother, Visser went to each one in turn, saying that he had been recommended by friends of Monsieur Rougemont. At the fourth his idea was proved to be good. The doctor in charge asked after the health of Monsieur Rougemont.

'I think that Visser derived a certain vulgar satisfaction from the thought of Dimitrios being cured of a heroin addiction. The cure is terrible, you know. The doctors go on giving the patient drugs, but gradually reduce the quantity. For him the torture is almost unbearable. He yawns and sweats and shivers for days, but he does not sleep and he cannot eat. He longs for death and babbles of suicide; but he has not the strength left to commit it. He begs for his drug and it is withheld. He . . . But I must not bore you with horrors, Mr. Latimer. The cure lasts three months and costs five thousand francs a week. When it is over the patient may forget the torture and start taking drugs again. Or he may be wiser and forget Paradise. Dimitrios, it seems, was wise.

'He had left the clinic four months before Visser visited it; and so Visser had to think of another good idea. He *did* think of it, but it involved going to Biarritz again and he had no money. He forged a cheque, cashed it and set off again. He reasoned that as Dimitrios and Madame la Comtesse had been friends, she would probably know his present whereabouts. But he could not simply go to her and ask for his address. Even if he could have invented a pretext for doing so, he did not know under what name Dimitrios was known to her. There were difficulties, you see. But he found a way to overcome them. For several days he watched the villa where she was staying. Then, when he had found out enough about it, he broke into her room one afternoon, when the house was empty except for two drowsy servants, and looked through her baggage. He was looking for letters.

'Dimitrios had never liked written records in our business, and he never corresponded with any of us. But Visser had remembered that on one occasion Dimitrios had scribbled an address for Werner on a piece of paper. I remembered the occasion myself. The writing had been curious: quite uneducated, with clumsy, badly formed letters and many flourishes. It was this writing that Visser was looking for. He found it. There were nine letters in the writing. All were from an expensive hotel in Rome. I beg your pardon, Mr. Latimer. You said something?'

'I can tell you what he was doing in Rome. He was organizing the assassination of a Yugoslav politician.'

Mr. Peters did not seem impressed. 'Very likely,' he said indifferently; 'he would not be where he is to-day without that special organizing ability of his. Where was I? Ah, yes! the letters.

'All were from Rome and all were signed with initials which I shall tell you were "C. K." The letters themselves were not what Visser had expected. They were very formal and stilted and brief. Most of them said no more than that the writer was in good health, that business was interesting and that he hoped to see his dear friend soon. No *tu-toi*, you know. But in one he said that he had met a relation by marriage of the Italian Royal family and in another that he had been presented to a Rumanian diplomat with a title. He was very pleased with these encounters, it seems. It was all very *snob*, and Visser felt that Dimitrios would certainly wish to buy his friendship. He noted the name of the hotel and, leaving everything as he found it, went back to Paris *en route* for Rome. He arrived in Paris the following morning. The police were waiting for him. He was not, I should think, a very clever forger.

'But you may imagine the poor fellow's feelings. During the three interminable years that followed he thought of nothing but Dimitrios; of how near he had been to him and how far he was now. He seemed, for some strange reason, to regard Dimitrios as the one responsible for his being in prison again. The idea served to feed his hatred of him and strengthen his resolve to make him pay. He was, I think, a little mad. As soon as he was free he picked up a little money in Holland and went to Rome. He was over three years behind Dimitrios, but he was determined to catch up with him. He went to the hotel and, posing as a

Dutch private detective, asked to be permitted to see the records of those who had stayed there three years before. The *affiches* had, of course, gone to the police, but they had the bills for the period in question and he had the initials. He was able to discover the name which Dimitrios had used. Dimitrios had also left a forwarding address. It was a Poste Restante in Paris.

'Visser was now in a new difficulty. He knew the name; but that was useless unless he could get into France to trace the owner of it. It was no use his writing his demands for money. Dimitrios would not go on calling for letters for three years. And yet he could not enter France without being stopped at the frontier or risking another term of imprisonment. He had somehow to get a new name and a new passport, and he had no money with which to do so.

'I lent him three thousand francs; and I will confess to you, Mr. Latimer, that I felt myself to be truly stupid. Yet I was sorry for him. He was not the Visser I had known in Paris. Prison had broken him. Once his passions had been in his eyes, but now they were in his mouth and cheeks. One felt he was getting old. I gave him the money out of pity and to get rid of him. I did not believe his story. I never expected to hear from him again. You may, therefore, imagine my astonishment when, a year ago, I received here a letter from him enclosing a *mandat* for the three thousand francs.

'The letter was very short. It said: "I have found him as I said I would. Here, with my profound thanks, is the money you lent me. It is worth three thousand francs to surprise you." That was all. He did not sign it. He gave no address. The *mandat* had been bought in Nice and posted there.

'That letter made me think, Mr. Latimer. Visser had recovered his conceit. He could afford to indulge it to the extent of three thousand francs. That meant that he had a great deal more money. Conceited persons dream of such gestures, but they very rarely make them. Dimitrios must have paid; and since he was not a fool he must have had a very good reason for paying.

'I was idle at the time, Mr. Latimer; idle and a little restless. I had my books, it is true; but one wearies of books, the ideas, the affectations of other men. It might be interesting, I thought, to find Dimitrios for myself and share in Visser's good fortune. It was not greed that prompted me; I should not like you to think that. I was *interested*. Besides, I felt that Dimitrios owed me something for the discomforts and indignities I had experienced because of him. For two days I played with the idea. Then, on the third day I made up my mind. I set out for Rome.

'As you may imagine, Mr. Latimer, I had a difficult time and many disappointments. I had the initials which Visser, in his eagerness to convince me, had revealed, but the only thing I knew about the hotel was that it was expensive. There are, unfortunately, a great many expensive hotels in Rome. I began to investigate them one after the other; but when, at the fifth hotel, they refused, for some reason, to let me see the bills for 1932, I abandoned the attempt. Instead, I went to an Italian friend of mine in one of the Ministries. He was able to use his influence on my behalf and, after a lot of *chi-chi* and expense, I was permitted to inspect the Ministry of Interior archives for 1932. I found out the name Dimitrios was using, and I also found out what Visser had not found out – that Dimitrios had taken the course, which I myself took in 1932, of purchasing the citizenship of a certain South American republic which is sympathetic in such matters if one's pocket-book is fat enough. Dimitrios and I had become fellow citizens.

'I must confess, Mr. Latimer, that I went back to Paris with hope in my heart. I was to be bitterly disappointed. Our consul was not helpful. He said that he had never heard of Señor C. K. and that even if I were Señor C. K.'s dearest and oldest friend he could not tell me where he was. He was offensive, which was unpleasant; but also I could tell that he was lying when he said that he had no knowledge of Dimitrios. That was tantalizing. And yet another disappointment awaited me. The house of Madame la Comtesse off the Avenue Hoche had been empty for two years.

'You would think, would you not, that it would be easy to find out where a *chic* and wealthy woman was? It was most difficult. The *Bottin* gave nothing. Apparently she had no house in Paris. I was, I will confess, about to abandon the search when I found a way out of my difficulty. I reflected that a fashionable woman like Madame la Comtesse would be certain to have gone somewhere for the winter sports season that was just over. Accordingly, I commissioned Hachettes to purchase for me a copy of every French, Swiss, German and Italian winter sports and social magazine which had been published during the previous three months.

'It was a desperate idea, but it yielded results. You have no idea how many such magazines there are, Mr. Latimer. It took me a little over a week to go through them all carefully, and I can assure you that by the middle of that week I was very nearly a social-democrat. By the end of it, however, I had recovered my sense of humour. If repetition makes nonsense of words it makes even more fantastic nonsense of smiling faces, even if their owners are rich. Besides, I had found what I wanted. In one of the German magazines for February there was a small paragaph which said that Madame la Comtesse was at St. Anton for the winter sports. In a French magazine there was a *couturier's* picture of her in skating clothes. I went to St. Anton. There are not many hotels there, and I soon found that Monsieur C. K. had been in St. Anton at the same time. He had given an address in Cannes.

'At Cannes I found that Monsieur C. K. had a villa on the Estoril, but that he himself was abroad on business at the moment. I was not discontented. Dimitrios would return to his villa sooner or later. Meanwhile I set myself to discover something about Monsieur C. K.

'I have always said, Mr. Latimer, that the art of being successful in this life of ours is the art of knowing the people who will be useful to one. I have in my time met and done business with many important people – people, you know, who are informed of what goes on and why – and I have always taken care to be helpful to them. It has paid me.

'So, where Visser might have had to prowl about in the darkness in search of his information, I was able to get mine from a friend. It proved easier than I had expected to do so, for I found that, in certain circles, Dimitrios, with the name of Monsieur C. K., had become quite important. In fact, when I learned just how important he had become, I was pleasantly surprised. I began to realize that Visser must be living on the money he got from Dimitrios. Yet what did Visser know? Only that Dimitrios had dealt illegally in drugs; a fact that it would be difficult for him to prove. He knew nothing about the dealings in women. I did. There must, I reasoned, be other things, too, which Dimitrios would prefer not to be generally known. If, before I approached Dimitrios, I could find out some of those things, my financial position would be very strong indeed. I decided to see some more of my friends.

'Two of them were able to help me. Grodek was one. A Rumanian friend of mine was another. You know of Grodek's acquaintance with Dimitrios when he called himself Talat. The Rumanian friend told me that in 1925 Dimitrios had had questionable financial dealings with Codreanu, the lamented leader of the Rumanian Iron Guard, and that he was known to, but not wanted by, the Bulgarian police.

'Now there was nothing criminal about any of those affairs. Indeed, Grodek's information depressed me somewhat. It was unlikely that the Yugoslav Government would apply for extradition after so many years; while, as for the French, they might hold that, as Dimitrios had rendered some sort of service to the Republic in 1926, he was entitled to a little tolerance in the matter of dealings in drugs and women. I decided to see what I could find out in Greece. A week after I arrived in Athens and while I was still trying unsuccessfully to trace in the official records a reference to my particular Dimitrios, I read in an Athens' paper of the discovery, by the Istanbul police, of the body of a Greek from Smyrna with the name of Dimitrios Makropoulos.'

He raised his eyes to Latimer's. 'Do you begin to see, Mr. Latimer, why I found your interest in Dimitrios a little difficult to explain?' And then, as Latimer nodded: 'I, too, of course, inspected the Relief Commission dossier; but I followed you to Sofia instead of going to Smyrna. I wonder if you would care to tell me now what you found out from the police records there?'

'Dimitrios was suspected of murdering a money-lender named Sholem in Smyrna in 1922. He escaped to Greece. Two years later, he was involved in an attempt to assassinate Kemal. He escaped again, but the Turks used the murder as a pretext for issuing a warrant for his arrest.'

'A murder in Smyrna! That makes it even clearer.' Mr. Peters smiled. 'A wonderful man, Dimitrios, don't you think? So economical.'

'What do you mean?'

'Let me finish my story and you will see. As soon as I read that newspaper paragraph, I sent a telegram to a friend in Paris asking him to let me know the whereabouts of Monsieur C. K. He replied two days later, saying that Monsieur C. K. had just returned to Cannes after an Ægean cruise with a party of friends in a Greek yacht which he had chartered two months previously.

'Do you see now what had happened Mr. Latimer? You tell me that the *carte d'identité* was a year old when they found it on the body. That means that it was obtained a few weeks before Visser sent me that three thousand francs. You see, from the moment Visser found Dimitrios, he was doomed. Dimitrios must have made up his mind at once to kill him. You can see why. Visser was dangerous. He was such a conceited fellow. He might have blurted out indiscretions at any time when he had been drinking and wanted to boast. He would have to be killed.

'Yet, see how clever Dimitrios was! He could have killed Visser at once, no doubt. But he did not do so. His economical mind had evolved a better plan. If it were necessary to kill Visser, could he not dispose of the body in some advantageous way? Why not use it to safeguard himself against the consequences of that old indiscretion in Smyrna? It was unlikely that there would be consequences, but here was his chance to make certain of the fact. The body of the villain, Dimitrios Mak-ropoulos, would be delivered to the Turkish police. Dimitrios, the murderer, would be dead and Monsieur C. K. would be left alive to cultivate his garden. But he would require a certain amount of co-operation from Visser himself. The man would have to be lulled into feeling secure. So, Dimitrios smiled and paid up and set about getting the identity card which was to go with Visser's dead body. Nine months later, in June, he invited his good friend Visser to join him on a yachting trip.'

'Yes, but how could he have committed the murder on the yachting trip? What about the crew? What about the other passengers?'

Mr. Peters looked knowing. 'Let me tell you, Mr. Latimer, what I would have done if I had been Dimitrios. I would have begun by chartering a Greek yacht. There would be a reason for its being a Greek yacht: its home port would be the Piræus.

'I would have arranged for my friends, including Visser, to join the yacht at Naples. Then I would have taken them on their cruise and returned a month later to Naples, where I would have announced that the cruise would end. They would disembark; but I should stay on board saying that I was returning with the yacht to the Piræus. Then I would take Visser aside privately and tell him that I had some very secret business to transact in Istanbul, that I proposed to go there on the yacht and that I should be glad of his company. I would ask him not to tell the disembarking passengers who might be angry because I had not asked them all and to return to the yacht when they had gone. To poor, conceited Visser, the invitation would be irresistible.

'To the captain I would say that Visser and I would leave the yacht at Istanbul and return overland, after we had transacted our business, to Paris. He would sail the yacht back to the Piræus. At Istanbul Visser and I would go ashore together. I would have left word with the crew that we would send for our baggage when we had decided where we should be staying for the night. Then, I would have taken him to a *boîte* I know of in a street off the Grande Rue de Pera; and later that night I would find myself poorer by ten thousand French francs, while Visser would be at the bottom of the Bosphorus at a place where the current would carry him, when he was rotten enough to float, out to Seraglio Point. Then I would take a room in a hotel in the name and with the passport of Visser, and send a porter to the yacht with a note authorizing him to collect both Visser's luggage and mine. As Visser, I would leave the hotel in the morning for the station. His baggage, which I would have searched overnight to see that there was nothing in it to identify it as Visser's, I would deposit in the *consigne*. Then I would take the train to Paris. If inquiries about Visser are ever made in Istanbul, he left by train for Paris. But who is going to inquire? My friends believe he left the yacht at Naples. The captain and crew of the yacht are not interested. Visser has a false passport, he is a criminal: such a type has an obvious reason for disappearing of his own free will. Finish!'

Mr. Peters spread out his hands. 'That is how it would occur to me to deal with such a situation. Perhaps Dimitrios managed it a little differently; but that is what might well have happened. There is one thing, however, that I am quite sure he did. You remember telling me that some months before you arrived in Smyrna, someone examined the same police records that you examined there? That must have been Dimitrios. He was always very cautious. No doubt he was anxious to find out how much they knew about his appearance, before he left Visser for them to find.'

'But that man I told you about looked like a Frenchman.'

Mr. Peters smiled reproachfully. 'Then you were *not* quite frank with me in Sofia, Mr. Latimer. You *did* inquire about this mysterious man.' He shrugged. 'Dimitrios does look like a Frenchman now. His clothes are French.'

'You've seen him recently?'

'Yesterday. Though he did not see me.'

'You know exactly where he is in Paris, then?'

'Exactly. As soon as I discovered his new business I knew where to find him here.'

'And, now that you have found him, what next?'

Mr. Peters frowned. 'Come now, Mr. Latimer. I am sure that you are not quite as obtuse as all that. You know and can prove that the man buried in Istanbul is not Dimitrios. If necessary you could identify Visser's photographs on the police files. I, on the other hand, know what Dimitrios is calling himself now and where to find him. Our joint silence would be worth a lot of money to Dimitrios. With Visser's fate in mind, we shall know, too, how to deal with the matter. We shall demand a million francs. Dimitrios will pay us, believing that we shall come back for more. We shall not be as foolish as to endanger our lives in the way. We shall rest content with half a million each – nearly three thousand pounds sterling, Mr. Latimer – and quietly disappear.'

'I see. Blackmail on a cash basis. No credit. But why bring me into the business? The Turkish police could identify Visser without my help.'

'How? They identified him as Dimitrios and buried him. They have seen perhaps a dozen or more dead bodies since then. Weeks have gone by. Are they going to remember Visser's face well enough, to justify their beginning expensive extradition proceedings against a rich foreigner because of their fourteen year old suspicions about a sixteen year old murder? My dear Latimer! Dimitrios would laugh at me. He would do with me as he did with Visser: give me a few thousand francs here and there to keep me from making myself a nuisance with the French police and to keep me quiet until, for safety's sake, I could be killed. But you have seen Visser's body and identified it. You have seen the police records in Smyrna. He knows nothing about you. He will have to pay or run an unknown risk. He is too cautious for that. Listen. In the first place, it is essential that Dimitrios does not discover our identities. He will know me, of course, but he will not know my present name. In your case, we shall invent a name. Mr. Smith, perhaps, as you are English. I shall approach Dimitrios in the name of Petersen and we shall arrange to meet him outside Paris at a place of our own choosing to receive our million francs. That is the last that he will see of either of us.'

Latimer laughed but not very heartily. 'And do you really suppose that I shall agree to this plan of yours?'

'If, Mr. Latimer, your trained mind can evolve a more ingenious plan, I shall be only too happy to . . .'

'My trained mind, Mr. Peters, is concerned with wondering how best to convey this information which you have given me to the police.'

Mr. Peters' smile became thin. 'The police? What information, Mr. Latimer?' he inquired softly.

'Why, the information that . . .' Latimer began impatiently and then stopped, frowning.

'Quite so,' nodded Mr. Peters approvingly. 'You have no real information to convey. If you go to the Turkish police they will no doubt send to the French police for Visser's photographs and record your identification. What then? Dimitrios will be found to be alive. That is all. I have not, you may remember, told you the name that Dimitrios uses now or even his initials. It would be impossible for you to trace him from Rome as Visser and I traced him. Nor do you know the name of Madame la Comtesse. As for the French police, I do not think that they would be interested either in the fate of a deported Dutch criminal or excited by the knowledge that somewhere in France there is a Greek using a false name who killed a man in Smyrna in 1922. You see, Mr. Latimer, you cannot act without me. If, of course, Dimitrios should prove difficult, then it might be desirable to take the police into our confidence. But I do not think that Dimitrios will be difficult. He is very intelligent. In any case, Mr. Latimer, why throw away three thousand pounds?'

Latimer considered him for a moment. Then he said: 'Has it occurred to you that I might not want that particular three thousand pounds? I think, my friend, that prolonged association with criminals has made it difficult for you to follow some trains of thought.'

'This moral rectitude . . .' began Mr. Peters wearily. Then he seemed to change his mind. He cleared his throat. 'If you wished,' he said with the calculated *bonhommie* of one who reasons with a drunken friend, 'we could inform the police *after* we had secured the money. Even if Dimitrios were able to prove that he had paid money to us, he could not, however unpleasant he wished to be, tell the police our names or how to find us. In fact, I think that that would be a very wise move on our part, Mr. Latimer. We should then be quite sure that Dimitrios was no longer dangerous. We could supply the police anonymously with a dossier as Dimitrios did in 1931. The retribution would be just.' Then his face fell. 'Ah, no. It is impossible. I am afraid that the suspicions of your Turkish friends might fall upon you, Mr. Latimer. We could not risk that, could we!'

But Latimer was scarcely listening. He knew that what he had made up his mind to say was foolish and he was trying to justify its folly. Peters was right. There was nothing he could do to bring Dimitrios to justice. He was left with a choice. Either he could go back to Athens and leave Peters to make the best deal he could with Dimitrios or he could stay in Paris to see the last act of the grotesque comedy in which he now found himself playing a part. The first alternative being unthinkable, he was committed to the second. He really had no choice. To gain time he had taken and lighted a cigarette. Now he looked upon from it.

'All right,' he said slowly; 'I'll do what you want. But there are conditions.'

'Conditions?' Mr. Peters' lips tightened. 'I think that a half share is more than generous, Mr. Latimer. Why my trouble and expenses alone . . . !'

'Just a moment. I was saying, Mr. Peters, that there are conditions. The first should be very easy for you to fulfil. It is simply that you yourself retain all the money that you are able to squeeze from Dimitrios. The second . . .' he went on and then paused. He had the momentary pleasure of seeing Mr. Peters disconcerted. Then, he saw the watery eyes narrow quite appreciably. Mr. Peters' words as they issued from his mouth were charged with suspicion.

'I don't think I quite understand, Mr. Latimer. If this is a clumsy trick. . . .'

'Oh no. There is no trick, clumsy or otherwise, Mr. Peters. "Moral rectitude" was your phrase, wasn't it? It will do. I am prepared, you see, to assist in blackmailing a person when that person is Dimitrios; but I am not prepared to share in the profits. So much the better for you, of course.'

Mr. Peters nodded thoughtfully. 'Yes, I see that you might think like that. So much the better for me, as you say. But what is the other condition?'

'Equally inoffensive. You have referred mysteriously to Dimitrios's having become a person of importance. I make my helping you get your million francs conditional on your telling me exactly *what* he has become.'

Mr. Peters thought for a moment, then shrugged. 'Very well. I see no reason why I should not tell you. It so happens that the knowledge cannot possibly be of any help to you in discovering his present identity. The Eurasian Credit Trust is registered in Monaco and the details of its registration are not therefore open to inspection. Dimitrios is a member of the Board of Directors.'

CHAPTER 13

RENDEZVOUS

It was two o'clock in the morning when Latimer left the Impasse des Huits Anges and began to walk slowly in the direction of the Quai Voltaire.

At the corner of the Boulevard St. Germain there was a café open. He went inside and was served with a glass of beer by the bored mute behind the zinc. He drank some of his beer and gazed vacantly about him like a person who has strayed into a museum for shelter from the rain. He wished that he had gone straight to bed after all. He paid for the beer and took a taxi back to his hotel. He was tired, of course; that was the trouble.

In his room, Latimer sat down by the window and gazed out across the black river to the lights which it reflected and the faint glow in the sky beyond the Louvre. His mind was haunted by the past, by the confession of Dhris, the Negro, and by the memories of Irana Preveza, by the tragedy of Bulić and by a tale of white crystals travelling west to Paris, bringing money to the fig-packer of Izmir. Three human beings had died horribly and countless others had lived horribly that Dimitrios might take his ease. If there *were* such a thing as Evil, then this man. . .

But it was useless to try to explain him in terms of Good and Evil. They were no more than baroque abstractions. Good Business and Bad

Business were the elements of the new theology. Dimitrios was not evil. He was logical and consistent; as logical and consistent in the European jungle as the poison gas called Lewisite and the shattered bodies of children killed in the bombardment of an open town. The logic of Michelangelo's *David*, Beethoven's quartets and Einstein's physics had been replaced by that of the *Stock Exchange Year Book* and Hitler's *Mein Kampf*.

Yet, Latimer reflected, although you could not stop people buying and selling Lewisite, although you could do no more than 'deplore' a number of slaughtered children, there were in existence means of preventing one particular aspect of the principle of expediency from doing too much damage. Most international criminals were beyond the reach of man-made laws; but Dimitrios happened to be within reach of one law. He had committed at least two murders and had therefore broken the law as surely as if he had been starving and had stolen a loaf of bread.

It was easy enough, however, to say that he was within reach of the Law: it was not as easy to see how the Law was to be informed of the fact. As Mr. Peters had so carefully pointed out, he, Latimer, had no information to give the police. But was that an altogether true picture of the situation? He *had* some information. He knew that Dimitrios was alive and that he was a director of the Eurasian Credit Trust, that he knew a French Countess who had had a house off the Avenue Hoche and that he or she had had an Hispana Suiza car, that both of them had been in St. Anton that year for the winter sports and that he had chartered a Greek yacht in June, that he had a villa on the Estoril and that he was now the citizen of a South American republic. Surely, then, it must be possible to find the person with those particular attributes. Even if the names of the directors of the Eurasian Credit Trust were unobtainable, it ought to be possible to get the names of the men who had chartered Greek yachts in June, of the wealthy South Americans with villas on the Estoril and of the South American visitors to St. Anton in February. If you could get those lists, all you would have to do would be to see which names (if there should be more than one) were common to the three.

But how did you get the lists? Besides, even if you could persuade the Turkish police to exhume Visser and then apply officially for all that information, what sort of proof would you have that the man you had concluded to be Dimitrios, was in fact, Dimitrios? And supposing that you could convince Colonel Haki of the truth, would he have enough evidence to justify the French extraditing a director of the powerful Eurasian Credit Trust? If it had taken twelve years to secure the acquittal of Dreyfus, it could take at least as many years to secure the conviction of Dimitrios.

He undressed wearily and got into bed.

It looked as if he were committed to Mr. Peters' blackmailing scheme. Lying in a comfortable bed with his eyes closed, he found the fact that in a few days time he would be, technically speaking, one of the worst sorts of criminals no more than odd. Yet, at the back of his mind there was a certain discomfort. When the reason for it dawned on him, he was mildly shocked. The simple truth was that he was feeling afraid of Dimitrios. Dimitrios was a dangerous man; more dangerous by far than he had been in Smyrna and Athens and Sofia, because he now had more to lose. Visser had blackmailed him and died. Now, he, Latimer, was going to blackmail him. Dimitrios had never hesitated to kill a man if he had deemed it necessary to do so; and, if he had deemed it necessary in the case of a man who threatened to expose him as a drug pedlar, would he hesitate in the case of two men who threatened to expose him as a murderer?

It was most important to see that, hesitation or no hesitation, he was not given the opportunity. Mr. Peters had proposed the taking of elaborate precautions.

The first contact with Dimitrios was to be established by letter. Latimer had seen a draft of the letter and had found it gratifyingly similar in tone to a letter he himself had written for a blackmailer in one of his books. It began, with sinister cordiality, by trusting that, after all these years, Monsieur C. K. had not forgotten the writer and the pleasant and profitable times they had spent together, went on to say how pleasing it was to hear that he was so successful and hoped sincerely that he would be able to meet the writer who would be at the So-and-So Hotel at nine o'clock on the Thursday evening of that week. The writer concluded with an expression of his *'plus sincere amitié'* and a significant little postscript to the effect that he had chanced to meet someone who had known their mutual friend Visser quite well, that this person was most anxious to meet Monsieur K. and that it would be so unfortunate if Monsieur K. could not arrange to keep the appointment on Thursday evening.

Dimitrios would receive that letter on the Thursday morning. At half past eight on the Thursday evening, 'Mr. Petersen' and 'Mr. Smith' would arrive at the hotel chosen for the interview and 'Mr. Petersen' would take a room. There they would await the arrival of Dimitrios. When the situation had been explained, Dimitrios would be informed that he would receive instructions as to the payment of the million francs

on the following morning and told to go. 'Mr. Petersen' and 'Mr. Smith'
would then leave.

Precautions would now have to be taken to see that they were not
followed and identified. Mr. Peters had not specified what sort of
precautions but had given assurances that there would be no difficulties.

That same evening, a second letter would be posted to Dimitrios
telling him to send a messenger with the million francs, in *mille* notes to a
specified point on the road outside the cemetery of Neuilly at eleven
o'clock on the Friday night. There would be a hired car waiting for him
there with two men in it. The two men would have been recruited for the
purpose by Mr. Peters. Their business would be to pick up the messenger
and drive along the Quai National in the direction of Suresnes until they
were quite sure that they were not being followed and then to make for a
point on the Avenue de la Reine near the Porte de St. Cloud where 'Mr.
Petersen' and 'Mr Smith' would be waiting to receive the money. The
two men would then drive the messenger back to Neuilly. The letter
would specify that the messenger must be a woman.

Latimer had been puzzled by this last provision. Mr. Peters had
justified it by pointing out that if Dimitrios came himself there was just a
chance that he might prove too clever for the men in the car and that
'Mr. Petersen' and 'Mr. Smith' would end up lying in the Avenue de la
Reine with bullets in their backs. Descriptions were unreliable and the
two men would have no certain means of knowing in the dark if a man
presenting himself as the messenger were Dimitrios or not. They could
make no such mistake about a woman.

Yes, Latimer reflected, it was absurd to imagine that there could be
any danger from Dimitrios. The only thing he had to look forward to
was the meeting with this curious man whose path he had stumbled
across. It would be strange, after he had heard so much about him, to
meet him face to face; strange to see the hands which had packed figs and
driven the knife into Sholem's throat, the eyes which Irana Preveza and
Wladyslaw Grodek and Mr. Peters had remembered so well. It would be
as if a waxwork in a chamber of horrors had come to life.

For a time he stared at the narrow gap between the curtains. It was
getting light. Very soon he fell asleep.

He was disturbed towards eleven by a telephone call from Mr. Peters,
who said that the letter to Dimitrios had been posted and asked if they
could have dinner together 'to discuss our plans for to-morrow'. Latimer
was under the impression that their plans had already been discussed,
but he agreed. The afternoon he spent alone at the Vincennes Zoo. The
subsequent dinner was tedious. Little was said about their plans, and

Latimer concluded that the invitation had been another of Mr. Peters' precautions. He was making sure that his collaborator, who now had no financial interest in the business, had not changed his mind about collaborating. Latimer spent two hours listening to an account of Mr. Peters' discovery of the works of Dr. Frank Crane and a defence of his contention that *Lame and Lovely* and *Just Human* were the most important contributions to literature since *Robert Elsmere*.

On the pretext of having a headache, Latimer escaped soon after ten o'clock and went to bed. When he awoke the following morning he actually had a headache and concluded that the carafe burgundy which his host had recommended so warmly at dinner had been even cheaper than it had tasted. As his mind crept slowly back to consciousness he had, too, a feeling that something unpleasant had happened. Then he remembered. Of course! Dimitrios had by now received the first letter.

He sat up in bed to think about it and, after a moment or two, came to the profound conclusion that if it were easy enough to hate and despise blackmailing when one wrote and read about it, the act of blackmailing itself called for rather more moral hardihood, more firmness of purpose, than he, at any rate, possessed. It made no difference to remind oneself that Dimitrios was a criminal. Blackmail was blackmail, just as murder was murder. Macbeth would probably have hesitated at the last minute to kill a criminal Duncan just as much as he hesitated to kill the Duncan whose virtues pleaded like angels. Fortunately, or unfortunately, he, Latimer, had a Lady Macbeth in the person of Mr. Peters. He decided to go out to breakfast.

The day seemed interminable. Mr. Peters had said that he had arrangements to make in connection with the car and the men to drive in it, and that he would meet Latimer at a quarter to eight, after dinner. Latimer spent the morning walking aimlessly in the Bois and, in the afternoon, went to a cinema.

It was towards six o'clock and after he had left the cinema that he began to notice a slight breathless feeling in the region of the solar plexus. It was as if someone had dealt him a light blow there. He concluded that it was Mr. Peters' corrosive burgundy fighting a rearguard action and stopped in one of the cafés on the Champs Elysées for an *infusion*. But the feeling persisted, and he found himself becoming more and more conscious of it. Then, as his gaze rested for a moment on a party of four men and women talking excitedly and laughing over some joke, he realized what was the matter with him. He did not want to meet Mr. Peters. He did not want to go on this blackmailing expedition. He did not want to face a man in whose mind the uppermost thought would be to kill him as quickly and quietly as possible. The trouble was not in his stomach. He had cold feet.

The realization annoyed him. Why should he be afraid? There was nothing to be afraid of. This man Dimitrios was a clever and dangerous criminal, but he was far from being superhuman. If a man like Peters could . . . but then Peters was used to this sort of thing. He, Latimer, was not. He ought to have gone to the police as soon as he had discovered that Dimitrios was alive and risked being thought a troublesome crank. He should have realized before that, with Mr. Peters' revelations, the whole affair had taken on a completely different complexion, that it was no longer one in which an amateur criminologist (and a fiction writer at that) should meddle. You could not deal with real murderers in this irresponsible fashion. His bargain with Mr. Peters, for example: what would an English judge say to that? He could almost hear the words:

'*As for the actions of this man Latimer, he has given an explanation of them which you may find difficult to believe. He is, we have been told, an intelligent man, a scholar who has held responsible posts in universities in this country and written works of scholarship. He is, moreover, a successful author of a type of fiction which, even if it is properly regarded by the average man as no more than the pabulum of adolescent minds, has, at least, the virtue of accepting the proposition that it is the business of right-thinking men and women to assist the police, should the opportunity present itself, in preventing crime and in capturing criminals. If you accept Latimer's explanation, you must conclude that he deliberately conspired with Peters to defeat the ends of justice and to act as an accessory before the fact of the crime of blackmail for the sole purpose of pursuing researches which he states had no other object than the satisfaction of his curiosity. You may ask yourselves if that would not have been the conduct of a mentally unbalanced child rather than that of an intelligent man. You must also weigh carefully the suggestion of the prosecution that Latimer did in fact share in the proceeds of this blackmailing scheme and that his explanation is no more than an effort to minimize his part in the affair.*'

No doubt a French judge could make it sound even worse.

It was still too early for dinner. He left the café and walked in the direction of the Opera. In any case, he reflected, it was too late now to do anything. He was committed to helping Mr. Peters. But was it too late? If he went to the police now, this minute, something could surely be done.

He stopped. This minute! There had been an *agent* sauntering along the street through which he had just come. He retraced his steps. Yes, there was the man, leaning against the wall, swinging his baton and talking to someone inside a doorway. Latimer hesitated again, then crossed the road and asked to be directed to the police *Poste*. It was three streets away, he was told. He set off again.

The entrance to the *Poste* was narrow and almost entirely concealed by a group of three *agents* deep in a conversation which they did not interrupt as they made way for him. Inside was an enamelled plate indicating that inquiries should be made on the first floor and pointing to a flight of stairs with a thin iron banister rail on one side and a wall with a long, greasy stain on it on the other. The place smelt strongly of camphor and faintly of excrement. From a room adjacent to the entrance hall came a murmur of voices and the clacking of a typewriter.

His resolution ebbing with every step, he went up the stairs to a room divided into two by a high wooden counter, the outer edges of which had been worn smooth and shiny by the palms of innumerable hands. Behind the counter a man in uniform was peering with the aid of a hand-mirror into the inside of his mouth.

Latimer paused. He had yet to make up his mind how he was going to begin. If he said: 'I was going to blackmail a murderer to-night, but I have decided to hand him over to you instead,' there was more than a chance that they would think him mad or drunk. In spite of the urgent need for immediate action, he would have to make some show of beginning at the beginning. 'I was in Istanbul some weeks ago and was told of a murder committed there in 1922. Quite by chance, I have found that the man who did it is here in Paris and is being blackmailed.' Something like that. The uniformed man caught a glimpse of him in the mirror and turned sharply round.

'What do you want?'

'I should like to see Monsieur le Commissaire.'

'What for?'

'I have some information to give him.'

The man frowned impatiently. 'What information? Please be precise.'

'It concerns a case of blackmail.'

'You are being blackmailed?'

'No. Someone else is. It is a very complicated and serious affair.'

'Your *carte d'identité*, please.'

'I have no *carte d'identité*. I am a temporary visitor. I entered France four days ago.'

'Your passport, then.'

'It is at my hotel.'

The man stiffened. The frown of irritation left his face. Here was something that he understood and with which his long experience had enabled him to deal. He spoke with easy assurance.

'That is very serious, monsieur. You realize that? Are you English?'

'Yes.'

He drew a deep breath. 'You must understand, monsieur, that your papers must always be in your pocket. It is the law. If you saw a street accident and were required as a witness, the *agent* would ask to see your papers before you were permitted to leave the scene of the accident. If you had not got them, he could, if he wished, arrest you. If you were in a *boîte de nuit* and the police entered to inspect papers, you would certainly be arrested if you carried none. It is the law, you understand? I shall have to take the necessary particulars. Give me your name and that of your hotel, please.'

Latimer did so. The man noted them down, picked up a telephone and asked for '*Septième*'. There was a pause, then he read out Latimer's name and address and asked for confirmation that they were genuine. There was another pause, of a minute or two this time, before he began to nod his head and say: '*Bien, bien.*' Then he listened for a moment, said: '*Oui, c'est ca,*' and put the telephone back on its hook. He returned to Latimer.

'It is in order,' he said; 'but you must present yourself with your passport at the Commissariat of the Seventh Arrondissement within twenty-four hours. As for this complaint of yours, you can make that at the same time. Please remember,' he went on tapping his pencil on the counter for emphasis, 'that your passport must always be carried. It is obligatory to do so. You are English, and so nothing more need be made of the affair; but you must report to the Commissariat in your arrondissement, and in future always remember to carry your passport. Good Day, sir.' He nodded benevolently with an air of knowing his duty to be well done.

Latimer went out in a very bad temper, Officious ass! But the man was right, of course. It had been absurd of him to go into the place without his passport. Complaint, indeed! In a sense he had had a narrow escape. He might have had to tell his story to the man. He might well have been under arrest by now. As it was, he had not told his story and was still a potential blackmailer.

Yet the visit to the police *Poste* had eased his conscience considerably. He did not feel quite as irresponsible as he had felt before. He had made an effort to bring the police into the affair. It had been an abortive effort; but short of collecting his passport from the other side of Paris and starting all over again (and that, he decided comfortably, was out of the question) there was nothing more he could do. He was due to meet Mr.

Peters at a quarter to eight in a café on the Boulevard Hausmann. But by the time he had finished a very light dinner the curious feeling had returned again to his solar plexus and the two brandies which he had with his coffee were intended to do more than pass the time. It was a pity, he reflected as he went on to keep his appointment, that he could not accept even a small share of the million francs. The cost of satisfying his curiosity was proving, in terms of frayed nerves and an uneasy conscience, practically prohibitive.

Mr. Peters arrived ten minutes late with a large, cheap-looking suit-case and the too matter-of-fact air of a surgeon about to perform a difficult operation. He said, 'Ah, Mr. Latimer!' and sitting down at the table, ordered a raspberry liqueur.

'Is everything all right?' Latimer felt that the question was a little theatrical, but he really wanted to know the answer to it.

'So far, yes. Naturally, I have had no word from him because I gave no address. We shall see.'

'What have you got in the suit-case?'

'Old newspapers. It is better to arrive at a hotel with a suit-case. I do not wish to have to fill up an *affiche* unless I am compelled to do so. I decided finally upon a hotel near to the Ledru-Rollin Metro. Very convenient.'

'Why can't we go by taxi?'

'We shall go by taxi. But,' added Mr. Peters significantly, 'we shall return by the Metro. You will see.' His liqueur arrived. He poured it down his throat, shuddered, licked his lips and said that it was time to go.

The hotel chosen by Mr. Peters for the meeting with Dimitrios was in a street just off the Avenue Ledru. It was small and dirty. A man in his shirt-sleeves came out of a room marked 'Bureau', chewing a mouthful of food.

'I telephoned for a room,' said Mr. Peters.

'Monsieur Petersen?'

'Yes.'

The man looked them both up and down. 'It is a large room. Fifteen francs for one. Twenty francs for two. Service, twelve and a half per cent.'

'This gentleman is not staying with me.'

The man took a key from a rack just inside the Bureau and, taking Mr. Peters' suit-case, led the way upstairs to a room on the second floor. Mr. Peters looked inside it and nodded.

'Yes, this will do. A friend of mine will call for me here soon. Ask him to come up, please.'

The man withdrew. Mr. Peters sat on the bed and looked round approvingly. 'Quite nice,' he said, 'and very cheap.'

'Yes, it is.'

It was a long, narrow room with an old hair carpet, an iron bedstead, a wardrobe, two bentwood chairs, a small table, a screen and an enamelled iron *bidet*. The carpet was red; but by the washbasin was a threadbare patch, black and shiny with use. The wall-paper depicted a trellis supporting a creeping plant, a number of purple discs and some shapeless pink objects of a vaguely clinical character. The curtains were thick and blue and hung on brass rings.

Mr. Peters looked at his watch. 'Twenty-five minutes before he is due. We had better make ourselves comfortable. Would you like the bed?'

'No, thank you. I suppose you will do the talking.'

'I think it will be best.' Mr. Peters drew his pistol from his breast pocket, examined it to see that it was loaded and then dropped it into the right-hand pocket of his overcoat.

Latimer watched these preparations in silence. He was now feeling quite sick. He said suddenly: 'I don't like this.'

'Nor do I,' said Mr. Peters soothingly; 'but we must take precautions. It is unlikely, I think, that they will be needed. You need have no fears.'

Latimer remembered an American gangster picture that he had once seen.

'What is to prevent him from walking in here and shooting us both?'

Mr. Peters smiled tolerantly. 'Now, now! You must not let your imagination run away with you, Mr. Latimer. Dimitrios would not do that. It would be too noisy and dangerous for him. Remember, the man downstairs will have seen him. Besides, that would not be his way.'

'What is his way?'

'Dimitrios is a very cautious man. He thinks very carefully before he acts.'

'He has had all day to think carefully.'

'Yes, but he does not yet know how much we know, and if anyone else knows what we know. He would have to discover those things. Leave everything to me, Mr. Latimer. I understand Dimitrios.'

Latimer was about to point out that Visser had probably had the same idea, and then decided not to do so. He had another, more personal misgiving to air.

'You said that when Dimitrios paid us the million francs that would be the last he heard of us. Has it occurred to you that he may not be content to let things rest in that way? When he finds that we don't come back for more money he may decide to come after us.'

'After Mr. Smith and Mr. Petersen? We should be difficult to find under those names, my dear Mr. Latimer.'

'But he knows your face already. He will see mine. He could recognize our faces, whatever we chose to call ourselves.'

'But first he would have to find out where we were.'

'My photograph has appeared once or twice in newspapers. It may do so again. Or supposing my publisher decided to spread my photograph over the jacket of a book. Dimitrios might easly happen to see it. There have been stranger coincidences.'

Mr. Peters pursed his lips. 'I think you exaggerate, but' – he shrugged – 'since you feel nervous perhaps you had better keep your face hidden. Do you wear spectacles?'

'For reading.'

'Then put them on. Wear your hat, too, and turn up the collar of your coat. You might sit in the corner of the room where it is not so light. In front of the screen. It will blur the outlines of your face. There.'

Latimer obeyed. When he was in position, with his collar buttoned across his chin and his hat tilted forward over his eyes, Mr. Peters surveyed him from the door and nodded.

'It will do. I still think it unnecessary; but it will do. After making all these preparations we shall feel very foolish if he does not come.'

Latimer, who was feeling very foolish anyway, grunted. 'Is there any likelihood of his not coming?'

'Who knows?' Mr. Peters sat on the bed again. 'A dozen things might happen to prevent him. He might not, for some reason, have received my letter. He may have left Paris yesterday. But, if he has received the letter, I think that he will come.' He looked at his watch again. 'Eight forty-five. If he *is* coming, he will soon be here.'

They fell silent. Mr. Peters began to trim his nails with a pair of pocket scissors.

Except for the clicking of the scissors and the sound of Mr. Peters' heavy breathing, the silence in the room was complete. To Latimer it seemed almost tangible; a dark grey fluid that oozed from the corners of the room. He began to hear the watch ticking on his wrist. He waited for what seemed an eternity before looking at it. When he did look it was ten minutes to nine. Another eternity. He tried to think of something to say to Mr. Peters to pass the time. He tried counting the complete parallelograms in the pattern of the wall-paper between the wardrobe and the window. Now he thought he could hear Mr. Peters' watch ticking. The muffled sound of someone moving a chair and walking about in the room overhead seemed to intensify the silence. Four minutes to nine.

Then, so suddenly that the sound seemed as loud as a pistol shot, one of the stairs outside the door creaked.

Mr. Peters stopped trimming his nails and, dropping the scissors on the bed, put his right hand in his overcoat pocket.

There was a pause. His heart beating painfully, Latimer gazed rigidly at the door. There was a soft knock.

Mr. Peters stood up and, with his hand still in his pocket, went to the door and opened it.

Latimer saw him stare for a moment into the semi-darkness of the landing and then stand back.

Dimitrios walked into the room.

CHAPTER 14

THE MASK OF DIMITRIOS

A man's features, the bone structure and the tissue which covers it, are the product of a biological process; but his face he creates for himself. It is a statement of his habitual emotional attitude; the attitude which his desires need for their fulfilment and which his fears demand for their protection from prying eyes. He wears it like a devil mask; a device to evoke in others the emotions complementary to his own. If he is afraid, then he must be feared; if he desires, then he must be desired. It is a screen to hide his mind's nakedness. Only a few men, painters, have been able to see the mind through the face. Other men in their judgments reach out for the evidence of word and deed that will explain the mask before their eyes. Yet, though they understand instinctively that the mask cannot be the man behind it, they are generally shocked by a demonstration of the fact. The duplicity of others must always be shocking when one is unconscious of one's own.

So, when at last Latimer saw Dimitrios and tried to read in the face of the man staring across the room at him the evil which he felt should be there, it was of that sense of shock which he was conscious. Hat in hand, in his dark, neat French clothes, with his slim, erect figure and sleek grey hair, Dimitrios was a picture of distinguished respectability.

His distinction was that of a relatively unimportant guest at a large diplomatic reception. He gave the impression of being slightly taller than the one hundred and eighty-two centimetres with which the Bulgarian police had credited him. His skin had the creamy pallor which succeeds in middle age a youthful sallowness. With his high cheekbones, thin nose and beak-like upper lip he might well have been the member of an Eastern European delegation. It was only the expression of his eyes that fitted in with any of Latimer's preconceived ideas about his appearance.

They were very brown and seemed at first to be a little screwed up, as if he were short-sighted or worried. But there was no corresponding frown or contraction of the eyebrows; and Latimer saw that the expression of anxiety or short-sightedness was an optical illusion due to the height of the cheekbones and the way the eyes were set in the head. Actually, the face was utterly expressionless, as impassive as that of a lizard.

For a moment the brown eyes rested on Latimer; then, as Mr. Peters closed the door behind him, Dimitrios turned his head and said in strongly accented French: 'Present me to your friend. I do not think that I have seen him before.'

Latimer very nearly jumped. The face of Dimitrios might not be revealing, but the voice certainly was. It was very coarse and sharp, with an acrid quality that made nonsense of any grace implicit in the words it produced. He spoke very softly, and it occurred to Latimer that the man was aware of the ugliness of his voice and tried to conceal it. He failed. Its promise was as deadly as the rattle of a rattle snake.

'This is Monsieur Smith,' said Mr. Peters. 'There is a chair behind you. You may sit down.'

Dimitrios ignored the suggestion. 'Monsieur Smith! An Englishman. It appears that you knew Monsieur Visser.'

'I have *seen* Visser.'

'That is what we wanted to talk to you about, Dimitrios,' said Mr. Peters.

'Yes?' Dimitrios now sat down on the spare chair. 'Then talk and be quick. I have an appointment to keep. I cannot waste time in this way.'

Mr. Peters shook his head sorrowfully. 'You have not changed at all, Dimitrios. Always impetuous, always a little unkind. After all these years no word of greeting, no word of regret for all the unhappiness you caused me. You know, it was most unkind of you to hand us all over to the police like that. We were your friends. Why did you do it?'

'You still talk too much,' said Dimitrios. 'What is it you want?'

Mr. Peters sat down carefully on the edge of the bed. 'Since you insist on making this a purely business meeting – we want money.'

The brown eyes flickered towards him. 'Naturally. What do you want to give me for it?'

'Our silence, Dimitrios. It is very valuable.'

'Indeed? How valuable?'

'It is worth at the very least a million francs.'

Dimitrios sat back in the chair and crossed his legs. 'And who is going to pay you that for it?'

'You are, Dimitrios. And you are going to be glad to get it so cheaply.'

Then Dimitrios smiled.

It was a slow tightening of the small, thin lips; nothing more. Yet there was something inexpressibly savage about it; something that made Latimer feel glad that it was Mr. Peters who had to face it. At that moment, he felt, Dimitrios was far more appropriate to a gathering of man-eating tigers than to a diplomatic reception, however large. The smile faded. 'I think,' he said, 'that you shall tell me now precisely what you mean.'

To Latimer, who would, he knew, have responded promptly to the menace in the man's voice, Mr. Peters' bland hesitation was maddeningly reckless. He appeared to be enjoying himself.

'It is so difficult to know where to begin.'

There was no reply. Mr. Peters waited for a moment and then shrugged. 'There are,' he went on, 'so many things that the police would be glad to know. For instance, I might tell them who it was who sent them that dossier in 1931. And it would be such a surprise for them to know that a respectable director of the Eurasian Credit Trust was really the Dimitrios Makropoulos who used to send women to Alexandria.'

Latimer thought that he saw Dimitrios relax a little in his chair. 'And you expect me to pay you a million francs for that? My good Petersen, you are childish.'

Mr. Peters smiled. 'Very likely, Dimitrios. You were always inclined to despise my simple approach to the problems of this life of ours. But our silence on those matters would be worth a great deal to you, would it not?'

Dimitrios considered him for a moment. Then: 'Why don't you come to the point, Petersen? Or perhaps you are only preparing the way for your Englishman.' He turned his head. 'What have you to say, Monsieur Smith? Or is neither of you very sure of himself?'

'Petersen is speaking for me,' mumbled Latimer. He wished fervently that Mr. Peters would get the business over.

'May I continue?' inquired Mr. Peters.

'Go on.'

'The Yugoslav police, too, might be interested in you. If we were to tell them where Monsieur Talat . . .'

'*Par example!*' Dimitrios laughed malignantly. 'So Grodek has been talking. Not a sou for that, my friend. Is there any more?'

'Athens, 1922. Does that mean anything to you, Dimitrios? The name was Taladis, if you remember. The charge was robbery and attempted murder. Is that so amusing?'

Into Mr. Peters' face had come the look of unsmiling, adenoidal viciousness that Latimer had seen for a moment or two in Sofia. Dimitrios stared at him unblinkingly. In an instant the atmosphere had become deadly with a naked hatred that to Latimer was quite horrible. He felt as he had once felt when, as a child, he had seen a street fight between two middle-aged men. He saw Mr. Peters draw the pistol from his pocket and weigh it in his hands.

'You have nothing to say to that, Dimitrios? Then I shall go on. A little earlier that year you murdered a man in Smyrna, a moneylender. What was his name, Monsieur Smith?'

'Sholem.'

'Sholem, of course. Monsier Smith was clever enough to discover that, Dimitrios. A good piece of work, don't you think? Monsieur Smith, you know, is very friendly with the Turkish police; almost, one might say, in their confidence. Do you still think that a million francs is a lot to pay, Dimitrios?'

Dimitrios did not look at either of them. 'The murderer of Sholem was hanged,' he said slowly.

Mr. Peters raised his eyebrows. 'Can that be true, Monsieur Smith?'

'A Negro named Dhris Mohammed was hanged for the murder, but he made a confession implicating Monsieur Makropoulos. An order was issued for his arrest in 1924. The charge was murder; but the Turkish police were anxious to catch him for another reason. He had been concerned in an attempt to assassinate Kemal in Adrianople.'

'You see, Dimitrios, we are very well informed. Shall we continue?' He paused. Dimitrios still stared straight in front of him. Not a muscle of his face moved. Mr. Peters looked across at Latimer. 'Dimitrios is impressed, I think. I feel sure he would like us to continue.'

When Latimer thinks of Dimitrios now it is that scene which he remembers: the squalid room with its nightmare wall-paper, Mr. Peters sitting on the edge of the bed, his wet eyes half closed and the pistol in his hands, talking, and the man sitting between them, staring straight in front of him, his white face as still as that of a waxwork and as lifeless.

The droning of Mr. Peters' voice was punctuated by silences. To Latimer's overwrought nerves those silences were piercing in their intensity. But they were short, and after each one Mr. Peters would drone on again: a torturer mumbling the repetition of his questions after each turn of the screw.

'Monsieur Smith has told you that he saw Visser. It was in a mortuary in Istanbul that he saw him. As I told you, he is very friendly with the Turkish police, and they showed him the body. They told him that it was the body of a criminal named Dimitrios Makropoulos. It was foolish of them to be so easily deceived, was it not? But even Monsieur Smith was deceived for a while. Fortunately I was able to tell him that Dimitrios was still alive.' He paused. 'You do not wish to comment? Very well. Perhaps you would like to hear how I discovered where you were and who you were.' Another silence. 'No? Perhaps you would like to know how I knew that you were in Istanbul at the time poor, silly Visser was killed; or how easily Monsieur Smith was able to identify a photograph of Visser with the dead man he saw in the mortuary.' Another silence. 'No? Perhaps you would like to be told how easy it would be for us to arouse the interest of the Turkish police in the curious case of a dead murderer who is alive, or of the Greek police in the case of the refugee from Smyrna who left Tabouria so suddenly. I wonder if you are thinking that it would be difficult for us to prove that you *are* Dimitrios Makropoulos, or Taladis, or Talat, or Rougemont, after such a long time has elapsed. Are you thinking that, Dimitrios? You do not wish to answer? Then let me tell you that it would be quite easy for us to prove. I could identify you as Makropoulos, and so could Werner or Lenôtre or Galindo or the Grand Duchess. One of them is sure to be alive and within reach of the police. Any of them would be glad to help to hang you. Monsieur Smith can swear that the man buried in Istanbul is Visser. Then there is the crew of the yacht you chartered in June. They knew that Visser went with you to Istanbul. There is the concièrge in the Avenue de Wagram. He knew you as Rougemont. Your present passport would not be a very good protection to a man with so many false names, would it? And even if you submitted to a little *chantage* from the French and Greek police, Monsieur Smith's Turkish friends would not be so accommodating. Do you think that a million francs is too much to pay for saving you from the hangman, Dimitrios?'

He stopped. For several long seconds Dimitrios continued to stare at the wall. Then at last he stirred and looked at his small gloved hands. His words, when they came, were like stones dropped one by one into a stagnant pool. 'I am wondering,' he said, 'why you ask so little. Is this million all that you are asking?'

Mr. Peters sniggerd. 'You mean, are we going to the police when we have the million? Oh, no, Dimitrios. We shall be fair with you. This million is only a preliminary gesture of good will. There will be other opportunities for you. But you will not find us greedy.'

'I am sure of that. You would not want me to become desperate, I think. Are you the only ones who have this curious delusion that I killed Visser?'

'There is no one else. I shall want the million in *mille* notes to-morrow.'

'So soon?'

'You will receive instructions as to how you are to give them to us in the morning. If the instructions are not followed exactly you will not be given a second chance. The police will be approached immediately. Do you understand?'

'Perfectly.'

The words were spoken levelly enough. To a casual observer they might have been concluding an ordinary business deal. But neither of their voices was quite steady. To Latimer it seemed as if it were only the pistol that prevented Dimitrios from attacking and killing Mr. Peters and only the thought of a million francs that prevented Mr. Peters from shooting Dimitrios. Two lives hung by the thin steel threads of self-preservation and greed.

As Dimitrios stood up an idea seemed to occur to him. He turned to Latimer. 'You have been very silent, monsieur. I wonder if you have been understanding that your life is in your friend Petersen's hands. If, for example, he decided to tell me your real name and where you might be found, I should very likely have you killed.'

Mr. Peters showed his white false teeth. 'Why should I deprive myself of Monsieur Smith's help? Monsieur Smith is invaluable. He can prove that Visser is dead. Without him you could breathe again.'

Dimitrios took no notice of the interruption. 'Well, Monsieur Smith?'

Latimer looked up into the brown anxious-seeming eyes and thought of Madame Preveza's phrase. They were certainly the eyes of a man ready to do something that hurt, but they could have belonged to no doctor. There was murder in them.

'I can assure you', he said, 'that Petersen has no inducement to kill me. You see . . .'

'You see,' put in Mr. Peters quickly, 'we are not fools, Dimitrios. You can go now.'

'Of course.' Dimitrios went towards the door, but at the threshold he paused.

'What is it?' said Mr. Peters.

'I should like to ask Monsieur Smith two questions.'

'Well?'

'How was this man whom you took to be Visser dressed when he was found?'

'In a cheap blue serge suit. A French *carte d'identité*, issued at Lyons a year previously, was sewn into the lining. The suit was of Greek manufacture, but the shirt and underwear were French.'

'And how was he killed?'

'He had been stabbed in the side and then thrown into the water.'

Mr. Peters smiled. 'Are you satisfied, Dimitrios?'

Dimitrios stared at him. 'Visser,' he said slowly, 'was too greedy. You will not be too greedy, will you, Petersen?'

Mr. Peters gave him stare for stare. 'I shall be very careful,' he said. 'You have no more questions to ask? Good. You will receive your instructions in the morning.'

Dimitrios went without another word. Mr. Peters shut the door, waited a moment or two, then, very gently opened it again. Motioning to Latimer to remain where he was, he disappeared on to the landing. Latimer heard the stairs creak. A minute later he returned.

'He has gone,' he announced. 'In a few minutes we, too, shall go.' He sat down again on the bed, lit one of his cheroots and blew the smoke out as luxuriously as if he had just been released from bondage. His sweet smile came out again like a rose after a storm. 'Well,' he said, 'that was Dimitrios about whom you have heard such a great deal. What did you think of him?'

'I didn't know what to think. Perhaps, if I had not known so much about him, I should have disliked him less. I don't know. It is difficult to be reasonable about a man who is obviously wondering how quickly he can murder you.' He hesitated. 'I did not realize that you hated him so much.'

Mr. Peters did not smile. 'I assure you, Mr. Latimer, that it was a surprise to me to realize it. I did not like him. I did not trust him. After the way he betrayed us all, that was understandable. It was not until I saw him in this room just now that I realized that I hated him enough to kill him. If I were a superstitious man, I should wonder if perhaps the spirit of poor Visser had entered into me.' He stopped, then added '*Salop!*' under his breath. He was silent for a moment. Then he looked up. 'Mr. Latimer, I must make an admission. I must tell you that even if you had agreed to the offer I made you, you would not have received your half million. I should not have paid you.' He shut his mouth tightly as if he were prepared to receive a blow.

'So I imagine,' said Latimer dryly. 'I very nearly accepted the offer just to see how you would cheat me. I take it that you would have made the real time for delivery of the money an hour or so earlier than you would have told me, and that, by the time I arrived on the scene, you and the money would have gone. Was that it?'

Mr. Peters winced. 'It was very wise of you not to trust me, but very unkind. But I suppose that I cannot blame you.' He rubbed salt in the would. 'The Great One has seen fit to make me what is known as a criminal, and I must tread the path to my Destiny with patient resignation. But it was not to abase myself that I admitted to having tried to deceive you. It was to defend myself. I would like to ask you a question.'

'Well?'

'Was it – forgive me – was it the thought that I might betray you to Dimitrios that made you refuse my offer to share the money with you?'

'It never occurred to me.'

'I am glad,' said Mr. Peters solemnly. 'I should not like you to think that of me. You may dislike me, but I should not care to be thought cold-blooded. I may tell you that the thought did not occur to me either. There you see Dimitrios! We have discussed this matter, you and I. We have mistrusted one another and looked for betrayal. Yet it is Dimitrios who puts this thought in our heads. I have met many wicked and violent men, Mr. Latimer, but I tell you that Dimitrios is unique. Why do you think he suggested to you that I might betray you?'

'I imagine that he was acting on the principle that the best way to fight two allies is to get them to fight each other.'

Mr. Peters smiled. 'No, Mr. Latimer. That would have been too obvious a trick for Dimitrios. He was suggesting to you in a very delicate way that *I* was the unnecessary partner and that you could remove me very easily by telling him where I could be found.'

'Do you mean that he was offering to kill you for me?'

'Exactly. He would have only you to deal with then. He does not know, of course,' added Mr. Peters thoughtfully, 'that you do not know his present name.' He stood up and put on his hat. 'No, Mr. Latimer, I do not like Dimitrios. Do not misunderstand me, please. I have no moral rectitude. But Dimitrios is a savage beast. Even now, though I know that I have taken every precaution, I am afraid. I shall take his million and go. If I could allow you to hand him over to the police when I have done with him, I would do so. He would not hesitate if the situation were reversed. But it is impossible.'

'Why?'

Mr. Peters looked at him curiously.'Dimitrios seems to have had a strange effect on you. No, to tell the police afterwards would be too dangerous. If we were asked to explain the million francs – and we could not expect Dimitrios to remain silent about them – we should be embarrassed. A pity. Shall we go now? I shall leave the money for the room on the table. They can take the suit-case for a *pourboire*.'

They went downstairs in silence. As they deposited the key, the man in his shirt-sleeves apeared with an *affiche* for Mr. Peters to complete. Mr. Peters waved him away. He would, he said, fill it in when he returned.

In the street he halted and faced Latimer.

'Have you ever been followed?'

'Not to my knowledge.'

'Then you will be followed now. I do not suppose that Dimitrios had any real hope of our leading him to our homes, but he was always thorough. He glanced over Latimer's shoulder. 'Ah, yes. He was there when we arrived. Do not look round, Mr. Latimer. A man wearing a grey mackintosh and a dark soft hat. You will see him in a minute.'

The hollow feeling which had disappeared with the departure of Dimitrios jolted back into its position in Latimer's stomach. 'What are we to do?'

'Return by Metro, as I said before.'

'What good will that do?'

'You will see in a minute.'

The Ledru-Rollin Metro station was about a hundred yards away. As they walked towards it the muscles in Latimer's calves tightened and he had a ridiculous desire to run. He felt himself walking stiffly and self-consciously.

'Do not look round,' said Mr. Peters again.

They walked down the steps to the Metro. 'Keep close to me now,' said Mr. Peters.

He bought two second-class tickets and they walked on down the tunnel in the direction of the trains.

It was a long tunnel. As they pushed their way through the spring barriers, Latimer felt that he could reasonably glance behind him. He did so, and caught a glimpse of a shabby young man in a grey raincoat about thirty feet behind them. Now the tunnel split into two. One way was labelled: '*Direction* Pte. de Charenton,' the other: '*Direction* Balard.' Mr. Peters stopped.

'It would be wise now,' he said, 'if we appeared to be about to take leave of one another.' He glanced out of the corners of his eyes. 'Yes, he has stopped. He is wondering what is going to happen. Talk, please, Mr. Latimer, but not too loudly. I want to listen.'

'Listen to what?'

'The trains. I spent half an hour here listening to them this morning.'

'What on earth for? I don't see . . .'

Mr. Peters gripped his arm and he stopped. In the distance he could hear the rumble of an approaching train.

'*Direction* Balard,' muttered Mr. Peters suddenly. 'Come along. Keep close to me and do not walk too quickly.'

They went on down the right-hand tunnel. The rumble of the train grew louder. They rounded a bend in the tunnel. Ahead was the green automatic gate.

'*Vite!*' cried Mr. Peters.

The train was by now almost in the station. The automatic door began to swing slowly across the entrance to the platform. As Latimer reached it and passed through with about three inches to spare, he heard, above the hiss and screech of pneumatic brakes the sound of running feet. He looked round. Although Mr. Peters' stomach had suffered some compression, he had squeezed himself through on to the platform. But the man in the grey raincoat had, in spite of his last-minute sprint, left it too late. He now stood, red in the face with anger, shaking his fists at them from the other side of the automatic gate.

They got into the train a trifle breathlessly.

'Excellent!' puffed Mr. Peters happily. 'Now do you see what I meant, Mr. Latimer?'

'Very ingenious.'

The noise of the train made further conversation impossible. Latimer stared vacantly at a Celtique advertisement. So that was that. Colonel Haki had been right after all. The story of Dimitrios had no proper ending. Dimitrios would buy off Mr. Peters and the story would merely stop. Somewhere, at some future time, Dimitrios might happen to find Mr. Peters and then Mr. Peters would die as Visser had died. Somewhere, at some time, Dimitrios himself would die: probably of old age. But he, Latimer, would not know about those things. He would be writing a detective story with a beginning, a middle and an end; a corpse, a piece of detection and a scaffold. He would be demonstrating that murder would out, that justice triumphed in the end and that the green bay tree flourished alone. Dimitrios and the Eurasian Credit Trust would be forgotten. It had all been a great waste of time.

Mr. Peters touched his arm. They were at Chatelet. They got out and took the Porte d'Orléans *correspondance* to St. Placide. As they walked down the Rue de Rennes, Mr. Peters hummed softly. They passed a café.

Mr. Peters stopped humming. 'Would you like some coffee, Mr. Latimer?'

'No, thanks. What about your letter to Dimitrios?'

Mr. Peters tapped his pocket. 'It is already written. Eleven o'clock is the time. The junction of the Avenue de la Reine and the Boulevard Jean Jaurès is the place. Would you like to be there, or are you leaving Paris to-morrow?' And then, without giving Latimer a chance to reply: 'I shall be sorry to say good-bye to you, Mr. Latimer. I find you so sympathetic. Our association has, on the whole, been most agreeable. It has also been profitable to me.' He sighed. 'I feel a little guilty, Mr. Latimer. You have been so patient and helpful and yet you go unrewarded. You would not,' he inquired a trifle anxiously, 'accept a thousand francs of the money? It would help to pay your expenses.'

'No, thank you.'

'No, of course not. Then, at least, Mr. Latimer, let me give you a glass of wine. That it is! A celebration! Come, Mr. Latimer. There is no taste in nothing. Let us collect the money together to-morrow night. You will have the satisfaction of seeing a little blood squeezed from this swine Dimitrios. Then we will celebrate with a glass of wine. What do you say to that?'

They had stopped at the corner of the street which contained the Impasse. Latimer looked into Mr. Peters' water eyes. 'I should say,' he said deliberately, 'that you are wondering if there is a chance that Dimitrios might decide to call your bluff and thinking that it might be a good idea to have me in Paris until you have the money actually in your pocket.'

Mr. Peters' eyes slowly closed. 'Mr. Latimer,' he said bitterly, 'I did not think . . . I would not have thought that you could have put such a construction on . . .'

'All right, I'll stay.' Irritably, Latimer interrupted him. He had wasted so many days: another one would make no difference. 'I'll come with you to-morrow, but only on these conditions. The wine must be champagne; it must come from France, not Meknes, and it must be a vintage *cuvée* of either nineteen nineteen, twenty or twenty-one. A bottle,' he added vindictively, 'will cost you at least one hundred francs.'

Mr. Peters opened his eyes. He smiled bravely. 'You shall have it, Mr. Latimer,' he said.

CHAPTER 15

THE STRANGE TOWN

Mr. Peters and Latimer took up their positions at the corner of the Avenue de la Reine and the Boulevard Jean Jaurès at half-past ten, the hour at which the hired car was due to pick up the messenger from Dimitrios opposite the Neuilly cemetery.

It was a cold night, and as it began to rain soon after they arrived, they stood for shelter just inside the *porte cochère* of a building a few yards along the Avenue in the direction of the Pont St. Cloud.

'How long will they be getting here?' Latimer asked.

'I said that I would expect them by eleven. That gives them half an hour to drive from Neuilly. They could do it in less, but I told them to make quite certain that they were not followed. If they are in doubt they will return to Neuilly. They will take no chances. The car is a Renault *coupé-de-ville*. We must have patience.'

They waited in silence. Now and again Mr. Peters would stir as a car that might have been the hired Renault approached from the direction of the river. The rain trickling down the slope formed by the subsidence of the cobbles formed puddles about their feet. Latimer thought of his warm bed and wondered if he would catch a cold. He had booked a seat in the Athens slip-coach of the Orient Express due to leave the following morning. A train would not be the best place to spend three days nursing a cold. He remembered that he had a small bottle of cinnamon extract somewhere in his luggage and resolved to take a dose before he went to bed.

His mind was occupied with this domestic matter when suddenly Mr. Peters grunted: '*Attention!*'

'Are they coming?'

'Yes.'

Latimer looked over Mr. Peters' shoulder. A large Renault was approaching from the left. As he looked it began to slow down as if the driver were uncertain of the way. It passed them, the rain glistening in the beams of the headlights, and stopped a few yards farther on. The outline of the driver's head and shoulders were just visible in the darkness, but blinds were pulled down over the rear windows. Mr. Peters put his hand in his overcoat pocket.

'Wait here, please,' he said to Latimer, and walked towards the car.

'*Ca va?*' Latimer heard him say to the driver. There was an answering '*Oui*'. Mr. Peters opened the rear door and leaned forward.

Almost immediately he withdrew a pace and closed the door. In his left hand was a package. '*Attendez,*' he said, and walked back to where Latimer was standing.

'All right?' said Latimer.

'I think so. Will you strike a match, please?'

Latimer did so. The package was the size of a large book, about two inches thick and was wrapped in blue paper and tied with string. Mr. Peters tore away the paper at one of the corners and exposed a solid wad of *mille* notes. He sighed. 'Beautiful!'

'Aren't you going to count them?'

'That pleasure,' said Mr. Peters seriously, 'I shall reserve for the comfort of my home.' He crammed the package into his overcoat pocket, stepped on to the pavement and raised his hand. The Renault started with a jerk, swung round in a wide circle and splashed away on its return journey. Mr. Peters watched it go with a smile.

'A very pretty woman,' he said. 'I wonder who she can be. But I prefer the million francs. Now, Mr. Latimer, a taxi and then your favourite champagne. We have earned it, I think.'

They found a taxi near the Porte de St. Cloud. Mr. Peters enlarged on his success.

'With a type like Dimitrios it is necessary only to be firm and circumspect. We put the matter to him squarely; we let him see that he has no choice but to agree to our demands, and it is done. A million francs. Very nice! One almost wishes that one had demanded two million. But it would have been unwise to be too greedy. As it is, he believes that we shall make fresh demands and that he has time to deal with us as he dealt with Visser. He will find that he has deceived himself. That is very satisfactory to me, Mr. Latimer: as satisfying to my pride as it is to my pocket. I feel, too, that I have, in some measure, avenged poor Visser's death. It is at moments like these, Mr. Latimer, that one realizes that if it sometimes appears as if the Great One has forgotten His children, it is only that we have forgotten Him. I have suffered. Now I have my reward.' He patted his pocket. 'It would be amusing to see Dimitrios when at last he realizes how he has been tricked. A pity that we shall not be there.'

'Shall you leave Paris immediately?'

'I think so. I have a fancy to see something of South America. Not my own adopted fatherland, of course. It is one of the terms of my citizenship that I never enter the country. A hard condition, for I would like for sentimental reasons to see the country of my adoption. But it cannot be altered. I am a citizen of the world and must remain so. Perhaps I shall buy an estate somewhere, a place where I shall be able to pass my days in peace when I am old. You are a young man, Mr. Latimer. When one is my age, the years seem shorter and one feels that one is soon to reach a destination. It is as if one were approaching a strange town late at night when one is sorry to be leaving the warm train for an unknown hotel and wishing that the journey would never end.'

He glanced out of the window. 'We are nearly home. I have your champagne. It was, as you warned me, very expensive. But I have no objections to a little luxury. It is sometimes agreeable and, even when it is disagreeable, it serves to make us appreciate simplicity. Ah!' The taxi had stopped at the end of the Impasse. 'I have no change, Mr. Latimer. That seems odd with a million francs in one's pocket, does it not? Will you pay, please?'

They walked down the Impasse.

'I think,' said Mr. Peters, 'that I shall sell these houses before I go to South America. One does not want property on one's hands that is not yielding a profit.'

'Won't they be rather difficult to sell? The view from the windows is a little depressing, isn't it?'

'It is not necessary to be always looking out of the windows. They could be made into very nice houses.'

They began the long climb up the stairs. On the second landing Mr. Peters paused for breath, took off his overcoat and got out his keys. They continued the climb to his door.

He opened it, switched on the light, and then, going straight to the largest divan, took the package from his overcoat pocket and undid the string. With loving care he extracted the notes from the wrappings and held them up. For once his smile was real.

'There, Mr. Latimer! A million francs! Have you ever seen so much money at once before? Nearly six thousand English pounds!' He stood up. 'But we must have our little celebration. Take off your coat and I will get the champagne. I hope that you will like it. I have no ice, but I put it in a bowl of water. It will be quite cool.'

He walked towards the curtained-off part of the room.

Latimer had turned away to take off his coat. Suddenly he became aware that Mr. Peters was still on the same side of the curtain and that he was standing motionless. He glanced round.

For a moment he thought that he was going to faint. The blood seemed to drain away suddenly from his head, leaving it hollow and light. A steel band seemed to tighten round his chest. He felt that he wanted to cry out, but all he could do was to stare.

Mr. Peters was standing with his back to him, and his hands were raised above his head. Facing him in the gap between the gold curtains was Dimitrios, with a revolver in his hand.

Dimitrios stepped forward and sideways so that Latimer was no longer partly covered by Mr. Peters. Latimer dropped his coat and put up his hands. Dimitrios raised his eyebrows.

'It is not flattering,' he said, 'for you to look so surprised to see me, Petersen. Or should I call you Caillé?'

Mr. Peters said nothing. Latimer could not see his face, but he saw his throating move as if he were swallowing.

The brown eyes flickered to Latimer. 'I am glad that the Englishman is here, too, Petersen. I am saved the trouble of persuading you to give me his name and address. Monsieur Smith, who knows so many things and who was so anxious to keep his face hidden, is now shown to be as easy to deal with as you are, Petersen. You were always too ingenious, Petersen. I told you so once before. It was on the occasion when you brought a coffin from Salonika. You remember? Ingenuity is never a substitute for intelligence, you know. Did you really think that I should not see through you?' His lips twisted. 'Poor Dimitrios! He is very simple. He will think that I, clever Petersen, will come back for more, like any other blackmailer. He will not guess that I may be bluffing him. But, just to make sure that he does not guess, I will do what no other blackmailer ever did. I will tell him that I *shall* come back for more. Poor Dimitrios is such a fool that he will believe me. Poor Dimitrios has no intelligence. Even if he finds out from the records that, within a month of my coming out of prison, I had succeeded in selling three unsaleable houses to someone named Caillé, he will not dream of suspecting that I, clever Petersen, am also Caillé. Did you not know, Petersen, that before I bought these houses in your name they had been empty for ten years? You are such a fool.'

He paused. The anxious brown eyes narrowed. The mouth tightened. Latimer knew that Dimitrios was going to kill Mr. Peters and that there was nothing that he could do about it. The wild beating of his heart seemed to be suffocating him.

'Drop the money, Petersen.'

The wad of notes hit the carpet and spread out like a fan.

Dimitrios raised the revolver.

Suddenly, Mr. Peters seemed to realize what was about to happen. He cried out: 'No! You must . . .'

Then Dimitrios fired. He fired twice and with the ear-splitting noise of the explosions Latimer heard one of the bullets thud into Mr. Peters' body.

Mr. Peters emitted a long-drawn-out retching sound and sank forward on to his hands and knees with blood pouring from his neck.

Dimitrios stared at Latimer. 'Now you,' he said.

At that moment Latimer jumped.

Why he chose that particular moment to jump he never knew. He never even knew what prompted him to jump at all. He supposed that it was an instinctive attempt to save himself. Why, however, his instinct for self-preservation should have led him to jump in the direction of the revolver which Dimitrios was about to fire is inexplicable. But he did jump, and the jump did save his life; for, as his right foot left the floor, a fraction of a second before Dimitrios pressed the trigger, he stumbled over one of Mr. Peters' thick tufts of rug and the shot went over his head into the wall.

Half dazed and with his forehead scorched by the blast from the muzzle of the revolver, he hurled himself at Dimitrios. They went down together with their hands at each other's throats, but immediately Dimitrios brought his knee up into Latimer's stomach and rolled clear of him.

He had dropped his revolver, and now he went to pick it up. Gasping for breath, Latimer scrambled towards the nearest movable object, which happened to be the heavy brass tray on top of one of the Moroccan tables, and flung it at Dimitrios. The edge of it hit the side of his head as he was reaching for the revolver and he reeled; but the blow stopped him for barely a second. Latimer threw the wooden part of the table at him and dashed forward. Dimitrios staggered back as the table caught his shoulder. The next moment Latimer had the revolver and was standing back, still trying to get his breath, but with his finger on the trigger.

His face sheet-white, Dimitrios came towards him. Latimer raised the revolver.

'If you move again, I shall fire.'

Dimitrios stood still. His brown eyes stared into Latimer's. His grey hair was tousled; his scarf had come out of his coat; he looked dangerous. Latimer was beginning to recover his breath, but his knees felt horribly weak, his ears were singing and the air he breathed reeked sickeningly of cordite fumes. It was for him to make the next move, and he felt frightened and helpless.

'If you move,' he repeated, 'I shall fire.'

He saw the brown eyes flicker towards the notes on the floor and then back to him. 'What are you going to do?' asked Dimitrios suddenly. 'If the police come we shall both have something to explain. If you shoot me you will get only that million. If you will release me I will give you another million as well. That would be good for you.'

Latimer took no notice. He edged sideways towards the wall, until he could glance quickly at Mr. Peters.

Mr. Peters had crawled towards the divan on which his overcoat lay, and was now leaning against it with his eyes half closed. He was breathing stertorously through the mouth. One bullet had torn a great gaping wound in the side of his neck from which the blood was welling. The second had hit him full in the chest and scorched the clothing. The wound was a round purple mess about two inches in diameter. It was bleeding very little. Mr. Peters' lips moved.

Keeping his eyes fixed on Dimitrios, Latimer moved round until he was alongside Mr. Peters.

'How do you feel?' he said.

It was a stupid question, and he knew it the moment the words had left his mouth. He tried desperately to collect his wits. A man had been shot and he had the man who shot him. He . . .

'My pistol,' muttered Mr. Peters; 'get my pistol. Overcoat.' He said something else that was inaudible.

Cautiously, Latimer worked his way round to the overcoat and fumbled for the pistol. Dimitrios watched with a thin ghastly smile on his lips. Latimer found the pistol and handed it to Mr. Peters. He grasped it with both hands and snicked back the safety catch.

'Now,' he muttered, 'go and get police.'

'Someone will have heard the shots,' said Latimer soothingly. 'The police will be here soon.'

'Won't find us,' whispered Mr. Peters. 'Get police.'

Latimer hesitated. What Mr. Peters said was true. The Impasse was hemmed in by blank walls. The shots might have been heard, but unless someone had happened to be passing the entrance to the Impasse during the few seconds in which they were fired, nobody would know where the sounds had come from.

'All right,' he said. 'Where is the telephone?'

'No telephone.'

'But . . .' He hesitated again. It might take ten minutes to find a policeman. Could he leave a badly wounded Mr. Peters to watch a man like Dimitrios? But there was nothing else for it. Mr. Peters needed a doctor. The sooner Dimitrios was under lock and key the better. He knew that Dimitrios understood his predicament and the knowledge did not please him. He glanced at Mr. Peters. He had the pistol resting on one knee and pointed at Dimitrios. The blood was still pouring from his neck. If a doctor did not attend to him soon he would bleed to death.

'All right,' he said. 'I'll be as quick as I can.'

He went towards the door.

'One moment, monsieur.' There was an urgency in the harsh voice that made Latimer pause.

'Well?'

'If you go he will shoot me. Don't you see that? Why not accept my offer?'

Latimer opened the door. 'If you try any tricks you will certainly be shot.' He looked again at the wounded man, huddled over the pistol. 'I shall be back with the police. Don't shoot unless you have to.'

Then, as he made to go, Dimitrios laughed. Involuntarily, Latimer turned. 'I should save that laugh for the executioner,' he snapped. 'You will need it.'

'I was thinking,' said Dimitrios, 'that in the end one is always defeated by stupidity. If it is not one's own it is the stupidity of others.' His face changed. 'Five million, monsieur,' he shouted angrily. 'Is it not enough or do you want this carrion to kill me?'

Latimer stared at him for a moment. The man was almost convincing. Then he remembered that others had been convinced by Dimitrios. He waited no longer. He heard Dimitrios shout something after him as he shut the door.

He was half way down the stairs when he heard the shots. There were four of them. Three cracked out in quick succession. Then, there was a pause before the last one. His heart in his mouth, he turned and ran back up to the room. It was only later that he found anything curious in the fact that, as he raced up the stairs, the fear uppermost in his mind was for Mr. Peters.

Dimitrios was not a pleasant sight. Only one of the bullets from Mr. Peters' heavy pistol had missed. Two had lodged in the body. The fourth, evidently fired at him after he had fallen to the floor, had hit him between the eyes and almost blown the top of his head off. His body was still twitching.

The pistol had slipped from Mr. Peters' fingers and he was leaning, with his head on the edge of the divan, opening and shutting his mouth like a stranded fish. As Latimer stood there he choked suddenly and blood trickled from his mouth.

Scarcely knowing that he was doing, Latimer blundered through the curtain. Dimitrios was dead; Mr. Peters was dying; and all he, Latimer, could think about was the effort required not to faint or vomit. He strove to pull himself together. He must do something. Mr. Peters must have water. Wounded men always need water. There was a wash-basin and beside it were some glasses. He filled one and carried it back into the room.

Mr. Peters had not moved. His mouth and eyes were open. Latimer knelt down beside him and poured a little water into the mouth. It ran out again. He put down the glass and felt for the pulse. There was none.

Latimer got quickly to his feet and looked at his hands. There was blood on them. He went back to the wash-basin, rinsed them and dried them on a small, dirty towel which hung from a hook.

He should, he knew, call the police immediately. Two men had killed each other. That was a matter for the police. Yet . . . what was he going to say to them? How was he going to explain his own presence there in that shambles? Could he say that he had been passing the end of the Impasse and had heard the shots? But someone might have noticed him with Mr. Peters. There was the taxi-driver who had brought them. And when they found that Dimitrios had that day obtained a million francs from his bank . . . there would be endless questionings. Supposing they suspected him.

His brain seemed to clear suddenly. He must get out at once and he must leave no traces of his presence there. He thought quickly. The revolver in his pocket belonged to Dimitrios. It had his finger-prints on it. He took it out of his pocket, put on his gloves and wiped it all over carefully with his handkerchief. Then, setting his teeth, he went back into the room, knelt down beside Dimitrios and, taking his right hand, pressed the fingers round the butt and trigger. Removing the fingers and holding the revolver by the barrel, he then put it near the body on the floor.

He considered the *mille* notes strewn over the rung like so much waste-paper. To whom did they belong – Dimitrios or Mr. Peters? There was Sholem's money there and the money stolen in Athens in 1922. There was the fee for helping to assassinate Stambulisky and the money of which Madame Preveza had been cheated. There was the price of the charts Bulić had stolen and part of the profits from the white slave and drug traffics. To whom did it belong? Well, the police would decide. Best to leave it as it was. It would give them something to think about.

There was, however, the glass of water. It must be emptied, dried and replaced with the other glasses. He looked round. Was there anything else? No. Nothing at all? Yes, one thing. His finger-prints were on the tray and the table. He wiped them. Nothing more? Yes. Finger-prints on the door-knobs. He wiped them. Anything else? No. He carried the glass to the wash-basin. The glass dried and replaced, he turned to go. It was then that he noticed the champagne which Mr. Peters had bought for their celebration standing in a bowl of water. It was a Verzy 1921 – a half bottle.

No one saw him leave the Impasse. He went to a café in the Rue de Rennes and ordered a cognac.

Now he began to tremble from head to foot. He had been a fool. He ought to have gone to the police. It was still not too late to go to them. Supposing the bodies remained undiscovered. They might lie there for weeks in that ghastly room with the blue walls and gold stars and rugs, while the blood congealed and hardened and collected dust and the flesh began to rot. It was horrible to think of. If only there were some way of telling the police. An anonymous letter would be too dangerous. The police would know immediately that a third person had been concerned in the affair and would not be satisfied with the simple explanation that the two men had killed each other. Then he had an idea. The main thing was to get the police to the house. Why they went was unimportant.

There was an evening paper in the rack. He took it to his table and read it through feverishly. There were two news items in it which suited his purpose. One was a report of the theft of some valuable furs from a warehouse in the Avenue de la Republique; the other was an account of the smashing of the shop window of a jeweller in the Avenue de Clichy and the escape of two men with a tray of rings.

He decided that the first would suit his purpose best, and, summoning the waiter, ordered another cognac together with writing materials. He drank the brandy at a gulp and put his gloves on. Then, taking a sheet of the letter paper, he examined it carefully. It was ordinary, cheap café notepaper. Having satisfied himself that there was no distinguishing mark of any kind on it, he wrote across the middle of it in capital letters: '*FAITES DES ENQUETES SUR CAILLÉ – 3, IMPASSE DES HUITS ANGES.*' Then he tore the report of the fur robbery out of the paper, folded it inside the note and put the two in an envelope, which he addressed to the Commissaire of Police of the Seventh Arrondissement. Leaving the café, he bought a stamp at a tobacco kiosk and posted the letter.

It was not until four o'clock that morning, when he had lain awake in bed for two hours, that the nerves of his stomach succumbed at last to the strain which had been put upon them and he was sick.

Two days later a paragraph appeared in three of the Paris morning papers saying that the body of a South American named Frederik Peters, together with that of a man, at present unidentified, but believed to be a South American also, had been found in an apartment off the Rue de Rennes. Both men, the paragraph continued, had been shot and it was thought that they had killed one another in a revolver fight following a quarrel over money, a considerable sum of which was found in the apartment. It was the only reference to the affair, the attention of the public being divided at the time between a new international crisis and a hatchet murder in the suburbs.

Latimer did not see the paragraph until several days later.

Soon after nine o'clock on the morning of the day on which the police received his note, he left his hotel for the Gare de l'Est and the Orient express. A letter had arrived for him by the first post. It had a Bulgarian stamp and a Sofia postmark and was obviously from Marukakis. He put it in his pocket unread. It was not until later in the day, when the express was racing through the hills west of Belfort, that he remembered it. He opened it and began to read:

My dear Friend,

> Your letter delighted me. I was so pleased to get it. I was also a little surprised, for – forgive me, please – I did not seriously expect you to succeed in the difficult task which you had set yourself. The years bury so much of our wisdom that they are bound to bury most of our folly with it. Some time I hope to hear from you how a folly buried in Belgrade comes to be unearthed in Geneva.

> I was interested in the reference to the Eurasian Credit Trust. Here is something that will interest you.

> There has been recently, as you may know, a great deal of tension between this country and Yugoslavia. The Serbs, you know, have reason to feel tense. If Germany and vassal Hungary attacked her from the north, Italy attacked her through Albania from the south and by sea from the west, and Bulgaria attacked her from the east, she would be quickly finished. Her only chance would lie in the Russians out-flanking the Germans and Hungarians with an attack launched through Rumania along the Bukovina railway. But has Bulgaria anything to fear from Yugoslavia? Is she a danger to Bulgaria? The idea is absurd. Yet, for the past three months or four, there has been here a stream of propaganda to the effect that Yugoslavia is planning to attack Bulgaria.

'The menace across the frontier' is a typical phrase.

If such things were not so dangerous one would laugh. But one recognizes the technique. Such propaganda always begins with words but soon it proceeds to deeds. When there are no facts to support lies, facts must be made.

Two weeks ago there took place the inevitable frontier incident. Some Bulgarian peasants were fired upon by Yugoslavs (alleged to be soldiers), and one of the peasants was killed. There is much popular indignation, an outcry against the devilish Serbs. The newspaper offices are very busy. A week later the Government announces fresh purchases of anti-aircraft guns to strengthen the defences of the western Provinces. The purchases are made from a Belgian firm with the help of a loan negotiated by the Eurasian Credit Trust.

Yesterday a curious news item comes into this office.

As a result of careful investigations by the Yugoslav Government, it is shown that the four men who fired on the peasants were not Yugoslav soldiers, nor even Yugoslav subjects. They were of various nationalities and two had previously been imprisoned in Poland for terrorist activities. They had been paid to create the incident by a man about whom none of them knows anything more than that he came from Paris.

But there is more. Within an hour of that news item reaching Paris, I had instructions from the head office there to suppress the item and send out a *démenti* to all subscribers taking our French news. That is amusing, is it not? One would not have thought that such a rich organization as the Eurasian Credit Trust would be so sensitive.

As for your Dimitrios: what can one say?

A writer of plays once said that there are some situations that one cannot use on the stage; situations in which the audience can feel neither approval nor disapproval, sympathy nor antipathy; situations out of which there is no possible way that is not humiliating or distressing and from which there is no truth, however bitter, to be extracted. He was, you may say, one of those unhappy men who are confounded by the difference between the stupid vulgarities of real life and the ideal existence of the imagination. That may be. Yet, I have been wondering if, for once, I do not find myself in sympathy with him. Can one explain Dimitrios or must one turn away disgusted and defeated? I am tempted to find reason and justice in the fact that he died as violently and indecently as he lived. But that is too ingenuous a way out. It does not explain Dimitrios; it only apologizes for him. Special sorts of conditions must exist for the creation of the special sort of criminal that he typified. I have tried to define those conditions – but unsuccessfully. All I do know is that while might is right, while chaos and anarchy masquerade as order and enlightenment, those conditions will obtain.

What is the remedy? But I can see you yawning and remember that if I bore you you will not write to me again to tell me whether you are enjoying your stay in Paris, whether you have found any more Bulićs or Prevezas and whether we shall see you soon in Sofia. My latest information is that war will not break out until the spring; so there will be time for some ski-ing. Late January is quite good here. The roads are terrible, but the runs, when one gets to them, are quite good. I shall look forward eagerly to learning from you when you will come.

With my most sincere regards,

N. Marukakis.

Latimer folded the letter and put it in his pocket. A good fellow, Marukakis! He must write to him when he had the time. But just at the moment there were more important matters to be considered.

He needed, and badly, a motive, a neat method of committing a murder and an entertaining crew of suspects. Yes, the suspects must certainly be entertaining. His last book had been a trifle heavy. He must inject a little more humour into this one. As for the motive, money was always, of course, the soundest basis. A pity that Wills and life insurance were so outmoded. Supposing a man murdered an old lady so that his wife could have a private income. It might be worth thinking about. The scene? Well, there was always plenty of fun to be got out of an English country village, wasn't there? The time? Summer; with cricket matches on the village green, garden parties at the vicarage, the clink of tea-cups and the sweet smell of grass on a July evening. That was the sort of thing people liked to hear about. It was the sort of thing that he himself would like to hear about.

He looked out of the window. The sun had gone and the hills were receding slowly into the night sky. They would be slowing down for Belfort soon. Two more days to go! He ought to get some sort of a plot worked out in that time.

The train ran into a tunnel.

The
Naked Runner

Francis
Clifford

THE NAKED RUNNER

For John Attenborough
and Robin Denniston

All men dream: but not equally.
Those who dream by night in the
dusty recesses of their minds wake
in the day to find that it was
vanity: but the dreamers of the day
are dangerous men, for they may
act their dream with open eyes, to
make it possible . . .
T. E. LAWRENCE
Seven Pillars of Wisdom

. . . a fear among fears
A naked runner lost in a storm of
spears.
ARTHUR SYMONS

CHAPTER 1

Sam Laker watched his son serve himself with a second enormous helping of breakfast cereal then top it over with sugar and cream. Lord, he marvelled, how they can put it away at fourteen. And this was merely a beginning, he knew. Bacon and eggs, half a dozen slices of buttered toast, perhaps an apple to round off with – and sure enough the hunger-pangs would be back well before lunch. Only last week Mrs. Ruddick had said that when Patrick was home from Greynham it was like shopping for an entire extra household. Still, Laker reflected, he looks damn well on it, and that's the main thing. Big for his age, and chunky. Helen would have approved – except perhaps for the present state of his hair.

He folded the *Telegraph*, drained his coffee and smiled. 'What's on the agenda for today?'

'The Planetarium.'

'Oh yes, you told me. You and Tim Maxwell.'

'That's right.'

'And afterwards?'

'We thought we'd come back to the river. If the weather lasts, that is. Otherwise I'll probably go over to his place and listen to records or something.'

'Didn't you do that yesterday?'

'Yes, but Tim's player packed in. He'll have had it fixed by this afternoon, though.'

'I see.' Laker paused uncertainly. 'Well, you're all organised then?'

'Just about.'

He rose, pushing away his chair. 'The Planetarium ought to be interesting.'

'Yes.'

'Enjoy yourself, anyway.'

'Thanks.'

'And don't try anything too clever if you do go on the water.'

'I won't. 'Bye.'

They never seemed to speak much in the mornings. Patrick was invariably late down and Laker made a point of being at Gale and Watts by nine-thirty. Not that breakfast, even at the week-end, was an especially communicative time; but it often struck Laker that leaving the boy to his own devices five days a week throughout most of the school holidays was a routine act of desertion. It would have been different if he weren't an only child, or if Helen had lived, but regrets like that offered no solution. On the credit side, Patrick was nothing if not self-reliant. And, by way of amends, next week's trip to Leipzig and West Germany would help to balance things up a bit.

The mail had come. Telephone account, a picture-card for Mrs Ruddick and a letter addressed to Patrick from Paris. *Patrick Laker, Esquire.* Laker opened the breakfast-room door and tossed the envelope on to the table.

'Just arrived. Which particular pen-pal would that be?'

'Gilles,' Patrick answered, straightening it. 'Gilles Leroux.'

'Formal type, eh?'

'How d'you mean?'

'Esquire.'

Patrick's eyes widened. 'Oh, glory.'

'Incidentally – '

'Yes?'

'Get your hair cut, will you?'

A grin from Patrick and Laker shut the door again. A minute or two later he looked into the kitchen.

'I'll be in at the usual time, Mrs. Ruddick. Around six-thirty.'

'Very well, Mr. Laker.'

'Patrick will be out most of the day as far as I can gather. Meanwhile he's busy taking on fuel.'

'It's a wonder where he puts it, and that's a fact. But they're all the same at his age.' Smiling, efficient, dependable Mrs. Ruddick. 'You ought to see my nephew.'

'By the way, there's a card for you,' Laker said. 'I left it in the hall.'

Except for a few curled feathers of cirrus the morning was cloudless. Rain wouldn't come amiss, Laker thought, glancing at the roses as he cut across the lawn to the garage. He didn't fancy an evening's watering, but all the signs were that he was in for one. He ran the Humber out, locked the garage after him, then headed along the tree-lined avenue.

It was five miles to Gale and Watts and he had twenty minutes. He slowed at the intersection, waited for a line of cars to pass, then nosed into the main road that would lead him through Oatlands and on past the filling-station and into Weybridge. The trees and bordering hedges wore a bloom of late summer dust. He wound the driving-window all the way down, letting the air whoosh in. In Oatlands he veered out of the traffic's stream, switched off, and crossed to the tobacconist's for cigarettes.

'Morning, sir.' From habit the man reached for the required brand and slid a pack of twenty across the counter. 'Another lovely morning.'

'Certainly is.'

'We deserve all we can get, that's what I say.'

Laker collected the change, nodded his thanks and stepped outside. Again and again he was to trace the nightmare back to that precise moment and wonder whether Slattery would in fact have got in touch if the next few seconds had never happened. But there and then he was aware only of the woman with the pram who was in the path of an oncoming truck. With abnormal clarity he saw the horrified expression of the driver in the high cab and the inevitability of disaster as the woman dithered between strides.

Instinct propelled Laker from the kerb. He sprinted, canted forward, going for the woman's waist, flinging himself at her in a rugby-tackle. She had begun to scream as his right shoulder crashed into her, and then she grunted, hands going up. In an overlapping blur of awareness he felt her moving with him and glimpsed the pram shooting clear and the bonnet of the truck shuddering towards them in a squeal of locked brakes that was merged with the hoarseness of a human voice somewhere in the distance. Then he was falling with the woman under him, rolling the instant they hit the tarmac, twisting away from the truck's towering bulk. With his eyes half-screwed he saw the red side of it loom vertically against the sky, going past him, the near wing brushing his clothes, and only then was he sure they were clear. The truck shook to a standstill with the cab-door immediately above Laker's head and the next thing he remembered with certainty was the driver staring down at him, eyes and face rigid with terror through sifting dust.

'You okay?'

Laker stirred. A wheel-hub was against his left calf. He tried to say 'I think so,' but there was a kind of dislocation between his brain and his tongue and all he could do was cough.

'*Jesus!*'

As the driver leapt from his cab Laker pushed himself on to his knees. The woman was stirring too, calling 'Michael? . . . Michael?' in a dazed sort of way. Two or three people were between the truck and the pavement, righting the pram which had fallen sideways.

'Jesus,' the driver said again to Laker, 'they were goners but for you. You okay?' His face was the colour of zinc.

'Yes.'

Laker stood up and helped the woman to her feet. She had a graze on her forehead and her eyes were frantic.

'*Michael!*'

The pram was upright now, the curly-haired child bawling but apparently unscathed. The woman ran to him, her voice breaking. All the voices seemed suddenly very loud, a little unreal. Someone said: 'He had a bump, that's all. Just a bump when the pram hit the kerb and toppled over. He's frightened, that's all. He isn't hurt.'

'They were goners,' the driver was insisting. 'She came straight out from behind that parked van. Didn't give me a chance.'

Laker went over to the pram. The woman had freed the child from its harness and was holding him to her, sobbing. She wasn't much more than a girl. Her yellow dress was streaked with tar and a man who'd apparently retrieved her shoes was offering them to her.

Laker said: 'Can I take you home?'

He reckoned she scarcely heard him. He was only one of many; part of the babel. Somebody from a shop had brought out a chair.

'A doctor, maybe? My car's here.'

She shook her head. A sizeable crowd had gathered. Laker looked at her. She'd be all right: no point in staying. He turned and made for the Humber, almost oblivious of the fact that the driver was asking: 'Where's the fellow that pushed 'em clear? They'd have had it but for him.'

He got into the car and drew away. His left knee throbbed and he was a shade light in the head, but it wasn't until he had nearly reached Weybridge that the reaction hit him in earnest. He pulled in to the side and felt the coldness blow through him and then the hot flush come. Everything went a greenish pink for a few moments and he rested his forehead on the wheel, eyes closed, blood and brightness beating together in his mind. A minute or two passed before the feeling of nausea began to ebb. Eventually, he broke the seal on the crushed pack of cigarettes and with trembling fingers lit up.

He'd scraped his knuckles, he noticed. He blew smoke against the windscreen, then took a deep lungful of air. Almost nine-thirty. Well, for once he'd be late. He wiped the chilly sweat from his face and sucked his knuckles, then prepared to drive on, a kind of disbelief possessing him as the scene began to run like a film across his natural vision. It had been close, all right, too close, and his nerves couldn't quite cope with it yet.

Gale and Watts designed and manufactured office equipment.

One of Laker's uncles, Charles Gale, had taken him into the firm soon after the war and for five years he served a kind of apprenticeship, 'a grounding' Charles called it, first in the factory and then in the office, transferring periodically from one department to another. Accounts, Costing, Sales, Publicity, Organisation and Methods, Welfare – Laker duly went through the mill. On his thirtieth birthday, two years after marrying Helen, he had been elevated to the position of Frank Watts' personal assistant and when Charles retired on medical advice in the late fifties Laker was elected to fill the vacancy on the Board.

It was a small company, with something under eight hundred employees, and the neat red brick and white stone offices which screened the factory bays from the road stood back from the entrance gates behind a spread of shrubs and flower-bordered lawn. Laker ran the Humber into a space in the frontal parking-lot and got out, extracting his brief-case before locking up. He was one of those men who looked taller than his true height, which was five feet ten and a half inches, and he went to the scales around one hundred and ninety pounds. Like Patrick he was very solidly put together. His dark hair was on the wiry side, a trifle crinkly, and when he smiled it was a generous smile, radiating crow's-feet from the outer corners of his eyes and showing strong, even teeth that were his own. Guessing his age, strangers usually underestimated: he was, in fact, forty-three. 'How d'you do it, Sam?' Baxendale, the sales director, had remarked only a couple of weeks earlier. 'What's the secret? I break my back on the rowing-machine and do thirty-six holes every Saturday and Sunday, and what happens? All I get is a twin-sized paunch and a flabby chin.'

Laker walked diagonally across the forecourt, the trace of a limp only slightly impairing his stride. MacDonald, the commissionaire, offered a bright 'Good morning, Mr. Laker' and held the door open. MacDonald had never really quit the parade-ground; he marched everywhere, his left arm scarcely swinging as if he permanently carried a rifle at the trail.

'Morning, John.'

It was a pleasant entrance-lobby with half a dozen watercolours framed on pastel-washed walls. 'No need,' Charles Gale used to say, 'for an office to look like a penitentiary.' Laker nodded to the girl in Reception, unaware as he mounted the stairs that her gaze followed him curiously. Ten to ten. Carol Nolan, his secretary, was busy typing as he entered his second-floor office.

'Hallo,' he said. 'Had you given me up?'

'I was beginning to wonder.'

'Well, I'm sure Gale and Watts is still solvent.' His smile changed to a wince as he sat in the swivel-chair. 'Any calls?'

'No,' she said. 'There's quite a post, though, and you've an appointment at eleven with Mr. Thornton of International.'

Laker nodded, glancing at the orderly presentation of his mail and the files already flagged for reference. Carol was the best secretary he'd ever had, and by far the most attractive; raven-black hair, lively brown eyes and long slim legs. Baxendale was for ever suggesting that she ought to come to him when his own Miss Grigg retired, if not sooner. 'She's just what's wanted on my front, believe me.' And then, invariably, the corny crack: 'To my mind Development can't do another thing for her.'

'What's happened,' Carol was saying now, 'to your jacket?'

'Where?'

'The shoulder. No, the other one – at the back.' She moved round the desk. 'It's torn.'

Laker craned his head. White padding bulged where the seam had come apart.

'And your hand. How – ?'

'That I knew about.' He sucked the scraped knuckles again. 'Get some tape, will you?'

'Did you fall or something?'

'Kind of.'

She eyed him uncertainly. 'Is that all you're going to tell me?'

'Let's say I had an argument with a truck.'

'Whereabouts?'

'Oh, not far from home.'

'Is the car damaged?'

'I wasn't in it.' He shifted in the chair. 'Look, be a good girl and get the sticking-tape, will you?'

'She knew him well enough not to press him. When she returned from First Aid she said: 'Can I have your jacket, please. You can't see Mr. Thornton if you're looking like that.'

Laker gave it to her and she carried it away for temporary repairs. His suède shoes were smeared with tar across the toes, but they'd pass. Routine imposed itself. He got down to his mail, but it was quite a while before the day took shape in the way that others did, building upon their sequence of events and problems. His mind repeatedly fled to the woman in the yellow dress. It was a long time since he had been within a hair's breadth of danger or had his nerves stroked by anything worse than some minor, passing fear. Now, in retrospect, the incident had a curiously static quality, though once he shuddered dismissively as memory and imagination swept him with the vivid reality of every split second.

Carol brought his jacket back ten minutes before Reception announced that Thornton had arrived. He was a frequent visitor, so there was no need for Laker to have to apologise for the quality of the canteen coffee. He wasn't one for hanging about, either. As soon as they had studied the drawings and discussed the test reports on a new plastic sheeting requirement, he left. It was only then that Laker discovered he had lost his wallet. Dining-room accounts were presented on the last Tuesday of the month and, as soon as Thornton had gone, Carol was in with various additions to the paper-work together with the August account. And he always liked to settle on the spot.

'You didn't see it when you were mending my jacket, did you?'

'No,' Carol said.

'Blast. Then it must have fallen out at Oatlands.'

'Is that where you had your so-called argument with the truck?'

'Yes. Ring the police, will you? Don't go into details. Just report the loss. Someone may have turned it in.'

No one had, she informed him a few minutes later.

He swore more forcibly.

'Was there much in it?'

'Driving licence, A.A. card – '

'Money, I meant.'

'About fifteen pounds.'

Carol made a pained face.

'Something from the Leipzig Fair people – flight particulars.'

'I've got your plane tickets,' she said. 'And your Fair Cards and traveller's cheques and hotel reservations. Are you sure you started out with the wallet?'

'Sure,' he said, then gave a resigned shrug. 'We'll just have to keep our fingers crossed.' Then again: 'Blast it!' Helen had given it to him.

He lunched with Baxendale in the private room reserved for directors. Baxendale was in his most button-holing mood, unloading all the stories he'd heard at the golf club the previous evening including the one about the lama who unscrewed his navel only to find that his behind fell off when he stood up – a story so ancient that Laker could only imagine it must be going the rounds a second time.

'How's the delectable Miss Nolan today? On the ball as usual?'

'I'm happy to say.'

'You ought to marry her, Sam. She's a guinea a box.'

Laker laughed. 'I thought you wanted her yourself to brighten your office.'

'All in all, I'm the most generous of men.'

'Where'd I find another secretary to come within a mile of her?'

'That'd be the last thing to worry me if I were in your shoes. Seriously, though, you ought to marry again. Margaret agrees with me. Mrs. Ruddick's a marvel and all that, but there's more to having a woman about the house than merely having a woman about the house.' The boom years showed in Baxendale's thick flesh and pouchy eyes. 'It'd be good for young Patrick, too – wouldn't it now?'

'I'll think it over,' Laker countered lightly.

'My eye, you will. By the way, when are you two off to Germany?'

'Tomorrow week.'

'Where are you going after you've done your duty at Leipzig?'

'The Rhineland. Ever been?'

'No.'

'It was Patrick's idea. The house has been full of maps and leaflets for months.'

'Well, I envy you. If Margaret has her way we'll never see anything except the bloody Costa del Sol. Oh, it's all right, I suppose, but it's too damned hot for golf unless you start before breakfast and the food's a bit off-putting. Those dreary paellas always look to me as if they've been regurgitated. Incidentally, what have you done to your hand?'

An incoming trunk-call summoned him away before he got an answer. Laker left shortly afterwards and went back to his office. Carol wasn't there, but she had pinned a note to the blotter. *1.10 p.m. Police rang to say crocodile wallet handed in. Thirteen pounds ten, A.A. card, driving licence, Leipzig letter and two photographs – C.N.*

Relieved, Laker mulled over the Minutes of the last Publicity Committee; he was due at the quarterly meeting at three. Apart from an occasional reminder either from his knuckles or his bruised knee the morning's shock had receded. If his thoughts wandered from the day's stint it was towards Patrick, wondering whether he was still in London or on his way back with Tim Maxwell. The weather had held, so they were probably bound for the river. Odd how one worried – out of a sense of inadequacy, he supposed. Yet Patrick did tend to be a shade impetuous; someone more accident-prone would have learned his lesson by now.

'What did you tell the police?' he asked Carol on her return from lunch.

'That you'd call for it on your way home.'

'Fine,' he nodded.

She took letters from him for the next three-quarters of an hour. Baxendale's remarks kept echoing in his mind and once he caught himself looking at her almost as if it were for the first time. There was a bond between them – respect, trust, loyalty. Now and then he'd driven her home to Woking. She'd dined with him once or twice and he remembered her birthday religiously. But that was all.

At the door on his way to the meeting he asked suddenly: 'How old are you, Carol?'

'Old?'

'That's right.'

'Twenty-three,' she said, colouring slightly. 'Why?'

'I just wondered.'

As if he didn't know. And Patrick was almost fifteen. But there it was; think an improbable thought and you got a very impractical answer.

The police-sergeant on duty asked if Laker could identify himself, then produced the wallet and turned the receipt book round for him to sign.

As Laker was checking the contents, the sergeant said: 'A great thing you did this morning, sir. Quick thinking.'

Privately, Laker had hoped that he wouldn't be associated with what had happened; but no such luck. He shrugged and countered: 'Who handed the wallet in?'

'Horne's delivery boy.' The sergeant consulted the book. 'Said he found it in the gutter.'

'Do you know him?'

'By sight, yes.'

Laker put a pound on the desk. 'Would you see he gets that?'

'I certainly will, sir. Yes, a fine effort on your part from what I've heard.'

'How's the young woman?'

'Right as rain, I gather.'

Curiosity got the better of Laker as he was turning to leave. 'Who decided it was me, anyhow?'

'I think it was the tobacconist, sir. He's the one who recognised you. You didn't give your name or anything, you see. By the time one of our men arrived the fellow from the local paper had done his work for him, you might say. And then the wallet sort of confirmed things.'

He ought to have guessed, Laker told himself, that the Press would latch on. There wasn't anything he could do except hope that some eager tyro wasn't going to overdramatise everything with the intention of catching the editor's eye.

On the way home he toyed with the idea of stopping off for a drink, but decided against it. At twenty-past six he ran the car into the garage and went through the side door into the house.

'Patrick showed up yet?'

'He just beat you, hardly five minutes ago.' Mrs. Ruddick looked at him more carefully than usual. 'Are you all right, Mr. Laker?'

He wasn't expecting her to have heard; not this soon, anyway.

'A reporter rang,' she said. 'A Mr. Case.'

'Oh.' That explained it.

'This morning.' She had a trace of a Gloucestershire accent which gave warmth to her voice. 'He wanted to get in touch with you, but I thought you wouldn't like to be bothered at the office so I told him you'd be away all day.'

'Thanks. I'm glad you did.'

'He mentioned what it was about, of course.'

Laker found the admiring, slightly anxious gleam in her eyes embarrassing.

'What else did you tell him?'

'Nothing. Oh no, Mr. Laker. Once I knew you weren't hurt I thought it best to let you deal with it yourself.'

'Thanks, Mrs. Ruddick.'

He nodded and made for the cloakroom. It had been a slack day, slack enough to feel almost guilty about, but the evening was close, sticky, and a wash revived him. When he eventually entered the living-room Patrick was already there.

'Hallo,' Laker said. 'What did you make of the Planetarium?'

'It was great.'

'Worth my going to some time?'

'I'd say so, yes.' With the air of a conjurer disclosing his next prop, Patrick produced the *Evening Standard* from behind his back. 'Seems to me you've been seeing stars yourself.'

'Meaning?'

'Look,' Patrick said, and gave him the paper, pointing to an item low down on the front page.

WAR HERO SAVES MOTHER AND CHILD
SCOOPED FROM LORRY'S PATH

Oatlands Village, near Weybridge in Surrey, was the scene of high drama at 9.15 this morning when a passer-by, Mr. Samuel Laker, flung himself in front of a heavily-laden truck to hurl a mother and her child clear of almost certain death.

The woman, Mrs. Edna Browning, was wheeling her eighteen-month-old son Michael across the road when the incident occurred. 'She gave me no chance,' lorry-driver Mr. Jim Smailes explained. 'They would have been goners if she and the little kid hadn't been shoved out of the way. It was about the bravest thing I've seen in fifteen years' driving.'

Mrs. Browning sustained slight bruising and shock. The child was completely unhurt. Mr Laker, 43, who lives locally at Roundwood, Mill Avenue, was not available for comment. During the war he was awarded the Distinguished Service Order and the Military Cross. A widower, with one son, he is a Director of Gale and Watts, the office-equipment manufacturers.

'Oh, hell,' Laker said quietly.

'Tim Maxwell spotted it. He was so impressed, in fact, that he paid the fares back.'

'They make mountains out of molehills, you know that.' Laker glanced at the by-line. *A Special Correspondent*: Mr. Case, no doubt. But whoever it was could certainly ferret.

Patrick was grinning like a Cheshire cat. 'Come on, dad. Cheer up. It's not as if they've said anything awful about you. A million people will have seen what's there. Don't you think I'm entitled to the full story?'

Laker moved his shoulders. 'They've made it full enough, flannel included.' He dropped the newspaper on to a chair and started to pour himself a whisky. 'It just happened – the way things do.'

A million people. That Martin Slattery might have been one of them never so much as entered his head.

CHAPTER 2

Case, the reporter, didn't call back, but the telephone started ringing later that evening.

Baxendale was the first to get on to him ('You old dog, you, hiding your light under a bushel'), then Cranston from across the road, then Mary Armitage, another neighbour, then a cousin from Hampstead. As a consequence Laker neither finished watering the garden, nor gave Patrick all the time he'd promised him on the holiday itinerary.

He was in two minds next morning about dodging the tobacconist's and getting his cigarettes elsewhere, but doing so would have no more than staved off the inevitable. He endured the plaudits and the insisted-upon handshakes only to find that there was no escape even when he arrived at Gale and Watts. MacDonald saluted him as if a guard of honour were drawn up awaiting inspection and on the way through to his office he collected more nods and 'Good mornings' than normally came his way in a week. Carol Nolan merely said: 'You realise, I suppose, that you've destroyed the image I'd cultivated about myself outside of here? When I got home last night I was the one person who didn't know. The *one* person, mind' – and she clenched her fist at him on her way back to her desk. Then the private calls began again, about one in every three, and Laker found a formula to cope with them.

Slattery came through the following day, on the Wednesday. The thing was as good as over by then and there was suddenly a pile of work, like a seventh wave, to set Laker's conscience to rights about having had too easy a time earlier in the week. He was in the middle of a hastily-convened meeting with Wilson and Farrow, from Design Group, trying to unravel a particularly knotty problem, when Carol's buzzer sounded.

'Yes?' He was on the brusque side.

'There's a Mr. Slattery wanting you. I know you said you weren't to be interrupted but he insists it's urgent.'

'What name?'

'Slattery. Martin Slattery.'

Laker frowned, memory spanning the years.

'Shall I put him through?'

He glanced across at the other two. 'Did he say *what* was urgent?'

'No.'

'All right, I'll take it.' He apologised briefly to Wilson and Farrow, then waited for the opening, 'Martin Slattery here. Who's that?'

'Sam Laker.'

'Sam! How are you keeping?'

'Fine.'

'I'm delighted to see that your reflexes are as good as ever.'

Even after so long a time the breezy, quick-fire delivery was instantly familiar.

'We must read the same paper,' Laker said.

'Could be. Well, what's it been, Sam? How long?'

'I hate to think.'

Farrow was pretending not to listen, whereas Wilson was making no bones about it.

'From the sound of things you're very much a tycoon these days.'

'Hardly.'

'Damned difficult to reach, anyhow. Almost easier to break into the Kremlin than get past your secretary.' Slattery laughed, the dryish cackle Laker imagined he had forgotten.

'I'm sorry about that, but – well – I'm at a meeting.'

'Then I won't keep you.'

'Something urgent, wasn't it?'

'I wondered if we could lunch.'

Laker raised his eyes to the ceiling. My God 'I'd like that, yes.'

'Tomorrow?'

'Tomorrow's a bit sudden.'

'I'm tied up the rest of the week, and most of next as well. Failing lunch, perhaps you'd dine with me?'

'Hang on, will you, while I look?' Reaching for his diary, Laker said: 'Where are you? In town?'

'Yes.'

'Still in the same business?' He was filling in.

'Not exactly.'

Tomorrow was clear, Laker saw. But it was short notice all the same. At any other time he might not have felt so pushed to give an answer, but Wilson was surreptitiously glancing at his watch and muttering *sotto voce* to Farrow. Why was it that a first-rate designer like Wilson had to be such a difficult cuss?

'Let's make it tomorrow then.'

'Splendid. Lunch?'

'Yes, lunch would suit me best.' He could look in on International; two birds with one stone. 'Where shall we meet?'

Slattery gave an address in Manchester Square. 'The bottom bell. Don't pay any attention to the name. The bottom bell, yes? And how about twelve-thirty?' The last thing he said was: 'It'll be really

marvellous to see you again, Sam. A hell of a lot of water's gone down the
Thames since we were within arm's length.'

Laker hung up and looked across at the others. 'Sorry,' he smiled.
'Now, where were we?'

He had met Martin Slattery in the penultimate year of the war, a few
weeks after D-day.

One of Laker's more lasting memories of the Special Operations set-
up in Grosvenor Gardens was the time they had spent together after his
return from Italy. Slattery's office was in an overflow building not far
from Victoria Station and Laker shared it with him, on and off, for a
couple of months. Slattery had a limp then, the result of some accident
on a grenade range, and what Laker particularly remembered was the
homily framed behind his desk; he was word-perfect in it even now:
*According to the theory of aerodynamics, and as may be readily demonstrated by
means of a wind tunnel, the bumble-bee is unable to fly. This is because the size,
weight and shape of his body in relation to the total wing span make flight
impossible. But the bumble-bee, being ignorant of these scientific facts and
possessing considerable determination, does fly – and makes a little honey, too.*

It was a bitter kind of honey, though. But amid the permissible
murder of war those two months of waiting were quite unlike any other
in Laker's experience. Office hours, bus queues, the tube, midday
sandwiches and beer in the pub round the corner. He was even able to
live at home in St. John's Wood.

Slattery was one of those responsible for briefing and debriefing what
were invariably described as 'foreign bodies'. Since Laker was due to be
dropped into Germany himself as soon as conditions were right he was
never present when these sessions took place: it was fundamental that
field-operators remained in the dark as to who else was involved, and
where, unless it directly concerned them. But while his own operation
was delayed he was attached to Slattery, helping out with the collation
of every scrap of general intelligence that came in, and there was a mass
of it coming in around that time: the lean, scavenging years were over.

Sandwiched between the fury of Italy, with its naked violence and
brutal hardship, and the gamble in store for him in Germany, an office
had seemed to Laker an unreal place in which to find himself. He was
never quite able to adjust his mind to the esoteric argot and the
academic approach of headquarters. But the work appeared tailor-
made for Slattery. He would have been about thirty then; plump, red-
faced and bespectacled. Whether the homily about the bumble-bee was
on his wall as a kind of self-justification for being chairborne, or whether

it somehow pleased him for its own sake, Laker never could decide. Mentally, he was very alert, with a remarkable aptitude for being able to discard inessentials and to strip a report, no matter how garbled, down to its bare bones. Though he fought his war by proxy he fought it with a quiet intent that only once during Laker's contact with him, hinted at some hidden fury.

They'd have a drink or two most evenings before going their separate ways, but Laker didn't really get to know him. Not that he was in the mood for developing acquaintances then: he was too on edge with what was coming. But Slattery was with him when he received the call about the flying-bomb near Lord's and for some reason it was Slattery he rang from St. John's Wood to say that his parents and sister were dead and it was Slattery he walked with in Green Park a night or two later when, sodden with whisky and hatred, he swore what he would do when they let him loose in Germany.

And Slattery who said: 'You do that, Sam. You kill the bastards. Kill every bloody one of them you can.'

Which he did. And when it was all over and he finally came home to the ruins and the emptiness, it was to Slattery that he made his last report before he was eventually demobilised and taken under Charles Gale's wing.

Laker spent a useful half-hour with Thornton at International's enormous glass-and-steel rabbit warren near Chiswick before driving on through Kensington High Street and around the outskirts of Hyde Park. The midday traffic was sluggishly heavy and new one-way streets seemed to be cropping up every week. Even reaching Manchester Square was easier said than done and when he got there he couldn't park. In the end he found a vacant meter on the fringe of Grosvenor Square (*Eisenhowerplatz* Slattery used to term it; strange how the trivia stuck) and walked across Oxford Street into the comparative quiet of the Georgian environs of the Wallace Collection.

The address Slattery had given him was on the west side of the square. The bottom bell was marked *Curtis* but he pressed it dutifully, wondering while he waited why Slattery should choose to meet him here when there were half a dozen good restaurants and hotels barely a stone's-throw away.

Only a few seconds elapsed before the door opened. Momentarily, a stranger stood framed in the gap, a shortish, bulky, balding man who, as recognition dawned, Laker realised was Slattery. The spectacles and brick-coloured complexion outweighed any slight hesitation.

'I'm late, I'm afraid.'

'Sam! . . . Come in, come on in.'

Slattery encouraged him with a gesture, remaining where he was as if to avoid the direct sunlight. Only when the door was closed did he shake hands, enthusiastically, as if he were presenting Laker with an award.

'Good to see you again, Sam. You're looking marvellous, I must say.'

'And you. Sorry about the time, but what with getting the car parked – '

'Oh, parking's murder around here. Murder.' Slattery gestured again like a helpful shop-walker. 'Go on through – first right.'

They crossed a wide, tiled hall under a chandelier. There was a staircase with a filigree railing sloping up to the next floor. Laker entered a lobby which led into a small room with numerous sporting prints and miniatures on the walls and dustsheets over the furniture.

'Keep going,' Slattery chuckled from behind. 'Civilisation's just ahead.'

There the room was spacious, bright, uncluttered. Striped paper, marble fireplace, deep brocaded chairs, rust-red drapes, a huge gilded mirror. One of the pictures might have been a Corot. Manchester Square looked misty beyond the window-length ninon.

'Would you like a wash or anything?'

'No, thanks.'

There was a pause, a kind of mutual uncertainty, during which they were strangers again. Probing, Laker said: 'You don't live here, I take it?'

'No. Cigarette? . . . No, it belongs to a friend. He lets me use it from time to time. No, as far as having an address goes, mine's in Kew. What will you have? . . . Sherry? Gin?'

'Sherry, please.'

'It's a fino. Too dry?'

'Absolutely right.'

Traffic rumbled vaguely in the distance, emphasising the quiet.

'Well, here's to you, Sam. It's certainly been a long time.'

He hadn't changed much, really. Less hair, a slight looseness about his suit as though he'd shrunk a little; and he seemed shorter, somehow. But the face was unlined, almost cherubic, and his speech was as quick as ever. Behind the thick-rimmed spectacles his eyes were eagerly attentive. And the limp had gone.

They sank into the chairs and Laker said: 'You stayed on, didn't you?'

'After the war?'

He nodded.

'Yes, I suppose you could say that.'

'And you're still at it?'

'After a fashion.'

'I guessed as much from the camouflage.'

'This place? Oh, that's more habit than anything else.' Beaming, Slattery crossed his legs. 'Tell me about yourself, Sam. Are Gale and Watts the people you joined when things folded up?'

'That's right.'

'One of them was an uncle of yours, wasn't he?'

'Charles Gale, yes.'

'I remember now. God,' he said, 'it's been a time, hasn't it?' He blew smoke. He was inclined to blink a lot. 'You married, didn't you? I believe I heard that.'

'Yes, but my wife died.'

'I'm sorry.'

'Eight years ago. Cancer. It was very sudden – mercifully so in the circumstances.'

'I'm sorry,' Slattery repeated.

'What about you?'

'Me? Oh yes, I'm married. Three children, what's more, all costing the earth.'

They compared notes, the conversation flowing more easily when they touched on common ground. And there were names to fall back on – Ayres, Bill Maltby, McBride, Harry Castle, Gemmell . . .

'What ever became of Polglaze?' Laker asked.

'I rather fancy he went to the States.'

'He and Harry Castle were always cheek-by-jowl in those days.'

'They were, weren't they? Harry's a solicitor. *Very* prosperous. Who said that crime doesn't pay?'

'D'you ever see Thompson?'

'I read him from time to time. He writes, didn't you know? Well, you haven't missed much. Not surprising considering the reports he used to put together.'

They laughed, Slattery tilting the decanter towards Laker's glass.

'There's a cold spread,' he said. 'D'you mind?'

'Sounds wonderful.'

He watched Slattery bring the trolley in. So he was still at it, still in the game – whatever the game was now. Did it never go sour on him, corrode, rot? Or was it always fresh and complicated and worthwhile; beautiful, even? He'd admitted to that once.

Laker said: 'Remember Erskine?'

Slattery paused, cocking his head. 'Vaguely. Polish Section, wasn't he? . . . That's one I've quite lost touch with' – and there was something just sufficiently contrived about the denial to make Laker guess that Erskine was still in the game too. Not that he was particularly interested: *chacun son goût.*

An hour passed. It was a simple yet excellent meal: melon, cold lamb, a strawberry mousse with cream. Once or twice it crossed Laker's mind that he had come a long way merely to ramble over old times, but the claret and the pattern of their talk disarmed any lurking conjecture. And when Slattery eventually asked, 'Is it next week you're going to Germany, Sam?' he let it drop like a stone.

'Yes.' Then, looking up in surprise: 'How the hell did you know?'

'I checked.'

'Checked?'

Slattery nodded, quite unabashed.

'My God,' Laker said. His lips curled in astonishment. 'What are you? Some sort of eyes and ears?'

'We still keep tabs on – though doing so isn't my particular pigeon.'

'Exactly what *is* your pigeon?'

Slattery avoided answering that.

Without hostility, Laker said: 'D'you mean to tell me that anyone who happens to be visiting Germany is automatically – ?'

'Of course not. But you're going to Leipzig.'

'So?'

'Leipzig's in the Russian Zone.' Slattery lifted his heavy shoulders. 'Look,' he then said cheerfully, leaning forward a little. 'There's no mumbo-jumbo about this. When I read about you in the *Standard* the other evening I simply thought: that's Sam Laker. Why not get together? . . . So I called you.'

'Having checked on me first?'

'I'm not apologising. Records are usually more rewarding than the *Directory of Directors*. It was just routine, Sam. You're an old pro, so you'll know how it is.'

'I don't believe I do. Are you telling me that all this time, all these years, I've been under someone's beady eye?'

'Not in the way you're implying, no.'

'But someone's kept tabs on – you said so yourself.'

'Only certain tabs.'

'Now you're talking in riddles.'

'It's a rough world, Sam. Putting it at its simplest, Leipzig is behind the lines. That's the kind of tab I mean, the kind that sticks.'

'I'm visiting the Trade Fair – about the largest, incidentally, and the oldest, in Europe.'

'Which is precisely what's logged on the file.'

'Your sources must be bloody good. All I've done is apply for Fair Cards and book a flight.'

'They're good,' Slattery said evenly. 'Not perfect, but good.'

Laker stirred his coffee. He couldn't help smiling. 'Is Leipzig my only black mark?'

'D'you really want to hear?'

'Of course, I'm fascinated – and a little indignant.'

'You've a boy, haven't you – Patrick.'

'Yes.'

'Since May last year he's been in touch with an address in Rostock. Lenin-Strasse 32, to be precise.'

Laker snorted derisively. 'A pen-pal. He's got about six of 'em.'

'A pen-pal in Halberstadt took the daughter of a certain Naval officer for a great ride a couple of years ago. Practically emptied her father's brief-case.'

'There's nothing in mine worth having. Besides, all Patrick's contacts are thoroughly genuine. As often as not I see their letters myself. "I am an East German boy, sixteen years old, and my hobbies are sailing, music and collecting postcards." They're as innocent as the day's long.'

'That's not the point, Sam. If you're using a net a whole lot of innocent fish swim into it.'

'But you tab them just the same.'

'As a matter of routine.'

'You must employ an army,' Laker said tartly. 'What else have you got on me?'

'Not a thing.'

'After so long?'

'There's the old stuff, of course. That's still there – in a class by itself.'

'I must be a disappointment to you.'

'It's only background, Sam. Don't get the wrong end of the stick.'

'I haven't. But I'll be a damn sight more careful in future.'

Part of him accepted the necessity of vigilance, part of him objected to the form it apparently took. On balance it struck him as pretty preposterous and he said as much.

'You wouldn't think that if you'd stayed on,' Slattery replied.

'I wasn't cut out for staying on.'

'Why not?'

'I couldn't have kept it up.'

'Kept what up?'

'Oh, I don't know.' Laker paused. 'But I couldn't play it as a sort of everlasting chess, not on and on, world without end.'

'Is that all you imagine it to be?'

'For want of a better comparison, yes.'

Slattery said casually: 'What kind of spur would you need, then?'

Laker hesitated. There was only one thing, one thing, but it was dead, thank God. Anyway, Slattery would remember; he was there in Green Park that night years ago.

He glanced at his watch. He didn't want a ticket on the car for overrunning his meter-time and it was quite a walk back to Brook Street. They talked more generally for a while, but the leads were tending to peter out. Once, the telephone rang. Slattery merely said 'Yes?' when he picked it up and 'Yes' twice more before he put it down. Presently Laker suggested that he ought to be going.

'Must you?'

'I'm afraid so.'

'It's flown, hasn't it? By the way, when are you off?'

'To Leipzig?'

'Yes.'

'Surely a little detail like that hasn't escaped your notice?' Laker could still smile, though a trifle sourly.

'Refresh my memory.'

'Wednesday. For forty-eight hours I'm picking other people's brains as regards office equipment, after which Patrick and I are spending about ten days in and around the Rhineland.'

'Very nice.' Slattery stubbed his cigarette, making an over-thorough job of it. 'Sam.'

'Yes?'

'I haven't been entirely honest with you.'

'I think I understand.'

'I don't mean that.'

'What, then?'

'I had a particular reason for getting you to come along.'

'Oh?'

'It was to ask a favour.'

'What kind of favour?'

'I'm hoping you'll deliver a message for me.'

'Where?'

'Leipzig.' Then quickly: 'There's no risk. Absolutely none.'

So that was his pigeon. 'Why me?' Laker said.

'Who better?'

'Have you run out of regular couriers, or what?'

Slattery blinked at him. 'It's our availability, Sam. Plus the fact that you're totally uncompromised over there.' The jargon hadn't changed. 'In point of fact it's not such an exceptional request these days.'

'A verbal message?'

'No. But that side of things will be taken care of.'

'Isn't this wildly unorthodox?'

'Not with someone like you.'

Laker looked away, watching a green car move towards Spanish Place through the sunlit fog of ninon.

'I'd rather not,' he said.

'It would take about ten minutes of your time, Sam. Hardly more.' Slattery waited, watching him. 'You'll remember better than most what hanging on can be like. Well, there's someone hanging on now. And you could have them off the rack on Wednesday.'

Laker kept his gaze on the windows. No, he thought.

'I'd more than hoped,' Slattery said. 'I was absolutely sure you'd agree.' He spoke as if Laker owed him something. 'It couldn't be more simple.' With a ghost of a smile, he added: 'No cloak, no dagger.'

'I dare say.'

'Think about it.'

'If I must.'

'Think about it and let me know.'

'All right,' Laker conceded.

'By this evening? It has to be by then.'

'All right. Where do I phone you?'

Slattery gave him a Gerrard number. They started through the room where the dust-covers were.

'It's important, Sam. I wouldn't have put it to you otherwise. I know what's on your mind – Patrick, Gale and Watts . . . I can understand your hesitation. It's a lot to ask, but as far as you're concerned it will be as uneventful as stepping out into the street.'

CHAPTER 3

Laker walked back to Brook Street, heeding the warning whispers. He hadn't collected a ticket, which was a relief. He sat in the car for a minute or two without attempting to drive, blind to the sauntering woman who slowed and offered a hopeful smile from the pavement.

It was a lot to ask, all right. And galling that he should have been asked at all. 'An old pro like you' – Slattery seemed to consider this sufficient excuse. Once in the game, always in it, always an honorary member – that was his line. 'When I read the file,' his parting words were, 'and where you were going, it was almost too good to be true.'

Irritated, Laker lit a cigarette. What galled him particularly was the implicit suggestion that if he refused he was letting Slattery down. 'There's no danger, Sam, absolutely none. I wouldn't have put it to you otherwise.'

One way and another lunch had been an eye-opener. It was surprising enough to have learned that one's associations with Communist territories were so meticulously recorded. Granted it was a suspicion-ridden world. Granted, the bureaucratic net couldn't be individually selective. But when one's willingness to be used was apparently more or less expected if circumstances provided the need, and the opportunity – that jarred.

And the proposition itself was so damned vague. If Slattery had been more forthcoming it might have been easier to have reached an out-and-out decision before leaving Manchester Square. As it was Laker couldn't for the life of him understand why he should continue to mull it over. 'A simple, straightforward person-to-person delivery . . . Ten minutes of your time.' To whom? he thought. Exactly how and where?

Brooding, he switched on and went into gear; drew away. The old-pals act was a kind of blackmail. And nothing was ever one hundred per cent safe. Nothing. Slattery could say what he liked.

Park Lane sucked him into its flow. No, he thought again. But as he headed towards Knightsbridge and the Brompton Road his initial hostility to the idea began to fade. Against his will Slattery's anonymous contact in Leipzig weighed with him. There wasn't much worse than being cut off. He didn't have to stretch his imagination to know what it was to wait, and go on waiting. Day by day the certainty of having been abandoned gnawed at the nerves. Silence of that kind was the most agonising silence of all. He'd experienced it once, and once was plenty.

The airborne assault on Arnhem was already poised when Laker was dropped in. He went in alone more than two hundred miles east of the Rhine, touching down in wooded country to the west of Gardelegen. A reception party was there to hustle him away – Karl and Günter and the girl. If the punch through Arnhem succeeded the way to the heart of Germany would be open, and each and every bridge that could be kept intact across the Aller would be worth its weight in gold: that was the scheme. But Arnhem failed and their radio failed and Karl and Günter didn't return from a raid on an explosives dump at Klötze.

In case they'd been taken alive, Laker and the girl left the protection of the crumbling farmhouse and holed themselves up in a thick patch of spruce overlooking the Magdeburg–Uelsen road. Night after night long convoys moved north-east and aircraft droned across the autumn sky. It was cold and it rained a lot. Laker roofed over a hollow and at night they would lie in it. Every day the girl would go down to one or other of the near-by villages and somehow find food; once she came back with a blanket.

A week after Karl and Günter were lost he got the set to work again and began calling at the specified times. There was never an answer but he went on calling long after he was certain he'd been written off. He did it more to encourage the girl than anything. She wouldn't leave him. She was thin and freckled and about eighteen years old. She could have gone; she had an uncle somewhere in the south. But no. 'You will starve,' she said again and again. 'Without me you will be finished.'

They were to have linked up with another group to the north of Gifhorn, but without instructions they didn't know how. So they continued to wait, Laker vainly risking his call-sign three times a day. Twice they were forced to move. They waited in hunger and desperation. It grew colder and they clung to each other for warmth. 'Sammy,' she called him. They waited five days more, trying to deduce from the movement on the road what might have happened to the distant front. Eventually Laker decided their only chance was to travel west, but on the evening they prepared to start the girl became ill. He could hear her lungs bubbling as she breathed and her skin burned in the cold. By midnight her speech was rambling. He wrapped her in the blanket and carried her to an isolated house from which she had sometimes stolen eggs. He laid her on the ground where the light would fall when the door was opened, knocked hard and ran – stopping only to check when someone came: an old man.

Then he went back to the spruces again, kicked the set to pieces and retrieved his carbine and some grenades. It took him twenty-nine days to reach the Allied lines and on the way he conducted a private war, the full volume of his hatred released at last for what had befallen his parents and sister and out of grief and uncertainty for the girl. He killed where he could and when he could – an isloated sentry, two Luftwaffe corporals cycling together, all the occupants of a staff-car, the crew of a stranded tank. There were others, too; he lost count. He did it out of a haunting fury and because he could shoot marvellously well. And by the time he got through to the Americans he was as wild-eyed as a hunted animal and grabbed instinctively for the carbine when he awoke from his exhaustion and found a nurse bending over the bed . . .

There were things one never forgot.

After Hammersmith he took the less direct route back to Weybridge – Richmond, Hampton, Sunbury. It was always pleasant along by the river with the boats showing through the weeping willows and there was little traffic to distract his mind. Inevitably, as he passed through Oatlands, he was reminded of the woman in the yellow dress: if it weren't for her he'd have been spared the favour Slattery expected of him.

Chance had the longest, most unpredictable arm of all.

He had no illusions. It was a different kind of war now – more complex, more sophisticated, yet equally ruthless, equally deadly. No holes in the sodden ground, little overt violence. A different kind of war, yes; but hanging on would be no less desperate . . . Everything, nothing had changed. And Slattery, blast him, knew that he knew what hanging on was like; and that knowing would probably help to tip the scales.

He arrived at Gale and Watts shortly before four. Carol had dealt with most of the chores, but there was a fair amount demanding his attention. He cleared as much as he could in fast time and telephoned the two people Carol had listed for him. Baxendale looked in briefly, ostensibly to put him on to one of Piggott's rides next day but more obviously to indulge his fascination for Carol's legs.

It was after five when Laker asked for a line and dialled the Gerrard number. A woman answered without indicating where she was speaking from.

'Mr. Slattery, please.'

'Who's calling?'

He told her.

'Is Mr. Slattery expecting you to telephone?'

'Yes,' he said and waited for the click and Slattery's voice. 'I'm at my office,' he began.

'Go ahead.'

'I'm not keen, but the answer's yes.'

Slattery didn't exactly indicate enthusiasm. 'Oh good,' was all he said – rather as if Laker had found that he was free for dinner or something.

'If it's really that important and there's no one else.'

'It is, Sam. And there isn't.'

'And provided it's as elementary as you made out.'

'It couldn't be more so.'

'All right . . . What now?'

'I'll be in touch. Incidentally, about your watch – '

'My what?'

'Your watch. I'm most dreadfully sorry. It was entirely my fault. I'm arranging for it to be collected in the morning.'

'In the morning?' Laker was a little slow.

'Sometime before noon if that's convenient.'

'Oh yes . . . Very well.' Suddenly there were a dozen questions welling out of last-second misgivings, but an open line made them impossible. 'Is that all?'

'For the present, Sam. And thanks. I was banking on you, you know.'

You bet, Laker thought. He fingered his watch, wondering how they would tamper with it; what it would carry. But at least he knew the means of delivery, and it wasn't difficult to guess how it was to be effected. The knowledge was curiously reassuring, underlining Slattery's insistence on the run-of-the-mill nature of what he'd agreed to do. Even so, how much of a fool was he to have committed himself?

He wasn't allowed to dwell on it without interruption. Carol plied him with a score of letters for signature and there was a joint report by Wilson and Farrow, suggesting a way out of the Design Group's difficulty, marked FOR URGENT COMMENT. Laker tried to concentrate on it there and then, but after a while he gave up. Leipzig kept intruding. Gale and Watts hadn't an export business worth talking about, so there was no possibility of doing them harm. And, as regards Patrick . . . Hell, if he started along those lines he'd better change his mind while he could. He was sufficiently lukewarm as it was without thinking in terms of a slip-up. Slattery had surely played his proxy game long enough now to have this aspect of it perfected. Behind the beaming smile and blinking, bespectacled eyes he was shrewd, a realist, and Laker's lingering doubts found refuge in that. Scores of export executives carrying their brief-cases around Europe must have acted as unpaid postmen over the last few years – Slattery had said as much. And this was about what it came to – being a postman.

He stayed on for half an hour after Carol left, but the Wilson–Farrow argument still demanded more of him than he seemed able to give, so he decided to take it home. Patrick was there when he arrived, the maps spread out, a sentence on one of his tour leaflets underlined: *A cable car will take you high above Rudesheim to the Germania Monument, erected in the last century as a symbol of Bismarck's united Germany.*

'There's nothing in the papers,' Patrick grinned meaningly, 'but what exciting thing's happened to you since breakfast?'

MacDonald rang through from Reception sharp on eleven next morning.

'Person for your watch, sir. Shall I come up or will Miss Nolan come down?'

'Come up, John.' Then: 'No, on second thoughts ask *him* to come up.'

'Right away, sir.'

Laker's curiosity didn't reward him with anything out of the ordinary. A rather thin young man with a spaniel-like face and a neat brown suit presently put his head round the door. 'Mr. Laker?'

'Correct. Come on in.'

The suit was good; the tie instantly recognisable. It would have been interesting to know what he did with the rest of his time. For an absurd moment Laker thought of asking him whether he was in the habit of collecting watches.

'Do I get a receipt?'

'I'll write you one if you wish.'

Laker shook his head. He unstrapped the watch and slid it into an envelope.

'Thank you,' the young man said.

'That's all, I take it?'

'I think so, Mr. Laker. Good morning.'

A minute afterwards Laker watched him from his window cross the forecourt and drive off in a plain, dark blue van. No one more casual entered the office throughout the day-long press of work; only the naked feel of Laker's left wrist kept sharply reminding him that the undertaking had moved a first stage from acceptance towards execution.

Slattery left him alone for twenty-four hours. It was noon on Saturday before he chose to telephone. Laker was in the book so it was no surprise to be caught at the house. But he said: 'Another few minutes and you'd have missed me.'

'Sorry, the week-end's always chancy, I suppose. Could we meet one evening?'

'When?'

'To-morrow?'

'I'm playing bridge tomorrow.'

'Monday?'

'It'll have to be Monday. Tonight I'm tied up and Tuesday's my last evening.'

'All right, then. Let's say Monday. And to spare you the burden of all the comings and goings, how about meeting half-way?'

'Where?'

'The Mitre, Hampton Court. Nell Gwyn bar.'

'Fine,' Laker said.

He arrived a quarter of an hour before the agreed time, ordered a Scotch and waited. He had managed not to think about Slattery too much over the rest of the week-end. But on the short drive from Roundwood, and now, as he looked about him at the prosperous self-sufficiency of the bar's occupants, an undercurrent of uneasiness tugged at him. Oh, he'd do it. He wouldn't cry off at this stage. But the sooner Wednesday had come and gone, the better. And in – what? – less than six days' time he'd be shot of Leipzig and Patrick's carefully-planned side of things would have begun – Heidelburg, Mannheim, Worms, Mainz, Rudesheim, Cochem, Coblenz . . . It was the boy's holiday, after all.

'Hello,' Slattery said, suddenly at his elbow. 'Have I kept you?' He pulled a vacant chair from the next table and sat down.

'What'll you have?'

'A pink.' He almost changed his mind. 'Yes, a pink . . . I did explain, didn't I, that I can't stay?'

'You did.'

'My wife's old father's been stomping round Kew Gardens all afternoon and he's dining with us. He's as deaf as a post and I'm the only one in the family whose voice has the right *timbre*, or whatever it is, so my presence is virtually obligatory on these occasions.'

He leaned back, brushing his sparse hair with the flat of his hands, blinking from table to table as if innocently in search of friends.

'Good luck, Sam,' he said when his gin came. 'And thanks again.'

Laker shrugged.

'Down to business?'

'I'm ready.'

'How good are you on telephone numbers?'

'It depends. I remembered the Gerrard one. Try me.'

'Double three, four two, eight six.' Slattery repeated it. 'Salt it away.' He tapped his head.

Laker's lips moved.

'Got it?'

'I will have.'

They were quite close; their voices sufficiently low.

'D'you know Leipzig?'

'I was once there as a kid, but it's all a blur now.'

'What's your hotel?'

'Astoria.'

Slattery nodded. 'There's a jeweller's in the Luisenstrasse – a five-minute taxi-ride. The description's flattering, I admit, but that's beside the point. The name's Kromadecka.' He spelt it out. 'All right?'

'Yes.'

'It's small, but you can't miss it. All you have to do is to ask them to fit a new watch-strap.'

'Nothing more?'

'Nothing more.' Slattery's smile seemed to be prompted by a memory. 'I told you, it couldn't be more straightforward.'

'When do I get the watch back?'

'There and then.'

'From you, I mean.'

'Sorry, stupid of me. I'll have it delivered on Tuesday evening, to your home.'

'I see.'

Slattery signalled a waiter. 'Scotch, is it?'

'Please.'

Neither spoke for a few moments. People were coming and going all the time. A girl laughed near by, content with the world she knew, safe. Leipzig seemed very remote. 'Happier about things now?' Slattery beamed.

'You haven't raised any goose-flesh, I grant you that.'

'Any questions?'

'Only why the hell I should be doing it.'

Slattery laughed his ridiculous cackle.

'This place, Kromadecka – '

'Yes?'

'Doesn't it matter who attends to me?'

'The problem won't arise. There's only one person there.'

'I don't need to furnish recognition aids or anything like that?'

'No. Merely ask for a new strap, wait while it's fitted, then push off. Get on over to the Fair and begin picking those brains you talked about. Start on your holiday, in fact.'

'And the number? – where does that come in?'

'It won't.' Slattery spread his hands almost apologetically. 'Call it insurance, Sam. Wise-virgin common-sense. Has it lodged, incidentally?'

'Three three, four two, eight six.'

'It's like the emergency handle on the train. It's a million to one against you having to use the thing but it's reassuring to know it's there.' He matched Laker's gaze for a second or two. 'Get me?'

'I get you,' Laker said. He drew on his cigarette. There was always an element of risk, no matter how infinitesimal, and he'd made his own assessment of it. But he'd somehow have liked Slattery more if there hadn't been such smooth denials at Manchester Square.

'And I'll tell you this. You'll never hook me another time.'

He smiled grimly and Slattery blinked back, fingering his glass.

'D'you want to recap?'

'Not really.'

'What time d'you touch down?'

'Around noon I've forgotten exactly.'

'Do it that afternoon, will you, Sam? On Wednesday. Don't wait until the next day.'

'I won't sleep on it, you can be sure of that. The quicker I'm through with being one of your acting unpaid supernumeraries, the better I'll like it, believe me.'

'Good man,' Slattery said. He drained his glass with a hint of finality. 'Now I'm the one who's against the clock. What are you doing?'

'Going home.'

They walked out together. After the artificial brightness the dusk seemed thicker than it was; the river air surprisingly cool. Beyond the wall and the trees across the wide road Hampton Court shaped the skyline. A man and woman passed, the woman carrying a small child, and the child was wailing out of weariness and the ancestral fear of what the gathering dusk might conceal.

Laker accompanied Slattery to his car – a grey Rover with a Royal Thames Yacht Club badge. The prefix to the registration number was UUU and Laker recalled a once-heard music-hall gag – 'Three Volunteers'. Slattery unlocked the door and turned – to shake hands, Laker assumed. But he said: 'There's something I haven't mentioned, Sam.'

'What?'

A bus trundled by, and Slattery waited. Laker could hardly see his face.

'What?' he asked more doubtfully, suspicious of postscripts.

'At Kromadecka's. You mentioned recognition.'

'Yes?'

Slattery cleared his throat. 'You'll know who it is.'

'How d'you mean – 'know'?'

'The person who'll fix your watch-strap will be Karen Gisevius.'

'Sammy,' she had called him.

'Karen?' Laker echoed. 'Karen?'

'That's right.'

'But – ' His thoughts seemed to be stumbling in several directions at once. He said stupidly: 'She's alive, then?'

'Oh yes.'

'My God.' He could grasp so much and no more. Seconds elapsed. 'My God,' he said. 'Why didn't you tell me the other day?'

'It wouldn't have been reasonable.'

'Reasonable?' Laker frowned.

'To use her as a lever. It might have come to that if you'd refused in the first place. Happily, you didn't. But it's only right that I should put you in the picture now.'

Slattery's head and shoulders were silhouetted against The Mitre's wistaria-covered, softly-lit façade.

'How long,' Laker began, faltered, then started again. 'How long have you known?'

'Known?'

'That she'd survived.'

'Some time, Sam. A goodish time.'

'Twenty years?' Something akin to resentment had entered Laker's voice.

'Ten's more like it.' Slattery delayed for a couple to pass near by through the parked cars. 'She was recruited in the mid-fifties but even then her name didn't ring an immediate bell. She's one of our best links. That's why it's so galling to have her out on a limb like this.' He seemed to imagine that more was expected of him, because he went on: 'There's been a misunderstanding. Not a slip-up. No one's been blown – nothing as serious as that. Otherwise I wouldn't be involving you. I can't explain, and you won't expect me to. But the result is that contact's been broken and it's imperative to make the damage good.'

Laker wasn't really listening. His mind was on the house and the gasping, blanketed body abandoned in desperation to the mercy of whoever came in answer to his rap on the door, the years telescoping as he thought of that and a score of related things, one of them being the day he sat in Slattery's Grosvenor Gardens office for the last time and worded his report about Karl and Günter and Karen Gisevius and the failure of the gamble called Operation Extension.

'I could have been told,' he said.

'Not once she was on our books.'

'Unofficially.'

'Hardly, old boy.'

Slattery's silhouette moved as he shifted his legs. The dusk seemed to be shrinking all the time and the cars dipping over the bridge were jostling into position for the roundabout ahead. It was a ridiculous place in which to talk about anything, let alone this.

'Why not?' Laker persisted.

'It never crossed my mind, Sam. And we'd lost touch, hadn't we? Gone our own ways.'

'Until it suited you.'

'Until I read the *Evening Standard* last week.'

'Oh balls,' Laker snapped quietly.

He was confused, filled with wonder that Karen lived yet feeling cheated for not having known of it and disturbed at the sudden prospect of meeting her again. It was too much to take at once and his mood compounded an unreasoning anger with Slattery that was shot through with distrust.

'If there's one thing I can't stand,' he said, 'it's being led by the nose.'

'Sam – '

'Once a pro, always a pro. It's your claim, not mine. You can't have it both ways.'

'I'm sorry. I had no idea – '

'Balls,' Laker snapped again. 'And another thing. D'you seriously expect me to walk into this place where she is and leave a handful of minutes later – just like that? Or have you forgotten you're dealing with people instead of little pins on the map?'

Judiciously, Slattery took his time. 'You'd rather not do it, is that it?'

'I didn't say that.'

'I don't think you've fully understood my position. The whole world might be making tracks to Leipzig, but I can't employ any Tom, Dick or Harry. *You* know that. It's a fluke if you like, about you and Karen, but these things crop up. And I certainly wasn't going to put pressure on you by mentioning her right away.'

'Ten minutes, you said. Then push off, get back to the Fair . . . As uneventful as stepping out into the street . . . What sort of person d'you – ?'

'I was merely underlining the extent of the commitment.' Slattery spoke as if he were justified by a set of rules. 'She'll be the judge of what's possible and what isn't.'

Laker pursed his lips, still confused, still bitter. It was late in the day to have baited the hook. He glared at Slattery in the dusk. Karen, Karen Gisevius . . .

'She's one of our best, you know.'

'I don't doubt it.'

It bewildered him to realise they weren't speaking of the past, or of the dead. The use of the present tense kept ramming home the shock, awakening memories which time had grafted on to him so that the longer he listened to Slattery the more moved he became. Question upon question began to queue in his mind, but Slattery's answers increasingly had the quality of protective gestures.

'Listen, Sam – and don't get me wrong. I'm not running an international social-contacts bureau, nor am I holding a gun to your head. You're still at liberty to cry off. It's up to you, entirely up to you. It has been from the start. But now you know it's Karen, I rather thought you'd be especially glad to help.'

'You make it sound like a good turn.'

'Isn't it?'

Christ, Laker thought.

'Isn't it?' Slattery insisted. 'Isn't that just what it is?'

Two worlds were overlapping as Laker drove back to Weybridge, thinking, thinking, sensing already that nothing could ever be quite the same again.

CHAPTER 4

The watch was brought to the house early on Tuesday evening. Laker had left the office before the usual time and was there to take it in. The small blue van looked as if it might have been the same one, but the man who came to the door certainly wasn't and he struck Laker as an unlikely accomplice – squat, middle-aged, untidy and badly out of condition if his shortness of breath were anything to go by. If Mrs. Ruddick had accepted the slim, brown-paper package it would have been odds on his getting a tip. As it was he simply asked Laker's name, nodded and walked away, his somewhat moody glance at the roses implying that, given the opportunity, he too could make use of leisure.

Patrick had gone upstairs to try and squeeze yet another afterthought into an already bulging suitcase and Mrs. Ruddick was quietly clattering in the kitchen. There was no writing or typed label on the package. Laker took it into the living-room and broke the seals, drew out the watch and examined the strap. Unmistakably, it was his own. Whatever had been done to it was completely invisible. They'd unstitched it, he presumed, but he couldn't detect the slightest trace of extra bulk or resewing. Slattery had been as good as his word on the score of technique ('Even you will doubt that you're carrying anything') and Laker had never been more than mildly curious regarding the details of the message he would be delivering at Kromadecka's. But from the moment Karen Gisevius was mentioned the project had taken on an entirely new dimension.

For a day and a night he had tried to convince himself that he had no reason to feel aggrieved at the way in which Slattery had played his cards. There was logic in his argument as to why he had avoided mentioning Karen until the last. But, knowing the potential of her name, it was naïve to imply that for ten years or more the thought of at least privately reporting her survival hadn't even crossed his mind. So was the specious nonsense about having lost touch when, only a couple of days earlier, he'd been quoting from Laker's file.

He wasn't easy to fathom, and renewed acquaintance had reminded Laker how slight their association ever was. Outside The Mitre his apparent insensitivity to everything except the main chance had injected anger into Laker's confusion, obliterating from the wake of the initial shock any purity of delight or astonished curiosity. These had emerged since, as Laker's resentment mellowed, and he tried to reason that Slattery was inhibited by a special code of laws and moralities.

Slattery's parting words had been: 'We'll meet when it's over, Sam.'
In the gloom he had fumbled a handshake like a Freemason searching
for the correct pressure-point. And only then, for the briefest possible duration, Laker had thought he detected the very slightest flaw
in the bland indifference. 'No hard feelings, I hope – now or at any
time.'

He gazed into the garden, thoughts focusing on Karen. She would be
about thirty-eight, thirty-seven or thirty-eight. He could only picture
her as she once was – thin, freckled and with eyes that burned with a
gravity beyond her years. Everything else was conjecture, what they had
shared being merely a spring-board for all the questions which filled his
mind as he tried to imagine what might have happened between his
leaving her at the house near Gardelegen and her now being at a
jeweller's in Liepzig. He thought about her with a curious sense of
unreality, as if he still couldn't completely accept that by tomorrow
afternoon he would have seen her, vaguely concerned with the shape of
his own life as much as with hers, drifting from one query to another, one
problem to another, thinking about survival, dying, being chosen and
not being chosen, recovery, living, about the war which had brought
them together and the kind of peace that would do so again.

He had never been back: Germany was split from north to south even
before he was out of uniform, with Gardelegen behind the wire and the
freshly-sown mines. He wrote, though. He wrote to the Red Cross and
other likely authorities, but they couldn't help. Twice he went as far as to
send letters direct, addressing them as a child might – *Large Grey Stone
House, 3 kms. South-West of Gardelegen* . . . But there was no answer and, in
his heart, he had scarcely expected one. Europe was a place of ghosts and
its desolation had swallowed her up along with the millions. She
remained a memory, as vivid and deeply-branded as the murders he'd
committed on his way out; dead, for all he knew, as dead as the hate that
had made them possible.

He had to keep reminding himself that she wouldn't realise he was
coming. It was useless to speculate on what had brought her back into
the game, yet the watch on his wrist and the telephone number stored in
the recesses of his mind were proof that tomorrow was first and foremost
Slattery's business. But Slattery wasn't the only one to have lost contact
and it was inconceivable that the Kromadecka shop on the Luisenstrasse
would lead to an exchange of watch-straps and nothing more.
Inconceivable, Russian Zone or no . . .

'Dad,' Patrick was calling from the stairs, 'what d'you think I should
do? Load my camera now, or in the morning?'

It was an early flight: 8.55 from London.

Low slicks of mist threatened the approaches to the airport, but there was no delay. Exactly on time the Viscount soared into the overhanging blue. Laker and Patrick were forward of the starboard wing and Patrick had the window-seat; he'd only flown twice before and it was still very much of a novelty. As soon as Laker released his belt he looked over his shoulder along the tube of the fuselage; much as he'd expected there was hardly a woman passenger to be seen. The man directly across the aisle was already browsing through a glossy catalogue of toys and construction kits and the hum of conversation somehow lacked the normal defensive arrogance of English travellers on holiday; it sounded more in keeping with any expense-account Pullman.

They were to put down at Amsterdam and Laker's guess was that ninety per cent of those abroad would transfer to the Leipzig connection. He eased back into his seat and stared past Patrick's profile at the mottled drift of Surrey and Kent. By the time the grey-and-pink encrustation of Canterbury was discernible on their left the morning's collation had been served, the flight particulars passed along and Patrick's concentration on the view was beginning to wane. He grinned at his father and fished out a German phrase-book.

'The postillion,' Laker said, 'has been struck by lightning.'

'That one's not here.'

'I honestly doubt if it ever was.'

'"Where can I obtain a good phrase-book?" – that is, though.'

'I don't believe it.'

'Cross my heart.'

Laker chuckled. His own German was excellent. 'What's "The Trade Fair"?'

'*Die Messe.*'

He took the book, opening it at random. 'How about "How do we get to the museum?"?'

Patrick screwed his face. '*Wie komm man –* '

'*Kommat. Wie kommt man . . .*'

'*Wie kommt man zu dem Museum.*'

'Full marks. They must be teaching you something at Greynham after all. Now . . . "Is there a price reduction for students, singly or in groups?"'

'Ouch.'

'No?'

'Definitely no.'

'Try "Are there any jelly-fish or dangerous currents?"'

Patrick deliberated, then retrieved the book. 'I'd better stop while I'm ahead. Anyway, who's swimming?'

'You never know. We'll be over the sea any minute.'

'Pessimist.'

Except for the eyes Patrick didn't much resemble Helen, but in this respect they were memorably alike – blue, with thick dark lashes. 'Look after him, Sam,' she had whispered that afternoon before they put her under for the unavailing operation. No one had told her, but she must have sensed it was hopeless. 'Look after him for me, won't you?' Laker glanced away almost guiltily, fingering his watch, torn between the slight yet ineradicable malaise that recurred every time he considered what he had undertaken on Slattery's behalf and the eagerness with which he anticipated the chance it had given. In the room looking out on to Manchester Square his rejection of the proposition had been quite automatic. No, he'd thought, the amateur in him instinctively on guard – and again as he'd brooded in the car in Brook Street. And then, somehow, by a series of mental stepping-stones which he couldn't precisely retrace, he had found himself swung over, unenthusiastic yet willing, arguing away the risk he might be running the further he committed himself until, finally, Karen dominated every aspect of the assignment.

'Did you know,' Patrick said, flicking through a leaflet now, 'that Bach was Cantor at the Thomaskirche in Leipzig?'

'If I did I'd forgotten.'

'I wonder if the Liverpool guides will mention The Beatles in a couple of hundred years' time?'

Laker winced theatrically.

'It's quite a thought, isn't it?'

'Everyone will be going to the moon by then,' Laker said.

A quarter of an hour passed. Toy ships floated in the wrinkled expanse of sea. Soon the coast of Holland showed, brown and wandering, flanking their line of flight. It was barely ten, but in a heavy Dublin brogue the man across the aisle asked the stewardess for a Jameson, and seemed genuinely put out when informed that Irish wasn't available: he settled for Scotch and two hundred cigarettes instead. Construction kits, Laker reflected, must be doing all right.

Presently a girl's voice clicked on, brittle with courtesy. 'In a few minutes we will be landing at Amsterdam, ladies and gentlemen. Would you please extinguish all cigarettes and fasten your seat-belts . . .'

There was the best part of an hour's hanging about at Amsterdam.

The transit-lounge was resonant with disembodied announcements and the occasional whine of aircraft. Outside the day was fine; the sky still cloudless. Patrick bought a Coca Cola from a machine and, through the windows, fired off a couple of shots with his camera at a Caravelle disgorging its load on the hard near by.

'By the way,' Laker said, 'I'd be careful about using that thing while we're in Leipzig.'

'Even at the Fair?'

He shrugged, aware that he was being absurdly inconsistent. 'It's the Russian Zone, after all.' Aware, too, that he had suddenly sounded like Slattery. 'Better check what the form is first.'

They flew on in a piston-engined aircraft operated by Czech Airlines; it looked like the old Dakota. After the Viscount's smoothness it was a bumpier, noisier ride, though the furnishings were a good deal more ornate: the windows had tasselled velvet curtains and the seats were covered in scarlet velour. 'Wow,' a bald-headed man in front exclaimed as everyone was settling in, 'it's like a whore's parlour,' and his companion said drily: 'You ought to know, George.'

No flight-maps were provided, but Patrick had brought the B.E.A. one along and it wasn't difficult to make an intelligent guess at their route. To begin with they headed into the sun, east, and they were low enough to interpret the shifting view – the metallic-looking Rhine, the industrial haze of the Ruhr far to the south; later the Ems with what could only be Munster dragging under the port wing.

Laker had been right: most of the London passengers were still with them. More names for Slattery's files – it was an odd and still unacceptable thought. Laughter, over-enunciated English to the stewardesses, voices raised above the engines' din: Spurs might have been playing in the European Cup. The person nearest to him caught his eye and asked: 'Didn't I see you last year?'

'In Leipzig?'

'Yes.'

'I wasn't there.'

'First time, eh?'

'Yes.'

'Odd. I could have sworn we'd met. What's your line?'

Laker told him.

'You're starting the young man early, I'll say that.' This with an amiable nod towards Patrick. 'My name's Black, incidentally. Dargle and Tait, Ilford . . . Optical Goods.'

Laker wasn't in the mood for shop, and to his relief the man seemed more or less content to let it go at that. Patrick was saying: 'D'you reckon that's the Weser?'

'Could be,' he answered, peering.

'It must be.'

'You're the navigator.'

It was impossible to block out the past. His first time to the Fair, yes; but he'd flown this way before, in cloudy moonlight, with a diversionary raid on Magdeburg to distract attention, and he suddenly remembered the dispatcher, a New Zealander, leaning back from the intercom and bawling: 'Skipper says we've passed the Weser. Hanover to starboard. Two-fifteen and not a mouse stirring . . .' And then he remembered another time, days later, when he lay with Karen in the covered depression among the spruce trees. Huddled close, her breath warm on his face yet frosting in the air, she had said 'D'you know what I'm thinking, Sammy? I'm thinking how normal tonight is for millions of other people – at home, out dancing, at the theatre maybe, sitting somewhere by a fire, having a bath, cooking, feeding the baby, making love . . . When is it going to be normal for us, Sammy?'

He closed his eyes and let the darkness in. No need for qualms. He was a postman. Only fools were picked up; fools and those who risked the deep water. For all he knew Leipzig would be swarming with front-and-cover organisations. Intelligence had become a major post-war industry. Getting rid of the strap would be child's-play. But meeting Karen again wasn't something that could be conducted across a counter in the space of a few brief minutes.

Surely, he thought, it was going to be possible to see her after that?

Clouds began to obscure the land. Towards noon they turned southeast, canting over, the sun swinging. They were due in at twelve-twenty. Patrick had put the map away. The white scar of an autobahn made itself visible and other gaps in the overcast offered tantalising glimpses of minor roads and railway-tracks spidered between towns and villages clustered about the grey-green countryside.

'D'you know what?' Patrick said. 'I'll send a card to Hans Meiner. That'll shake him.'

'Which is Hans?'

'The boy in Rostock.'

'Ah.' Slattery was inescapable. 'What about the others?'

'Oh, I'll do them too. Gilles, Paris; Erich, Hanover; Jenny, San Francisco; Manuel Chapi, Barcelona . . .' Patrick ticked them off on his fingers.

'Only one girl?' Laker smiled. 'What happened to that glamorous thing who used to write from Athens?'

'I wish I knew. She was a bit square, though.'

'Don't forget Mrs. Ruddick.'

'And Tim Maxwell. Still, the point is to get one off to Hans when I'm on his side of the fence. You know – wish you were here; having capitalist time.'

Patrick laughed, pleased with his joke, and Laker fisted him playfully on the shoulder. Once, a year or so ago, when they were searching the store-room at Roundwood, Patrick had come across the box containing Laker's decorations and medal ribbons, but there was no mention of Karen in the citations and Laker had never spoken about her. What would he tell him now, supposing they all could meet? 'A friend,' would he say? 'Someone I worked with during the war, long before you were born, before I even knew your mother, someone I believed I would never see again . . .'

The stewardess with the severely swept-back hair and the trained smile that could have masked contempt had started along the gangway, signalling everyone to fix their belts. They were lower already, the vibration more marked, wallowing a little on the up-currents.

Cloud streamed like mist past the windows and, quite suddenly, the outskirts of Leipzig slid obliquely into view like a multi-coloured street-map. Instinctively, Laker pointed. The aircraft seemed to search for a line, then chose one and held it, slanting in, wheels down, flaps down, throttled back, flattening out as the runway rose abruptly out of a smear of crops and hedgerows.

'Dead on time,' Patrick said like a seasoned traveller as soon as the jolt was over.

The airport formalities weren't prolonged. An announcement, first in English, then in French, greeted them as they filed indoors: 'Passengers are requested to present their passports and Fair Cards at the Immigration Bureau. Facilities are also available for currency exchange. All enquiries regarding the Trade Fair should be addressed to the Information Department in this building or to the Foreign Visitors' Centre at the New Town Hall . . . Thank you.'

They had to queue at Immigration, but there were no difficulties. Returning to Dover after a day-trip to Calais couldn't have been easier. A page of their perforated Fair Cards was stamped and detached; a nod and they were clear. Perhaps because the Customs official hadn't expected Laker to answer in German he chalked squiggles on their luggage without asking for anything to be opened and even went as far as to wish them a pleasant stay in the German Democratic Republic. Then they were free to move into the high, echoing Arrivals hall and pass under the flags and welcoming banners which draped the exits.

Outside, another queue waited for taxis. Theirs, when it came, was a Skoda, newish, with a photograph of Ulbricht stuck on the windscreen like a talisman and a driver who wore a black plastic cap with a duck-bill peak.

'Astoria Hotel,' Laker said.

He was sweating thinly, and Patrick remarked on it. He shrugged: 'It's a bit stuffy.' But he glanced at the rear-view mirror all the same, deriding his caution even as he did so, aware only then of the effort the Customs had cost him. And yet they'd waltzed through. He watched Leipzig straggle towards them, alien and unrecognisable. Roundwood, Gale and Watts, Mrs. Ruddick, Carol Nolan – all at once they seemed immensely remote, in time as well as distance.

The city took shape, graceless and functional, the heavy Russian style of the outlying tenement blocks and the more central commercial area only partially redeemed by the temporary rash of decorative bunting. The treeless squares were as drab as parade-grounds and there was a heavy sprinkling of uniforms on the thronged pavements. Laker had forgotten who had recommended the Astoria, but he'd booked weeks in advance and even then it meant Patrick sharing a room with him. As they entered the foyer the Irishman from the plane was already on his way out, giving them the thumbs-down sign as he passed.

'Mr. Laker?' a plump woman-receptionist inquired, studying the hotel's letter of confirmation he'd produced. 'Mr. Laker and son?' She pronounced it 'Larker', but he let it go. He nodded and they waited. The décor was confused, modern pastel incongruously burdened with Edwardian gilt; and the place seemed packed. When the woman spoke to them again it was in English. She hadn't much charm but she was certainly efficient. 'Yes, that is in order, Mr. Larker. You have a reservation for two days. You will both complete and sign the register, if you please.'

They did so, and she said: 'Your room is number fifty-four.' She couldn't manage the 'r' and it sounded like 'womb'. Then she pinged a bell and a cadaverous porter collected the key and their luggage. The elevator whined them up to the third floor.

'You're busy,' Laker remarked to the porter.

'Busy, yes. Oh yes. Fair-time is always busy.' He looked as if life had tried to crush him, and might do so yet. 'The whole world visits Leipzig for the Fairs.' When it came to a tip he asked for cigarettes instead of money.

The room was on the small side, but adequate. Twin beds, a handbasin, a single wardrobe. The atmosphere seemed heavy, as if peat were burning somewhere. Patrick opened a window and they stared out. Beyond the immediate solidity of the neighbouring façades there were vacant, rubble-heaped lots and bomb-truncated ruins. Nearer, a poster implored housewives to collect scrap. Everything looked grey and it had begun to spit with rain.

'Well,' Laker said. 'What d'you think?'

'It's different.'

'From what you imagined?'

'No. Just different – like the old news-reels. Does that make sense?'

'After a fashion.'

Patrick unslung his camera and tested one of the beds. 'Still, the womb's all right.'

Laker smiled. Fourteen, he thought.

'Shall we lunch now? 'I'm starved.'

'Right away.' But he delayed at the window, wondering where the Luisenstrasse was.

It was a reasonable meal. The dining-room was loud with the collision of voices. Laker recognised at least three of the London passengers scattered about: Black was one of them and he seemed to be fraternising to good effect. He waved vaguely in Laker's direction.

Laker took out the folder into which Carol had put all the Fair particulars and glanced through them. There was no reason why they should go to the Foreign Visitors' Centre; he'd changed twenty pounds at the airport and had no desire to 'meet and converse with trade partners in your particular sphere of interest,' as one of the leaflets worded it, either at the New Town Hall or at the Messedienst – 'a must for information and assistance in the advancement of international Fair business.'

He wasn't there for that, or for the junketing. From the first his intention had been to make a couple of visits to the Fair itself, one general, one more specifically on behalf of Gale and Watts, and to fill in with some routine sightseeing for Patrick's benefit. A few hours' snooping round the Business-Systems section was the most he'd envisaged and even before he was hooked by Slattery he had decided to leave that side of things until the following day. The general tour of the Fair could start after lunch, so nothing had changed – nothing, that was, except having to leave Patrick to his own devices for a short while.

He said: 'I'll have to duck away for a bit this afternoon. You know – business. It would only bore you.'

'For how long?'

'Not so long. We'll get over to the Fair as soon as we've unpacked and then, say about four, I'll leave you to browse on your own for a while. Okay?'

He was restless now, wishing the damn thing off his wrist; but not on that account alone.

They had the choice of a dozen or more exhibition buildings and the overall effect on Laker was rather as if Earls Court and Olympia and the old British Industries Fair had been lumped together in the city's centre. Once off the streets and confronted with the panoply of the various trade displays it was hard not to forget that, in Slattery's phrase, they were behind the lines. Plush carpeting, ingenious presentation, subtle dioramic lighting – it was the same shop-window world with the same eye-catching gadgetry, the same kind of product demonstrators, the same extrovert bonhomie of the salesmen with the same smoky stuffiness, the same sort of voices and earnest gropings. Jerry Baxendale would have been in his element.

Laker went through the motions of showing interest, but his mind was elsewhere. The television and musical-instrument section was like the Radio Show in miniature and it seemed the best possible place in which to leave Patrick. Time was getting on: time to go.

'You'll be all right?'

'Sure.'

'It's almost four now. I'll be back before five. But just in case I'm not, or you get bored around here, push off to the hotel.'

'Okay.'

He handed Patrick some money. 'Don't blue it all on records.'

Patrick grinned and he left him, suddenly uneasy, regretting the necessity. At the exit he turned and looked back, as if the scene would somehow offer reassurance, then made his way into the street. It was still spitting with rain. He found a taxi-rank under some plane-trees at the corner of the first block and asked for the Luisenstrasse.

'Whereabouts?' the man said. 'What number?'

'Twelve,'' he answered, guessing, not wanting to give the name or to be vague.

He sat on the edge of the seat. Fair directions were everywhere but he had no idea which way they were heading. 'A five-minute ride' – though that was from the Astoria. Off to the right he glimpsed a railway-station, then a square dominated by an ungainly piece of statuary. Thereafter the concentration of flags and banners began to peter out: there was another Leipzig and it came quickly, more nakedly drab, the hoardings no longer proclaiming a welcome.

EVERY INCREASE IN OUTPUT IS A NAIL IN ERHARDT'S COFFIN . . . WE ARE LEARNING FROM SOVIET SCIENCE, THE MOST PROGRESSIVE IN THE WORLD . . . DO YOUR SHARE AND STRIKE A BLOW FOR THE GERMAN DEMOCRATIC REPUB-LIC . . .

Bicycles were everywhere. Lights delayed them and Laker watched the passers-by: they were cosmopolitan no longer and their faces showed evidence of the hard life. Some stared, as if a taxi were a novelty, and the stares gave him a disturbing sense of isolation, of having strayed out of bounds. This was far enough, he kept thinking, far enough. And then, as if in obedience to his silent urging, the taxi made an abrupt right turn and cruised to a halt in front of a second-hand clothing shop.

It was an unlikely destination to have chosen. He climbed out and paid the man off, then made a pretence of tying his laces, giving the taxi time to draw away. The rain had stopped. There were shops on both sides of the street, two-storeyed mainly, a run-down look about them: a queue of women gossiped outside a baker's opposite. He lit a cigarette and started walking. It was a hundred yards or more before he saw Kromadecka's – just as he was beginning to have an awful feeling that he must have come to the wrong place. It was diagonally across the street, narrow-fronted, the name lettered in black on a yellow ground. In the minute it took him to reach it, he twice looked over his shoulder. He would have felt less exposed amongst a crowd, but the Luisenstrasse had none to offer. Apart from the queue it seemed almost unnaturally quiet – few people, no cars, hardly a cyclist.

He walked at an even pace. 'Nothing to it, old boy . . .' He had talismans of his own. 'Couldn't be more elementary . . .' But there was more to this than actively taking sides in a war and, despite the tension, he was strangely elated. Ten yards away he slowed, keeping to the outside of the pavement so as to widen his view of the shop. A clock centred in the window showed that it was a little after a quarter-past four. There was a hand-written notice in German taped to the inside of the glass.

WATCH REPAIRS
ESTIMATES FREE
PRICES MODERATE

It greeted him like an invitation, something meant for him personally, and he reached for the door, eager to make an end of being manacled to Slattery and effect a beginning of his own.

CHAPTER 5

A bell above the door tinkled as he went in. The place was small, cluttered, glass cases forming a counter on three sides. Through a curtained opening he could see the base of some stairs leading out of a back room.

'A moment, please.'

It was a woman's voice; soft, quite cheerful. Time had blurred how Karen had sounded, but it could only be hers – Slattery had said so – and Laker heard the intensified thud of his heart above the irregular ticking of several clocks. The walls were hung with them. In the cases were cutlery sets and a few pieces of silver plate, embossed pottery, tankards and some glass; after the lavish sophistication of the Fair everything looked pitiable. He wiped his face and waited, suddenly caught between anticipation and a kind of dread, staring about him, wondering. There was a selection of watches in a wall-cabinet and an old square safe screwed to the floor in the opposite corner.

A truck ground past just as he heard her on the stairs. Before she came through the curtains she was saying, 'I'm sorry, sorry.' And then she was there, the curtains closing behind her. 'Good afternoon. Can I help you?'

Perhaps it was vanity, but he thought she hesitated when she saw him. For a second or two it seemed as if her face clouded with incipient disbelief, her brows knitting slightly as she moved behind the counter. But, for his part, he had no need to rack his memory; reality matched the basic image. He would have picked her out in the street, in a restaurant –

anywhere. The gentle freckling, the broad mouth, the blonde hair; above all, the eyes – as brown and grave as he'd remembered.

'What was it you wanted?'

He mastered emotion. Again, momentarily, he believed he detected the beginnings of a frown of recognition.

As dutifully as a boy on an errand he said: 'A new watch-strap.'

If she felt anything she didn't show it. She gave nothing, absolutely nothing away. 'Any special kind?'

'Something like the one I'm wearing will do.'

He took the watch off and handed it to her. She had dropped her gaze now.

'It's an English strap, isn't it?'

'Yes,' he said. 'I got it in London.'

She nodded and reached for a batch of cards, each displaying a choice of samples. She was very calm, very practised.

'I can't give you leather. Imitation is the best I have; the alternative would be plastic.'

She wore a darkish orange costume of tweed-like material and a white bead necklace. Her lips were only lightly reddened and her hair curled softly away from the forehead. The skin was a fine, delicate colour. When she placed the cards in front of him he saw how slender her fingers were. There was no ring, he noticed.

'Imitation will be all right.'

And suddenly it seemed beyond reason that he should continue his part of the masquerade. He couldn't be bothered with the cards. He said quietly: 'Don't you remember me, Karen?'

If she bore scars at all they were in her eyes. Now, as she lifted them to his, he saw for a fleeting instant not merely wariness but a whole background of apprehension, like an illness she had learned to live with.

'Sam,' he said. 'Sam Laker.' Then, as if it were a codeword: 'Sammy.'

There was nothing then but the sound of the clocks. For a long time that was all. He thought her stare would never end.

'Sammy?'

Smiling, he watched her expression as she made the leap in time, her eyes widen a fraction, the line of her mouth alter. He didn't know what he expected – delight, wonder, incredulity; any or all of these. The incredulity was dawning, but there was something else as well: dismay, perhaps – he couldn't decipher it. She lifted a hand to her throat.

'No!' she said. 'Oh, no!'

'Am I so different?'

She didn't answer.

'Am I?'

She shook her head, staring still, searching his face. Slowly, she began: 'I didn't expect –'

'How could you have done?' He leaned nearer, Patrick forgotten, Slattery forgotten. 'You look fine, Karen. You haven't changed.' Matured, filled out, but not changed. 'As soon as you came through the curtains – '

'I . . . I can't believe it,' she said. She shook her head again, closing her eyes momentarily. 'Sammy Laker' – and now when she used his name the wonder was there.

'You frowned when you saw me. I thought perhaps – '

'It was the light,' she said. 'You were against the light.'

'You didn't guess?'

'No.'

'And now?'

'There's no need to guess now.' Her lips trembling.

'I thought you were dead, Karen – until forty-eight hours ago, that is, when they asked me to do this.'

Laker gestured towards the watch lying between them; they were safe here. Thoughts a million times faster than speech were racing through his mind. He began to talk about the Red Cross, about the letters to the house near Gardelegen, very moved suddenly, and all the time she gazed at him as if certainty hadn't quite enveloped her yet. Little by little she seemed to be shedding her dismay or whatever it was he imagined he saw; but there was no smile.

'How long have you been in Leipzig?'

'Since 'forty-seven.'

'And in this shop?'

'Twelve years. It was my uncle's. When he died I kept it going.'

'Do you live here?'

She raised her eyes to the ceiling. 'Upstairs.'

They paused then. She had hardly touched the watch.

'I wondered about you,' Laker said.

'So did I,' she said. 'I wondered, too. Many, many times.' A kind of tremor seemed to pass through her. 'I still haven't grasped it, Sammy . . . You.'

He nodded. 'And they say miracles never happen.' He offered her a cigarette but she refused, with a fluttering gesture. 'Tell me about yourself.'

She shrugged.

'Were you ill for long?'

'At that house?'

'Yes.'

'Not so long. They were very kind.'

He had the feeling that she couldn't give her mind to what had happened all that time ago. Biting her lower lip she stared at him, denied in some way the ease to let her wonder live and grow out of the passing moments. They both faltered sometimes, lost for words. Behind Laker's back a clock whirred and struck the half-hour. He'd almost forgotten what had brought him there. Even in the silences he seemed to be rediscovering something about her. He wasn't sure whether Karen asked him or not, but he found himself telling her what he had done since the war; about Helen. She must have asked, otherwise he would hardly have been speaking about Helen so soon, but he was confused himself, split by many emotions.

'There are children?'

'A boy – Patrick. Not that he's a child any more. He's with me in Leipzig, incidentally.' Another clock was chiming. 'Are you married?'

'No,' she said.

'Were you?'

'No.'

Someone went by in the street, a woman wearing a headscarf, blinking in the light from the window as she passed. Karen glanced quickly that way and he realised how tense she was.

'You will have to go,' she said.

'Not yet.'

'Soon.' Slattery's comment echoed in her tone – 'I'm not running a social-contacts bureau, Sam.'

'You've got to fix my strap first.'

She picked up the watch and reached into a drawer for a pair of sharp-pointed pliers.

'How many years have you been fixing straps?' he asked. 'Straps from London?'

She frowned over the watch, probing with the pliers, but refrained from answering.

'Or shouldn't I ask things like that?'

Without looking at him she said: 'You have never done this before, have you?'

'Does it show so much?'

She nodded.

'There's a whole lot more I want to ask.'

'There won't be time.'

'I'm here until first thing Friday morning. At the Astoria. Couldn't we meet there?'

'It would not be wise.'

'Tonight, for dinner?'

'No, Sammy.'

'Why not?'

'You know why.'

'But, hell –' he began, the amateur in him hurt. He thought of Black, Black who could fraternise openly in the hotel's dining-room, and the score of animated meetings he'd witnessed during that self-same afternoon. Leipzig was packed with foreigners, its arms flung wide in the interests of trade. Openly, in the Astoria's bar, with Patrick, and then to dine, the three of them – where was the harm?

He tried to put it to her, but she only shook her head.

'I can't.'

'Do you want to?'

'Of course,' she said. 'Of course.'

'But you won't?'

'It's not a risk I can take.' She looked at him. 'Believe me, please.'

Once she had risked so much, survived so much. They both had. Suddenly he remembered that other time, and her saying: 'When is it going to be normal for us, Sammy?' Suddenly he realised that in a few minutes he would be out in the street. One wing of the strap was already detached and she had started picking at the fastening of the other. Slattery loomed once more. The Mitre, the flat in Manchester Square and the plain blue van. 'She's one of our best, Sam . . . There's been a misunderstanding. You can get her off the rack.'

Laker stubbed his cigarette. 'I can phone you, surely?'

'No.'

He stared at her, striving to accept that her coolness towards him wasn't wilful.

'I can't just go,' he said. 'I can't just walk away. Not after twenty years. I can't just say "Good-bye" and not see you again.'

'You must.'

'Can't you suggest something? Isn't there a park, or a square, or a café – ?'

'Don't push me, Sammy. It's no good.' She unclipped the other wing of the strap, more clumsily than before, her movements showing signs of stress. 'Don't you understand?'

'I do, but – '

'Already you have stayed too long.'

'Ten minutes?'

'They must have told you how it would be.'

He said nothing.

'I didn't know you were coming.' Now, all at once, she was near to tears. 'I didn't know *who* was coming, or even when it would be. I'm not expected to know, I'm not expected to ask. That isn't my part of it.' Her eyes burned, brown and huge; yet her face still held its fine colour. 'I thought you were dead, Sammy. And not until forty-eight hours ago. Until just now . . . It's harder for me – can't you see? I didn't know it was going to be you standing here.' Her lips trembled again. 'Oh, God,' she finished wretchedly.

'I'm sorry,' Laker said. 'I'm sorry, Karen.' He seemed tongue tied. Impulsively, reaching forward, he touched her on the cheek. For a moment she didn't draw away, but suddenly she stiffened.

'No.'

Her voice was sharp. She pulled back and bent her head over the watch. Outside, there was the drag of footsteps.

'Vopos,' she whispered tersely.

'Who?'

'Vopos.'

The light faded as the window was partially blocked. Out of the corner of his eyes Laker saw two members of the People's Police, one taller than the other, and the taller of them was leaning forward as he peered in, hoisting his shoulder-slung carbine.

'Which strap have you chosen?'

Karen's tone had utterly changed: the cards shook slightly as she held them in front of him.

Laker pointed. 'I'll take that one.'

The light swelled again as the figures moved. He thought they were going away, but he was wrong. When the door-bell tinkled his neck prickled coldly. They came in, heavy boots gritting on the worn linoleum, and stood behind him, close because of the lack of space. For an awful moment that seemed quite interminable he remained woodenly at the counter, expecting them to speak, to challenge him even. The two wings of his old strap lying on the glass looked frighteningly conspicuous.

Karen finished unfastening the new one from the display-card before addressing them. 'Can I help you?' It amazed Laker that she should have the ability to smile.

One of the two cleared his throat. 'You have a brooch in the window.'

Over his left shoulder Laker focused briefly on to a fleshy, constipated face under a green fore-and-aft cap, a young face with thick lips and snub nose. Then he turned his head away.

'Would you like to show me which one?'

'I will wait.'

'It's no trouble. You can be making up your mind while I finish with this gentleman's watch.'

Karen moved to the window; the Vopo who had spoken followed suit. 'There,' he said. 'There, yes, that's it.'

She returned to where Laker was standing without so much as glancing at him. In his relief he marvelled at her control, but there was lead in his heart. A kind of angry dejection filled him as she began fixing the new strap into position. It was almost unendurable to wait to be dismissed, unable to speak with her again, let alone to make one more plea that their reunion shouldn't end in such a fashion. Behind him the two Vopos muttered over the brooch. 'What d'you think?' one of them said. 'Will it do?' and the other answered: 'Do? She'll fall for it. Look, if I hold it you can see it better.' As if mesmerised Laker stared across the counter, watching Karen's small-boned hands fold the last clip down with the pincers.

Then she was saying: 'There, sir . . . I think you'll find that's satisfactory.'

Sir . . . He took it from her, vainly hoping to hold her gaze if only for a second, aware that she was facing the Vopos, yet hoping despite that. 'Thank you.'

There were a thousand questions, but nothing was possible. He paid with a note. The till was on a shelf fixed to the wall and as she turned she casually picked up the pieces of the strap and dropped them into the open drawer, for all the world like a woman for whom tidiness was everything. And when she spoke to him again, counting out his change, he might have been exactly what he was meant to be – a stranger.

'Thank you, sir. Good afternoon.'

The sound of the door-bell seemed to mock him as he walked away. Yet the resentment locked within his feeling of deprivation wasn't directed against her. The Vopos had served to remind him of the dangers. Until they came the shop had seemed quite safe: Slattery's game – her game – a shade unreal, undeserving of extreme caution. But now that alarm had brushed his own nerves he more fully understood the high wire on which she existed, and it was this that he hated – its discipline and its denial.

For what? Yes, for what?

He crossed the street, his mind whirling, selfishly grateful that she had almost reached the brink of tears. The past meant something, then. He hadn't nurtured an illusion or romanticised a memory.

It was getting on for a quarter to five. An enormous effort was required to bring his thoughts to bear on where he had arranged to meet Patrick. He walked briskly, heedless of his surroundings, hoping to find a taxi. There was a telephone booth at the first intersection. She had insisted that he mustn't call but he went in and looked for Kromadecka in the tatty directory, scribbling the number, the number only, hurriedly in his diary. He wouldn't use it for a while, perhaps never; but he couldn't accept that he had seen the last of her. Tomorrow, perhaps, he might return to the shop, ostensibly to buy something. He would have to think what to do, what was best – weighing the possible risk to her against what the last fifteen minutes had aroused in him.

He walked with his shoulders hunched, embittered by the irony of the situation, unable to think very clearly. After several hundred yards he found himself passing a bookshop. ART IS A WEAPON, the window-display proclaimed. Inside, he asked where he could get a taxi and the assistant, speaking slowly as if unsure of Laker's command of the language, directed him to a rank a couple of blocks away. The driver at the head of the rank accepted him without enthusiasm and crunched through the gears on his way to the Astoria. Patrick would almost certainly have gone back to the hotel; it was as near to five as made no difference.

The streets spread themselves as they approached the area of the Fair. Under the bunting and the banners there were crowds again, people moving with varying degrees of purpose, the stiffening of uniforms amongst them. He was in the clear now, a postman no longer, so the uniforms conveyed no sense of personal threat; yet they were the outward and visible reason for care before he made a second move towards Karen.

He recognised the Ring-Messehaus, with its fringe of flags hanging limply after the rain, but he failed to see the railway station he had passed on the previous journey. Vaguely, he suspected the driver was giving him a tourist's run-around and soon he leaned forward, saying 'Astoria' in such a way as to indicate that he knew his Leipzig, only to find that he didn't. Hardly had he spoken than they were drawing up outside the hotel, scraping the kerb.

He suffered the driver's smirk, paid, and turned towards the steps. The heavy peat-like scent enveloped him as he entered the foyer. There was no sign of Patrick. He hesitated, wondering whether to wait for him there or to go on up to their room. And, as he hesitated, a man in a light raincoat rose from one of the tables near the entrance and approached: a shortish man with a slightly lopsided face.

'Mr. Laker?'

He didn't use the broad 'a'. With affected ease Laker said: 'That's right.'

'Mr. Samuel Laker?'

'Yes.'

'I have some unfortunate news, I'm afraid, Mr. Laker.'

'Oh?'

'There's been an accident.' He stuttered slightly. 'I'm sorry to say that your son has –'

'Accident?' Scalp tightening, Laker snatched at the words. 'What happened?'

The man started on some rigmarole about stairs, a fall, but Laker couldn't wait for him to finish.

'Is he badly hurt?'

'He was unconscious when they put him in the ambulance.'

'Where is he?'

'At the University Clinic.'

'God!' Laker said.

He wheeled blindly for the doors, isolated by the shock, unaware that he was followed. But on the steps his arm was grabbed.

'This way, this way . . . I have a car.'

He remembered being guided to an old grey Mercedes and getting into the back seat, the man in the raincoat lurching against him as the door was slammed. Another man was already at the wheel and they started to move almost immediately, nosing into the traffic.

'When did it happen?'

'Half an hour ago.'

'How's he injured? Is it his head, or what?'

'I couldn't say exactly. But don't alarm yourself too much. I don't think you will find his condition too serious.'

'Unconscious, you said.'

'Yes, but –'

'Did you see him?'

'Not personally, no.'

'Was it at the radio-and-television place?'

'Yes, yes; that's right.'

'God!' Laker said again. He felt sick; stunned. 'I left him alone for a while because there was some business I had to attend to and I thought it would bore him. I wondered at the time whether I was making a mistake. But his German's not bad, d'you see, and he's normally quite capable of looking after himself.' Anxiety, self-reproach spilled over. The streets blurred past. 'How far's the hospital?'

'Not too far, Mr. Laker.'

His hands wouldn't remain still and he brought them together, the knuckles bone-white. He heard himself say: 'It's very good of you to help like this. I appreciate it.' By talking he could at least keep his imagination under control. 'How did you recognise me?'

'Please?'

'How did you know me? Or that I'd be at the Astoria?'

'Your son said you would be there.'

'Laker frowned. 'He *was* able to speak, then?'

'I understand so. To begin with.'

He found himself looking at his companion as if for the first time. The man had a hat on now, a brown trilby. The person at the wheel was bareheaded, wearing a black leather jacket; around the cropped blond hair-line his neck was inflamed with boils. 'Take a left,' the one with the hat said, and Laker felt the centrifugal tug as the tyres snickered. Since the shock hit him he had been in a daze, apprehensive of what awaited him, oblivious of the distance they were covering. The minutes passed. He couldn't for the life of him understand how Patrick had come to pitch down a flight of stairs, but his questions increasingly drew a blank, a shrug. Suspicion was some way from taking hold, but his wits were thawing a little and it struck him that the man was losing interest, more concerned with their route and issuing directions. Twice in succession they bore right. There was less traffic and the streets had narrowed: it was the other Leipzig again, cheerless and gaunt with factories squatting amid old untended scars.

Laker said urgently: 'What's the hospital called again?'

'The University Clinic.'

'Are we nearly there?'

'Soon.'

But there was no indication of it. On edge, he said: 'Wasn't there anything more central?' He glanced at his watch. Time suddenly took meaningful shape. Where were they? They were moving fast and the city was running more and more to seed.

'Who are you?' he said, alarmed by a wild doubt.

The man shifted position, but didn't answer. Small, bright eyes; a crease-bracketed mouth.

'Look, where's my son been taken? Where's this hospital?'

'Keep quiet, Mr. Laker.'

Laker stiffened, heart missing a beat.

'There is no hospital and there has been no accident.' The slight stutter emphasised the injection of menace. 'Keep quiet and don't try anything foolish.'

'What the hell are you talking about?'

'I'm talking about you, Mr. Laker. Do as I say and you will come to no harm.'

As casually as if he were about to offer a cigarette the man withdrew his right hand from inside the raincoat. Dropping his gaze Laker saw an automatic pistol.

'Otherwise,' the man said, 'I will have no alternative but to kill you.'

CHAPTER 6

Laker stared at the gun with incredulous dismay. Fear crawled clammily over his skin.

'Is this a joke?' he managed thickly. 'Some kind of a joke?'

'No joke, Mr. Laker.'

They must have covered a quarter of a mile before another word was spoken and throughout that time his thoughts spun in chaos.

Karen, Kromadecka's.

He achieved that one coherent deduction before the confusion regained its hold. With as much control as he could find he said: 'What's the meaning of this? Just what d'you think you're doing?'

Except with his eyes the man ignored him.

Laker licked his lips, desperately seeking to pacify himself, not to bluster. 'Look,' he said, 'I don't know who you are, and I don't care, but you've made a mistake. A bloody silly mistake.' But it was hopeless and he already knew it. Something had gone wrong, terribly wrong; the gun and the two men and the story about Patrick were an integral part of disaster.

'Where are we going?'

No reply.

'What about my son? Where's he?'

'In good hands, Mr. Laker. Safe and sound.'

'Where?' he shouted. Then he tried again, more persuasively. 'I'm a British subject. This is ridiculous. Intolerable' – echoing the protests of all those who had ever walked into a trap; and again, even as he formed the words, he knew the futility of them. Appeals, bribes – these were out, too. He'd fallen for the oldest trick of all and it was twenty years since he had been within reach of a weapon, twenty years since he was trained in the unarmed skills that might have led to a physical break. Pressing against his side of the car he felt unable to move, held by the gun and the other's eyes, his groping relief that Patrick was uninjured whirled away by apprehensions so tortured that they amounted almost to a physical pain.

'Who are you?' he demanded. 'Police?'

'We aren't kidnappers, Mr. Laker.'

'Who, then? And what am I supposed to have done?'

'You will find out.' A joyless, off-centre smile. 'But, if it is any comfort to you, my colleague and I have offical blessing.'

They were leaving the fringes of the city; numbly Laker was aware of a smear of crops behind the man's head, trees dotted about an untenanted green slope. For a moment or two his thoughts seemed to reach a state of appalled calm, but before he could attempt to reason the confusion began to renew itself, repeating his mind's instinctive cry of dismay when he first saw the gun. Patrick was at the heart of it, Patrick and Karen and Slattery. And there were others, others who were involved in that they were a part of the pattern of his life, faces and places near and far, all frenetically scrambled together, kaleidoscopic images sweeping him as if he were drowning.

Christ, he thought, Oh Christ.

He started feeling for his pockets, but the man checked him.

'I want a cigarette,' he said.

'Use these.'

A pack was tossed across together with some matches. Laker lit up clumsily, fingers shaking, narrowing his eyes against the smoke. Another weakening rush of panic surged through him. There had been nothing to arouse his suspicions, no evidence of being followed, no feeling the weight of another's scrutiny. Lies, denials; he must cling to these now. Karen would and so must he. They'd have picked her up as well; everything pointed to the inevitability of that. It couldn't be him without her. Her without him, yes, but not him without her.

Oh Christ, he thought again.

Pines stood along each side of the road. 'Where are you taking me?' he asked a second time, but he might have been talking to himself. The sun flickered like a signal-lamp through the trees and the driver grunted, reaching to retrieve dark glasses from the empty seat beside him.

They were heading north-east and it had passed the half-hour. A sign pointed to Berlin and Laker felt an inner cold blow through him, chilling him in the marrow. Minute after minute he was stumbling around in his mind for a clue to what might have betrayed them, yet his most desperate anxiety was still for Patrick.

'What d'you mean by "in good hands"?'

'Exactly what the phrase implies, Mr. Laker.'

'But where is he? . . . What's he been told? I was meeting him at five.'

A shrug.

'He's fourteen. Fourteen – a kid. And he's only once before been away from England.'

He waited, but there was no answer.

'Are you deaf?' he suddenly raged through his distress. 'Why the hell can't you explain what this is all about?' Then, finally, in English: 'You bastard. Whoever you are, you sodding bastard.' And he saw the man's eyebrows contract and knew he'd understood.

An autobahn crossed their path like a dyke. They took the looping underpass and gradually the trees straggled back to fence the road. They must have been seven or eight miles from the outskirts of Leipzig before the driver cut his speed. A track led off to the right. They nosed clear of the tarmac and headed into the pines, the car slewing a little as the wheels shuddered in and out of some ruts. Laker stared about him, sensing the journey was almost at an end yet baffled by the sudden change of route. The pines hemmed them in. After about half a mile the track branched and they bore left, not far, debouching eventually into a small clearing in which there was a log-hut. If Laker had anticipated anything beyond the certainty of an interrogation it wasn't this.

'Listen,' the man in the raincoat stuttered quietly. 'No foolishness. Get out and remain still. Don't move. Don't do something you might regret.'

Laker obeyed woodenly. The driver had beaten him to it. Until his companion had rounded the back of the Mercedes he stood close to Laker, close but not too close, as watchfully as a wrestler. But specks were sand-blasted into the coarse facial skin and the mouth was sullen. Over Laker's shoulder he must have received a signal because he nodded and turned towards the hut.

'Follow him, please.' This was from behind.

Three wooden steps led up to door. There were several windows, none of them curtained. A board fixed to the nearest side of the hut stated in red on white FIRE CONTROL. B SECTOR. The driver fished a key from his leather jacket, unlocked the door and pushed his way inside. Laker entered as cautiously as the pistol at his back allowed. Everything seemed dark for a moment or two and then, as his vision adjusted, he found himself in a squarish room in which was nothing except a table and a few hard chairs. Another door led out of the room, but this was closed. A single bulb with a white enamel shade hung from the central rafter.

'Sit down.' The man in the raincoat elbowed the door to, then removed his hat, motioning with the automatic as he did so. 'Sit at the table and empty your pockets.' What passed for a smile pushed his features askew. 'Everything, mind.'

Laker glared at him, risking stubborness. 'Who the devil are you? Just what authority have you got?'

'This.' The gun. 'This will do for now. And if you think I wouldn't use it you are very much in error.'

The room was resonant and their voices bounced off the bare walls. Laker emptied his pockets slowly, the only show of defiance remaining to him. Wallet, pen, nail-clippers, comb, handkerchief, cigarettes and lighter, some loose change, diary . . . Panic could still block his thoughts to reason and, as he put the diary on the table, he remembered with a prickle of alarm that it contained the Kromadecka number.

'Anything else?'

'No.'

'It would be wise for us to make certain, don't you think? Take your overcoat and jacket off. And your trousers.' There was a pause, during which Laker did nothing. 'You have no option, Mr. Laker. Hurry now.'

The driver went over them as minutely as if he were looking for lice. All he found were a couple of old cinema-ticket stubs, but the seam which Carol Nolan had re-sewn on the right shoulder of the jacket interested him. He produced a claspknife, slit it open and explored the wadding, ignoring Laker's protests. Eventually, after a shake of the head, he tossed the clothes on to the nearest chair.

Laker put them on again, his anger as impotent as his desperation. 'What did you expect?' he bellowed. 'Look, this is monstrous. I demand an explanation. I'm in Leipzig for the Fair, a *bona fide* visitor, and my son's expecting me at the Astoria Hotel. You've made a mistake, I tell you, and the sooner –'

'If there has been a mistake, Mr Laker, you will be entitled to, and will receive, the fullest amends. Meanwhile we can only wait and see.'

'Wait?'

'Wait, yes.'

'How long, for God's sake? What for?'

'I mentioned, didn't I, that your arrest had offical blessing?'

'Arrest? Now look here – '

'The last half-hour has perhaps been a little unorthodox. However, Colonel Hartmann will be here at six and he, better than anyone, will be in a position to judge whether a mistake has been made. Colonel Hartmann, you see, is head of S.S.D. – the State Security Service.'

With that the man picked up the diary, crossed his legs and began to turn the pages. 'Watch him,' he said, and Laker saw that the driver had a pistol, too.

Again the milling confusion of mind descended. And again Slattery was there – 'No one's been blown; nothing like that . . .' Well, Karen was blown now, and he was linked with her. The two Vopos? . . . No, no. How, then? He still couldn't think straight. There was an awful feeling of emptiness in him, as if his strength had been sapped.

It was ten to six, and the sun was splintering lower through the pines. He went to the nearest window and stared out. The immediate landscape wasn't irrelevant to his fears. Why had they brought him here instead of to some urban headquarters? He turned nervously, in need of another cigarette, but the driver warned him away from those he had left on the table and threw him one of his own instead.

'Mine aren't poisoned,' Laker said bitterly, but the man only cleared his throat and rubbed the barrel of his automatic on his sleeve. You lout, Laker thought. He looked at the one leafing through the diary, and as if he had been given a cue the man said: 'I see your son's birthday is the same as mine – June 14th.'

Laker glared, hating him. It was imbecilic to have noted the Kromadecka number, yet it would be equally mad to deny having been in the shop. He would have admitted that in any case. They knew, anyway. Karen was the focal-point of what had happened and for him to be here at all could only mean that she must have been under suspicion long before he set foot in the Luisenstrasse. Why else had he been hi-jacked? And so promptly? If only he could calm his mind . . . He smoked about half-way down the cigarette, weakness returning like a fever. Then the one in the raincoat rose and dropped the diary on the table. He had given no indication of having noticed the number; in fact he'd appeared to be more interested in the London underground map than anything.

'You were a busy person, Mr Laker,' he remarked. 'You lived a full life back there in England.'

He said it as mildly as a priest reproving a common vice. At any other time Laker might have fastened in alarm on to the use of the past tense, but for some inexplicable reason he was suddenly aware of the correct pronunciation of his name. The receptionist at the Astoria had called him 'Larker', but this man had never made that mistake. Not once. He had been right from the very beginning ('Mr. Laker? . . . Mr. Samuel Laker? . . .'), and the only other person in Leipzig who'd addressed him accurately was Karen.

A terrible possibility entered his head. He tried to shove it aside, attributing the accuracy to Patrick, but it insisted, boring in. With an almost convulsive movement that tore skin from dry lips he snatched the cigarette from his mouth, searching his memory for Slattery's exact words outside The Mitre – 'A misunderstanding. I can't explain and you won't expect me to. But contacts have been broken . . .' In disbelief he then remembered something else. 'No!' Karen had said when she recognised him. 'Oh no!' – and with a sense of derangement he found himself interpreting her look of dismay as one of guilt. Had she been aware of what was going to happen? Could it be that she was blown *before* Slattery ever approached him; her shock principally that of discovering whom she was forced to expose? 'Oh God,' she had uttered finally. 'I didn't know it was going to be you standing here . . .'

It was unbelievable that he should be thinking of her as if she were a kind of enemy when only an hour ago he had been moved by her very closeness. Yet the fact remained that within fifteen minutes of his leaving Kromadecka's the Mercedes was at the hotel, *waiting for him*, along with the lies about Patrick and this devastating, slowly burgeoning seed of Laker pronounced as it should have been . . .

If she had been under duress he was sunk. He heeled out the cigarette on the floor, subsided on to a chair and for barren moments afterwards rested his head in his hands. He didn't hear the car coming. The others did, and the man in the raincoat went outside. But after perhaps a minute he was conscious of voices, the one that stuttered and the one he didn't know, and the clatter on the steps.

He was expecting someone in uniform, but he was wrong. Hartmann was wearing a dark brown belted overcoat and a black velour trilby, the brim of which was turned down back and front. He was tall, lean, older than Laker, and his eyes had a slightly fixed stare, like a ventriloquist's. He paused when he saw Laker, looked at him for a long moment, then motioned to the driver who had stopped leaning against the wall and was suddenly at attention.

'I'll use the other room.' The voice was throttled, as if he had had laryngitis.

'Yes, colonel.'

The driver opened the communicating door and snapped on a light. The other two went through and the door was shut, leaving Laker and the driver alone. Laker sweated, listening to the murmur which reached them through the partition, protest and apprehension compounded. Several minutes elapsed before the door opened again and the man in the raincoat emerged.

'All right,' he said, and jerked his head.

It was a similar-sized room, with a table and only two chairs, but the whole of one side was stacked with buckets, bags of sand, coiled lengths of hose and long-handled birch brooms. All but one of the windows were obscured, so the electric light was necessary. With a renewal of bewilderment Laker questioned why he had been brought to such a place. He felt scared, scared and irresolute, as if he sensed that he wasn't far from the border-line of nightmare.

'I understand you speak German.'

'Yes.'

'Very well. Sit down.'

They faced each other across the empty table. Hartmann's swarthy complexion seemed to emphasise the blueness of his eyes. Narrow nose, straight grey hair. His hat had left a pressure-weal angled across his forehead and he rubbed it gingerly.

'The two in the other room aren't the only ones who are armed.' The strained voice, the ventriloquist's stare. 'Is that clear?' He didn't wait. 'Now tell me something about yourself, Mr. Laker.' The 'a' was correct again, feeding Laker's new-found conclusion.

'I want to know why I'm here first.'

'We'll come to that.'

'I want to know now. And I want to know what's become of my son.' He was like an actor with no faith in the weight of his lines. 'If you can't tell me I insist on being taken to someone who can.'

'To whom, for instance?'

'I don't give a damn as long as I get some answers.'

'And an apology, I suppose?'

Laker shifted position.

'What would you expect this apology to cover?'

'My God,' Laker snapped. 'What d'you think?'

'False arrest? Or is your objection to the manner in which it was carried out?' Hartmann seemed amused. 'There was no violence, was there? If you cast your mind back you will realise that my colleagues employed the Judo technique of using their opponent's muscles.'

Laker leaned towards him. 'I was told my son was at the University Clinic. But since I now know that was a lie, where is he? Who's looking after him? What kind of explanation's he been given about this . . . this nonsense?'

'The story is that you've been called away.'

'He won't accept that.'

'He really doesn't have any choice.'

Laker clenched his hands. 'Where am I supposed to have been called to? For what reason? And for how long? . . . I've a right to know. And I've a right to be told on what grounds, what possible grounds –'

'We aren't here to discuss your son. And rights, you will discover, begin and end with me.' Hartmann paused to rub the diminishing weal. 'You should have taken his welfare into consideration before you came to the Democratic Republic.'

'I don't follow.'

'No?' The tone was almost conversational, but his eyes never once left Laker's face. 'You will, though. I am certain you will . . . Now, what brought you to Leipzig?'

'I came for the Fair.'

'On your own account?'

'No.'

'What line of business are you in?'

'We design and manufacture office equipment.'

'"We"?'

'My firm. Gale and Watts.'

'In London?'

'No.'

'Where, then?'

'In Weybridge, Surrey.'

'I see . . . And have you found our Fair worth the visit?'

'What I've had time for, yes.'

'How about your particular trade section?'

'I haven't been to it yet.'

'When did you arrive?'

'This morning.'

'By air?'

'Yes. I applied for Fair Cards at your Agency office in London two months ago – for myself and for my son.'

'Never having been here before?'

'Not since I was a child.'

Hartmann nodded. 'How did you and your son spend this afternoon?'

'On a general look-round.' Laker tried to match the stare. Now the crux was coming.

'A general look-round at what?'

He moved his shoulders 'Sports goods, photographic equipment, radio and television –'

'So you didn't visit the section you specifically came to Leipzig to see?'

'We're on holiday as much as anything and I gave the boy his head this afternoon. Tomorrow, though – '

'Where else did you go, Mr. Laker?'

'Personally?' He hadn't meant to stall, but he couldn't seem to help himself.

'Personally. What decided you to separate from your son?'

'I went to get something done to my watch.'

'What, exactly?'

'It needed a new strap.'

'And where did you go?'

'To a shop in the Luisenstrasse.'

'The Luisenstrasse?'

'Yes.'

'And the name of this shop?'

'Kromadecka.'

Another skilful, demoralising pause. The overhead light seemed to burn brighter.

'Why there?'

'How d'you mean?'

'What made you choose that particular shop?'

'It was recommended.'

'Oh yes?'

'I broke my old strap on the plane. One of the passengers suggested I ought to go to Kromadecka.'

'Mr. Laker, 'Hartmann said, 'there are half a dozen places which you could have gone to within walking distance of the Astoria Hotel.'

'I wasn't aware of that. I haven't been in Leipzig for over thirty years.'

'So the distance to the Luisenstrasse surprised you?'

'Yes – I suppose it did.'

'You went by taxi?'

'Yes.'

Hartmann rested his chin on his knuckles. 'Your only reason for going to Kromadecka was to have your watch attended to – am I right?'

'Quite right.'

'There was no other motive?'

'No.'

'You would swear to that?'

'Certainly.'

For a lunatic moment Laker thought it possible that there was some sort of hope. But almost at once this died.

'When did you write the Kromadecka number in your diary?'

'On the plane.'

'Why not the address?'

'I wasn't given the address.' Suddenly he was floundering.

'A telephone number only? By a stranger in an aircraft?'

'Yes.'

'You expect me to believe that?'

'It happens to be true.'

Seconds elapsed. Then, gazing across at him with what could have been pity, Hartmann said. 'You are very much a novice, Mr. Laker. Those people who sent you – '

'Gale and Watts?'

'The people who sent you to Kromadecka . . . Didn't they tell you the cardinal rule?'

He stood up, walked to the door and opened it. The man in the raincoat was there, like an eavesdropper.

'Bring the Gisevius woman in,' Hartmann said, and Laker's heart plummeted as he spun round.

Apart from the first frightened glance she would not look at him. She was dressed exactly as when he saw her last except that the white bead necklace had gone. Her hair was slightly disarranged. She came in as if she had been pushed, then halted abruptly, swaying a little, terribly pale.

'Do you know this man?' Hartmann asked.

'Yes.'

'Explain how you know him.'

'He called at my shop.' It was a whisper, almost inaudible, but there was no hesitation.

'When?'

'This afternoon.'

'For what purpose?'

'To renew the strap of his watch.'

Laker had got to his feet. Wheeling on Hartmann he protested desperately: 'I told you. I told you this.'

Hartmann's face was expressionless. 'What was sewn into the old

strap, Fräulein? The one he left with you?'
'Microfilm.'
An insect pinged against the light. Hartmann glanced sidelong. 'You
see, Mr. Laker? Or do you still insist that your arrest is without cause?'
'I don't know what the hell you're talking about.'
'No?'
'No,' Laker shouted, dismay absolute.
'Are you making out that we have confronted you with a liar?'
Laker chocked back the instinctive assent. Karen's eyes were averted
from him. Hartmann allowed time for an answer, then nodded to the
other man.
'Very well. Take her away.'
She went without prompting, as if she wanted to run from the room,
but in the doorway she turned suddenly and met Laker's gaze, sobbing,
defeated. 'I'm sorry . . . I'm sorry . . .' The man in the raincoat shoved
her into the other room. Laker heard them cross to the outer door, heard
it opened and slammed. The grass killed their footsteps after that but the
sound of her crying seemed to go on and on, bitter and broken, matching
his own wretchedness.
And Hartmann's throttled voice was saying: 'Spare me, please, the
story that you were merely doing a friend of yours in London a favour. I
have heard that one before, and there is nothing more tiresome than
repetition.'

For perhaps another quarter of an hour Laker denied everything
except having visited Kromadecka's; either that or he met Hartmann's
leads with a dogged silence. In a mood of heart-break and recrimination
the ragged edges of his mind isolated themselves from the reality of
Hartmann's presence and turned in hostility upon the mainspring of
disaster, Slattery – Slattery who must have been aware that, at best,
Karen was on thin ice and that anyone sent to contact her was running
an abnormal risk. *Must* . . . So he should have been told, warned; instead
of which he'd been criminally misled. And now, as at Gardelegen years
before, he was as good as written off, Slattery's get-out number as useless
as the wireless-set which wouldn't work. And this time he was trapped,
without choice of action, run to earth on behalf of an organisation he
didn't know or belong to and which would almost certainly disown him.
Whose game *was* this? Whose war? . . . Not his. Not Patrick's.
Hartmann had just said: 'You are either an unfortunate fool, Mr.
Laker, or a benighted idealist. The Gisevius woman is clearly the latter –
though in her case, since she is a German, such a phrase is a euphemism.'

The ventriloquist's stare was there again. 'Which are you, Mr. Laker?'
Laker looked through him.

'Did it not occur to you that this might happen? How much did they
tell you in London before they borrowed your watch?'

He didn't answer. They knew more than he did. Karen had branded
him from the doorway, and the remembered sound of her voice sent a
pang through him as stunning as grief. She must have been as powerless
as he was now. Chance had worked against them both, lain in wait for
them after half a lifetime, and London would have ditched her as well.
Nothing he said could help her. And he owed Slattery nothing,
absolutely nothing. His first loyalty was to himself and to Patrick and it
was better to stick to the lies and protestations than offer one word too
many. Co-operation wasn't a way out. What was on the microfilm?
What kind of postman had he been?'

'I want to see my son,' he cut in on Hartmann.

'That will not be possible.'

'Why not?'

'There won't be time.'

Time? Time? 'I want to write to him, then.' He licked his lips. 'A note.
I'm . . . I'm trying to be practical. He's got no money, to start with,
and – '

'That side of things has been taken care of.'

'Who by?'

'By my department.'

'He's fourteen, Laker said, veins swelling in his temples. 'If there's a
spark of sympathy in you – '

'I'm aware of the boy's age.'

'He hasn't done anything.'

'I'm aware of that, too. But, as I said earlier, we didn't meet to talk
about him. And remember this, Mr. Laker. You are a long way from
home. What's more, your country does not recognise the German
Democratic Republic. This, as you will discover, is greatly to your
disadvantage since it means that what are sometimes called your
interests cannot be safeguarded.'

Again, for a fleeting moment, Hartmann's face seemed to register a
hard-held pity. Then, abruptly, as if he had come to a decision with
himself, he got to his feet and went out, taking his hat, leaving the door
open. Laker heard a muttered conversation in the other room. Craning
round, he saw the driver framed by the doorway, arms crossed,
watching him. Half a minute later someone left the hut – Hartmann, he
presumed – and presently he heard a car retch, roar, then purr away.

He moved to the solitary window, thoughts churning frantically. It was small, too small, the frame heavy. Daylight still held in the clearing and long shadows were printed across the grass. Why here? he questioned again. And what would follow? What happened to the others? – those one read about? A People's Court? . . . He couldn't understand why Hartmann had left without pressing him further, but his mind had been stretched beyond conscious usefulness and he could find no answers – to that or to anything else.

They left him alone for a few minutes. Presently the driver came to the door, the automatic like an extension of his right arm, and ordered him out. The man in the raincoat followed and the three of them walked across the clearing towards the Mercedes. The air seemed cold and Laker shivered involuntarily. A stained wash of clouds patched the gaps in the pines. Far off, a train rattled. He slowed as he neared the car, but to his surprise the driver said: 'Keep going.' Puzzled, Laker started to round it, imagining that he was expected to get in from the far side, but the driver waved him on. When he hesitated the other one stuttered: 'Into the trees, Mr. Laker.'

Alarm entered him then. 'Why?'

'Into the trees. Go on – move.'

He obeyed, tightness gripping his stomach. Perhaps thirty paces brought them to the edge of the pines and his panic mounted with every step.

No, he thought. No. They couldn't.

The driver was three or four yards behind. 'Where are you taking me?' Laker demanded, but there was no answer. The light faded as he entered the trees. The ground was springy, deadening their footfalls. The trees were well-spaced. He stopped again.

'What's the idea?'

Their faces confirmed his fears. Unnerved, he stared at them. *Jesus* . . .

'Hurry, Mr. Laker.'

He seemed to have lost the ability to move. Suddenly the nightmare was on him, insanely improbable, yet happening, actually happening. He started to say something but his lips stuck to his teeth and a kind of leer resulted, dragging the corners of his mouth.

'Walk,' the driver snapped. 'Turn round and walk. Otherwise you can have it here.'

Laker made about ten paces, a withering contraction shrinking his insides, numbing him through and through.

'Stop.'

Almost immediately a rope was flipped over his shoulders, pinning his

arms. He struggled as if an icy douche had restored his senses. The man
in the raincoat stood with the pistol pointed at Laker's chest while the
driver looped the rope round the nearest tree, then hauled so that Laker
stumbled back. He began to bawl at them, demoralised, swept by a kind
of frenzy, fighting against the rope, kicking, dread and disbelief
compounded into an electric terror.

From behind, the driver fastened the rope across Laker's ankles,
whistling tunelessly as he did so. Then he stood up, fumbled inside his
jacket and brought out a thick brown paper bag. The last things Laker
saw before the bag was shoved over his head were the blond hairs poking
through the driver's chin and the smoke from the other's cigarette
hanging on the air like ectoplasm.

The sugary smell of the bag and the acrid stink of his own sweat
enveloped him. He stopped shouting, jerking his head, trying to toss the
bag away. The driver was backing with the alacrity of someone who had
lit a fuse; Laker could hear the crushing of pine-needles. Light blurred
through a small hole on one side of the bag. It wouldn't shift. Now,
straining his ears, he tried to stifle the monstrous hammer-blows of his
pulse, desperate to identify the slightest sound.

His guts seemed to be liquidising. Stiff against the tree, fingernails
digging into the bark, teeth beginning to chatter.

No! . . . No! . . .

Silence.

Where were they?

A bird twittered somewhere in the branches. A cough, several yards
away, its hoicking rasp muffled by the bag. A whisper. A metallic click . . .
Time seemed to run to a halt. Laker screwed his eyes, images sweeping in
raving disorder across the throbbing, blood-red darkness – Patrick,
Slattery, Helen, Patrick, Hartmann, Karen . . . Patrick . . .

Body arched, the back of his legs beating a flabby tattoo against the
tree, bladder beginning to empty.

Silence.

A tiny thread of awareness made him understand that time was
moving on again. He cocked his head.

Nothing.

Then a sound, slow and deliberate. The soft crunch of someone
walking. Half right. Coming closer. Laker held his breath. His lips
moved, but nothing escaped them. His wits were resurrecting, clinging
to life. The footsteps approached casually. Two or three paces from him
they stopped.

Another silence that seemed to last as long as the spinning, recollected years. He flinched from whoever was there, whatever was happening. Finally the man in the raincoat spoke.

'Not today, Mr. Laker.' It came with a rush as the stutter broke. 'We'll forget about it this time.'

And Laker vomited into the bag.

CHAPTER 7

They helped him to the car, linking him in an underarm grip. One of them gave him some rag to wipe himself and afterwards, when he had slumped into the back seat, a metal flask was pushed into his hands.

'Cognac.'

He shook his head.

'Cognac. You need it.'

Through a blur of awareness he tilted the flask. The cognac caught at his throat and he started coughing. He pushed the flask away, bending over, heavily gasping for air. Then he slumped back again and closed his eyes, horror beating through him.

'Let's go,' he heard.

Icy ripples were moving everywhere over his skin. The car lurched as it met the ruts and he swayed with it, limp and unprotesting. Shivering, hugging himself, he had no control over the reflexive spasms which occasionally twitched his body, nor could he unlock his jaws. He could smell the bag still and the foulness of his soiled clothes wafted up at him, reviving the tidal-wave of terror and release that had buckled his knees and made him sag on the rope.

Several minutes have passed before the violence of the trauma began to ebb a little. After a while he opened his eyes and stared glazedly through the window, dimly conscious of speed, cars flickering the other way, the rubbery lick of tyres. The sun had dropped below the horizon and the slopes were darkening below their gilded rim, but this didn't register. Questions were drumming a shaky tattoo against his senses, demanding an explanation. One thing and one thing only was clear – he wasn't alive because of any sudden change of heart. What had happened had been intended to happen.

A feeling of vertigo assailed him. Something else was in store, but it was beyond his powers of recovery to grapple with what it might be. He wound the window down and raised his face to the draught, ashen, oblivious of the driver's curiosity reflected in the quivering rear-view mirror or the other's sideways glance.

They corkscrewed under the autobahn. Soon, Leipzig began to fashion itself, the scattered fringes rising out of the shrinking dusk.

'More cognac?'

The stutter, more than the voice itself, seemed to summon the enfeebling nausea. Laker groped forward, a gargling noise in his throat, but nothing came.

'Pull over, Hans. I don't want him messing the car.'

They slowed and the man in the raincoat watched him as anxiously as a parent.

'All right?'

Laker nodded, threads of spittle hanging from his lips, wondering how much longer he was to be toyed with, cat and mouse, and to what end. Solicitude was as much a part of the nightmare as survival.

Where he was taken he didn't then know. It seemed to be the back of a building towards the city's centre. A narrow entrance, a dozen or so stone steps and then a small rope-operated elevator which moaned them up to about the second floor. Several right-angle turns brought them to an expanding metal gate which snapped behind them. The driver didn't accompany them beyond the gate, but the other one directed Laker along a short, ill-lit corridor. Nobody else was in evidence. They passed a number of plain grey doors, each with an exterior observation shutter. At the end door on the left Laker was told to halt. The man produced a key and tossed it to him, taking no chances even here, the pistol bulging his right-hand pocket.

'Inside, Mr. Laker.'

There was a steel bunk, a wooden table and a galvanised slop-bucket; nothing else. Walls and ceiling were whitewashed. High up, set in a chute, a small barred window framed a square of near-darkness. Two lights burned, one above the bunk, the other from a plug directly below the chute.

As soon as Laker stepped inside the door closed and he heard the lock go on. Without as much as looking round he flung himself on to the bunk. For what seemed an immense amount of time he remained motionless, as if he had been pole-axed, staring blankly at the opposite wall, chained to a succession of appalling cameos that flitted across the surface of his consciousness. When he eventually gazed along the length of his body and saw what he had done to himself he lacked any sense of shame. Thoughts stirred and eddied, shying from the edges of reality. But there was no refuge, no escape from whatever unfinished crisis chance and Hartmann had chosen for him, and the question-marks continued feebly in the background with disordered insistence.

Soon after eight he heard movement in the corridor. He sat up, muscles rigid by the time the door was opened. Someone he had never seen before came in, a youngish, dark-haired individual with a long penitential face who wore a white shirt and black trousers that could have belonged to a uniform. He was carrying a plastic bowl in one hand, a towel in the other.

Putting the bowl on the table he said impatiently: 'I want your clothes.' Then, as the towel landed on the bunk: 'Your clothes. I haven't got all night.'

Laker stripped to his shirt and underpants without a word, defiance bludgeoned out of him. There was warm water in the bowl and a cake of brown soap wrapped in the towel. When he was alone again he washed, then pulled a blanket over his shoulders and sat huddled on the bunk with his back against the wall, desperately trying to still his mind and to get a grip on himself.

'Not today, Mr. Laker . . .'

Whatever was coming he could find no basis for hope. Pencilled on the wall to his left were someone else's initials together with a year-old date, and there were others when he looked for them, half a dozen or so, one spidered into the brickwork as if with a thumbnail, the date more recent. From the depths of shock Laker wondered who these people were and whether secrecy and half-truths had erupted into madness for them, too.

Towards eight-thirty the same man kneed the door open and brought in a tray on which were soup, a hash of some kind, coarse dark bread and a mug of coffee. On his way out he delayed to drop matches and a pack of cigarettes on to the bunk, but Laker was beyond the reach of surprise. The sight of the food almost turned his stomach; he couldn't touch it. He drank the sharp black coffee, though, and lit up, inhaling so fiercely that it made him dizzy.

Patrick, Karen, Slattery – his mind revolved endlessly. It was absolutely quiet except for the small sounds of his own making and these seemed to increase his isolation. A star or two glittered in the dark square of the window. The hash formed a wrinkled skin as it grew cold. For what might have been hours he relived what the day had done to him, travelling again through expectancy charged with tension, tension with action, action with dismay, dismay with that awful escalation of fear; and now the savage, impenetrable remorse.

God, what a fool he'd been. What a blind, uncalculating fool . . .

But it wasn't hours: when he next heard movement in the corridor he saw that it was only ten-past nine. The man entered again, this time fully uniformed in black, carrying Laker's suit draped across his arm. His eyes, his expression, conveyed nothing.

'Put it on,' he said, and waited.

The suit had been sponged and pressed; the tear in the right shoulder re-sewn.

'Where am I going?'

'Colonel Hartmann wants you.'

Laker had guessed as much, but he was too exhausted to care. When he started to walk his legs felt as though he'd been bedridden for weeks.

To reach Hartmann's office they descended a spiral iron staircase to the next level and made their way through a maze of windowless, yellow-brick corridors that smelt of disinfectant. Again they passed no one, saw no one. Presently they reached a door with a green light glowing on the lintel. The man ordered Laker to stop, then motioned him in, not following, closing the door as soon as Laker had passed through. And Hartmann was there, behind a desk in the centre of a largish room, waiting for him with the choked, unforgettable voice.

'Sit down, Mr. Laker.'

There was a chair on the near side of the desk and Laker went to it, dry in the mouth. Hartmann studied him in silence, reverting at once to this particular weapon in his armoury, using it now almost as if he hoped it would produce a reaction: hatred, perhaps.

'How d'you feel?'

Laker swallowed.

'How was it in the pines with a bag over your head?'

No reply.

'An experience, eh? To be remembered?'

His shoulders were so square that he might have had the chairback under his jacket.

'To be remembered?'

'Yes.'

'Not pleasant, eh? Not willingly gone through again?' He tapped the desk. 'Answer me.'

'No.'

Framed behind his narrow head was a colour print of a healthy-looking Ulbricht. The desk was empty of papers. Glass ashtray, blotter, two telephones – that was all. Some filing cabinets lined one of the walls; slatted blinds shut out the night. But Laker's gaze didn't wander far.

'Why d'you suppose you continue to be alive, Mr. Laker?'

'I don't know.'

'Have you wondered?'

'Of course.'

'Have you also wondered how it came about that you were ever taken into the pines?'

'Yes.'

Hartmann cleared his throat to no effect. 'With more success?'

'I can only think that you must imagine me to be somebody else.'

'Somebody else?' It seemed to surprise him.

'Yes.'

'Who, for instance?'

'Somebody more important.'

'You aren't being very logical. The Gisevius woman identified you.'

Laker gestured weakly. He would have tried to shield her once, but that was hours ago. Lies, denials, pretence – these were pointless now. She was sunk, too. There was no one to betray. 'In which case,' he said, 'you've thrown her away on account of a nobody.'

'"Thrown her away"?'

'As far as using her's concerned.'

'Is that what you are? A nobody?'

'Yes.'

'You're too modest. I wouldn't say that. I wouldn't say that at all.' Hartmann leaned back, crossing one leg over the other. 'In time I shall explain.' He swung his free leg and let the silence settle for a few moments. With a kind of admiration he then said: 'You are remarkably resilient, Mr. Laker. Not many could sit there and be so self-possessed so soon after what has happened. It was an outrage, was it not?'

Laker clenched his jaws.

'An outrage,' Hartmann repeated as if he found pleasure in the word. 'And I shouldn't like you to think anything so drastic is normal practice. The S.S.D. and its agencies have certain responsibilities, certain functions, within the Democratic Republic. I won't bother you with what they are. But, in the usual way, when a courier is intercepted he – or she – is most rigorously interrogated. How rigorously I am sure you can imagine. In your case, however, interrogation has been kept to a bare minimum. This is not because the Gisevius woman has volunteered all we might have wanted to know about you. Far from it. The fact is that, for once, we aren't particularly interested. All that interests us is your being here.' He flicked a speck of dust from the blotter. 'Does any of this make sense?'

'No.'

'We have plans for you, Mr. Laker. You are about to work for us . . .

Oh, yes. There is a job to be done. A very special job. It will mean your being taken from here and set free.'

Laker frowned.

'I assure you. Tomorrow you will be on your way. And you will do the job as surely as a puppet dances when the strings are pulled.'

'I don't understand.'

'Soon you will. First, though, I want you to get used to the idea.'

'And if I can't?'

'You are not in a position to object. You're as good as dead, Mr. Laker. Don't tell me your memory's that short.'

Now it was Laker who paused. 'You said I would be released.'

'That is so. By tomorrow evening you will be in Copenhagen.'

'*Copenhagen?*'

Hartmann nodded.

'Why? What for?'

'To kill someone.'

'*What?*'

'To kill someone,' Hartmann repeated evenly. 'Does it shock you so?'

He was met with an appalled stare. Laker heard himself say: 'You must be mad.'

'We're talking about you.'

'I couldn't do it.'

'You could, Mr. Laker. And you shall.' Hartmann leaned on the desk. 'I can read you like a book. I can almost see your mind working – do you know that? Copenhagen, you are thinking. How will he make the puppet dance at such long range? I will have a frontier behind me. He can't control me then. Why should I kill anyone for him? The idea's preposterous.'

Laker dropped his gaze.

'Am I not right?'

'You underestimate me if you believe I'm so naïve.' Suddenly there was a trace of venom. 'I thought you would be quicker to appreciate the situation. Must I explain what will operate the strings?'

A fearful possibility had begun to dawn, but Laker couldn't bring himself to utter it.

'Why do you think you were made to stand against that tree? . . . No? All right, I shall enlighten you. Imagination is a poor substitute for experience, Mr. Laker. You were put there so that you would know exactly what your son will experience if you fail in Copenhagen. The only difference being that, in his case, there will be no last-second reprieve . . . Have I made myself clear? From the moment you are liberated until you complete this assignment it is going to be – how shall I say? – zero hour for him.'

Hartmann watched the blaze of horror in Laker's bloodshot eyes.

'This is the crudest form of blackmail, I admit. However, I can assure you that the old-fashioned pressures are far and away the best. A few hours ago you were terrified in the marrow of your bones – and who can blame you? This is not to say that you wouldn't offer to be taken into the pines again to spare your son. It would be a natural enough gesture. Unfortunately for you, *I* choose who goes there and who doesn't.'

Laker's voice shook. 'You can't mean that.' The nightmare had reasserted itself with the same demented improbability. 'You can't . . . You wouldn't dare. He's innocent.'

Hartmann blew through his lips. 'I'm not concerned with that. But you are, which is as it should be.'

'He's a schoolboy. A schoolboy, d'you hear? On holiday. He was keeping me company, that's all. After tomorrow we were going back to the West, to the Rhineland.' The protests spilled over, words, words. 'You can't mean this, any of it. You *can't.*'

But he did. Oh Christ, he did.

'I want to see someone else.' Panic brought Laker to his feet. 'Where am I? Where is this place?' Desperately he struggled to control himself. 'Who are you to decide what becomes of us. Look . . . listen to me. I want to speak to someone else. All I've done – '

'There *is* no one else – not for you. Contrary to what you may believe the Soviets give us a very free rein in certain matters. Now sit down. This is between you and me, Mr. Laker.'

In vain Laker searched for the glimpse of pity he had once detected. But Hartmann's fixed blue stare was implacable. He looked very sure of himself, as if he'd inhabited this room for a long time, proposed such things before. Even as his thoughts reeled and blundered Laker knew the futility of pleading.

'Where's my son now?'

'Unaware that he is under discussion, I promise you.'

'That's not an answer.'

Hartmann half-smiled, as if a thought had that moment struck him. 'All this has come at you very quickly. How much of it do you doubt, I wonder?' He reached for one of the telephones and dialled a number, unhooking the ear-piece extension as he did so and pushing it in Laker's direction.

Laker lifted it in time to hear: 'Astoria Hotel, good evening.'

'Reception, please.' Then, when they were connected: 'I'm enquiring about two of your guests. They are British, and the name is Laker . . . Laker, yes. L,A,K,E,R . . . Can you tell me if they are still with you? The room number is fifty-four, I believe.'

Hartmann's fingers drummed the desk. A hum throbbed along the line. Muffled voices sounded in the background – sane, unaware.

'Are you there, caller?'

'Yes.'

'The people you are inquiring after checked out earlier this evening.'

'Thank you.' Hartmann hung up. 'You see, Mr. Laker? . . . I have your luggage, incidentally. Only yours, of course. Your son has kept his own.'

Laker swore at him.

'You can say all you wish, but it will change nothing. And you have only yourself to blame. Deep waters are for those who can swim. You should have reckoned on the possibility of getting beyond your depth. Now, for want of a better phrase, you are an instrument about to be put to practical use. And, human nature being what it is, you will take every care to see that you operate with maximum efficiency.'

Silence and heart-break closed in on Laker. 'You're asking the impossible.'

'I think not.'

'You've got the wrong man. I'm not a murderer.'

Hartmann pressed back in his chair. 'You are old enough to have been in the war. Were you in the war, Mr. Laker? A soldier, perhaps?'

'What's that got to do with it?'

'Killing was a duty then. A daily duty.'

'I wasn't in the S.S.'

Hartmann coloured slightly. 'All it needs is provocation. Provocation or necessity. Listen very carefully. If you change your mind and don't go through with this, your son will never rejoin you, safe and sound. And if you try, yet fail, the result will be the same. Either way I promise you that on whatever you care to name as sacred.'

Laker closed his eyes, what remained of his spirit crumbling.

Hartmann was saying: 'The psychology is soundly based. I am quite certain you will give me your fullest co-operation. We're continuing with the Judo technique, d'you see? Everything has been most thoroughly considered. On the face of it you will be your own master. You will go to Copenhagen, you will take certain actions, and you will ensure that the job is successfully completed. Then, and then only, will you and your son be reunited.'

'How can I be sure of that?'

'You have my word.'

Clutching at straws now, Laker said thickly: 'If my son were harmed in any way there'd be an outcry. What you've done already is a violation of every international – '

'Listen, Mr. Laker. Keep listening. I've no qualms about the story you'll tell London when you eventually return there. But do you suppose the people who sent you will care to broadcast it to the world at large? Two years ago something went badly wrong for a certain Mr. James Wyatt. Were you, as a member of the British public, ever made aware of Mr. Wyatt's objectives or what became of him? Was there an outcry then? Have you ever heard of him, in fact? . . . No. And why not? Because, unless the circumstances are exceptional, outcries are an embarrassment to those who make them. They should have told you of this in London. In effect, Mr. Laker, you and your son have ceased to be public property. Here, in this room, you may well be of the opinion that there is no such thing as justice. But you will find it doesn't exist where you come from either. Sympathy there may be; generosity, no doubt, if your silence has to be bought. But if your son suffers as a result of your failure in Copenhagen the world will never be allowed to know. London will see to that. They have too many skeletons in too many cupboards. They'll go along with our account of an accident; accept our post-mortem certificate. You yourself will know it's all a lie and so will they. But an outcry? . . . No, Mr. Laker, particularly in view of the seriousness of what we can level against them and the degree of your involvement.'

Laker looked away, overwhelmed by the imagery of vicarious terror, trapped and committed by it. A shudder racked his shoulders.

'Now do you understand?'

He didn't answer.

'You have no choice, d'you see?'

Laker ungummed his lips. In a low voice he said: 'What am I to do?'

'I told you. You will go to Copenhagen and kill a man.'

'Who? How shall I know him?' Christ, he thought hysterically, what's happening to me?

'We have photographs. Have you ever been to Copenhagen?'

'No.'

'Denmark?'

'No.'

'We will brief you before you go, both as regards the city and the person concerned. We will speak about the details tomorrow. You will be given every possible aid. But the timing must be yours and yours alone. And you must not fail – remember that should freedom affect your judgement.' Hartmann yawned almost theatrically. 'Now, though, I suggest you sleep on it. There has been enough for one day, wouldn't you agree? Unless, that is, you have any questions?'

He was cold, ruthless, perfectly equipped for the business of murder. And yet, when he indulged what could only amount to a sadistic pleasure, there was something contrived about his manner as if at all costs he wanted the satisfaction of Laker's hatred before he was done.

'Do you believe it yet?' he tilted his head. 'Or do you imagine it all a joke? An elaborate, unforgivable far-fetched joke?'

Laker dug his nails into his palms.

'Like this evening's charade in the pine trees, perhaps?'

'No.'

'What, then? . . . This room, S.S.D. headquarters, you who were so very nearly dead – and the talk is of Copenhagen and your son and London and an assassination.' His leg swung back and forth, back and forth. 'It's not a dream, d'you suppose? A bad dream that morning or some other awakening is going to wipe away?'

'No,' Laker heard himself answer. 'It's not a dream.'

CHAPTER 8

In the labyrinth of empty corridors that led back to the cell Laker's despair was like darkness, like night, and when the lock crunched home, shutting him away, he lay on the bunk in the grip of an awful stillness.

The enormity of the blackmail was too appalling for reasoned thought. He kept telling himself that, given time, he would find a way out – tomorrow, the next day. But now he was weak with the assault of weariness and shock, hollow, a sensation that was mental as well as physical, and while it lasted he numbly accepted that his will was tied.

The wall close to his face and the scrawled initials and the barred window reinforced reality. He fell asleep and woke and fell asleep again, over and over. Always when he woke the lights were burning. Sometimes a dream broke into his sleep like an intruder, once bringing him out of it in a fit of shaking, propped on the bunk, hearing the tail-end of his own voice. There was a time when he found himself running along an echoing passage vainly searching for a door; another when he was talking to Karen and Slattery in the forecourt of Gale and Watts, looking across Karen who was at the wheel of the blue van with Slattery

sitting beside her, and Slattery beamed: 'Tell me, Sam – what's
Hartmann like? What trick d'you fancy he might have up that S.S.D.
sleeve of his? . . . Incidentally, I warned you about him, didn't I?'
  No! . . . No!
  Towards five he surfaced once more and remained awake. He chain-
smoked despite a fierce thirst, the intimidation and the purpose of it as
devastating as before, his mind back on the treadmill. He couldn't even
begin to make a coherent assessment of what might be possible until
Hartmann told him more. Disbelief was stone-dead. Yesterday's terror
had hammered acceptance into him. He was being sent to murder
someone.
  Who? . . . How? . . .
  In desperation he drove his thoughts elsewhere. Jerry Baxendale,
Carol Nolan, Mrs. Ruddick, Roundwood, the Humber in the garage,
Mill Avenue, Oatlands, the woman in the yellow dress with the pram . . .
They had receded, yet always, always, they drew back to Slattery and
what had followed since and the monstrosity of what was still to come.
He watched the new day beginning to fill the small, high window,
wondering where Patrick was, thinking of him with terrible grief and
guilt, thinking of Helen and the last time, other times, Karen, vainly
trying to to be confronted with the question of how he could ever bring
himself to kill in cold blood and what was promised if he failed.
  His suitcase was in the cell, unopened. He was in his pants and shirt.
For the fifth time within an hour he lit a cigarette. Presently he put his
shoes and suit on, then either walked up and down or sat on the edge of
the bunk, fretting for someone to come and take him back to Hartmann
so that he could know all there was to know.

  He was fed first – black bread, some mottled slices of cold sausage, the
same sharp, gritty coffee. This was around seven-thirty. The man who
brought the food didn't speak, either then or when he returned to take
the tray away. Laker found his razor in the suitcase; plugged it into the
socket below the window-chute, shaved, then sluiced his face in the bowl
of water the man had brought when he removed the tray.
  Another hour dragged by after that. Death and violence were
commonplace when he had found it possible to kill. The whole world
was at it then. But he had grown, learned to pity, acquired sentiment,
softened. Jesus, how could he go about it now – even for Patrick's sake?
  There were no more cigarettes. He put his head in his hands and
stared at the floor, trembling.

Hartmann was seated behind his desk in the same attitude as when Laker had last seen him, for all the world as if he hadn't moved. It was just nine o'clock. A grey brick wall showed through the open blinds.

'Did you sleep well?' Hartmann asked with soft hoarseness.

'I slept.'

'And so, I understand, did your son. That will be a relief to you, I'm sure.' The taunting smile. 'When did you last handle a gun Mr. Laker?'

'What kind of a gun?'

'Any gun.'

'In nineteen forty-five.'

'Not since then?'

'No.'

'You don't possess one – privately?'

'No.'

'Then the first thing on this morning's agenda will be for you to get some practice. I told you, didn't I, that you would be assisted as much as possible?' He glanced at his watch. 'However, there is a little time yet . . . I have no doubt you've given the proposition plenty of thought. Who wouldn't, in your shoes? So I ought to touch on something which must have crossed your mind.' He paused briefly. 'Rid yourself of any idea of approaching your Embassy in Copenhagen or telephoning your associates in London. Inevitably, they would take steps to see that the person in question is removed from harm's way. And that, in the circumstances, is precisely what you cannot afford to have happen. D'you follow? This is between you and me, Mr. Laker. Until everything is over you have no alternative but to keep it so.'

'When will that be?' That Laker could even ask was the measure of the hold on him.

'By Saturday. The moment we have confirmation that you have successfully completed the assignment your son will be on a London-bound plane.' Hartmann studied his finger-nails before glancing up. 'It's an ugly business isn't it, Mr. Laker? Medieval one might say – without the medieval sanctity, that is.'

Saturday . . . Two days. Two days from now.

Hartmann went on: 'We'll come to the person's identity presently – after you've practised at the gallery. But in case your imagination is running away with you, let me tell you now that I doubt if you will ever have heard of him. He isn't the Mayor of West Berlin, or the American Secretary of State, or the Secretary-General of the United Nations. The history books won't be interested.' He glanced at his watch again, like a man who calculated every move. 'What kind of marksman were you, by the way?'

With sudden dread Laker burst out: 'Why me? Why've you picked on me?' All at once it had struck him that there might not be a loophole after all. Incredibly, everything was pointing to his doing exactly what Hartmann had planned. 'You want a killer, an out-and-out killer . . . a professional.' His voice cracked. It was the nearest he came to abasing himself.

Hartmann stood up, smoothing his jacket. 'You suit me very nicely, Mr. Laker. When the time comes I am certain we will find that you excel yourself.'

They rode down in the elevator, as close as friends, as silent as strangers, then descended the flight of stone steps. An official on duty at the exit into the street saluted as Hartmann approached. A dark green saloon was drawn into the kerb. The official hurried out and opened the near-side door. Hartmann motioned to Laker to get in, then joined him, rounding the car and squeezing behind the wheel.

The street was narrow, one way. They swung into a crescent-shaped thoroughfare with tall buildings on one side and a railed enclosure on the other. Only yesterday, watching the flocks of pedestrians, Laker had presumed of their joylessness natures corrupted and made stone-hard by promises and exhortations; and pitied them. But now, as the car threaded through heavy bicycle traffic into the world of posters and statues and other bolsters of hope, a crushing envy filled him for the sheer drab normality of their lives. From nowhere, ringing in his mind as if it were an echo-chamber, he remembered the girl in The Mitre laughing happily while he and Slattery sat together and he said: 'You haven't raised any goose-flesh yet . . .'

Hartmann turned left and right, then left again. Laker glimpsed a string of lettered bunting forming the word TEXTIL and some coloured direction indicators, but the Fair and everything to do with it seemed utterly unreal. Except that they appeared to be leaving the city's centre he hadn't the least notion where they were. PEACE IS OUR PROFESSION a hoarding announced. Within five minutes they were crowded by warehouses and the gaunt shards of some derelict buildings. Soon afterwards Hartmann nosed into a cobbled street and brought the car to rest outside what looked as if it might have been a bowling-alley.

'We have numerous rifle clubs and galleries in the Democratic Republic, Mr. Laker. Shooting is a very popular activity – in the schools, among factory organisations.' Hartmann spoke like a guide.

'Mainly it is the responsibility of the Association for Sports and Technology, but this particular gallery is administered by the Leipzig Division of the State Security Service. I think you will find it more than adequately equipped.'

They got out. The entrance was round a corner. Half a dozen steps led up to a reinforced glass door. Hartmann let them in with a key. A cloakroom led off the tiled lobby and there was also a door marked GUN-ROOM. The enclosed air had the stale tang of expended cordite.

Hartmann said: 'Normally a caretaker would be here, but on Thursdays the gallery is closed. There are two ranges, one for recruits, one for those who are more advanced. It would be sensible – don't you agree? – to treat you as a beginner.'

Laker didn't reply. It was all a nightmare.

'No stupidity, Mr. Laker. I'm armed, remember – though that isn't the real deterrent. You're a marionette already, as you surely know.'

He opened the gun-room, selected two rifles from the racks and took some ammunition cartons from a drawer. Emerging, he pointed: 'That way.' Laker walked along a short passage which brought him to another door. 'Go on through,' Hartmann said, flicking some switches, and Laker found himself in the intense brightness of what looked to be about a twenty-five-yard range.

The were fibre mats for six firing-points on a low, planked dais. The walls were a light grey except for the far one, which was black, and this was spattered raw above the sand-bagged, boxed-in target area. The air's bite was very strong, catching the throat. The door padded behind Hartmann who went immediately to the control-panel and started extractor-fans humming. He placed one of the rifles and a carton of ammunition on the dais, returned to the panel, fiddled with it for a few moments, then raised a small, ringed target on the butt numbered 3.

'Get down on the mat and load. I've given you a Walther ·22. It's single shot and the magazine holds a clip of eight. The catch on the side releases the magazine.' Hartmann moved round behind Laker. 'One last thing. We aren't expecting the impossible of you in Copenhagen. Average ability will suffice and this is your chance to bring yourself up to that standard . . . Now, take your time.'

Laker made a deliberate botch of thumbing a clip home, muddled snapping in the magazine, then settled into position on the mat. Even after so long a time the rifle had an easy, natural feel, but he made a show of awkwardness. With what he believed was cunning he aimed interminably before snatching at the trigger. Nothing happened and he tried to look puzzled.

'Push the safety-catch forward.'

He did so, aimed slightly off and fired. Sand spurted.

'Again.'

Another miss, well wide.

'Again,' Hartmann said tartly.

Laker missed six times in succession before Hartmann told him to stop.

'You aren't that incompetent.'

'I am. And I always was.'

'Try once more. Finish the clip.'

The target remained untouched.

'What kind of idiot are you, Mr. Laker? Don't you value your son's life?'

'Not everyone can shoot,' Laker gritted.

'All but the blind can do better than that. Get this into your head, once and for all. You've a job to do. In terms of skill required it won't be so difficult. And I've given you the best incentive I could think of.'

'Why me?' Laker shouted once more. 'Why not do your own filthy work?'

'A wise dog never fouls his own doorstep, Mr. Laker.'

'What's that supposed to tell me?'

'You'll find out. Now – reload and try again.'

Laker obeyed, anger filling him; helplessness. He took a sighting shot and squeezed the trigger, shutting his mind to thoughts of bone and muscle, flesh and blood. The electrical device above the target area recorded an inner at two o'clock.

'That's more like it,' he heard Hartmann concede.

He fired again, cutting the black edge of the bull on approximately the same radial line.

'Good . . . Good.'

With sudden contempt Laker emptied the magazine at speed, the crack of each shot punctuated by the trickle of ejected shell-cases on the floor beside him. Five clear bulls and one just clipping the line were recorded. He heard the hiss of Hartmann's indrawn breath.

'Good. *Very* good.' For once there was neither threat nor mockery in the voice. Hartmann crossed to the control-panel and switched the extractors off. 'You make a poor actor, Mr. Laker. How long is it since you used a rifle?'

'I told you.'

'Twenty years?'

'I told you.'

'It's hard to believe.'

'I don't give a penny damn what you believe.'

'Isn't it a relief to you that your son's future may not be so precariously balanced after all? It certainly is to me. Come – I want to see how you make out on the other range.'

In size, colouring and layout the second range was a duplication of the first. They reached it through a pair of communicating steel doors. This time Laker was given the other rifle.

'It's a Russian weapon,' Hartmann said. 'It has recently been superseded as a standard infantry issue, but it will serve your purpose very well and approximates in calibre and velocity to the one you will use. Make yourself familiar with it for a few moments. Then at five-second intervals, I shall raise a selection of random targets.'

Laker got down on the mat, legs splayed. He was shackled by a situation that was foul and crude and utterly compelling. Whatever chance there was of breaking free of it lay in the future, and the future was unmapped territory which his mind shrank from examining too closely lest he became convinced that it would offer nothing but the same hopeless subservience. He could not, dared not, think about it.

'Are you ready?'

He nodded, propped on his elbows, waiting, the catch off. Hartmann pressed a button on the control-panel and a small white pear-shaped metal cut-out sprang up to the right of the butt's centre. Laker fired and missed; nothing showed on the electric indicator-board. Hartmann grunted. The cut-out was already on its way down when Laker fired again, and this time he clipped it, taking Hartmann by surprise. Almost immediately another target appeared ten degrees or so to the left, identical but higher, wobbling on its arm. Laker scored a hit. The rifle was beautifully balanced, the recoil hardly noticeable. He missed the third cut-out, got the next, drew a blank on the indicator with the fifth, then put in two shots at the sixth, scoring both times, five seconds already seeming an overgenerous exposure.

'Try again,' Hartmann said. 'Reload and be ready for a three-second interval only. And a different target order.'

Laker scored seven hits. He was a born shot, relaxed, controlled, rock-steady, and he used the rifle now as if what remained of his pride depended on it. After he had emptied the magazine he loaded another and, on instructions, took the cutouts from a standing position, Hartmann mixing both their order and the duration of exposure. When the last puff of dust erupted from the protective wall of sandbags a full eight hits had been registered.

Hartmann nodded approvingly. 'Remarkable, Mr. Laker. Quite remarkable. I would say you are exceptional. Chance isn't always so obliging. It was a fortunate day for me when you decided to go to the Luisenstrasse.' He smiled. We have a saying; perhaps you know it? If you start with certainties you can end in doubts. But if you start with doubts, and are patient with them, you can end in certainties . . . I don't think we need continue with this, do you? The most useful place for both of us is back in my office.'

They were there by ten-thirty. It had begun to seem to Laker that there had hardly been a time when he hadn't faced Hartmann and met or avoided the pale-blue stare, hardly a time when his mind hadn't hovered between dread and loathing and despair.

'Now,' Hartmann said, lighting a cigarette. 'About this person of ours in Copenhagen.'

A thin stream of smoke flattened and spread as the desk deflected it. He withdrew a pink folder from the drawer in front of his stomach. Opening the folder he tossed a photograph towards Laker: it was about half-plate size.

'There,' he said. 'As I told you, the history books won't be interested. You won't achieve fame, Mr. Laker. It won't be like Dallas, Texas.'

Laker picked the photograph up. A broad, heavily-jowled face confronted him. Bushy hair, thick eyebrows, nipped-in ears, bulbous nose with flared nostrils, large mouth with a slightly pendulous lower lip.

'Who is he?'

'Rudolf Frenzel.'

The eye looked more Slavic than German. And surprise was in them, alarm, as if they had begun to flinch from the flash or even from the upward movement of the photographer's hands.

'If you were a student of the Democratic Republic's affairs, Mr. Laker, you would recall that Frenzel was once a member of the Politburo of the Socialist Unity Party. Four years ago he defected to the West. Until quite recently he hid himself away. But at last he has ventured out of his hole. He has become a sort of errand-boy – in which connection doesn't matter. What does is that tomorrow he visits Copenhagen.'

'How d'you know?'

'We know,' Hartmann said, and the manner of his saying it somehow reminded Laker of Slattery. 'We know where he will have travelled from, the time of his arrival, the time of his departure. And we also know where he will be most exposed during his stay.'

He seemed to think that Laker would ask him where this was, but

Laker was staring at the photograph. 'Did you hear me?' The tone was harsh again. 'When you arrive in Copenhagen yourself you will realise that we have given you what help we could. Nothing can be perfect, of course, but fear can remove mountains, I assure you.' He raised a finger as if he were at an auction. 'The photograph, please.'

It skidded across the desk and fell to the floor, but Hartmann didn't bother to retrieve it. Laker's expression seemed to gratify him.

'You will be supplied with another picture before you leave, more convenient for your pocket. It would be rash to rely too much on your memory. After all, when you are about to kill a man it is important to be certain you have picked the right one – isn't that so?' Hartmann opened the folder again and glanced at some typewritten notes. 'Our friend has a reservation at the Metropol Hotel and my information is that he has been allocated room sixty-eight. When you are contacted in Copenhagen you will realise the significance of this.'

'Contacted?'

'Your passport photograph has been copied and prints sent in advance. You'll be recognised, don't worry.' He picked up the typewritten sheet and passed it over. 'It would be better if you looked at this while I explain.' He might have been discussing a sales campaign, a holiday schedule – anything; anything except the preliminaries to a murder.

Laker read:

Axel Bar, Tivoli. Thursday 20.30
Copenhagen-National, Sunderspladsen. Friday 10.00–15.00:17.00–18.00
Metropol Hotel, Halmstergade. Friday 18.00–Saturday 1400.

'This afternoon,' Hartmann said, 'you fly to Copenhagen via Schônefeld, Berlin. You will be there – in Copenhagen, that is – around seven. Contact wil be made at the Axel Bar at eight-thirty tonight. Not only will you find that accommodation has been provided for you, but once you have taken your bearings you will discover also that it is directly across the street from where Frenzel will be staying. A narrow street – no wider than the range where you have so reluctantly demonstrated your skill.'

He paused. He was talking about a real place, a real man. And Laker could not hold his gaze.

'Frenzel arrives tomorrow, on an S.A.S. flight from Paris, due at six in the evening. He leaves again next afternoon – on the Saturday. That means you will have a maximum of twenty hours, during a proportion of which he will be as close as I can bring him to you. Across a street, Mr. Laker, a narrow street. Third-floor window to third-floor window. His will be the one directly in front of yours. With a telescopic sight it will seem almost as if you are prodding him.'

He paused again, stubbing his cigarette in the glass tray. 'You see there is reference to Copenhagen-National.'

'Yes.'

'Copenhagen-National is a bank. We have rented a safe deposit for you in the name of George Marshall. In it a rifle is waiting to be collected. The rifle is in a special case and no one will raise an eyebrow. The fact is that you will be in no personal danger until the moment you decide to put an end to Rudolf Frenzel's existence. Then, of course, your real difficulties will begin. But you can be down a fire-escape and on a bus or in a taxi within three minutes of pressing the trigger. It has been timed, Mr. Laker. We gave it what we call a dry run.'

He kept using 'we', but as far as Laker was concerned there was no one but Hartmann. And every time Laker's mind moved he was there to block it.

'You can't afford to fail; I hope I have made that crystal clear. By three o'clock on Saturday afternoon, at the very latest, we will know whether you have succeeded or not, and I won't labour the consequences. We want Frenzel dead, Mr. Laker. Dead at all costs – even if it means jeopardizing your own chances of escape. If time begins to whittle down or there are other difficulties it may be that you will have to abandon the role of sniper and seek him out – cross the street, go to his room. These will be things for you to decide. But remember this – the Danish police are very efficient. The more you expose yourself the greater will be the risk of their laying hands on you. And – should that happen – I cannot warn you strongly enough not to open your mouth until you have been advised by your colleagues in London what to say. They will think of something, Mr. Laker. What is more, they will expect to be given the opportunity. Never forget that. They used you in the first place, after all. They will have something at stake too, remember.'

A muscle was jumping in one side of Laker's face. 'When will I see my son?'

Hartmann consulted the folder. 'Assuming all goes well his plane will reach London at eleven o'clock on Saturday night. Incidentally, there is a letter for him here which you have to complete.'

He pushed it across. It was typed, bore yesterday's date and was headed Leipzig Airport.

I'm terribly sorry. After I left you this afternoon I got caught up in some urgent business which has made it essential for me to travel to Copenhagen immediately. I tried to find you, but couldn't. The only thing I could do was to ask Mr. Rauter to keep an eye on you while I'm away and he has kindly agreed to do so. He suggests you ought to stay at his house rather than at the Astoria and this of course you will be doing before this hurried letter reaches you.

Expect to see you by Saturday at the latest. If I can't manage to rejoin you by then I have asked Mr. Rauter to put you on a flight to London that evening. Then we'll be able to start for the Rhineland and pick up the planned schedule. Once again I'm very, very sorry, but it couldn't be helped. Mr. Rauter will have explained.

Enjoy yourself meanwhile. I've had to dictate this, by the way.

'Who is Rauter?'

'A family man. He has a pleasant apartment, a homely wife, two children of his own. As long as your mission is successful I can promise you that your son will have nothing but happy memories of his time in Leipzig.' Hartmann gestured. 'Sign the letter, Mr. Laker. We've done our best not to alarm him, and you of all people should approve of that. Sign it, then listen.'

Laker fumbled for his pen. *Dear Patrick,* he wrote; then, *Your affectionate father* and his initials.

'Listen,' Hartmann said. 'Your own flight is at 14.40. Your passport is in order. You will be provided with ample funds. Before you leave Leipzig you will have memorised the details on that piece of paper – the Axel Bar and so on. Above all you will have memorised the deadline.'

He waited, watching, always watching.

Laker ran his hands over his face. A full minute must have elapsed. Faintly, from the street below a horn blared like a cry of pain. He felt stunted, smashed. Mercy was what men wanted most; quarter. And Hartmann was able to offer it – at a price.

'If I do this – '

'Yes?'

'What can you promise for Karen Gisevius?'

'Who?'

'Karen Gisevius.'

Hartmann leaned forward, one eyebrow raised. 'Why should she interest you?'

'I know her.'

'Naturally.'

Laker shook his head. 'During the war. I worked with her. I haven't

seen her since. Until the other day I thought she must be dead. She . . .
She was . . .' And suddenly he couldn't go on. All he could do was to stare
and see Hartmann slowly dissolve, solidify.

Through a blur, as if from a long way off, he heard: 'You have enough
to worry about.'

'What will happen to her?'

'Does it matter?'

'Yes. *Yes*.'

'Then I am sorry for you.'

Once before Hartmann had come to an abrupt decision with himself,
and so it was again. He pressed the buzzer on the desk and rose.

'That's all, Mr. Laker. Go and memorise those Copenhagen details.
In – what? – something over three hours your plane will be leaving. On
it there are likely to be businessmen. But not one of them, I assure you,
will be *en route* for home with a contract more binding than yours.'

CHAPTER 9

Leipzig Airport sank below. Soon it was smothered by clouds – the
ragged fringes of the city, too; everything.

Laker pressed back in his seat. The last thing Hartmann had said was:
'There's no way out, Mr. Laker. Racking your brains won't help. The
longer you live with the situation the more you will realise that you have
to go through with it to the end. One word to anyone – *anyone* – and you
know what that will mean. We have our reasons for wanting Frenzel
killed just as you have reasons for making sure that he is. Until then this
is between you and me. Always remember that. You and I have become
partners.' And in the shadows of Laker's mind his narrow face presented
itself, half-smiling, eager for drama, looking for it with eyes for the most
part empty of anything except a cold, lonely light.

The twin-engined aircraft was about three-quarters full but mercifully the seat beside Laker was vacant. He couldn't have coped with a
stranger intent on trivialities about the Fair. He had clung to the hope
that once he got away he would somehow be able to detach himself from
the dementia of the past twenty-four hours, continuing to cling to it long
after he knew in his heart that freedom would alter nothing, clinging to it
even now when doing so was no more than an act of despair. Hartmann
held the strings. Distance was irrelevant. He had two days in which to go
about Patrick's salvation, two days in which the memory of yesterday's

terror in the pines was to goad him into becoming an instrument of vengeance.

He shook his head. Things like this happened to others; never to you and yours.

Behind his back someone was saying in a flat, Midlands' brogue: 'I found 'em charming. Couldn't have been friendlier. It's dreary there, God knows, but they're all right. If you ask me there's a damned sight too much drivel talked about the Curtain and all that. I'm not denying it's a fact, any more than I'm saying there isn't a flaming great wall across Berlin. But what I *am* saying is that the whole political thing doesn't make the sense it once did . . .' The knowing voice insisted through the engines' roar. 'The tension's easing all the time. We aren't at each other's throats any longer. If we imagine we are it's largely the fault of the Press and the television people. They need news, that lot, so they balloon every trivial little incident in the hope it'll burst and make a bang. That's my view, and I've been here twice now. Seeing's believing after all . . .'

Laker opened his eyes and fixed them blankly on the empty sky. Patrick, fresh from some junior book of instant knowledge, had once said: 'People think the sky's blue, but it isn't, not really – did you know that, dad? When you get beyond a certain point it's black, pitch black.'

It seemed fantastic that he should be scared to make a move when he was within arm's length of people who could pass a message for him. Inaction seemed a crime, yet it was part of the measure of reality. He was even nervous of being spoken to; when the stewardess offered him coffee he was brusque and dismissive, as if he were under surveillance from somewhere in the rear.

He thought of Frenzel, Frenzel with his hours already counted. Frenzel was the lynch-pin. Warn him, spare him, fail to get him – and Partick paid; those were the equations. 'An outcry, Mr. Laker? Oh no. You and your son have ceased to be public property. You should have asked more questions than you did before you so casually set out for Leipzig . . . And another thing. We'll want proof about Frenzel. Nothing short of a 22-carat job will do, and we have means of telling whether you will have undertaken it honestly or not . . . I'll know, Mr. Laker.'

He was in quicksands, trapped. And if he struggled or called for help they would close over Patrick's head, not his. The more he strained his mind the more scared he found himself, the more crammed with useless hatred. And, deep down, he was aware that if the nightmare persisted, if he lived it through in puppet-like obedience, self-disgust would be the final horror.

The man behind was still ploughing on: 'East Germany's all right. And it's got a tremendous market potential if only the British Government would take its finger out over the recognition business. The people I met were touchy about that, and no wonder. Still, I got nothing but courtesy wherever I went, and I'm damned certain no one comes to any harm nowadays unless they deliberately go looking for it . . .'

Laker stared at the sky's immaculate blue, lost in bitterness and abandonment.

It was a short flight to Schönefeld: forty minutes. They were down punctually at three-twenty, down through the clouds, and everything was grey again. The accents were different, but the uniforms were the same.

There were almost three hours to wait for the Copenhagen connection and to Laker they seemed interminable. He sat in the peeling transit-lounge along with a score of people, men mostly, some of them bleary from lunch and liquor who sprawled on the couches and dozed. Every half-hour or so a cafeteria trolley was wheeled round. On and off he paced the floor, submerged within himself. If he didn't contact London he felt he would go mad before the next forty-eight hours were over. But he seemed to have lost any capacity for trust, in Slattery most of all. Slattery had bungled where Karen was concerned, miscalculated – and he might again. By comparison with Hartmann he now seemed a child, an amateur, a dabbler; but there was nobody else to bring pressure to bear. He might have strings of his own . . . *Might.*

And Hartmann was there at once to push the pendulum the other way – 'One word to London and, inevitably, Frenzel will go back into his hole. You can't afford to have that happen.'

Laker's throat burned from incessant smoking. He couldn't remain still for long. Sometimes when he glanced at his watch he thought it must have stopped. The new strap, the wad of Kroner in his pocket, the safe-deposit key, the deckled edges of the photograph he dared not look at – there was no refuge. Tides of panic ebbed and flowed as his thoughts swung between Slattery and Hartmann. Slattery would have no choice but to act, and act quickly. Patrick was his responsibility. Or was the situation so insane that he would be forced to yield to Hartmann's stranglehold himself?

One moment such a thing seemed inconceivable, the next a terrifying probability. Hartmann had been so sure, so cast-iron sure, as if he knew exactly how far London would be prepared to go. 'There are unwritten rules in this business, Mr. Laker. And one of them is to be wary of having your own dirty washing blown into the scandalised face of the world. London, believe me, has more than a fair share on its hands and they will guard it more jealously than you would think possible. They'll muzzle you when the time comes – quite shamelessly if their treatment of Mr. Wyatt's unfortunate widow is anything to go by. Meanwhile, Frenzel is valuable to them and they won't willingly allow him to be obliterated. London, I suggest, would only confuse you. So keep away from your Embassy, Mr. Laker. And don't ring anyone – I'd take it as a sign of weakness, d'you see?'

But he would. He must.

And yet . . .

The Copenhagen flight was called at ten to six. Along with thirty or so others Laker trailed across the oil-slicked hard to a turbo-prop Ilyushin. With the resignation of the powerless he belted himself in and gazed out at the red-black-and-gold flags fluttering lazily along the rim of the airport buildings. The nightmare had been many things already; now, once more, it took the form of finding himself surrounded by people whose lives were wholly normal.

He wanted to shout at them, to protest, to shake their smugness, their boredom, to confide. Above all, to confide. There were files in London, he wanted them to understand, in which the names of every one of them armed with a British passport were automatically recorded once they ventured to this side of the Curtain. And there were men like Slattery who would use them if time and opportunity provided a need and they were fools enough to acquiesce. And there were men like Hartmann who could manipulate them to such a degree and with such cold certainty that they could find themselves inhabiting the same world as everyone else yet secretly terrorised, unable to cry out, committed to something that, only hours before, they would have considered utterly impossible.

With a whining crescendo the Ilyushin lifted off, graceful and buoyant, the violence of the noise and the feeling of thrust diminishing. Second by second the horizons widened. Berlin tilted like a display model beyond the port wing and every head turned. Then the clouds intervened and spread below like crusted pack-ice.

The thick-set crew-cut man beside Laker was galloping through a Swedish translation of Fleming's *Casino Royale*. Laker shut his eyes. Hartmann's stare and throttled voice, the sound of Karen's sobbing as she was taken from the hut, Patrick's parting grin as he left him, the ghastly stutter muffled by the paper bag, Slattery's bland elusiveness, Frenzel, Rudolf Frenzel – all were there again to torment and tear at his mind and his heart together with the remembered feel of the rifles and the smell of cordite in the shooting-gallery and the prospect of a strange city and a rendezvous at the Axel Bar at eight-thirty. And then . . .

The palms of his hands were unnaturally moist. Twice he lit a cigarette only to stub it out after a few nervous draws. The man in the next seat smiled and turned yet another escapist page. Time passed. Coffee was served again, but Laker ordered a cognac and drained his glass in a single gulp. After a longish while he heard someone say, 'Rostock, I reckon.' Peering down he saw an amoeba-like sepia smudge at the centre of a radiation of lines and scratches and the apparently motionless sea pressed against the map of the coastline. 'Having capitalist time, wish you were here' – Patrick's joke echoed brutally. Then Slattery claimed priority: 'Since May last year he's been in touch with an address in Rostock: Lenin-Strasse 32, to be precise' – Slattery who knew so much, so bloody much, Slattery of the homily about the bumble-bee, of the time before and after the Gardelegen débâcle, Slattery of The Mitre and the room in Manchester Square and the talk of helping out – 'No risk, old boy. Absolutely none . . .'

Never-do-it-yourself-Slattery. What match was he for Hartmann? As an ally he'd diminished, yet who else was there?

The Ilyushin made short work of the Baltic. Copenhagen was under them several minutes before the scheduled seven o'clock. The tanned young Customs officer who eventually dealt with Laker said, 'Holiday or business?' as a brisk preliminary to letting him go and Laker answered, 'Business', at the mercy even of a chance word.

He slumped in the coach that would take him to the terminal. A B.E.A. Trident screamed in while they waited for the coach to fill and the sight of it made London seem closer suddenly: attainable. Why delay? There were telephones in the Arrivals building . . . The pendulum started swinging again. But he was suspicious of freedom, suspicious of everyone in the immediate vicinity. Wait. Lose everyone first. Wait until they all reach town; scattered. And then . . . Should he? Christ, should he? The power of decision was draining out of him.

Anxiously, as the coach began to roll, he glanced at his watch: seven-twenty. 'How far's the terminal?' he asked a stout woman beside him. Fifteen minutes . . . There'd be time enough to call London – yet what if Slattery made another balls of everything? And he could. One rash move, one hasty indiscretion, and Hartmann would complete the equation. But would Slattery believe that? Could he make him understand – quickly, and on a public line – how desperate the balance truly was? . . . Panic renewed itself the nearer he came to chancing it. If he didn't, now or later, there was only one alternative.

Copenhagen's outskirts scarcely made a mark on his mind. A bridge and the evening glint of water, some laden coal barges – not much else registered. A man near by remarked as if he'd seen an old friend: 'There's the Europa' – but Laker didn't even look. He stared straight ahead, rehearsing what he would say, compressing it, trying to keep Hartmann's threats at bay. 'Listen, Slattery. They were waiting for me. Kromadecka's was blown before I got there. They picked all three of us up – Karen, Patrick and me. I'm in Copenhagen now and this is why, this is what's happened . . .'

The light was still good. He noticed trees; a verdigris-covered spire. Some of the passengers were already getting to their feet. Two minutes after the half-hour . . . The coach turned right and veered towards the kerb. 'Is this it?' somebody asked as movement ended. Laker took his turn at the door. Neon blinked and cascaded palely around a large square. He collected his suitcase then walked away, anywhere, anywhere, it didn't matter. Several times he glanced back, but signled no one out. He left the square and crossed a street, passed through an arcade, then turned left, mingling, one of many, moving faster than most though not conspicuously so.

After a few minutes he paused in a shop doorway; there was a post office opposite with telephone booths flanking the entrance. Several people passed, one with a brown dog on a lead, and the dog sniffed at his ankles. But there was no other interest taken in him, nobody loitering to keep their distance. He delayed for some cars to go by, then went over to the post office, certain he wasn't followed. Inside at the counter, he asked the cost of a call to London. The clerk, who spoke English, changed two 100-Kroner notes for him. There were booths along the facing wall but the clerk said: 'We close at eight. I suggest you use those in the street. You may have some delay on a call like that.'

Laker nodded and went outside. One of the booths was occupied. He stepped into the vacant one, put his suitcase down and studied the English version of the procedure instructions. The booth was glass on three sides. He looked all round; no one watched or waited, yet the back of his neck prickled. A moment's hesitation, then he dialled.

'I want to make a person-to-person call to London . . . London, England, yes . . .'

A click and a different voice, slightly sing-song, very precise. He gave the Gerrard number, repeating it twice, touched by a sudden alarm that Slattery might not be there at such an hour.

'Is there a delay?'

'I don't think so. There wasn't half an hour ago. What is your number, please?'

Laker read it out.

'Have you the right money?' The girl quoted the tariff.

'Yes.'

'What is the name of the person to whom you wish to speak?'

Laker ran a hand through his hair. 'Look,' he said urgently, 'I don't want it person-to-person, after all. I want a straight call on the Gerrard number.'

'Not person-to-person?'

'No.'

His alarm grew. Say no one was there? Suddenly everything had narrowed down to this. All he could remember was that Slattery lived in Kew.

'Hold the line, please.'

He straightened, moving his feet. Turning slightly he glanced out. A short, hatless man was leaning against the post-office wall, reading a newspaper. For a second or two Laker had no qualms. Come on, he urged, as the wire cracked. Come *on* . . . Then he realised that the man was looking at him over the top of the page.

A tentacle of suspicion fastened around Laker's heart. He tried to drag his eyes away, but couldn't. For what seemed an impossible length of time he stared back. Then the man lowered the newspaper, making no bones about his purpose, and with a chilling stab of dismay Laker recognised him. He had been on the plane from Leipzig, in the transit-lounge at Schönefeld, on the Ilyushin. In the toilets at Schönefeld they'd been alone, just the two of them, shoulders almost touching . . . Suddenly Laker was certain. His brain seemed to stall as the man prolonged the blatant warning, pushing away from the wall and moving nearer.

'Have your money ready, please. I will have London for you in a few mo – '

Laker's nerve broke then. He slammed the receiver down, grabbed his suitcase and backed out of the booth. And he ran – as if something were yapping at his heels. Only when he found himself in the square where the coach had deposited him did he slow to a walk. He rested against a lamp-standard, sucking in air. Despite the fading light he attracted attention: somebody stopped and spoke to him, hand on arm. Laker shook his head and walked on, frightened still, very frightened. Leipzig was three hundred miles away, behind the Curtain. But he wasn't free, he couldn't choose. Hartmann had as good as twitched the strings to prove it.

The dark was coming. Blocks of light fell from expanses of plate-glass window and the pulsing neon took a more gaudy hold. It was five past eight and his legs ached. Someone was still on his tail; he could sense it. He hadn't tried to lose himself again. Sick in the stomach he had stayed with the crowds; conformed. 'Don't allow Copenhagen to affect your judgement, Mr. Laker . . .' Hartmann kept pace with him like a second shadow, Hartmann whose mind was sharp with years of suspicion and who wielded the power of life and death. 'I'll know if it does, you see. I'll know for sure.'

Near a bicycle-park Laker hailed a cruising taxi. 'Axel?' the driver queried. 'Tivoli?'

It was only a short ride. He was put down at one of the entrances to the Gardens. The driver tried to explain something, pointing, but the Danish defeated Laker. He went to the arched gateway where he spoke to an attendant. 'Axel Bar?' he asked uncertainly and was rewarded with a nod. He paid to pass through the turnstile. There was a restaurant immediately to his right, the Wivex, and he heard the throb of music. Pustules of coloured lights bordered a choice of paths between avenues of brilliantly-lighted trees. A direction-arrow showed him which to take. Couples strolled hand in hand under the faery glow, animated, dreaming, the world shut out for a while. Presently he passed an open-air stage where a clown was performing on a trampoline before a seated audience. Some scattered applause startled him, reminding him that he was different from everybody in this place, from everybody in Copenhagen, and again he felt the swift breeze of fear in his belly.

Lugging his suitcase he walked perhaps another hundred yards before he saw AXEL in electric blue on the fascia of a small, low building. As he approached he wondered if the same man would again disclose himself. Some of the tables were alfresco, spaced about a hedged enclosure, and others were roofed over behind a glass screen. He chose not to go inside. A waitress with a pink beret came for his order. He didn't want anything but he asked for a beer. Then he lit a cigarette, apprehensive, heedless of the sauntering passers-by, suspecting that his contact was already present.

A military band played in the tinted distance. He sat alone with the suitcase beside him, fingering the chequer-board cloth. Again and again he checked his watch. Eight-thirty . . . Eight-thirty-two . . . Eight-thirty-five . . . No one yet. But there would be. Someone was waiting to show him where his room was, biding his time before closing in. There was beginning to be a dreadful inevitability about everything now.

'Can you manage a light?'

It was a girl's voice, the accent transatlantic. Laker jerked round, taken off-guard. Unknown to him she had seated herself at his table.

'A light?' she said.

Dark eyes, dark hair, white teeth, a mouth redder than blood – his glance was cursory. He nodded and fumbled in his pocket. She looked like a tart. As the flame spurted he held it to her cigarette and she steadied his hand, fingers touching his. Fawn coat, collar up.

'Thanks.'

The smoke swirled. He was turning his back on her.

'The picture didn't do you justice.'

He frowned.

'You were very punctual, I'll say that.'

Now he stared, pulse quickening. 'Aren't you making a mistake?'

'Hardly.' She smiled. 'Shall we go? I don't want a drink.'

He didn't move.

'It isn't far. And it's getting chilly here.' She smiled again. 'Yes?' she prompted.

He emptied his glass. They rose together. As they moved away under the lights she said: 'Tivoli closes next week for the winter, did you know?' But she was talking to someone who wasn't altogether listening.

CHAPTER 10

When they reached the exit by the Wivex he asked if they needed a taxi, but she said they didn't. It was the only time he spoke to her on the way. They walked for about five minutes, her heels clacking briskly as she strutted by his side. Familiar names occasionally showed amid the indecipherable welter – PETER O'TOOLE . . . CARLSBERG . . . ELIZABETH ARDEN . . . SHELL – but to Laker they seemed to belong to some other stage of his existence.

They turned a couple of corners; crossed a tram-clanking street. The crowds thinned out; soon they were almost alone. They were passing a line of shops when the girl stopped by a door next to a delicatessen.

'Here we are.'

Opposite were more shops with five or six rows of windows above. Laker glanced at them quickly before following her in. There was a small hallway with stairs leading up. She went first, slim calves level with his face. On the first landing she said: 'Are you fit? There are two more yet,' and again there was that smile. Already Laker was confused. He had expected an anonymously-rented room, bare perhaps, and then to be left alone – watched and followed only when he went out. But he was wrong. On the second landing he suspected it, on the third he was sure. He wasn't to be trusted for a minute.

Even so he asked: 'D'you live here?'

'Of course.'

She let him in, surprise in her tone. He found himself in a comfortably-furnished bed-sitter. Doors opened off to either side of a curtained window. Quilted double divan, a radio, some framed photographs, a square table with some bottles on it, a couple of deep, soft chairs – these were among his first impressions.

She tossed her coat on to the divan and bent to plug in an electric fire. A wild doubt took Laker to the window. He pulled back the curtains.

'Where's that place?'

'Across there?'

'Yes.'

'The hotel, d'you mean?'

'What's it called?'

'The Metropol.'

He turned, the enslaved part of his mind bewildered, unable to grasp that these terrible hours were to be shared. There had been no mention of it in Leipzig.

He said: 'Are you here all the time?'

'Of course,' she said again. 'Where else?' And then she said: 'My name's Anna. What's yours?'

He didn't answer.

'Knowing it will make things easier.'

'David.'

David would do. In one respect he'd been right about her. Men came here in search of an hour's safety, an hour's trust, release, a breath of comfort. But Laker had forgotten what desire was. He studied the room again, his thoughts racing a full round of the clock ahead, entering a new dimension of uncertainty.

'Are you tired? You look tired. There's Scotch if you want it.' She chuckled softly, kicking off her shoes. 'It's all paid for. Everything is – so make yourself at home. Everything's paid for the two days – so that's out of the way.'

'Who paid?' He was cautious.

Again she seemed surprised. 'I could describe him.'

'When?'

'This morning.'

He poured a whisky. There was no sign of a telephone.

'Where do those doors go?'

'Bathroom there. Kitchen there.' Sitting on the divan she watched him check. Her lips curled. 'Why not look under here as well?'

He shrugged. He felt caged.

'Are you English?'

He hesitated, unsure to what extent he was bound, not knowing whether to lie, how much would be reported back, what mattered and what did not. Hartmann had left such details in the air.

'Well, are you?'

'Yes, I'm English.' Then, probing once more: 'What about you?'

'Oh, I'm a local girl.'

'Not German?' She could have been. The transatlantic veneer camouflaged another, more basic, accent.

'No.'

She laughed, tossing her hair, and the laughter mystified him. She seemed so at ease, so indifferent to why he had come. Yet the Metropol was across the street and tomorrow he was expected to bring a rifle here; kill from here. She knew that, she must know that . . . He pulled the curtains aside once more, peering at the window directly opposite. It was in darkness, but several others were lit and in one of them, a floor down, he could see a maid turning back the bed-covers. She was close, all right; against his will the fact registered.

'When are you going to relax?'

He swung round, facing the unfamiliar room. The girl was putting a match to a cigarette. As if for the first time he noticed that she was wearing a green skirt and a white, frilled blouse. Twenty-five or -six; it was hard to tell. She proffered the pack.

'D'you want one?'

He shook his head.

Her eyes lacked something; the mouth, too. Whore's eyes, hard yet friendly, bold yet cautious, never quite certain. 'What's your work?'

'Office work.'

'In England?'

He avoided answering. He drank, haunted by others, further confused, wishing he were alone. He hadn't reckoned on this. Nothing was constant except the guarantee of climax. Desperation could drive him in search of another telephone; he could even take a plane to

London – somewhere, sometime, he'd already considered that. Yet what would Slattery *do*? What *could* he do? . . . That was the ultimate uncertainty. Hartmann had been in no doubt, and he believed Hartmann; the clearing in the pines and the bag over his head encouraged him in whom to believe. 'A joke, Mr. Laker? A dream? . . .' Neither; Jesus, no. Something filthy instead, filthy and cowardly and merciless. Something he didn't know the half of, yet which had him by the throat whichever way he turned.

'Have you eaten?'

'I'm not hungry.'

'It's no trouble to fix something. *Smørrebrød*, say? Yes? . . . I'm going to the kitchen anyway.'

'All right.'

He was curt. She was linked with Hartmann, paid by Hartmann, and that was enough to stoke what he felt. He went to the window for the third time, thinking distractedly. No one, as far as he could tell, stood in a doorway or in the bars of shadow between the shops on the other side of the street, but he was past being deceived or deceiving himself. They had warned him off Slattery once and the moment he left this room they'd be told; she would see to that.

He poured another whisky, numbing a little of the crisis within him and the stark chill of many fears. He moved nearer the fire. A tear-off calendar on the wall carried a thought for the day, attributed to Ibsen: *'I' is the capital city of the underworld in which all things happen to us.* Close by there was a coloured print of the Matterhorn framed in black passe-partout, and over the divan a beach-scene with the girl in a bikini waving at the photographer: *Klampenborg, August* was scrawled in ink across one corner.

She was singing quietly in the kitchen. They would have made plans for her; there was no other answer. For him there was a fire-escape – off the landing, probably: three minutes to a bus or a taxi . . . He remembered everything, every word. They'd done a dry run, timed it. So she was aware of what was to happen – and she would hardly wait to be a witness. She would go while the going was good, before a light showed where it mattered across the way, before six tomorrow evening when Frenzel was due. Surely . . .

His thoughts jerked on and on. Yet she lived here; it was a home. Clean, cared-for. His eyes travelled over the pictures again, the furniture, the strewn magazines, the bright dressing-table with its glass top, the amassed trivia, the long mirror facing the divan . . . Would she abandon it all? He was mystified still – and frightened simultaneously that he should be thinking this way, weighing only this, as if he knew in his heart of hearts that for him there might be no option.

'Switch on the radio, will you?'

The whisky in him obeyed. He went to the table and poured another glass, then sat down, staring at the coiled red bar of the fire. Presently he took out his wallet and extracted the picture of Frenzel, studying the startled eyes, the flared nostrils shadowed by the flash. 'One of those for whom the world will never be safe, Mr. Laker. And it shows, don't you see?'

'There,' the girl said, emerging with a tray. 'Was I long?'

He shoved the photograph away like someone found out. She set the tray down on the table which she then drew closer to the chairs and the fire.

'I made coffee,' she said. 'Okay?'

Her face was conventionally attractive, well-boned, a fringe of dark hair low on her forehead, her skin ivory smooth. The eyes were green, he saw now, not black as he'd supposed them to be under the Tivoli lighting. He tossed back some more whisky, feeling its full glow. She reduced the radio's volume to a background throb, then settled into the other chair, legs curled up.

'Better?' Smiling, she took a plate from the tray.

'Better?' he countered.

'When you came in you were wound up like a spring.' She held herself stiffly. 'Like that – you were, you know.'

She baffled him. What she had brought him there to do would incriminate her if he went through with it. Unless he could wriggle free, devise something – either in conjunction with Slattery or alone – she was involved up to her slim white neck. Yet she was there to prevent him from doing just that, a jailer, ready to report on his comings and goings.

He said: 'How long have you lived here?'

'A couple of years.'

'D'you rent it?'

'Uh-huh.' She was eating.

'So everything in the place is yours?'

'Except the bath and the wallpaper. D'you want a bath, by the way? The water's hot.'

He shook his head.

'Aren't you going to eat?'

There was ham garnished with lettuce and shrimps on light rye bread. He munched without really tasting anything. He was beginning to feel so weary that everything was muted – the play on his nerves, the gnawing sense of dread, the mental confusion. She didn't look like a fanatic or someone on the eve of drama. She looked slim and young and unconcerned and well content. This was where the abandoned rifle would be found, but she didn't seem to care. He couldn't fathom her; couldn't think properly.

She sipped her coffee. 'Tell me about yourself.'

He was silent.

'You're quite a way from home.'

Oh God, he thought, caught on a backwash of panic.

'Don't tell me nothing interesting has ever happened to you. Interesting things only seem to happen to interesting people, and you're interesting. Very.'

The sensation of madness seemed to touch him again. He rose from the chair and went to the whisky bottle. She more than most would know what it was to receive confidences: men must have fed her with them, unloading their complaints, their failures, sure of sympathy, buying that too. Yet he dared not speak about Frenzel. Hartmann's warnings to stay mute couldn't apply where she was concerned; she'd already been bought – with one specific thing in view. So why not have it in the open? There was so little time. But he could not. He had doubts about her, and they were growing. Once, when a backfire in the street made him start, she chuckled: 'Easy. You've too much imagination. This is a quiet neighbourhood.' Right or wrong he was ready to consider that she didn't know about Frenzel after all. Somewhere in the tired depths of his mind he was finding reasons to believe that she might have been lied to, misled. For all he knew she had been deceived about him and would be sacrificed when the time came. It was possible. Nothing about her was clear-cut any longer except the certainty that she expected him to share the divan, make love, sleep, wake and perhaps make love again when morning came. It was part of his right, paid for, but he was far from sure to what extent she had sold herself. Yet precisely because she had made the Axel rendezvous and had brought him to where Hartmann had promised it was dangerous to assume too much. Either way he couldn't trust her, couldn't ask whether there was a telephone in the building, couldn't chance the offer of a bribe or think of pleading.

The whisky spun his brain. If he broached the truth and discovered that she was, in fact, ignorant of it, disaster could ensure. She would turn him out, call the police, warn the Metropol – any or all of these. When he thought of her as someone tricked and used like himself he read into her a capacity for horror and instant action. Frenzel would survive, but there would be another victim; Hartmann had left him with the certainty of that and it governed him.

Some of the time he matched her small-talk, sometimes not. She seemed to fence when he questioned her obliquely as to what she knew, yet she warmed to him with explorations of her own as if anxious – and grateful – to be spared for once some hasty, wolfish stranger. She laughed frequently, juggling almost coyly with words and meanings, but her eyes, her gestures, made it plain that she would ease his nerves, deaden whatever tortured his mind, whenever he wanted.

Eventually she turned off the radio. Laker put down his glass, seeing nothing, never so alone. And weary beyond words, exhausted by everything the endless day had done to him. He gazed at the ceiling as if he were suffocating. Tomorrow he would think again, balance every-thing, think and decide which gamble to take, with her, with Slattery.

'Have a bath and freshen up.' She was calling him 'David' now. She came to where he sat and knelt in front of him. 'Yes?'

He shook his head. It had gone ten-thirty: when he glanced at his watch the new strap claimed his thoughts, dragging them back through the nightmare's web.

'Bed, then?'

He shrugged. She took his hand, leaning closer, smiling, enjoying the unaccustomed luxury of play.

'There's nothing like it.'

He got up again, abruptly. She watched him confidently. He drank another whisky, as if he were in a hurry, then went to the bathroom. His reflection greeted him in the wall-mirror and he stared at it as if amazed by the sanity of his appearance. He washed his hands and face, then returned to the room. All the lights were out except the one beside the divan. Without surprise he saw that the girl was wearing only pants and brassière and he remembered thinking how full her black-cupped breasts were. But he felt nothing, not even when she released the brassière, turning expectantly as she did so. Nothing. He took off his jacket and slung it on a hook on the kitchen door, then pulled the two soft chairs together.

'What are you doing?'

He didn't answer.

'David!' She made it a complaint.

'I'm sorry,' he said.

She came towards him, silhouetted. 'Don't joke.'

'I'm not.'

'Nonsense.' A little laugh. 'Nonsense.'

'I mean it.' He punched the cushions. 'I'm sorry, but there it is.'

For a moment he was prepared for an outburst, but it didn't come. For what seemed a long time as he softened the cushions he was aware of her standing close, aware of a tiny part of him numbly crying for comfort and escape, aware of her lips parted in astonishment.

'Truly?'

Then she knew it was truly.

'Are you married?'

'No.'

'Why, then?'

He shook his head and started unknotting his tie, still expecting anger, scorn – he wasn't sure what it would be. But, instead, her mouth twisted.

'Well, that's the first time ever. I'd like you to know that – the first time ever.'

She went to the divan, pulled back the covers and tossed a blanket at him before flouncing between the sheets, indignation in the violence of her movements. But she said nothing more. Laker heeled off his shoes, got out of his trousers, then fitted himself on to the chairs and covered himself over.

The girl switched off the light almost at once. The sodium-white blur of the street-lamps softly filled the room through the curtains. And Laker lay heavily on his side, huddled as if in protection against the coming day of obligation.

Karen whispered: 'Sammy? . . . Sammy? . . .' She was clinging to him in the hollow and the cold was like death. Even in the shadow-play of the dream he knew that the memory would brand him throughout his lifetime; that heart-break would come of this. 'When will it be normal for us, Sammy?' He held her tight, close, their breath like ghosts, her face pinched and freckled, her eyes burning with the onset of fever. 'We'll have to go,' he said. 'We'll have to work west. It's no good waiting. They've given us up. We're no use to them any more.' She was coughing already. 'You know best, Sammy.' He gazed down at her, moved, frightened for her. She'd never make it. There were planes droning in the sky. 'Now?' she asked. 'Right away?' But he shook his head. 'When it's dark.'

The picture fragmented. For a while he seemed to be nowhere, floating, not cold. He felt his body heave. He heard the crack of his carbine and saw a helmeted figure double up, saw another opening the lid of the stranded tank, aimed quickly, fired and ran. Then he was floating again, aware of the stench of decay, of destruction. And Slattery was saying: 'And then, Sam? What happened then?' – Slattery blinking across the desk in the Grosvenor Gardens office, tapping his teeth with a silver pencil. 'How many did you get, Sam?'

Then everything was changing once more, dissolving, focusing anew. 'A favour, old boy, that's all. Nothing to it. I wouldn't be asking you otherwise . . .' In a voice that didn't sound like his own he heard himself answer: 'I couldn't do it. I couldn't. Besides, Patrick will be with me.' Slattery beamed: 'Do what?' There were stars now, darkness, a child wailing. 'Kill anyone. That's what you're asking, isn't it?' Slattery had vanished, though Laker could still hear him – 'You did once, so why not again?' He began to shout back: 'I had a reason, the only reason. I hated them then. *You have to hate.*' And all at once it wasn't Slattery any more, but Hartmann, Hartmann with his head tilted, saying: 'Either that or you need an incentive, Mr. Laker. And I've seen to it that you've been given the best there is.'

The dream went out of him with a rush. He was mumbling, grinding his teeth. It was night and he knew where he was, remembering the room, the girl, the reasons why – everyone, everything.

'What is it?'

He grunted, twisting on the chairs.

'What's the matter?'

The lamp clicked on and he squeezed his lids together. He could smell her scent, the room's stuffiness. Gradually his eyes took the brunt of the light. Sitting up, she was holding the sheet across herself, alarm making her seem prudish.

'Were you dreaming?'

'Time.' He licked his lips. He was in a sweat. 'What's the time?'

'You scared me.'

'Huh?'

'You were saying things. Shouting.'

'What?'

'Names.'

'What names?'

'Frankel.'

He stared.

'Frankel, Frenzel – something like that.'

'Frenzel?' he said thickly.

'Yes.'

He paused, then tried it. 'Who's Frenzel?'

'God knows. It was your dream.' She frowned. 'Are you in some kind of trouble?'

'Is that what you were told?'

She shook her head. 'I'm guessing.'

'What *were* you told?'

'That you wanted a girl.'

'Just that?'

'Just that. I must have got the story wrong, though.' The hurt was still there. She gazed at him for several seconds without speaking. 'Is it bad? Something bad?'

He lay back. So she didn't know. That at least was clear. He believed her. His briefing had been incomplete. Hartmann hadn't warned him she would be a stumbling-block.

'I thought you were in town for some kind of conference.'

'That's right,' he lied.

But she wasn't satisfied. 'What is it, then?' she said after a pause.

'Nothing.'

'You sounded terrified. And now you look like death. And when you first came in tonight you were –'

'It was a dream,' he said.

He wiped the sweat from his face, suddenly afraid that she might not be prepared to harbour him. Her anxiety didn't sound as if it were altogether unselfish. And he'd wounded her pride as it was. Yet it was vital to stay. He must. This place was his last resort. Indeed, he might have to get her out of here – and keep her out.

'Nothing worse than that?'

'No,' he forced himself. 'Nothing.'

He could feel her eyes on him. Inwardly he groaned. 'The old-fashioned pressures are still the best, Mr. Laker.' He turned away from her. God, oh God. He didn't hate Frenzel.

CHAPTER 11

They must have slept again. A whimper of tyres in the street finally made Laker stir. He awoke quickly, tense at once, reality boring in. He got up immediately and went to the window; looked across. In the dullness of morning the window facing him seemed almost opaque: he couldn't see to any depth beyond the open slats of the blinds. A pigeon perched itself contentedly on the sill. Peering right he noticed that the entrance to the hotel was at the corner of the block. It was early for crowds, and those who walked moved briskly, intent on destinations, unaware of Frenzel, of Patrick, of Hartmann, buying their newspapers from a shop away to the left, glancing at the headlines as they hurried out, informed of violence and disasters and tyrannies around the globe, but ignorant of what fear was doing to someone above their heads, what tomorrow's editions might carry.

He let the curtain swing back and pulled on his trousers, then lit a cigarette. The girl was still sleeping. He gazed at her for a moment, then took his razor and a towel from the suitcase. The sharp click of the locks roused her. She rolled lazily on to her back, the sheet slipping from her breasts as she stretched.

'How long have you been up?'

'A couple of minutes.'

'Is it late?'

'Five to eight.'

She yawned and made a long arm for the radio. He entered the bathroom, shaved and washed. He ached from the chairs. He sat on the edge of the bath when he'd finished. Hartmann's remote control guiding the rabid course of his thoughts, endlessly warning him, daring him. After some time the girl thumped on the door and he opened it. She was in a pink housecoat. 'I reckoned you must have made camp,' she said tartly, brushing past. He was drawn to the window again, held there as if by a magnet. The light had improved and now he could vaguely discern the interior of Frenzel's room-to-be – a cupboard, part of a mauve-covered bed . . . But there was a point beyond which his mind refused to go.

He turned away sharply, a tightness in his chest. Yesterday's date had been torn from the calendar. *Do not men die fast enough*, he read, *without being destroyed by each other?* Friday . . . Almost with disbelief he realised that he and Patrick were to have been *en route* to Heidelburg. 'Lucky mortals,' Baxendale had said. 'Heidelburg, eh?' It seemed a lifetime ago.

He looked out on to the landing. It was squarish, the walls papered in silver grey, the carpet dark blue and showing signs of wear. There were two doors, one presumably the entrance to another apartment. The second was in the angle of the stairs. He went to it quickly. There was no lock. It opened outwards on to an iron platform and he saw the steps leading down, wire-meshed on both sides and roofed with corrugated sheeting. Below were garages and the service-yards to the ground-floor shops; beyond, a tangle of buildings, the partial view of a back street where traffic crawled as if in obedience to a promise. Three minutes? . . . Instinctively, the query lodged.

He returned to the girl's sitting-room and a calypso jerking from the radio. She emerged from the bathroom shortly afterwards and dressed in front of him with complete indifference, once asking 'Hungry?' but saying nothing more. They ate in the small kitchen – boiled eggs, toast and coffee. Her mood had changed. He was wary of her, sensing that her doubts about him were unallayed. The green eyes, a little puffy now, bleary, wanted no problems, no trouble. But at least he could be open about one thing.

'Where's the nearest telephone?'

'In the shop – the delicatessen.'

'Not downstairs?'

'No.' Her tone was surly. 'Will you be at your conference today?'

He nodded, remembering.

'What time?'

'Ten.'

'Where?'

He named the place where the bank was, Sunderspladsen, and she repeated it, correcting his pronunciation with a touch of scorn. Last night she would have teased him, but she'd made a bad bargain and her feelings showed.

'And then?'

'Then what?'

'What will you do?'

'I don't follow.'

'You won't want to come back here.'

'Of course.' Alarm chilled him. 'Of course I will,' he repeated.

'Why?'

'Why not?' he stalled.

'What's wrong with the Metropol?' She tossed her head. 'You look across there often enough.'

'This place is fine.'

'For what?'

'It suits me.'

With difficulty he held her gaze.

'On a couple of chairs?' she said. 'You get a bed in a hotel.'

He tried to laugh.

'There's no need to go on with it. Mistakes happen. How were they to know you didn't want a girl? You'd be better off elsewhere.'

'I like it here.'

'But I don't. It's . . . it's stupid. If you're sick or something, okay. Let's forget it ever happened.' More than pique was niggling her. 'Or is there another reason – one I haven't been told about?'

He snapped: 'You took the money, didn't you?'

'That was yesterday.'

'And tomorrow I'll have gone.'

'I'm counting the hours.'

She ground her cigarette in the saucer and went into the other room. Laker ran his hand over his face, dreading the depths of self-discovery to which he might yet be dragged. He had to keep a foothold here. And then, if need be, take the place over. God alone knew how. The imperatives controlling him made her presence unforgivable. Because she menaced an act that stabbed his mind with horror she prompted a terrible malice in him. He was too far gone in desperation to appreciate the irony. All he knew was what Hartmann had done to him, what Hartmann wanted, what was at stake.

The girl was straightening the crumpled divan when he left the kitchen. As if from habit he glanced towards Frenzel's room, the marksman in him automatically noting snags, thinking in terms of fleeting opportunity.

Nine twenty-five . . . Eight and a half hours before Frenzel's plane touched down; ten, say, before he was installed. So there was time yet. Time and Slattery. For too long he'd discounted Slattery. More and more he needed him, despite the risks, the misgivings. Alone he would crack.

'Have you got a spare key?'

'I'll be here,' the girl said.

'Say you aren't?'

'I will be.'

He didn't press it. He took his coat from its hook and went out on to the landing. In case she listened he walked all the way down. There were glass panels to either side of the front door and he studied the street through one of them. Nobody obviously waited for him, but he was taking no chances. He opened and shut the door loudly enough for the girl to hear, then went quietly up the first flight of stairs to the fire exit.

Again there was no evidence of being under observation. The fire-escape put him down by an outside lavatory at the rear of the delicatessen. The yard was stacked with wooden crates and a delivery van was parked close to the wall. No one was about. Laker walked between the crates and entered a storeroom where a woman was loading shelves with jars of pickle. She didn't notice him. He elbowed through a door into the shop, surprising an overalled youth on a ladder at the near end of the counter, but drawing no comment. It was a long rectangular shop. Half a dozen customers were either being served or waiting their turn. A solitary telephone-booth stood in an alcove. Laker checked his mass of small change, then stepped inside. A light clicked on as the door thudded. He paused before dialling, staring blankly at the activity behind the counter, the cheeses, the cooked meats, the patés, the hung salamis and knackwursts, isolating himself, visualising Slattery, putting his trust in him.

'London?' a voice echoed. 'A moment, please.'

And when it began again, the repetition, the waiting, the rising tension. 'No delay for London. Shall I book the Gerrard number?'

Three minutes after the half-hour. Someone would answer. Someone would be there. Laker closed his eyes, willing it, praying for it. The wire hummed, clicked, gabbled unintelligibly. An assistant sliced ham on a machine, a customer loaded her shopping-basket . . . If Slattery wasn't available they would tell him where he could be found. He'd make them. And Slattery would have a solution, institute counter-measures . . . Hope fed upon hope.

Every second lengthened, every minute. The booth was stifling. Outside, a man pointed at some mortadella, nodding, lips moving soundlessly. All the time people were either entering or leaving the shop.

'Hold for London, please.'

He had the money ready on a ledge, a pencil to hand. Aloud he urged: 'Hurry, please . . .' Another pause, another clash of tongues. On instructions he thumbed a succession of coins into the slots, waited, hands restless, eyes fixed, whispers like the sea filling his head. All at once there was silence, a moment's complete silence, before he heard the Gerrard number quoted. He hesitated, somehow unable to release himself from an intolerable strain.

'You're through, caller,' the operator prompted.

He swallowed. 'Mr. Slattery, please.'

'Who's calling?'

It sounded like the same person, the woman who'd answered when he rang from Gale and Watts. He told her, adding 'It's urgent.' But she stuck to her careful drill.

'Does Mr. Slattery know you?'

'Yes.'

'Is he expecting you to telephone?'

'Yes,' he snapped.

He waited again, trying to prepare his mind. Then, following a final click, Slattery was there at last, incredibly clear, seemingly in the booth with him, as close as ever he'd been. And cautious.

'Sam?'

'Listen – '

'Where are you?'

'Copenhagen.'

'*Where?*'

'I'm in trouble. Bad trouble . . .'

It came in a spate. He was never able to remember where he began or exactly what he said once the initial rush spilled over. He knew it was vital to be precise, chronological, absolutely accurate, but Slattery's interpolations confused him from the start – 'Hang on, Sam . . . Hold your horses . . .' He ignored them for a while, blundering on, but they became more frequent, louder, sharper, eventually cutting him off between words.

'You're on an open line, man. *An open line.*'

'I've no choice.'

'Then use your head. Scramble. Wrap it up.'

'How can I?'

'Try.'

'To hell with that. Listen – '

'I'm warning you.'

Laker bit back another retort.

'Do it my way,' Slattery said. '*My* way.'

'Very well.'

'Question and answer.'

'All right.'

The sound of Slattery's breathing raced along the line. 'You dropped in at K's?'

'Yes.'

'And found you were expected?'

'Yes.'

'After which they had a talk with you?'

'Yes.'

'Who did the talking?'

'Hartmann, S.S.D.'

'About Patrick?'

'In part.'

'Patrick's stayed on, I take it.'

'Yes.'

Slattery delayed for a second or so. He hadn't missed much. 'I didn't get the other person's name.'

'Rudolf Frenzel . . . He flies out of here tomorrow afternoon, at two.'

'Is he there now?'

'No. Tonight at six. From Paris.'

'And it's a case of either, or. Either, or – is that the proposition?'

'Yes.'

Silence.

Very quietly, Slattery said: 'Christ.'

'What are you going to do?'

'Give me time.'

'I tried to get to you last night, but they objected.'

'From Copenhagen?'

Yes.'

'Someone's with you?'

'Not at the moment. But I may not be able to contact you again.'

The wire spat. Laker licked his lips, staring as if mesmerised at a shop-assistant weighing cheese.

'Slattery?' he asked sharply by the lack of response.

'I'm here. Got my thinking-cap on . . . Is Patrick aware of the situation?'

'He's been told he's with friends of mine.'

'When did it come to a head?'

'Wednesday afternoon.'

'At K's?'

'After I left. Karen's been arrested. I saw her – '

'Easy, Sam.'

'She was blown. They knew I was coming – '

'Simmer down!'

Laker glared, seething. 'Get Patrick back and I'll simmer down.'

'All right, all right. But – '

'I'm not asking a favour. It's a matter of life and death. No one's playing a game at this end.'

'Look,' Slattery said. 'I'll alert Paris – that's the first thing. Our friend won't fly, d'you understand? He won't arrive.'

'That's no help.'

'It'll take the pressure off you while we – '

'It won't, it won't.' Frantically, Laker beat a fist against the coin-box. 'He's got to be here. *Got* to be. Don't stop him coming, for Christ's sake. They threatened me about that. He must arrive. Must, d'you hear?'

'To be an Aunt Sally?'

'It's him or Patrick.'

He began to talk about Hartmann, the words pouring from him again. He couldn't stop himself, straining desperately to convey the terror to which he had been subjected, the certainty that Hartmann wasn't bluffing, quoting him, restating the equation. Slattery seemed to have given up trying to interrupt.

'I haven't any choice, don't you see? Unless you intervene I've got to do what he wants.'

'You couldn't.'

'Put yourself in my position.'

The operator cut in to say that his time had expired. Urgently he asked for an extension, for Slattery to accept the charges, and Slattery agreed.

When it sounded as if they were once more alone Slattery said icily: 'Listen, Sam. I've got the message. If you go off the rails like that again I'll hang up – is that clear?'

'You wouldn't dare,' Laker snapped. 'You got us into this. Now get us out.'

'That's easier said than done.'

'Why?' He was trembling. 'If anything happens to Patrick I'll raise the roof. You'll have to answer for it – I'll see to that. You, personally. So think of something. And it had better be effective.'

'Such as?'

'How the hell d'you expect me to know? But you aren't powerless, are you?' He paused hopefully, but there was no answer. 'Are you?' he echoed.

'I'll do what I can. It's tricky, though.'

'Can't you offer anything more than that?'

'Not off the cuff, no.'

Laker gazed wildly at the continuing mime in the shop. A woman in a fur coat waited near the booth. Slattery was saying something about 'Playing it by ear'. Despite his blandness he sounded harassed and the jargon had a terrible sterility. In utter dismay, Laker shouted: 'What are you going to *do?*'

'Good God,' Slattery retorted. 'What d'you expect? I can't promise miracles. And even if I could I wouldn't be fool enough to broadcast them.'

The woman was tapping on the glass. Laker turned his back on her.

'Don't side-track Frenzel,' he urged Slattery. 'I want him here – tonight.'

'Look – '

'He's the only safeguard I've got.'

'Sam, listen – '

'You listen,' Laker shouted, beyond himself. 'Leave Frenzel alone.'

A frizzling noise filled the line. Through it Slattery was saying: 'I'll be in touch.'

'How?'

'Ritchie Jackson, at the Embassy.'

'I can't go there. Haven't you got the picture yet?'

'Can't you telephone?'

'I'm not sure I can risk it.'

The woman tapped on the glass again, harder now.

Almost hysterically Laker flung out: 'Hartmann said that Patrick and I had ceased to be public property. He said that because of circumstances I don't know about you'd be unwilling to lift a finger. Well, if you won't or can't, I will. I'll have to go through with it – and don't try and stop me. Leave word at the Metropol. The Metropol. If there isn't something by six tonight I'll know where I stand. And, so help me, I'll lay the whole bloody issue at your door when the time comes, whatever happens . . .'

He went on, goaded towards a kind of dreadful bravado. But after a while he was aware of a dribbling sound in his ear; he was talking to himself. Like someone betrayed he hung up and backed out of the booth. '*Tak!*' the woman said with heavy sarcasm. He stood amid the bustle and sudden chatter of the shop in a daze of anger and confusion. Whatever hopes he'd had had dwindled. But the upstairs room, the problem of the girl, the rifle awaiting collection at the bank – these were certainties, as real as the shoulders that jostled him.

Behind the counter an assistant cocked his head 'Nothing,' Laker muttered. 'Nothing.' Turning away he wished to God he'd had the sense to withhold Frenzel's name.

He went out through the back, crossed the yard and mounted the fire-escape. Then he walked down to the front door and let himself quietly into the street. After a few paces he paused to light a cigarette, glancing both ways as he did so. Once again no one caught his eye, but this time the feeling of menace was there. Where the block ended he waited for the lights to change before going over to the Metropol. It was shaped like a blunt V with traffic flowing along both sides. He made his way past the cars squatting in the forecourt and entered the deep-carpeted foyer.

The tall blonde on duty in Reception smiled politely, waiting to discover what language she was expected to match.

'I'm enquiring after a Mr. Frenzel.'

'What name?'

'Frenzel. Rudolf Frenzel.'

She consulted a list, running a scarlet nail down the side of the type. 'Frenzel,' she said, reminding herself.

'That's right.'

'There's a Mr. Frenzel expected. He has a reservation from this evening.'

Laker could see the number against her finger-nail: 68. And Hartmann loomed as if to remind him that one more thing had been proved; one more guarantee honoured.

'Mr. Frenzel would hardly be here yet, sir. Overnight visitors do not vacate their rooms until midday, but I can have him paged if you wish.'

'No, thank you.'

'Will you leave a message?'

'No.' Laker shook his head. 'Thank you,' he repeated, then walked away.

She would remember him, but he had hardly begun to concern himself with hazards of that sort. He was still trying to assess Slattery's tone, his attitude, still dismayed that his reaction hadn't been more appalled, more encouraging. Incredibly, his main concern had seemed to be for Frenzel. Nobody else could twist Hartmann's arm, and unless that were done there could only be one end. And Hartmann had been certain what that end must be; confident. 'I wouldn't care to be in London's shoes, Mr. Laker. No one likes humiliation, London least of all. But then, if I *were* in London's shoes, I wouldn't be aware of the situation, would I? You wouldn't have been stupid enough to tell me about Rudolf Frenzel, would you?'

For a while Laker walked aimlessly, blinkered by old and new fears, willing Slattery to act, to better Hartmann in some way, yet dreading a blundering, helping move which would result in catastrophe. For a day and a night he had never quite abandoned faith in Slattery's ability, but he was nearer to it now than ever before. Yet his hatred was for Hartmann, Hartmann who knew the lethal fury to which a person could be driven and who chose the victims and set a zero hour. Hartmann deserved what he meted out to others.

Thirty to forty yards to the rear a man in a dark overcoat kept his distance. He looked like the one who'd been in the foyer of the Metropol, but Laker wasn't sure about him and he didn't experiment. But he thought: All right, all right. So you know why I went there . . .

It was after ten and the banks were open. He would collect the rifle; he must. He was a puppet still. Nothing had changed.

A taxi brought him to the Sunderspladsen, a neat cobbled square centre on a fountain with a church filling most of one side and what Laker took to be municipal offices on the other. They had crossed a bridge to get there. The Copenhagen-National branch occupied a corner position. He paid off the driver and went in, affecting unconcern, as George Marshall requesting access to his deposit box. Once again the stepping-stone was ready and waiting; there were no snags. A clerk accompanied him down to the strong-room, used his master-key on Laker's locker, then discreetly withdrew. Hartmann's key opened the steel door. Inside was a narrow black case, about three and a half feet long and ten or twelve inches high. It wasn't new; the rexine covering was worn along the edges and slightly scratched. Laker slid it out and took it to one of the cubicles at the end of the room. To his surprise the case was secured only by catches. He sprung them simultaneously, then lifted the lid.

The weapon nestled in a bed of yellow velvet – the stock, the barrel and the telescopic attachment, each separate. Laker didn't touch them. They looked immaculate; the polished wood, the thin film of oil on the blue-black metal, the protective caps over the sight's ends, all gleamed dully under the overhead strip of light. In a recess at the top right-hand corner was a brown fibre box and he opened that, discovering what he expected – rimless ammunition packed in cotton-wool. A dozen rounds or so; he didn't count. There was an envelope taped inside the lid; 'Key' was written on it in German. He removed this and shut the case, locked it, putting the key into his hip-pocket as he left the cubicle.

The clerk said: 'Are you taking the case with you, Mr. Marshall?'

'Yes.'

'I see.' He was inclined to fuss. 'And are you continuing to rent your compartment?'

'Yes.'

'Very good.' He pushed the door to. It snapped shut and he turned the master-key, giving Laker a conspiratorial smile. There was nothing to sign, but the clerk entered the date in his ledger against the locker number.

'Thank you, sir.'

They walked up to the ground floor together. A nod, another smile, and they parted. Laker was sweating slightly, his face set. The case was heavier than its slimness suggested. He stepped out into the quiet square, armed now, equipped, yet as unremarkable as a musician on his way to rehearsal or a salesman hawking his particular brand of samples.

It was barely half-past ten. Only the waiting and the hoping remained, but he couldn't go back to the room so soon. He must use up a few hours. The girl was the major flaw in Hartmann's planning. And as he walked from the bank he once more began to realise how much hinged upon his ability to handle her – the lies, the blandishment, the persuasive wheedling that might be necessary; even the violence. But he had to have that room.

CHAPTER 12

He couldn't make up his mind whether anyone tailed him or not, but he took no deliberate avoiding action. It was strangely inefficient tailing, crude, apparently spasmodic; either that or immensely skilled. After a while he found himself on a tree-lined embankment overlooking a stretch of water in which the morning's white, ribbed clouds were mirrored. He paused there, the case at his feet, studying his wavering reflection.

Slattery would fail him; the feeling grew. For the hundredth time he went back to their meetings in Manchester Square and at The Mitre, appalled again by the amateur enthusiasm and cheerful understatement which had roped him in. If only he'd refused him at the outset, never learned of Karen's existence, been spared that aching wound along with the blackmail and its merciless inducement. Karen was already in the net by the time he was recruited, as helpless as he and Patrick were now. And Slattery should have known it; the secret wastes beneath the surface of daily living were his province.

It was futile to theorise, yet the question-marks persisted, throbbing through layers of hostility and desperation, blaming the years of deceit which had blunted Slattery's once sharp-eyed keenness for detail and his almost reflexive ability to read between the lines. At the very least Karen's position must have been suspect. Yet all he had thought necessary was to throw in a Leipzig telephone number – and that almost apologetically, as if it really weren't done even to imply that anything could go wrong.

Laker gazed into the water. The rhythmic clatter of a train reached him, making him raise his head and stare blankly at the buildings opposite. How glib Slattery had been. 'Wise-virgin common-sense, Sam . . .' That was then; and just now he was cagey, slightly flustered, not shocked enough, as if he still didn't fully understand what he'd started, what Hartmann would finish. *Not shocked enough.*

Laker moved on, scared again as his thoughts clipped nearer and nearer to Frenzel, picturing the hotel window with its slatted blinds. Say they were kept closed? Would he be forced to go to Frenzel's room – confront him? The sense of panic was never far off, and now it swept him anew. Aloud, almost dementedly, he heard himself ask: 'Why me? . . . Why me?' – and a couple passing on the embankment glanced at him with surprised amusement.

Intermittent sunshine cast his shadow on the paving-slabs; that of the case looked out of proportion, elongated. He crossed the road, a prisoner within himself, unaware of the car forced to swerve and the driver who shouted. Soon there were shops to either side. He went into a café and ordered a cognac, needing its fire, its strength. For a while as he sat there his mind fastened wildly on to the possibility of somehow entering into collusion with Frenzel, enlisting Jackson at the British Embassy, the Press and the police, between them faking a story and a photograph that would fool whoever waited to inform Hartmann of what had happened. But the idea withered like others before it.

The self-sufficient chatter at the neighbouring tables filled him with an extraordinary viciousness which presently drove him into the streets once more. He paused outside a newspaper office, its windows filled with enlargements of a military parade, the King and Queen arriving at the ballet. 'One word to anyone, Mr. Laker. *Anyone* . . .' The throttled dictum stayed with him, warning him that Slattery was hamstrung, too – 'An outcry, Mr. Laker? Public outrage? . . . Oh no' – reminding him all over again that Frenzel and Patrick were privately in the balance and must remain so. Yet hope could be stubborn. He dared not chance another personal visit to the Metropol, but under the pressure of stress he impulsively waved a cruising taxi into the kerb.

'D'you speak English?'

'Some. Where you want?' Cropped hair, blue eyes, a jaw like a boxer's.

'The Metropol.'

'Okay.'

'Go there for me. Ask at the desk if there is a message for Laker. Then come back here.'

'A message?'

'For Laker.' He spelt it quickly.

'You don't come?'

'No.'

A frown. 'You stay here, is that it?'

'Yes.'

'Okay – but for twenty Kroner.'

'All right.'

'Twenty Kroner first.'

Laker paid, repeating the name, the hotel.

'Okay,' the driver said. 'Five minutes.'

He drew away, grinning, and Laker waited nervously. He wasn't clever, but it was the best he could do. For what seemed a very long time he gazed into a window where a model of a black bull, pinned with paper banderillas, blinked electric eyes at him amid a display of sherries. He watched the traffic's flow in the glass, convinced he wasn't watched in turn. But he fidgeted, on edge, then paced up and down. Just as he was beginning to conclude he'd allowed himself to be robbed, the taxi slid in from behind a grinding tram.

'No message.'

'Are you sure?'

'Sure. Nothing for Laker.'

A muscle flicked by Laker's mouth. It was early yet, only ten to twelve. Even so . . .

'Thanks,' he said.

'Okay.' The driver grinned again. 'Perhaps she send word another time, eh?'

Laker decided to give Slattery another couple of hours. Meanwhile there were practical things to be done, preparations to be made. He couldn't cling indefinitely to straws.

He found his bearings, then explored the area to the rear of the delicatessen, timing himself over the distance between the service-yards and the nearest taxi-rank, walking briskly towards the street he'd seen from the top of the fire-escape earlier in the day. It took him almost six minutes, but that included mistakenly entering a cul-de-sac. The second trip took under five, the third, cutting corners, only a fraction over four. And this was walking; against that there were three levels of fire-escape to be negotiated. It was an all-night rank, he noted.

Eventually he took a taxi and was driven to the B.E.A. office. There were several flights to choose from and he booked on one leaving for London at four-thirty on the Saturday afternoon, two and a half hours after Frenzel's own proposed exit from Copenhagen. That part of him which had already lost confidence in the chances of a reprieve was dismayed by the gap between the unpredictable moment Frenzel was going to be squarely in his sights and four-thirty on Saturday. It might amount to hours, half a day, perhaps a night as well. There were so many imponderables. Where would he go after that headlong rush down the fire-escape? The Embassy? His mind wouldn't stretch that far. Self-preservation was the least of his concerns.

He chose a place to eat within a stone's-throw of the Tivoli. It was small, crowded, and he shared a table with a middle-aged man with a voracious appetite who read a newspaper and whose feet kept coming into contact with the gun-case. Twice Laker moved it, apologising. He wasn't hungry. He was killing time. He could only toy with the food, but he drank three large whiskies and several cups of black coffee. At a quarter to two he pressed some Kroner into the waiter's hand and asked him to ring the Metropol. The reply was the same: nothing, no message. Anxiety hounded him into the streets again, the weight of the case insisting that the nightmare was going to run its prescribed course after all, all the demented way.

He followed the route he and the girl had taken the previous evening. As he neared the delicatessen his eyes went up to her third-floor window and the one directly opposite. The sun glinted like gold on Frenzel's.

'Fear can remove mountains, Mr. Laker . . .'

He pressed the door-bell and thought of Patrick.

'Oh,' she said when she saw him. That was all – 'Oh,' without inflexion.

She let him in and he followed her up the steep stairs. The room seemed to have shrunk since he was last there. A cigarette burned in a tray beside the divan and the covering was pulled back, the pillows dented. He put the case down at the foot of the divan and tossed his coat over it. She was wearing dark slacks and a striped sweater and there was a pale-blue velvet band across her hair. Last night she'd been bright, talkative, eager to draw him out and have him relax, to have him laugh. But he'd put paid to that and the grudge still showed.

He muttered something about a wash: 'Please yourself,' she said and curled on the divan, reaching for the magazine.

The bathroom window was narrow and rather high. Laker moved the plastic curtain aside and gazed across the street. It surprised him how much of Frenzel's room he could see now that the sun was behind him, streaming in. He could even pick out the light-switch by the white door through which Frenzel would come and go. He wouldn't inevitably be deciphering shadows, then. And, sometime or other, Frenzel would surely attend to the blinds – close them, open them; it didn't matter much. A couple of seconds would be long enough, a couple of heart-beats. Four windows to the left a plump, bald man was at that instant polishing his spectacles and Laker drew an imagined line on him. It would be easy, given the occasion, given the chance of maintaining a vigil.

He felt no relief; every fibre of him ached to be spared. In an hour or two, somehow, he would check with the Metropol again. Meanwhile he must consolidate his position and make the vigil possible. Everything hung on what was said, how it was said. He sluiced his face from the cold tap, then looked at himself, in the grip of his own helplessness. His vision seemed to cloud. He was a businessman, a widower with a house in Weybridge. Weybridge, Surrey . . . England. Who was Frenzel? – Frenzel who would never know Patrick and whom Patrick would never know? What had Frenzel done except to change sides? . . . But he mustn't start thinking about Frenzel – not as a man, not like that. Only of what he must do and how to cope with the girl.

He finger-combed his hair and joined her in the room, mastering his nerves. She glanced up from her magazine, then went on reading.

'Have you been out?'

'No.'

'You're missing a fine day.'

She shrugged. He sat in the chair nearest to her and fastened his shoe-laces. Money might interest her, but first he had to establish rapport. She had gone cold on him; the glance just now was full of surly surmise.

'Where did you learn your English?'

'Huh?'

'Your English. It's good.'

'At school. Here and there.'

'It's good,' he said lamely.

'I was with S.A.S. for a while. That helped.'

'Flying?'

'For a while.'

She sounded bored, as if she had been asked these things a thousand times. Laker watched for a smile, some softening of her features, but there was none. He asked about her flying, the places she'd been, in what aircraft, where she liked best, not caring what her answers were, not interested, his mind in the employ of a situation three hundred miles away. If she warmed to him it was barely noticeable. He got up and went to the table where the bottles were, the lava flow of doubt and anxiety endlessly pressing through him.

'D'you want one?'

She shook her head. He poured himself a whisky, deliberately avoiding looking towards the window, seeing in her green eyes a lurking background of suspicion. Given time she would probably relent; tenderness was her professional stock-in-trade. If he had been hungry for her he would have had confidence in his ability to thaw her out. He carried the glass back to the chair and sat with is fingers locked round it, trying to hide his thoughts, afraid of showing that he was afraid.

'How was the conference?' she asked.

'All right.'

'Isn't there an afternoon session?'

'No.'

'Don't tell me you came to Copenhagen just for a morning's meeting.'

'We started yesterday,' he lied.

'On what.'

'Business efficiency.'

It was twenty to three. He began talking again, about her, working for a return of the smile which would be a beginning. Hartmann's funds weren't exhausted and he had traveller's cheques of his own; together they totalled around two hundred pounds. She could have the lot if need be. For money like that she might be willing to leave, stay the night somewhere, allow him the run of the place until the following afternoon. It was possible. It would be tempting. Two hundred pounds and no questions asked – yes?

He finished the whisky, reached over and switched on the radio. She arched an eyebrow, measuring him with a look while he struggled to mask his nerves, his tension.

'I'm sorry about last evening. I . . . I'd had a hard day – you know how it is.'

She didn't answer. He lit a cigarette, the hard core of his mind intent, the rest uneasy, uncertain. If he couldn't buy her absence he would somehow have to keep her prisoner – that or quit the room entirely and haunt the Metropol until Frenzel arrived and could be tackled squalidly at close quarters. For two days now he had existed in loneliness, anguish burning into him, destroying hope and pity and self-respect. It was worse than fever, worse than hysteria. Yet he was absolutely clear as to what the issues were, feeling Hartmann's corrective tug whenever he asked how it could possibly be that he was committed to a killing while the world went by outside and neither he nor Slattery could let it know. 'There are rules to this game, Mr. Laker . . .' Memory never let up.

'Anna,' he said.

He moved to the divan and sat beside her. She turned her head on the pillow, wary still. He took the magazine, sliding it from her grip, and tossed it aside.

'What's become of that smile?'

'It's not my smiling day.'

'Why not?'

She shrugged again, lifting her shoulders like a piano-player, narrowing them.

'Come on,' he said.

She grimaced, lips pressed together.

'Is that the best you can do?'

'I'm not a tap,' she said.

'I'm sorry about last night.'

'I heard you the first time.'

He still believed it was only a matter of patience. He touched her callously, as if he were just another man for whom machine-like response would suffice. 'Anna,' he said, despising himself, reduced to this so that she might feel sorry for him, glad to be necessary, and then be ready to listen, more willing to consider what he had to propose.

'What's got into you?' she said flatly.

She was stiff, unyielding. He ran his fingers over her white neck and into the softness of her hair. He felt no thrill, no excitement. He was using her, or seeking to. They would find the rifle here, but he didn't care. The contract permitted no stab of regret. Only the end mattered, and she was in the way of Frenzel's mortal danger.

She didn't move. Her eyes seemed harder, as if he were one of those who haggled when everything was finished.

'Where's this conference of yours?'

'The Sunderspladsen.'

'Where in the Sunderspladsen?'

'Where?'

'Where, yes.'

'Near the bank.'

She glanced away from him. The radio was pulsing out a staccato beat. Laker should have been warned, on his guard; but no. Ruthlessly he traced the line of her lips.

'You're lying,' she said after a few moments.

'Lying?'

'There is no conference.'

'Nonsense.'

'Not in the Sunderspladsen.'

'Of course there is.' He forced a laugh.

'I checked,' she said.

He saw the spiky glint of anger as she pushed his hands down. He sat back, alarm knotting in his chest.

'Look,' he began, 'this is ridiculous.'

'No, it isn't.'

'What's a conference got to do with us?'

'There isn't any conference.'

'All right. Have it your own way. But how does that matter?'

'It matters.'

'Tell me how.'

She twisted off the divan and reached for a pack of cigarettes, fumbled one loose and lit it. He watched her, thoughts in turmoil. Later, time and again, he was to recall how she looked at him then.

'I want you to go.'

'Why?'

'I do, that's all.'

'Listen –'

'You can have the money back.'

'It's not mine.'

'The one who laid on your fun, then.' Her nostrils flared. Instinct was warning her, it could only be that, warning her not to allow herself to be involved in something she sensed yet did not understand. 'I don't want you here any more.'

He got up. 'You're being stupid.'

'Perhaps.'

'You are.'

'That's my affair.'

'Anna,' he said desperately. He took hold of her, making one last try, fondling her roughly in the way she knew best, his mouth finding hers. 'You must be out of your mind.'

She wrenched herself free. 'I mean it.' She reached for a bundle of notes on the mantelshelf. 'Here,' she said furiously.

'I'm staying.' His voice had thickened. 'You can't turn me out.'

'I can and I will.'

She flung the money at him and started for the door. He caught her by the arms as the notes scattered about his head.

'Be reasonable, for God's sake.'

'Let – me – go!'

Even then he could hardly believe that disaster was land-sliding down in a cheap brawl. If she hadn't struggled he might have been able to control himself, quieten her – at least quieten her. But she was vicious, kicking at his shins, her voice rising all the time and the sound of it sliced into his brain like a knife. He slapped her, horrified by what she was doing, knowing that it had to be stopped. She spat at him, kicking again.

'Don't be a fool!' he shouted. 'Don't be – '

She was strong, absolutely wild. They crashed into the table and all the bottles went over. He freed a hand and slapped her a second time, hard, full on the cheek-bone. She screamed. He tried to drag her towards the divan but she broke away, her gaping red mouth destroying Patrick – in panic he could think of nothing else and in panic he went after her, thrashing round the cluttered room. With a convulsive movement she grasped one of the bottles. He closed, warding off the expected blow, but before he could check her she hurled the bottle through the window. For a moment they both stared, panting, silent until the sound of the brittle smash below reached them and a yell came from the street. And then she ran to the broken window and screamed piercingly again, with her hands clenched beside her head.

Laker seemed unable to move any more. Aghast, he watched her retreat from the window and sink on to the arm of the nearest chair, shaking, sobbing now. He felt as if the whole of his stomach was going to come up.

'Go away,' she moaned. 'Go away.'

Vaguely he was aware of a noise in the street; feet thudding on the stairs. Stunned, he couldn't think. He heard himself say: 'D'you know what you've done? Oh Christ, d'you know what you've done?'

Someone banged on the door. The girl scurried to open it. A uniformed policeman came in, then another, big men who seemed to fill the room. There was a brief interchange between them and the girl before they motioned Laker out. He could understand so much, but no more. He thought he was merely being ejected and he picked up the gun-case and his coat and the suitcase. With a hand to her swelling cheek the girl flinched as he drew level. He paused, staring into her uncomprehending face, trying to speak; but words wouldn't come.

The taller of the policemen pushed him on to the landing. It was only then and on the way down the stairs between them that he realised they were taking him with them.

CHAPTER 13

In a daze Laker leaned against the side of the wagon jolting him away. There had been people on the landings, people around the street doors, people outside the delicatessen – all watching as he was bundled across the pavement. He hadn't protested; he seemed to have been deprived of his strength, his will, his wits. And now, sitting between the two policemen in the enclosed back of the wagon, he was still beyond reasoning, the girl's screams still vibrating in his ears. 'Where am I going?' he kept asking, but either they didn't understand him or they weren't disposed to answer.

When the wagon stopped, the rear doors were opened and he lurched out, clutching his coat and the two cases. One of the policemen attempted to grasp him by the arm, but he shook the hand away, beginning to react at last.

Stone steps led up to heavy double doors. Inside was a brightly-lit lobby with corridors branching left and right. He was taken past a railed barrier and brought to a standstill in front of a counter where his escorts conferred with the grey-haired policeman on duty.

Without fluency this one asked him: 'What is your name?' A sheet of paper was briskly torn from a pad. 'Name?'

Laker stared at him, shattered, thoughts beginning to race. He was sweating.

'Name?'

'Laker.'

'Other name?'

'Samuel.'

'English? American?'

'English . . . Look,' Laker blurted, 'you aren't thinking of keeping me here, are you?'

'Passport?'

'What?'

'You have passport?'

Laker drew it from his inside pocket and the photograph of Frenzel nearly came out, too. Glimpsing that startled expression again all but overwhelmed him. The light above his head was clinical and fierce and he was suddenly unnerved lest someone decided to examine what was in the black case.

'Will there be a fine?'

The policeman pursed his lips and turned the pages of the passport, studying the visa stamps with earnest, puckered eyes.

'I'm in a position to pay if there's a fine. Or if there's any damage to be made good.'

Laker faltered, every moment of the brawl fresh and stark; frantically asking himself how it could conceivably have happened. There hadn't been reason enough; she'd almost manufactured it. He wiped his face, obsessed by what she had cost him in terms of angles and opportunity; what she might cost him yet. A clock behind the counter showed a minute or two past three.

'There was a misunderstanding.' He pressed against the counter. 'A misunderstanding. The window was broken by accident . . .' He swallowed. 'If you'd only listen I'd like to explain – '

Ominously, the passport was set to one side.

'You wait,' the duty man said, then corrected himself. 'You *will* wait.'

'What for? . . . For how long?'

'Long?'

'When can I go?'

'Not to go. Wait.'

'Yes, but for how *long?*'

There was no answer. 'Look here,' he exploded, then stopped, warned by a hint of exasperation in the other's stolid glance. More quietly he managed: 'Am I being charged – and, if so, what with?'

'Charged?'

With as much calm as Laker could dredge he said: 'If there's any question of my being held I insist on being put in touch with the British Embassy – a Mr. Jackson. A Mr. Jackson at the British Embassy, is that clear?'

It didn't seem to be. He leaned across the counter and snatched up a pencil; swivelled the pad round. *Mr. Jackson,* he wrote, *British Embassy.* 'Yes?'

The man nodded. 'Understand,' he said. 'But now you wait.'

Laker fought down another distracted protest. With his coat draped across the gun-case he went where the escort directed, turning into a corridor, entering a room the door of which was opened for him. The window was barred, but it was more like an interview-room than anything, with a trestle-table and some tubular steel chairs, cream-painted walls, red linoleum. Outside, cars were parked in a courtyard. He put the cases on the floor and sat at the table, trembling so much that he could hardly light a cigarette, reliving the swift crescendo of words and scuffling which had ruined Hartmann's basic plan, still flushed and sweating ice and fire.

He had botched everything. He'd never set foot in that room again, so there was only one course left – sickening even to contemplate, yet imperative, Hartmann's threat more urgent now than ever. He shuddered. Once he got out of here he would have to go on, on, with his senses gutted and his mind like that of a hunting animal, deprived even of the sop to his conscience which the width of a street, the impersonal pressure on a trigger, might have given.

They hadn't locked the door; he tried it after a while and looked into the corridor. But he wasn't tempted. It would be madness to cut and run; the exits were sure to be guarded. What was more they had his passport. And he needed to contact Jackson – not merely so as to smooth his release but because Jackson was his link with Slattery, perhaps the only one now.

Less than three hours remained to Slattery: six o'clock was his dead-line for producing a formula. And, if he couldn't, if there wasn't one, Frenzel was as good as dead. This was what terror did to you; what Hartmann had achieved by threat and argument and what he'd known could be sustained on the strength of a promise.

Nerves several times propelled Laker to the door during the next half-hour. Once a girl passed carrying some files, and she smiled at him, interested. Shortly afterwards what he took to be an officer went by with a couple of civilians; these all ignored him. At twenty to four a policeman came into the room with a cup of tea. Laker was too eager to talk with him to be surprised. 'Have you been in touch with the British Embassy? . . . Is Mr. Jackson on his way? . . .' But he got nowhere. Even when he followed the man into the corridor in an attempt to persuade him to fetch someone with a better understanding of English or German he failed to extract more from him than a series of gestures, shrugs and one repeated word – 'Soon.'

But for the rifle he would have stormed back to the counter in the entrance-lobby. There was nothing to stop him, yet he was afraid of incurring official enmity by creating a scene. If they took it into their heads to retaliate by checking his luggage, his pockets, inevitably he would find himself the focus of attention. Instead of being left to cool his heels there would be questions, questions he couldn't satisfactorily answer, and he might be held indefinitely, pending further enquiries. A sordid little shouting-match with a tart was one thing; explaining away a sniper's rifle would be a very different matter.

He left the door open to minimise the feeling of being cut off. Four o'clock gradually came and went. He couldn't settle. His thoughts grasshoppered interminably between past and future. At ten minutes after the hour the same man returned to collect the cup. 'Soon,' he said when Laker tackled him.

'Soon what?'

'Yes.'

A nod and he left. Jesus . . . Another thirty minutes elapsed, inflaming Laker's despair, stretching his control almost to breaking-point. It was nearly five before anyone else acknowledged his existence. Then an officer put in an appearance, a blond giant with protruding ears and an unexpectedly amiable manner. Laker hardly gave him a chance to shut the door.

'How long am I to be detained like this?'

'That is what I have come to explain.' At last the English was excellent. 'It depends.'

'Depends?'

'On whether the young woman decides to take action against you.'

'Prefer charges, you mean?'

'Exactly. Unfortunately, she has gone out. So far we have not been able to check with her.'

'But that's ridiculous. I've already been here two hours.'

'I realise that.'

'Am I under arrest?'

'No.'

'What could she charge me with?'

'Assault.'

'Say she did – what then?'

'You will be released on bail pending the hearing. And we will continue to keep your passport.'

Laker somehow kept a grip on himself. 'I asked at the desk for a Mr. Jackson at the British Embassy to be contacted.'

'That has been done.'

'Is he coming?'

'I could not say, but he has been informed.'

The officer turned to leave. Laker could feel the veins bulging in his temples. 'You can't hold me indefinitely.'

'Not indefinitely, of course.'

'Overnight?'

'I should not think that would be likely.'

'Can't you be more precise.'

'I have told you – it depends. The woman should have been brought here at the same time as you. That is the normal practice. She would then have had the opportunity of asserting her rights and you would have been spared this rather unfortunate delay.' In the doorway he paused as if anxious to show that he wasn't without sympathy. 'However, it may be for the best. She might not want her pound of flesh – is that what you say, her pound of flesh? – once she has calmed down. Her sort rarely do.'

A meal was brought to him around seven. Earlier a young policeman came with a tattered copy of *Reader's Digest*. They meant well. Laker touched neither. Imperceptibly the sky darkened. The lights were put on. Most of the cars in the courtyard drew away. Twice, imprudently, he quit the room and went to the entrance-lobby asking for news of the girl, of Jackson, once insisting that the Embassy was telephoned in his presence, and the imperturbability of those on duty, their stubborn adherence to a petty technicality, seemed more and more like a grotesque conspiracy.

Frenzel was installed in the Metropol by now. And Slattery had failed, failed even to respond, Slattery who outside The Mitre had said: 'No hard feelings, I hope, Sam – now or at any time.' Jackson was a dead loss, too. It was unbelievable; unforgivable. Laker rocked back and forth on a chair with his eyes hard closed, wishing to God in a kind of delirium there had never been any woman in a yellow dress with a child in a pram and a lorry bearing down on them all that distorted lifetime ago.

With an enormous effort he gathered himself together, knowing the futility of questioning anything, steeling himself to be patient, trying not to dwell on what he was being patient for. Yet he took Frenzel's picture from his pocket and stared at it, feeling hollow, drained, asking why either of them had been born.

Jackson arrived at twenty-five-past eight. Laker guessed who it was from the slightly drawled 'This way?' that heralded his approach along the corridor. And then he was there, about Laker's age, slight, sandy-haired, a dinner-jacket showing beneath his unbuttoned overcoat. 'Thank you,' he said to the accompanying policeman. 'Thank you very much.'

He stepped into the room offering a well-trained smile and a seemingly boneless handshake.

'Ritchie Jackson . . . I'm sorry to have been so slow. I gather you've been kept dangling for quite some while.'

'Since three o'clock.'

'As long as that?'

'At least.'

'I really am sorry. But I didn't get your message, d'you see? I wasn't in my office during the afternoon and it was only just now, half an hour or so ago, that the Embassy switchboard knew where they could catch me – glass in hand, as it were.'

Laker didn't know whether to believe him; not that it mattered. Tersely, he said: 'They're holding me on an idiotic technicality. I'm not under arrest and yet they say I can't leave – not, that is, until they know whether or not a complaint –'

'It's all fixed,' Jackson cut in smoothly. 'I've had a word with 'em.'

'I can go?'

'Yes. They're feeling quite a little guilty – and no wonder. They really didn't need much persuasion. They reckon the, er, other person concerned has had every chance, so they've agreed to forget there was ever any trouble. It was pretty much a storm in a teacup from what I hear, anyway. So –'

He spread his hands, smiling like a magician awaiting the applause. Laker's relief was minimal. He was searching for an indication that Jackson appreciated he wasn't rescuing just another tourist who'd run out of money or gone off the rails. But there was no sign of it, no hint that Jackson realised what was at stake. He closed the door.

'Slattery told me to ask for you.'

'Oh yes – I was coming to that.'

'Well?'

'He wanted you to know he's doing everything he can.' Jackson paused. 'Everything he can, unquote.'

Laker's mouth dragged at the corners. 'Is that all?'

'As far as I know. The switchboard passed the message on, d'you see, while I was drinking the Italian Ambassador's health.'

'When was it received, for God's sake?'

'About five, I understand.'

'And there was nothing else?'

'No . . . Does it make the sense it should?'

Laker was incapable of answering. Desolation ploughed through him. For an awful nauseous moment a part of him recoiled from what now seemed inevitable. All day he had clung to one last shred of hope, and it was part of the nightmare that Slattery's uselessness should be conveyed at second-hand, casually, with gin on the breath and small teeth bared in an anxious little smile.

'Does it?' Jackson repeated like a fool. 'You fellows always – ' And then he stopped, on the fringes of the game and keeping there.

Dumbfounded, Laker picked up the two cases and his coat. Jackson opened the door and they walked the corridor's length to the counter, where the grey-haired policeman interrupted booking a drunk to give Laker his passport.

'Can I drop you somewhere?' Jackson asked. 'My car's round the corner – unless it's been pinched, that is.'

The night air was cool. Jackson drove with a flourish. He was wearing a hat now, its angle slightly jaunty. When Laker recognised the square where the airport coach had put him down the day before he said curtly. 'This'll do,' and Jackson edged into the side.

'Sure?'

'Quite sure.'

'You don't want a hotel?'

Laker shook his head. Neon jazzed through the windscreen.

'Well, if there's nothing else,' Jackson said, holding out a hand and smiling the smile he did best, 'I'll be off to claim my wife before all that Italian charm bowls her over. Glad I was able to help. A police-station's no place to spend one's time and I'm only sorry I couldn't get to you earlier. Still, better late than never I suppose.'

Laker got out. From the kerb, he said: 'How soon can you get word to Slattery?'

'Practically right away.'

'Tell him I had no choice, no choice at all.'

'Just that?'

'"No choice at all" – will do.'

'There's more.'

'Yes?'

'Tell him also that if Patrick suffers as a result of this, I want him to know in advance that my name isn't Wyatt . . . James Wyatt.'

Jackson frowned. 'You can't enlarge a bit, I suppose? Or will that be clear to him?'

'It'll be clear,' Laker said.

His voice shook, yet he was unnaturally calm. He watched the car ease into the traffic, then began to walk. It had ceased to concern him whether he was tailed or not. Hartmann had all-but won. Shrink from murdering Frenzel and Patrick vanished, fail to murder Frenzel and Patrick vanished . . . Nothing had changed; nothing *could* change. He now realised he had asked the impossible of Slattery. The blackmail embraced them both. But he'd never excuse the callousness of almost total silence, the apparent indifference, the continued implication that once a pro always a pro and that, as such, he must fend for himself.

From the girl's room Laker would have been forced to take the first chance that presented itself, not knowing if another would follow. If she hadn't screamed him out of there Frenzel might have been dead already, the hunt in full cry. But he could delay now, choose his time – and pay the price in terms of horror. He walked slowly, on the lookout for a telephone, mentally leap-frogging forward to the moment when Patrick would touch down at London Airport tomorrow night, trying to reconcile everything with that.

It was nine when he found a public booth. Three hours had elapsed of Frenzel's twenty. He got the Metropol's number from the book, then dialled.

'Reception, please.' When he was connected he said: 'Have you a Mr. Frenzel with you? Rudolf Frenzel? . . . Yes, that's correct.'

He waited, beginning then to screw himself up for what would follow this preliminary reconnaissance. He could hear a rustle of papers; somebody coughing in the background.

'Did you say the name is Frenzel?'

'Yes.'

Another crisp rustle.

'No, caller, there's no Mr. Frenzel booked here.'

'There is,' Laker retorted. 'I checked earlier in the day.'

Alarm was slow to spiral. The plane must be late. Frenzel had delayed booking in . . . Yet he was saying urgently: 'Mr. Frenzel has been allocated room sixty-eight. Rudolf Frenzel – from Paris.'

'When did you check, caller?' The voice was helpful.

'This morning.'

More rustling; a mutter. Then: 'Ah yes, I see it now. Frenzel, sixty-eight . . .'

'Thank you.'

And then it came.

'But since then, caller, the reservation has been cancelled. Mr. Frenzel relinquished his booking at four o'clock this afternoon.'

It must have been five minutes before he could get a taxi. He had no recollection of hanging up or quitting the booth. In a frenzy of disbelief he signalled every passing cab, bawling at them through the traffic's rumble until at last one acknowledged him and took him to the Metropol. And there, by a quiet-spoken woman with blued hair who met the full force of his distress with impeccable politeness, his despair was made absolute.

He turned from her with a dead, beaten stare. By the Enquiries desk he stopped and asked if there was a message for him, doing so with the numbness of a person whose mind had congealed beyond sensible usefulness. And there was one. He snatched it from the man who took it from the pigeon-hole, capable as he did so of assuming that Slattery finally had a germ of hope to offer, guidance, instructions, even an explanation that the miracle had been achieved and Frenzel kept out of harm's way as a precaution.

He fumbled open the folded slip. *You should not have contacted London.* And the sender's name leaped at him – *Hartmann.*

CHAPTER 14

He moved blindly out into the night, oblivious of the flow of people, the gaggles of traffic, the guano-green fairy-tale roofs above the floodlit buildings. He felt his legs would give and he entered a bar and sat there staring, motionless, leaving untouched the whisky he never realised he ordered. Then he walked again. Finally, on a public bench under a street-lamp, he extracted the slip of paper which was crushed between his fingers and the handle of the gun-case and gazed at the scrawled writing of whoever had taken the message down. *Message for:* Mr. Samuel Laker. *Received by:* Telephone. *Time:* 16.50. The printed headings were in three languages. *Message:* You should not have contacted London. *Sender's name:* Hartmann.

He read it over and over, protest groping in the stupefied darkness of his brain. And every time it turned in agony on Slattery for what had been done Hartmann was there to intervene, claiming priority, inviting the hatred he had seemed to relish from that initial meeting in the hut.

'Between you and me, Mr. Laker. Always remember that . . .'

Laker crumpled the paper into a ball, split beyond control, guilt and rage beating behind his eyes. He should never have given Slattery Frenzel's name. Slattery could wait, though. Slattery was a reckless incompetent and would answer for it. But Hartmann was a destroyer, the begetter of horrific sins for whom mercy was a word, pity a word. 'Then I am sorry for you,' he had said when Laker pleaded for Karen – and sorrow was a word, too.

'You and me, Mr. Laker . . .' So be it. There was another kind of equation now and it had Laker silently in tears. He felt an urge like lust, ugly and savage, demanding satisfaction, deeper than the will to live or preserve life.

He was going back to Leipzig.

He nursed the hatred, letting it fester, drawing on it to drug his grief. He put on his coat, picked up the cases and walked until he reached another bar; and this time he drank, blinkered by the fierceness of his intent, numbing what he could of a hundred other memories. He drank until the place closed at midnight; heavily, effectively, but he was steady on his feet when he left.

It would be morning before he could make a move, nine o'clock at the earliest before he could set about getting himself another Fair Card, nine before the air-line ticket-offices opened. Despite the drink, and the pain that drink could never tranquillise, he saw the essentials clearly. He wandered into a park at one time, alone by a small lake except for some furtive lovers. The streets were emptying now; more and more he had them to himself. Nobody kept that careful distance and the fact showed that Hartmann had finished with him – emphasising what this meant, what it could only mean. He believed Hartmann. All along he'd believed him. He'd have made himself kill for Hartmann, so there was no chance of not believing him now. 'On whatever you care to name as sacred, Mr. Laker . . .'

Only revenge was left, and he felt the lust for it grow in the sodden depths of his spirit as he walked the night.

Sometime in the small hours he found himself passing the air-line terminus. He entered and sank on to a vacant couch, aching in thighs and calves, surrounded by a scattering of passengers waiting for dawn flights. The effect of the whisky was wearing off and he knew how close he was to breakdown. His jaw-muscles quaked as if a fever threatened. He shut his eyes, clinging to hatred as once he had to cling to hope, bolstering himself with it. The place filled up. People moved back and forth, bored, expectant, their hand-luggage labelled, carrying guide-books and magazines, about to venture somewhere new, returning home.

Home. Jesus, what could home be now?

He watched a coach-load depart. An indefatigable porter came to take his cases for weighing-in, but Laker stopped him.

'What is your destination, sir?'

He shook his head. Perhaps he looked ill, lost, incapable; perhaps he'd been there overlong.

'Do you know your flight number?'

'I'm all right,' he retorted hoarsely. 'All right.'

He searched the leaflet-racks. S.A.S. listed a Czechoslovak Ilyushin at

12.15, arriving Schönefeld 13.20. The fact registered dully. S.A.S. would confirm the time of the Leipzig connection when he bought his ticket. He'd be there before evening. The temporary visa that went with the Fair Card would see him through. There was one unavoidable hurdle, but he would face that when it came.

He urged the time away so that he could make a start. There was a discarded newspaper on the couch: the *Express*, yesterday's. He dragged it towards him distractedly. HELICOPTER SNATCH OFF BEACHY HEAD . . . 'I WON'T BUDGE': FRANCO . . . RECORD POOLS WIN . . . His eyes glossed over the headlines, the centred wedding pictures, the Lancaster cartoon, and it all seemed totally unreal. ALBRIGHT HERE, MOSCOW SAYS . . . *Matthew Albright,* he read, *the Sino-Soviet expert missing for several months from the U.S. State Department was today officially admitted by Moscow to be in the Soviet Union. This is the first time Russia has disclosed Albright's whereabouts, though the West has known since May that he had defected. As in the case of Pontecorvo, Burgess, Philby . . .*

Names, names.

A smudge of dawn was showing in the street. Laker stared at it, thinking of Frenzel whose ghost would haunt him to the end, Frenzel who had once defected too, earned a paragraph, if that, and whose life had been balanced against Patrick's.

He took up his cases and went stiffly into the morning's pearly chill. 'Provocation or necessity, Mr. Laker; they're the two incentives. You're an instrument about to be put to practical use.'

Not any more. Of his own free will, of his own choice – as at Gardelegen all that time ago, before Patrick ever existed.

He ate breakfast in a café where labourers and tram-crews apparently began their day. It was a quarter to seven when he paid the bill and left; eight before he found a barber's open and got a shave. A poster in a travel agent's window enticed the world to visit the Leipzig Fair. At half-past eight he was in the Farimagsgade, waiting for the Fair's office to start business. Sharp on nine he was admitted and by twenty minutes past he was out again, the forms completed, his passport details logged, the fee paid, the Fair Card in his wallet.

The S.A.S. booking-clerk was no less obliging. The Schönefeld flight connected with one for Leipzig at 14.40; Leipzig arrival time was 15.10. Would that be satisfactory? A traveller's cheque? Certainly . . . She bore no resemblance to the girl who yesterday had seemed to have loosed disaster upon him, but the S.A.S uniform and a certain similarity of speech dragged his mind back to the room and the window opposite and what he had prepared for then, what had bound him then. Watching her make out the flight-ticket he pieced the broken jigsaw together once again, and with hindsight he saw a pattern of inevitability in what had happened, step by step, Slattery's use of him and Hartmann's use of him sucking him down into the dark mouth of this funnel of vengeance.

He rode in a taxi to the airport. He was there with more than an hour to spare. A dozen times on the journey he must have tested the locks on the black case, yet his trust in them diminished as his luggage was weighed and heaved out of sight. But it was early yet to worry on that score; the hazards were still three hundred miles away. He went into the departure lounge and wrote a bitter cable for Slattery, but even the most vicious phrasing was inadequate and, in the end, he sent nothing. Nothing to Gale and Watts either. Nothing to Roundwood. Nothing to anyone, lest in doing so he should somehow weaken and waver, remember friends, sanity, remind himself that he would never get back.

When his flight was called he filed out with only a handful of others, fifteen at the most, and about half of them seemed to consist of a delegation of some kind; they all knew one another and solemnly filled a block of seats just aft of the wings. Except for a woman wearing a headscarf who sat immediately in front of him Laker was quite alone. He had never seen a plane more empty. He felt exhausted, yet his thoughts were measured, held by the savage fatalistic mood.

He watched the runway blur beneath him, the airport sink below, the green earth bank and wheel and level off. Presently he took out the Fair Card and thumbed it through, drawing what encouragement he could from it, keeping his anxiety about the coming Customs' confrontation battened down. Over the Baltic he dozed fitfully, never quite under. A stewardess startled him when she served coffee and from then on he was wide-awake, staring at the broken German coastline dead ahead, then at the slow slide of the land itself.

The weather was clear as far as Berlin and for some of the time he looked westward in the direction of Gardelegen and the River Aller, recalling how his father often used to say that when a man turned his back on something it usually got him again before the end, seeing a resemblance between that wartime gamble and this, that prolonged bout of murderous rage and this, gazing out on the country once openly trampled and fought over which was now the hunting-ground of back-room entrepreneurs who'd devised their stealthy games of blackmail and death, catch-as-catch-can, their own dirty laws, their own ethics. And hating them for it, each and every one; but Hartmann above all.

They whined into Schönefeld within minutes of the scheduled time.

They had flown south, yet it was colder; on the walk to the airport buildings Laker felt a nip in the air. Along with the delegation and most of the others he was herded into the transit-lounge, the same peeling place he'd waited in the other day with the same waxen-faced woman trundling a trolley round and the same take-away Fair leaflets scattered on the tables between the couches along the wall. *During eight centuries the servant of peaceful trade and understanding between the nations . . . A many-sided event, much more than the normal Trade Fair, set in a city where the hospitality of its inhabitants has become a byword throughout the world . . . Meet and relax in Leipzig . . .* Through the window he glimpsed his first Vopos – a pair of them patrolling the perimeter of a half-empty car-park – and another kind of chill fingered him. He'd almost come full-circle.

The delay was quite short. A juddering piston-engined aircraft punctually lifted them off, bucking on the up-currents after it had gained height and set course above the overcast. There was no passenger service now, no drinks, no cigarettes. Laker didn't unclip his belt. He sat alone, more closely hemmed about than before but insulated from the alien chatter by a steadily-generating tension. He had only the sketchiest of plans, and he couldn't grapple with what lay beyond the next thirty minutes or so. They would be down by then and everything would hang on some anonymous official's whim. That was part of the gamble, the part over which he had absolutely no control. From the first he had known it, accepted it, and now it was coming. But without the rifle he would be harmless: impotent.

The minutes passed, elongated by stress. He listened to the change of tone which marked the start of the descent. Scarves of cloud streamed over the wings. 'Fasten your seat-belts, please . . .' With a pang he remembered the previous nosing in; Patrick's 'Dead on time' as the wheels touched – and now it was beginning again, the plane's shadow racing across the tarmac to join them, the bump, the throttled roar, the ponderous run towards the hard, the final lurch and the silence.

The doors opened and the steps were angled into position. Laker took his turn, head buzzing with the sensation of continued movement. WELCOME TO LEIPZIG was emblazoned across the front of the Arrivals building. Inside, the metallic greeting of the public-address system vibrated in his altitude-clogged ears – 'Passengers are requested to present their passports and Fair Cards at the Immigration Bureau . . .' Beneath Ulbricht's blown-up, stony stare he completed the formalities and changed his money. There were fewer passengers to be attended to than before and the queues were shorter, but nerves made everything seem more prolonged. The thin person in cadet grey who studied

Laker's passport took his time, squinting carefully at the dates of the smudged visa stamps.

'You were here earlier in the week.' It was a statement, but an answer was expected.

'Yes.'

'On business?'

'Yes.'

That was all, but there was a dragging sensation in Laker's stomach. He walked into the Customs bay, wondering which of the knot of waiting officials would pronounce sentence on him. To claim the black rexine case when the baggage arrived called for a feverish brand of courage. He picked it up and set it on the bench beside his suitcase; clumsily lit a cigarette. In a state of terrible fascination he watched the nearest official's technique with the person next to him. Farther along someone's luggage was being rummaged. Then it was his turn: two hands descended on the cases.

'Both yours?'

'That's right.'

Small brown eyes held Laker's as he struggled not to bluster; held them but told him nothing.

'You are here for the Fair?'

'Yes.'

The man looked down; stroked the suitcase leather admiringly. Then he tapped the other one.

'And here you have – ?'

'Samples.' Laker could feel the sweat breaking like pins-and-needles in his neck hair. 'Trade samples.'

'Such as?'

'Precision instruments.'

A gesture, a chalked hieroglyph, and he was dismissed. He nodded and backed away; moved into the crowded Arrivals lobby. He was trembling violently. There was no sense of triumph. He pushed out into the open and stood on the steps. For a full minute he paused there, trying to give the impression that he couldn't make up his mind whether or not to join the taxi-queue; then, with a gesture meant to indicate to an observer that he'd that moment remembered something, he swung on his heels and returned inside. But no one seemed in the least interested; he knew the feeling now.

The delegate group was being officially greeted by a trio of smiling men with identification-tags in their square-cut lapels. Laker passed them all by, making for the battery of telephone-boxes in the far corner of the lobby. For hours he had known what he was about to do. He selected the centre one of three vacant booths and pulled the door across; grimly fumbled for change.

Double three, four two, eight six.

'Like the emergency handle on a train, Sam. Long odds against your having to reach for the thing, but it's reassuring to know it's there . . .'

He thumbed in the coin. After that blinding decision back in Copenhagen this had been the first practical idea to come to him, and it had come effortlessly. And the awful irony was with him again as he dialled – that Slattery had his uses at last.

'Salt it away, Sam . . .'

. . . eight . . . six.

He waited then, fingers drumming a tattoo, mind riveted by the repeated bleeps.

A woman answered with a marked Saxonian accent, almost adenoidal. For some reason he hadn't expected to hear a woman. He hesitated, then spoke the introductory phrase that had been buried in the retentive pit of his brain along with the number.

'Peter told me you have a room to let.'

'Who?'

'Peter. I was told you had a room.'

There was no change of tone. 'That is correct, yes.'

'Would it be convenient if I called to see it?'

'Of course. How soon will you be coming?'

'In about half an hour?' he suggested.

'Very well.'

She enunciated the address carefully, like a school-mistress dictating to a backward pupil. Laker hung up. As he slid the door open he found the exit blocked by someone in the black uniform of the S.S.D. and a spasm of fear gripped him. Self-control demanded a tremendous effort. But almost at once he realised that the man had stepped aside and was giving him the right of way. He brushed by, muttering thanks. Badly shaken, warned, he went outside and joined those waiting for transport.

At least he had somewhere to go, some kind of sanctuary. Next he needed information; more than that he couldn't expect. But he had to discover what had happened, exactly how, precisely where and when. What he did then was his concern, no one else's.

And Hartmann had armed him for it; the irony had no end.

CHAPTER 15

There were a few isolated spots of rain, as heavy as bird-droppings, before Laker reached the head of the queue. A converted Wartburg saloon picked him up. He didn't give the address, only the street, and he took his cases into the back with him, his eyes on sentry-go as they pulled away.

They went nowhere near the centre of the city, turning right once they were past the outlying tenement blocks, dog-legging through the scruffy wilderness of the suburbs. But it wasn't a long run: fifteen minutes, if that.

Laker walked for a while after settling with the driver, then made his approach. It was a sombre residential street and the house was as drab as its neighbours, of blemished brown stone and with tall windows draped with lace curtains: in the one to the left of the front door a 'ROOMS' notice was propped against the inside of the glass and Laker guessed it had been placed there for his benefit. Some children squabbled on the pavement; a white cat fled from the steps. Chimes ding-donged softly when he pressed the bell and the door opened almost before he had glanced both ways.

The woman was in her middle fifties, dumpy, greying, red-cheeked, with an apron over a flowered dress. She was wearing slippers.

'Was it about the letting?'

He nodded. The smile was cautious, but it welcomed him in. She remarked on the weather. Wiping her hands on the apron, she showed him into the front room, an overcrowded place in which the air seemed absolutely motionless, as in a museum. A horse-hair settee, a weighty table as a centre-piece with carved straight-back chairs, china cabinets, decorative plates around the walls. In the window, flanked by aspidistras on brass stands, was a caged macaw.

'Isn't he beautiful?' the woman remarked, removing the paste-board notice.

She seemed a highly unlikely ally. The macaw clambered on to the side of the cage and tried its great beak on the woman's proffered knuckles.

'How long would you require the room?'

'I'm not certain.'

'I let by the week.' She quoted the rate, explaining that this was inclusive of meals. 'Would you like to see it?'

'Thank you.'

She wagged a finger at the macaw. 'Naughty,' she smiled, then took Laker upstairs. It was a back room, small, with an iron-framed single bed and an old-fashioned marble-topped washstand. They were there for only a minute or two. Downstairs again she asked if he thought it would be suitable, and there was something disturbingly ordinary about the whole business, as if Laker had made a fantastic mistake and arrived at the wrong house. There was no indication that he hadn't. As he counted out a week's money she told him that soap and towels would be put in his bedroom and explained various domestic details about hot water, times of meals, the lights on the upper landing. He wasn't really listening. Having to pay worried him. Did you pay for a bolt-hole? – for that was what this was. Surely. 'Just in case, Sam . . .'

'I imagine you'll be staying in for the time being?' the woman said.

'Yes.'

'There'll be a key if you want one later.'

'Thank you.'

'You have only to ask.' She took the money from the baize-covered table. The macaw eyed them beadily through the bars. 'Don't you stick your little black tongue out at me,' she reprimanded it. 'And be nice to the gentleman. He's our guest – remember that.'

She smiled at Laker, only then dispelling his anxiety. 'Someone will come,' she said.

'When?'

'Before too long.' And with that she left him.

After a little while he heard her go upstairs and come down again. He went up himself then; towels and soap were on the washstand. He slid the catch on the door, then went to the window. The room wasn't overlooked. Walls jutted out to either side and there was a narrow view towards the rear of some other houses which were partially screened by trees. Beyond them was the silvered dome of a gas-holder. He unlocked the rexine case and took out the dismembered rifle; fitted it together. It was only the second time he had looked at it and he remembered how the first had destroyed the last flimsy shreds of hope that he was somehow at the centre of a vile, unfathomable hoax.

All markings had been obliterated. He wiped it clean of the film of oil, slotted the telescopic attachment into position and removed the protective end-caps. It was a precision instrument, all right: self-loading, single-shot. He didn't fill the magazine, but he reckoned it would take six. The balance was perfect and the shaped cheek-rest fitted snugly against the side of his face. Standing well away from the window he sighted on the lopped end of one of the branches of the nearest tree and the magnification brought it in from about fifty yards to what seemed to be no more than arm's length, so close that he could see the growth rings in the exposed wood. For perhaps twenty minutes he acquainted himself with the rifle's handling, selecting an occasional snap target – a bird, a man at work on a distant roof – and every alignment amazed him with its apparent shrinkage of distance, the hair-line accuracy at his command. Frenzel wouldn't have had a chance.

He broke the weapon down and re-packed it in the velvet recesses; put on the locks. The house was very quiet, though once he thought he heard the woman talking, perhaps on the telephone. It was a quarter to five. He lay on the bed, wondering who would come, thinking. The unrelenting fury smouldered like a coal. But he seemed to have absorbed fatigue and mostly his mind was sharp and clear, no longer fogged with stupefaction, not so frantic. Time was at a discount now. He'd got back; found shelter. The rest would follow – somehow, somewhere.

He smoked a cigarette and watched a drizzle begin to blur the panes.

The door-bell chimed soon after five. He got off the bed at once. He could distinguish voices, pitched low – the woman's and a man's. After a short while footsteps padded softly on the stairs and someone knocked.

'Come in,' he said.

The man was shorter than Laker, and older, perhaps ten years older. He was wearing a dirty raincoat. His face was long and heavily lined, pallid, and his mousy hair was cut short, like a soldier's or a prisoner's. The blue eyes seemed to lack any capacity for surprise.

'Good afternoon.' His grip was like a vice. 'Is the room satisfactory?'

'Thank you.'

'There's no need to confine yourself to it. You can use the living-room if you wish. I'm sure my wife mentioned that.' There was a wine-coloured birthmark on one side of his neck just above the collar-line.

'She did, yes.'

'Shall we go down? It is more comfortable there.'

'All right.'

A bicycle had been wheeled into the hall and there was a cloth bag slung on the cross-bar. Perhaps he was a plumber. Askew on the front of the cage the macaw clucked at them drily as they entered the room.

'D'you want names?' Laker asked.

'The fewer the better.'

'Mine?'

'No.'

The man shook his head. They continued to stand.

He said: 'When did your friend Peter recommend us?'

'Earlier this week.'

'Never before?'

'No.'

'So this is your first time?' The glance implied that beginners usually made their own trouble.

'Yes.'

'And you arrived . . .?'

'On Wednesday.'

'When did anything go wrong?'

'That afternoon.'

'Three days ago?'

'Yes.'

'How wrong?'

'I was arrested.'

'By?'

'The S.S.D.'

'When were you released?'

Laker shook his head. 'It wasn't like that.'

'I'm sorry, but I don't understand. Where have you come from? – today, I mean. Now.'

'The airport. Copenhagen.'

The man frowned. He motioned towards the settee and they sat down. 'Tell me,' he said. 'Tell me from the beginning.'

'And then?'

'We'll see what can be done.'

'You don't know what I want.'

'Tell me, and I shall.'

It didn't take long. Laker phrased the story carefully, selectively. He mentioned only Patrick and Hartmann by name. Kromadecka and Karen he left out of it; Frenzel too. He didn't once refer to Slattery or to London. The man listened in silence, without interrupting, poker-faced; mostly he stared at his grimy finger-nails. It was a mercy to be able to talk at last, like a letting of blood. Laker said nothing about the girl either. He kept to the essentials, beginning with the mock-execution in the pines and ending with the cancelled reservation at the Metropol which had brought despair and hatred to a white heat. And as he underlined the pressure put upon him and the promised consequences of failure he felt that he was speaking to someone who understood the realities of living – the potential terrors, the springs of desolation that only one in a million were aware existed. Whoever he was he looked a person who had suffered, for whom pain and violence weren't abstractions.

Laker finished and the man glanced up at him. For a long moment he was quiet, then nodded several times, lips pressed tight.

'You say you came on Wednesday?'

'To start with, yes.'

A pause, 'Kromadecka?'

'Yes.'

'Ah.' He had it now; Laker watched him: it was all of a piece. 'Ah,' he said and nodded again. Then he muttered: 'Bad, this is bad,' and his breath made a long sigh.

'Can you help?'

'With regard to your son?'

'I have to know what happened.'

'Of course, of course.' He got up, rubbing his birthmark, his attention seemingly held by something in the street. 'How did you return – on a Card visa?'

'Yes.'

'You'll never get out the same way – you realise that?'

Laker shrugged.

'Not even if you tried to go now, not in view of what you've told me. The machinery isn't slow to function. They'll have the shutters up already.'

'I dare say.'

'Something can be arranged, though. It can be done, but not before Monday.' The man turned and studied him. As if it were a duty he said: 'Don't pin your hopes for your son too high, my friend. I have to say this. Don't hope too much.'

Laker made no reply. He didn't need telling, but to hear it said fell on his heart like a blow. He squeezed his hands together, looking down between his knees.

'Forgive me,' the man said gently, 'but I know Hartmann. I know the kind of person he is. He is warped; there is a flaw of honour in him. Himmler had the same kind of flaw. In his case he was incorruptible where money was concerned. Hartmann's flaw is that he keeps his word.'

'For what?' Laker burst out. 'He could force me to do what he wanted, but once I'd failed, once that booking was cancelled . . .'

He choked to an end, Hartmann's image looming in his mind. The macaw skittered amiably about the cage. The man went to a cupboard and filled a glass.

'Here,' he said. '*Schnapps*. Take it.' He sat beside Laker again, his lined face very grave. After a while he said: 'I can help in two ways. I can find out about your son. I can also get you across the frontier.' He waited, then went on: 'What more is there? You can't stay here, not indefinitely.'

Laker drained the glass. At last he had someone to rely on – at last, and too late. He rose from the settee.

'There's a third thing, he said thickly.

'Yes?'

'You can tell me where Hartmann lives.'

'He has an apartment at S.S.D. headquarters.'

'Nowhere else?'

'No.'

'Where he goes, then. What his movements are.'

The man regarded him quizzically.

'I want to know,' Laker insisted.

'What can you do? What can you do with your bare hands? . . . It would be suicide, my friend.'

'He provided me with a sniper's rifle.'

'In Copenhagen.'

'I brought it back.'

'Here?' At last there was surprise.

'Here, yes. It's upstairs.'

'My God,' the man said slowly. 'Now I have heard everything.' He stared, as if making a reappraisal of the forces at work in Laker. 'You carried it with you – openly?'

'Yes.'

'My God,' he said again, this time almost in anger. 'The risk you ran. Do you realise the risk you ran?'

An obsession diminishes perception. With infinite weariness Laker lifted his shoulders, let them drop. 'I've been out on a limb for three whole days and no one's lifted a bloody finger – not until now. You're the first.' He hadn't meant to say this, but his voice had a steely edge. 'London led me by the nose, then dropped me. Three days ago I was just another businessman. I was beginning a holiday with my fourteen-year-old son. There was also someone I knew – Karen Gisevius . . . And now? . . . Who am I now? What am I?' There was no self-pity; only the terrible emptiness, the unquenchable loathing. 'I'm entitled to take all the risks I choose.'

The man hadn't moved his eyes from him. 'I can get you out,' he repeated, the anger, the alarm, quickly gone. 'Remember that.'

'I want Hartmann first.'

'But say your son is alive. Say, for once, Hartmann hasn't – '

'I don't believe he is.'

'But you must have proof. At least you must wait for that.'

'I know. I know.' Laker's vision blurred. 'I was told he was staying with someone called Rauter. I . . . I signed a letter, explaining my absence. He wouldn't have believed it, though. I don't write letters like that . . .' Again he didn't finish, sick with the numbness.

'I have a friend who will know where to enquire.'

'How soon?'

'I can't tell. It depends. But I will go and see him.'

'When?'

'Now. Immediately.' The man started to button his raincoat; he hadn't taken it off. 'Rauter, was it?' He tightened the frayed belt.

'That's right.'

At the door he turned, and Laker saw a look of pity which was akin to another he'd glimpsed somewhere back in the nightmare – whose he had forgotten. 'My wife will be here,' the man said. He made an attempt at a smile. 'You'll find her an excellent cook if you want anything.'

Laker heard him cross the hall; a muttered exchange – in the kitchen, he supposed. Then the front door opened and he saw the man wheel the bicycle out and pedal away, shabby yet nondescript, along the drenched, dusky street.

Almost at once the woman entered the room. She pulled the curtains carefully before switching on the lights, as if a blackout were in force. Normally they had supper at nine, but if he was hungry . . .? Some coffee and biscuits, perhaps? . . . No; Laker thanked her and went upstairs, threw himself on the bed. Hope was spent. There was nothing left to revive. He was sure about Patrick already, absolutely sure. All day he'd been sure; all night. Hartmann had conditioned him. Hope had shrivelled and died in the Metropol's foyer in one chilling moment of certainty.

The room darkened; the last of the daylight vanished. He thought a thousand things, confusedly, without sequence, in the way the drowning are said to do – except that there was no rush, no panic-stricken compression. Strangely, it was the memory of Patrick's penfriends which moved him most, as if only now he had discovered there must have been loneliness.

· 'Look after him for me, Sam . . .'

It had gone eight when he heard the chimes and the woman slop in her slippers into the hall. His pulse quickened sluggishly, but he didn't move. He listened to the steps approaching on the stairs, on the landing, and even before the knock sounded he knew exactly what he was going to learn. He was resigned to it, ready, and the man's reluctance to speak was proof in itself.

Yet he said: 'Well?'

'It is as you feared, my friend.'

Laker closed his eyes. There was silence.

Then the man said awkwardly: 'Shall I put on the light?'

'No.'

'There is a paragraph in *Neues Deutschland*.'

'What does it say?'

'D'you want me to read it?'

'Yes.'

The man leaned into the wedge of light that came from the landing and peered short-sightedly at a clipping.

'"A foreign youth, identified from papers on his person as Patrick Laker, last night received fatal injuries believed to have been caused by a motor vehicle in the Walder Platz. He was dead on arrival at the University Clinic. Enquiries are proceeding."'

Silence again, longer. 'London will go along with our account of an accident, Mr. Laker. They'll accept our postmortem certificate . . .'

'I'm sorry,' the man was saying. 'Very, very sorry.'

He didn't seem to know what to do with his hands. He came to the side of the bed and, in the gloom, put the cutting on the table there. Then he went back to the door where he paused, his face strained.

'What can I say? . . . Such an act is senseless. Meaningless . . . Is there nothing I can do?'

'No.'

'When it suits you we will talk some more. Any time . . . When you wish it.'

No answer.

He closed the door behind him, shutting the darkness in.

An hour must have passed before Laker went downstairs. The man and woman were eating in the kitchen and he joined them, the worst of his agony shed. There was cold meat, bread and soup, and he ate a little. The other two didn't speak much; when they did their voices were subdued. Laker drank a good deal of wine and afterwards he and the man went into the front room.

The first thing he said was: 'I won't involve you. It's my affair. You've got something to lose.' He was quite calm. 'All I want is information concerning Hartmann's whereabouts.'

'That won't be so easy. He doesn't parade himself.' The man slipped a dome of green baize over the macaw's cage. 'And that's what you're asking for, isn't it – a sitting target?'

'I'll take what offers.'

'Listen. I know something about abominations, my friend. Both of us do in this house, believe me. But we also know something about survival – and the way your mind is now you will never see London again. What's more, you *would* involve us – inevitably, and that would mean our involving others. A chain-reaction would start. Few of us are ever as strong as we pray to be. A litre of castor-oil, electrodes against the genitals, ice-cold immersion – the threat alone is often quite sufficient. I hardly need explain what fear can do to a man.'

A car was splashing through the wet. He cocked his head, his eyes following the sound along the street.

'We operate an escape route, my wife and I. People come here in order to survive, to get clear and lick their wounds in safety. That's our function.' He drew in his breath slowly. 'We tell ourselves it's a worthwhile occupation.'

He opened a drawer in one of the china cabinets and extracted a map. 'You've misunderstood me.'

'I don't think so.'

'I haven't said I won't help. But I *am* insisting on conditions.' He glanced earnestly at Laker, and again there was that built-in pity. 'I can't stop you from leaving this house whenever you choose. But they're on the lookout for you. And they'll pick you up before you even get wind of Hartmann, let alone squeeze a trigger.' He was spreading the map on the table, flattening the creases. 'I can't stop you. But I can argue with you. I can make the point that you weren't given this telephone number in order to endanger others on account of a personal vendetta.'

Laker gazed with suspicion at the grey, cadaverous face. 'What conditions?'

'One, that you're patient. Two, that I decide what is possible, and relate it to the problem of getting you back where you belong.' A bruised finger-nail stubbed the map. 'You're a hundred and fifty kilometres from the frontier. Even if you managed to get that far – alone – you'd never cross the death strip.'

'How patient?'

The man shrugged. 'Getting out may be secondary to you, but it isn't to me. I want you off our hands, my friend.' He offered Laker a cigarette. 'You aren't the first to have wished Hartmann dead. But yielding to instinct won't achieve it. If you're going to succeed you need more than a few scraps of information and advice. I'll give you all there is, and practical help as well, but you must accept that it will have to be tied in with getting you away.'

He coughed. 'Besides, I should imagine you have good reason for wanting to return to London. From what you tell me I'd say they also have something to answer for.'

It was almost midnight before they finished. Laker was so weary by then that he could scarcely employ his mind, but he had a dread of being alone again. Towards the end he was using the man as a safety-valve, unburdening himself, as confiding as a solitary drinker in a bar. The woman came in eventually and offered him a couple of sleeping-pills. He took them and the session ended. At the foot of the stairs he said to the man: 'Don't try and fob me off, that's all I ask. You'll be wasting your breath.'

'I won't, my friend. I promise you' – and Laker gripped his bony arms in a spasm of emotion.

The cutting was beside the bed and the gun was in its case. But oblivion came fast and, mercifully, there were no dreams.

CHAPTER 16

Twice next morning Laker heard the telephone. The first time it woke him to the waiting desolation; the second took him to the bedroom door, listening. But he deciphered nothing: on both occasions the woman was speaking. He lay in the bed until ten o'clock, then slowly shaved and dressed. While he was in the bathroom he thought somebody used the front door, but he wasn't certain.

There was a place set for him at the kitchen table. The woman greeted him with the same ingenuousness as when he'd first arrived. 'I thought you'd like to rest,' she said, clattering at the stove. 'Did the pills help?'

'Thank you.'

'You can get over-tired, can't you? They're useful then.'

'Yes.'

'It looks like rain again. And we had a lot in the night, too.'

The perfection of the lie she was living never varied, somehow raising an echo of the blatant disbelief that had unsuccessfully tried to hold Laker in the moment of waking. When he asked where her husband was she said: 'He's just gone to the shops for cigarettes. He won't be long' – and he wondered how much she really knew, how much her red-cheeked smile masked a longing for peace and safety.

He finished her strong, ersatz coffee and went into the living-room, restless already, watching the street. Last night, sprawled on the settee, he had talked with an abandonment that was rare for him, wretchedness loosing his tongue. It had come piecemeal, in no chronological order, yet it had made a kind of whole – mainly about Patrick, but about Helen too, about Weybridge, Gale and Watts, Roundwood, about the war and Karen Gisevius; all that. And now, remembering some of the things he had said he also remembered how the man had listened and how his sympathy had once or twice mounted almost to visible distress so that his willingness to assist in dealing with Hartmann grew like a bond between them. In the hall, when they were about to go upstairs, there had been a glint in his eyes which had reminded Laker of that night in Green Park half a lifetimes before when Slattery had suddenly burst out: 'You kill the bastards, Sam. Kill as many of them as you can.'

Just one this time. Just one to clean something out of his mind, out of his heart, out of his insides. And then, with what was left over, to face Slattery.

No, he hadn't done with London; the man was right. If it were possible Slattery wasn't going to get away with it either.

Half an hour elapsed before the familiar figure cycled shabbily into view along the street. The lack of haste wasn't encouraging. The macaw squawked and fluttered excitedly when the front door opened and again when the man entered the room: simultaneously the telephone rang. He hesitated, ready to go, ready to stay, waiting tensely as the woman took the call.

'Yes, he's here,' she said, and the man returned to the hall.

'That's right,' Laker heard. 'Yes . . . With pleasure . . . Certainly . . . But not for two or three days. On Wednesday, perhaps. May I call and discuss it with you? . . . Very well . . . Yes, I'll do that. I will be in touch. Without fail.'

He was smiling grimly when he rejoined Laker. 'A lady wants her kitchen painted.'

So that was his cover. He tossed his cap on to the table. He hadn't shaved and he looked tired. 'It's early yet. Don't expect too much all at once. It's going to be like walking in long grass for a while . . . Did you sleep well?'

Laker nodded.

'How good are you with a rifle?'

'According to Hartmann, exceptionally good.'

The man savoured that quietly. 'You'll need to be. You won't find him hanging about, asking for it.'

'Where is he now?'

'At headquarters. At least, his car's there.'

'A green one? Dark green?'

'A Moskvitch, yes.'

He took a folder from his breast-pocket and shook it open – a street-map of Leipzig. 'Hopeless,' he said. 'Hopeless. You wouldn't stand a chance in the city. Yesterday, for instance, he was here . . . and here . . . and then here, in the Alte Markt.' He used his hands dismissively. 'Hopeless. Impossible. You're going to have to wait until he travels farther afield.'

'When's that likely to be?'

'Perhaps days.'

'For God's sake!'

'How should I know?' He seemed on edge. 'I'm not a prophet. But I am a realist, and what might suit you tactically might not suit me. Be reasonable . . . Yes, reasonable.' he repeated tartly. 'Don't expect me to produce Hartmann for you like something out of a hat. I shudder when I think what has been done. Words are inadequate. But what you are asking has to be planned, thought about, worked on. Without help you'd achieve nothing except the certainty of disaster for others. So save up what you feel, my friend. Be patient.'

The morning passed. The man left the house around noon, on foot. Laker hadn't asked what his sources of information were, and he didn't want to know. But the restraint, the frustration, were almost unendurable. He went up to the bedroom for a while, assembled and practised handling the rifle. Somewhere he hadn't bargained on a lengthy delay. On a base, yes; but not on caution, not on being cooped-up, not on marking time. In the demented haze of his return he had imagined something reflexively swift, unaided, a snarling pent-up release that would find satisfaction in seeing Hartmann crumple and go down. Now he must wait for it; curb himself. He recognised the necessity. But grief was like a wound; the real pain was slow to come, and it was still spreading, raw now, giving existence to depths of him long since insensible.

And this was Slattery's territory; that worried him. Already Slattery would be wondering where the hell he'd got to. He would have begun to check and counter-check – and even a fool like Jackson would very soon find out. If Slattery put two-and-two together it was possible that he would attempt to warn the local network off. Almost certain, in fact. Karen had been lost to him already and he wouldn't want any more casualties. As a side issue he might approve of Hartmann's death, but not if it meant jeopardising his listening-post, his contacts, his go-betweens – all those who earned him dividends, showed returns. Someone would replace Hartmann, anyhow. The game would go on, Hartmann or no Hartmann, and for people like Slattery the game was the thing. In that ivory-tower of his what mattered was to keep his pins firmly on the map . . .

Stay out of this, sod you, Laker thought. You've done enough – or haven't you heard yet?

He hung about the living-room, anxiously watching the street.

The man was soon back, but only to shrug. Nothing yet . . . Towards one o'clock the telephone rang and he grunted cryptically several times into the mouthpiece, but all he said to Laker afterwards was: 'Still at headquarters.'

The three of them ate together in the kitchen. It was strange, but when the woman was present it was as if Laker and the man shared a secret from which she was excluded: the masquerade took over. But this time, as they were finishing, she suddenly remarked: 'You didn't mind about the money, did you?'

Laker frowned.

'The rent.'

'No.' He fingered his glass, puzzled, dragging his thoughts away from where they swarmed. 'No.'

The man leaned forward. 'My wife always insists that the labourer is worthy of his hire, no matter what the circumstances. But we aren't mercenaries, my friend, and if she has given you that impression she does herself less than justice.' Quietly he said to her: 'Show our guest your arm . . . Go on.'

The woman slid back the right sleeve of her blouse. Three or four inches above the wrist a six-figure number was crudely tattooed on the pink skin. Laker had no need to ask what it signified or when it had been put there.

'Ravensbruck,' the man said. 'And memories are just as indelible. I told you, we know something about abominations.' He gestured.

'Perhaps our willingness to help you is more understandable now. London would hardly approve, but that is neither here nor there. They spin the webs, but they don't live in them . . .'

It was as if he had been reading Laker's mind.

He went out again presently, on foot once more; where, why, he didn't say. He never said.

There was little movement in the street – an occasional cyclist, a scooter or two. A dog barked periodically from the broken railings on the other side and a handful of people walked by, women mostly, sometimes pausing to gossip. Laker's agitation reached a new peak; drove him upstairs. From the window there the dome of the distant gasholder had sunk from view; almost twenty-four hours had frittered away since he first saw it. He lay on the bed, but soon got up and returned to the living-room. There was no sign of the man and the telephone remained silent. Gone three . . . The macaw ground its beak furiously on the cage-wire; the clash of crockery sounded from the kitchen.

Half-past three. He'd never stand another day of it. Another day chained like this and something would snap. For the second time that afternoon he returned to the bedroom and lay there smoking, staring at the ceiling, watching the sagging grey sky, his face recording ugly inner journeys.

It was twenty to four when the telephone rang. He listened, head cocked, but for all he could tell it was another false alarm. Then he heard the woman on the stairs and he didn't wait for her to knock.

'Yes.'

She might have been coming in to turn the bed-covers down, or change the towels. 'My husband asked me to tell you to be ready in five minutes.'

Laker's heart lifted urgently. He nodded. 'Very well.'

'With both your cases. And would you please wear these.'

She dropped some old blue overalls on to the end of the bed.

'All right.'

He didn't question why. She left him and he put them on, dry in the mouth, his pulse quickening. The overalls were tight under the arms, but otherwise the fit was good enough. After a momentary indecision he folded his topcoat and pressed it into the suitcase, then hurried downstairs.

'Would you like some coffee?' The woman amazed him to the end. 'It's on the stove.'

'No, thanks.'

He followed her into the living-room where she remarked to the macaw: 'Our guest is going. Aren't you sorry to lose him?' The bird clawed clumsily round the cage. She stroked its gaudy head, but her eyes were on the gap in the draped lace curtains. Very soon she said: 'This is him now,' and Laker saw a small battered open truck rattling along the street.

'Stay here,' she said, a soft command in her tone for the first and only time. 'Let him come in first.'

The truck shook to a standstill and Laker watched the man get out and saunter towards the steps. The woman waited for the bell before she went to open the door. 'Is he ready?' Laker heard, and her quiet 'Yes.' He moved into the hall. The man looked at him and nodded meaningly. The two cases were at the foot of the stairs. Laker picked them up, but the man took the suitcase from him. 'I'll attend to this.'

'Good-bye,' the woman said. 'Good-bye. I'm pleased to have met you.'

She would baffle anyone, Laker felt, even under blinding lights.

He shook her by the hand, moved suddenly. 'Good-bye.'

The man went first. He slung the suitcase into the back of the truck and covered it over with a square of perished tarpaulin. Laker clambered into the driving-cab, shoving the black case between his knees. It was a rickety vehicle, the blue-grey paint chipped and scored and patched with rust; the off-side wing was badly concertinaed and Laker could see the ground through a hole in the flooring.

The man climbed in behind the wheel, fastening the door with a twist of string. He had left the engine running. With a crunch of gears they drew away. Laker didn't look back; never saw the woman again.

'Well?' This before they'd shuddered twenty yards.

'He's gone north, towards Dessau.'

'How far's that?'

'Seventy, eighty kilometres. But he'll be turning round at the district border, which is only half as far, and coming south again. And he's had a fair start, so we're against the clock.' They swung left, clipping the kerb. 'He'll be on the autobahn, understand?'

'Travelling?'

'Travelling, yes.'

That meant anything up to a hundred miles an hour; perhaps more. Daunted, Laker screwed his eyes, doubts and protest rising together.

'Listen,' the man said loudly above the clatter. 'At one point the south-bound slow lane is under repair. There are warning notices out. Traffic's down to about half-speed over a longish stretch.'

Sixty, say. Even so . . . It could be lunacy. Laker bit his lips, questioning his companion's judgement.

'You might wait a week and never have as good a chance. There's a party on its way from Berlin and Hartmann's taking over escort duty at the district border. It isn't often that he strays so far from home.'

They were rattling between drab rows of suburban shops.

'How's the time?'

'Four,' Laker said. Then, uneasily: 'I hope to God you know what's possible and what isn't.'

'You want everything guaranteed, don't you?' Suddenly the man was nettled. He wrestled the wheel, glowering. 'You want the work done for you, the risks all – '

'No, but – '

'Wait and see, then.' He dabbed the brake-pedal to avoid a cyclist; swore. 'I made conditions, remember. There are other necks at stake beside yours. I tell you Hartmann's as vulnerable as ever he'll be, but more important as far as I'm concerned is what happens afterwards.'

Laker was silent.

'I can get you away,' the man said, calming again. 'And that matters. Any fool can commit suicide. Tonight you'll be over the frontier. We aren't waiting for Monday.'

They were nearing the city's centre, the Fair's flags and streamers, the Sunday afternoon crowds. LEIPZIG – ANOTHER NAME FOR HOSPITALITY . . . Laker felt exposed, the overalls no protection against the attention attracted by the truck's racketing progress. A siren wailed behind them and his heart-beat thudded; there was no rear-view mirror. For an awful moment it seemed as if the man were pulling into the side, but he was merely getting out of the way. An ambulance slid past, and Laker's skin crawled with relief.

'There's a map under the seat,' he was told.

Traffic-lights delayed them as he groped. A black saloon drew alongside and its uniformed passenger stared broodingly at the truck from a distance of three feet.

'National People's Army,' the man muttered from the side of his mouth. 'General.' Then, when the lights changed and they had jerked into the car's wake: 'We're taking the Halle road . . . Halle, got it? Through Schkeuditz.'

'Yes.'

'We hit the autobahn after leaving Schkeuditz. It's marked E6. The slow section I mentioned is about four kilometres north of the junction. That's where I'll put you down.'

'And then?'

'The details don't make sense until you've seen the ground. But west of E6, running parallel, there's a minor road.'

Laker peered, trying to steady the map. 'About a kilometre west?'

'That's the one. We'll rendezvous there.'

The man's voice was taut, authoritative. He was allowing Laker no choice. His plans were made, but they had the vagueness of something hurriedly thrown together. Laker managed to hold his uneasiness in check, focusing his mind on an imagined stretch of autobahn, picturing a vehicle at speed, thinking about angles, height, time, distance . . . It was going to be now or never.

'How will I know which car is his?'

'That's taken care of. I'll explain when we're on the spot.' A clock showed four-twelve. They passed the Ring-Messehaus and its frontal gardens, then the Astoria where the nightmare had begun with stuttered explanations from a stranger in a raincoat, then the square where Hartmann had driven to the shooting-gallery.

Laker needed no reminders. He pressed his calves against the rexine case, keeping it steady. A few storm-drops struck the windscreen and he willed the sky to hold off, clenching his hands as he squinted upwards.

'Time?' the man asked hoarsely.

'Four-fifteen.'

They were heading west now: a sign pointed to Schkeuditz and Halle. All the din in the world seemed to be concentrated inside the draughty cabin as they passed through a succession of cobbled streets. Shops, houses, factories, a ruined church, more factories, wasteland, rubble – gradually the city fell away. A stream meandered in to flank them on the left and there were meadows to either side, dotted with oaks and larches. The road was mostly straight but the truck swayed dangerously, buffeted by a gusty cross-breeze, and the man crouched at the wheel, working the loose steering. They covered the distance to Schkeuditz at a kilometre a minute, slowed there to the permitted maximum, sweated out a traffic jam, then picked up speed again, steam issuing from the radiator. The countryside widened, more thickly wooded, slightly undulating. Northwards, slanting cords of rain darkened the horizon.

'How long have we got?' Laker shouted.

'You ought to be in position by five.'

'That rain will be on us by then.'

The man risked a sideways scowl and grunted. He looked drawn and the creases in his forehead glistened. The grunt was his only comment.

Five kilometres brought them to the autobahn's approach. The road climbed a shade, veering right, then topped a low crest, and all at once the autobahn was there, as wide as an airport's runway, split by a humped strip of grass. Tucked in behind an ancient Porsche they filtered into the first lane and the man opened the throttle again, steam flattening continuously over the shaking bonnet.

Hartmann would be coming south. South, on the other carriageway.

The traffic there was light, unevenly spaced. Laker singled out two or three of the faster cars, watching them swell from the size of toys and flash past, blurring as they went. Short white markers were planted at intervals along the far verge, behind which was a post-and-rail fence and then a broken fringe of pines. He was going to need cover and it looked as if he'd get it twenty or thirty yards from the carriageway; but the speeds had shaken him – even allowing for the fact that he was trying to assess them while the truck was flat out in the other direction.

A slightly-banked curve and the entire autobahn changed course, heading towards the blue-black clouds along the northern rim. As they roared beneath a bridge the man suddenly pointed half left 'There . . . There,' and beyond the humped divide Laker saw the beginnings of a long line of red-and-white tar-barrels which sealed off the opposite outer lane. They drew level; continued on by. The obstruction lasted a full two kilometres and the traffic was noticeably slower. The bulldozers and cement-mixers were ideal: Sunday. Beyond the heaps of sand and steel mesh and broken concrete and the gangers' huts a bank sloped up to the perimeter fence and the trees.

It would be there, then. Somewhere over there.

The man had the accelerator against the floor. Twenty to five. They continued north for another couple of minutes, then looped off, spiralled, crossed the autobahn, looped down and rejoined it, heading south. The warning-signs began almost at once. ROAD WORKS . . . REDUCE SPEED . . . TWO LANES ONLY . . . NO OVERTAKING . . . Then the first of the barrels was in sight. ROAD NARROWS . . . SLOW . . . SLOW . . . Brake-lights blinked dutifully on the saloon ahead of them. Angled trestles squeezed them into what was normally the centre lane and the man eased his foot from the throttle. They cruised for about a third of the obstruction's length before he chose a gap between barrels, nosed through and came to rest in the lee of a covered tarring-machine.

'Now,' he said immediately. 'Now what I tell you will make sense. Get out and pretend to look at the engine with me. For once she has boiled to order.'

They climbed down. He lifted the bonnet. Steam rose in clouds from the spitting radiator-cap. He nodded towards the crossing they had just used.

'That's where I'll be – on the north-bound shoulder. I'll be pulled off with the bonnet up, the same as now. Hartmann's escorting two other cars, so they'll come together, the three of them in convoy. I've some binoculars here which I'll give you in a minute. Keep me in view from wherever you locate yourself. Watch me all the time. When Hartmann comes through the underpass you'll see me slam the bonnet down and prepare to drive away. Is that clear?'

Laker nodded.

'There will be three cars, remember. I'll give my signal immediately they emerge from the underpass. You can't possibly make a mistake. You'll see them all the way from here. And the green Moskvitch will almost certainly be in the lead.'

Laker nodded again. A lorry whined by, wet, wipers still working. Speed and rain – it would be touch and go. A chill moved through him.

'Hartmann has a driver,' the man said, 'so he'll be riding in the back seat.'

'What else should I know?'

'Afterwards go due west. Through the trees. Keep going until you reach the minor road you saw on the map. Then wait there. Wait until we pick you up.'

'We?'

'I'll have switched to a car, but I can't say what kind it will be. Possibly a Volga. Just wait, that's all. And get rid of your overalls.'

'All right.'

The man leaned under the steering-wheel and brought out a pair of binoculars. Laker shoved them into a pocket and pulled the black case from the cabin. Air beat over them from a passing car.

'Now it's up to you,' the man said. 'I've done the best I can. Select your position, then watch for me on the shoulder by the underpass. I'll be there in five minutes.' He clamped the bonnet shut, heaved himself aboard and switched on. The engine raced. Pulling away he wound the window down and pumped his arm to indicate urgency. Above the roar he shouted: 'Good luck, Mr. Laker.'

Laker didn't reply. He cut between the tarring-machine and a stack of steel pipes and loped up the grass slope towards the fence, bending low as if he were under fire. The grass was soggy, sucking softly at his shoes. He climbed the fence and made for the trees, a kind of nausea welling up. And as he ran he began asking himself how the man had got to know his name.

He went a short distance into the wood, then dropped on to one knee and snapped the case open. In the couple of minutes it took him to assemble the rifle the query persisted.

How? . . . Last night, when distress and fatigue had made him talk so much – had it slipped out then? He didn't believe so. And there was more. The man had known what name to look for in *Neues Deutschland*. Only now this other fact struck him, now when action was all that mattered.

He must have told him. *Must* have done . . .

He broke open the carton of ammunition and loaded the magazine, thumbing the rounds in separately. He put in four against the pressure of the spring, hesitated with a fifth, decided against it, and rammed the magazine home. Two was about all he'd be able to use and an over-full magazine could jam; from twenty years ago he remembered. He stood up, pivoting on his heels. He was deep enough into the trees for the autobahn to be almost invisible. The sound of the traffic was pierced by a bird singing somewhere overhead.

'Good luck, Mr. Laker . . .' It wasn't a time for question-marks.

He left the case where it was and moved to the edge of the cover. He was ten yards from the fence and the fence was about fifteen from the white markers along the carriageway's border and those, in turn, were ten from the line of tar-barrels. There were better places: he was quick to decide. Off to his right the trees receded up the slope, then spread down again almost to the fence. He ran there, slithering on the carpet of pine-needles, impelled by a devil of instinctive obedience that was unleashed at last – like the time he'd kicked the radio-set to pieces and started his own war, skill and hatred fused, all the layers by which he recognised himself stripped away, peeling away now as he came to the fence and studied the line of fire the new position gave him, possessed by the same terrible hurt as then, the same elemental lust as then, except once it had been for Germans, any Germans, faceless, anonymous enemies, and now it was solely for Hartmann, Hartmann who had asked for this from the moment they first met.

Laker went prone behind the fence. Perhaps three-quarters of a mile separated him from the underpass; a quarter from where the south-bound carriageway narrowed. He was about eight feet above road-level with an uninterrupted view between a steam-roller and one of the deserted gangers' huts. SLOW . . . NO OVERTAKING . . . SLOW – over his right shoulder he could see the warnings repeated behind him along the whole length of the obstruction. He took out the binoculars and fixed them on the underpass: there was no sign of the truck, but the rain had spread nearer, blue and obliterating.

Five o'clock exactly . . . The ground was uneven so he wriggled back a few feet, angling his body about fifteen degrees from the fence. Emerging from the underpass the cars seemed to crawl. Where the slow section began they rocked minutely in tell-tale fashion from a touch on the brake or a sudden easing of the throttle, yet when they were about two hundred yards away the head-on effect rapidly diminished and it appeared as if they were actually accelerating as their individual detail loomed and they bore obliquely past with a rubbery whine.

The truck crashed along the north-bound track as he was slipping the end-caps off the telescopic sight. He watched it, the query renewing itself, niggling, the man's willingness to be an accessory suddenly suspect.

Disturbed, he sighted on an approaching Skoda, splaying his legs. It was sharp and clear when he picked it up at three hundred yards. For about four seconds the hair-line cross centred on a heavy face in the dark V cleared by the windscreen wipers; then the swift traversing movement began and Laker couldn't hold the aim without slewing. He took a line on the next two cars, concentrating on the rear seats through the spattered side windows, coldly, expertly, a culmination coming, the scent of the near-by pines a needless mnemonic of fear, manipulation and murder.

If the rain held off he had a sixty-forty chance. But would it? Christ, would it?

The truck had limped on to the shoulder just short of the underpass and the man had the bonnet up: the binoculars made him seem within shouting distance. Six minutes after five . . . Laker's mouth was as dry as a kiln and the truck moved in and out of focus with every hammerstroke of his heart.

Why such risks for a stranger? . . . What had been plausible an hour ago, a day ago, was increasingly in doubt. Who else could have disclosed his identity?

A solitary lorry crept through the underpass.

Slattery?

Sweat dribbled from Laker's eyebrows and he blinked it away.

Slattery?

A couple of cars, abreast. A light flurry of rain. And the growing confusion, the whirling suspicion that, even now, he was somehow being used.

The man was going through the motions of tinkering with the engine. The binoculars trembled in Laker's hands. With the distrust of the abused he tried to ask himself if it could possibly be that he was still a puppet, Slattery's now, led unknowingly as if he were in his sleep to settle some score that wasn't his. And as he groped for an answer that made even a freakish hint of sense he knew that such a thing was inconceivable. Patrick was dead; the score was his and his alone. 'Between you and me, Mr. Laker . . .'

Nothing through the underpass.

Frenzel was alive and Patrick was dead. The equation was Hartmann's, *the weapon was Hartmann's.*

Another lorry, another gap, then an old grey saloon. In ten minutes the rain would have engulfed the underpass.

Five-twelve.

Laker eased his weight from one elbow to another, fiddling the binoculars into sharper focus. As he did so he saw the man suddenly drop the truck's raised bonnet and three cars come out of the underpass in line astern, the Moskvitch in the lead.

His scalp tightened. The overalls split at the armpits as he reached for the rifle. Three-quarters of a mile . . . A deluge of noise was filling his ears. He pushed the safety-catch forward, not hearing the click, deaf to everything except the crescendo of the blood-beat inside himself. Vaguely he was aware of the truck moving off the shoulder and heading the other way but his stare was riveted to the convoy: the cars were still small to the naked eye, like models, one green and two black, seeming to inch clear of the underpass.

He shifted position slightly, tensing, raising the rifle. The grey saloon had swept by where he lay. At half a mile he saw the nose of the Moskvitch dip as it approached the warning-signs and he knew it was cutting speed. Six hundred yards . . . Nothing but the noise in his head, no conscious thoughts, no last-second spurt of rage, everything instinctive.

Five hundred . . . He nestled against the cheek-rest and took preliminary aim. The car was shedding a misty spray. Wipers going, peaked cap behind the wheel, Hartmann in the back, alone, blurred by the smeared side-windows. A peep-show, crossed by the hair-lines, enlarging . . . First pressure already on the trigger, the squeeze beginning. Another second. The angle widening, the apparent acceleration. An infinitesimal moment more –

Now!

Laker felt the jolt, saw the glass splinter and the simultaneous clutching movement inside the car. In an intensity of awareness he fired again, the aim held, the window frosting a hand's-width from the first point of impact, the figure slumping, hat askew – all this he glimpsed in the identical jarring instant, all at telescoped distance.

Then the lightning traverse to the right began and his chance of a third shot had gone. And he was stumbling to his feet, discarding the rifle, running.

He ran with his head down. The trees hid him almost immediately. The roar in his ears cleared for a moment, like enormous bubbles bursting, and he heard the savage whimpering of tyres. After a short distance he stopped and looked back through a gap in the pines. The three cars were at a standstill, askew on the track, men leaping from them. The driver of the Moskvitch had opened the near-side door and Laker could see the overcoated figure sprawled head and shoulders on to the carriageway, motionless.

He didn't wait. One glance was enough. He turned again and ran on, a choking sensation in his throat. The sounds of the autobahn receded. After a little he slowed, but the possibility of pursuit kept him going. The pines gave way to fields and he felt rain on his face as he moved into the open. Six or seven minutes brought him to the road, the self-same scenes flickered vividly across his vision. The road was sunken, unsurfaced, narrow. He stripped the overalls off and tossed them into a clump of bushes, then climbed some barbed wire and clambered down the bank. The rain was intensifying. He sheltered against the trunk of a huge beech, breathing hard, mind churning, an exultant shiver once racking him like an ague.

It seemed a long while before he heard something coming. Fifty yards away the road cornered gently and disappeared from view. He quit the protection of the tree and started to move in the direction from which the promised car was approaching. He'd taken about ten paces before he saw it, a mud-flecked Volga. He raised a hand in greeting and stopped. It came quite fast, in low gear, almost filling the width of the road. Several people seemed to be in it, but the rain hid their identities. As it braked to a standstill Laker started forward again, thumbs up. In the same moment doors opened on either side and the front-seat occupants got out. And with a blow of incredulous dismay he recognised the blond, black-jacketed driver and the man in the raincoat with the lop-sided face who'd been his captors once before.

For a lifelong moment he was rooted where he stood. Then he turned and fled, mind and body temporarily dissociated – the one stunned, the other in a paroxysm of movement.

'Mr. Laker!'

He sprinted along the road. A stuttering voice repeatedly bawled at him to stop. Doors slammed and he heard the car start after him. With a despairing effort he flung himself up the bank, expecting a shot. He clawed his way up frantically, reached the top as the car drew level below, then went to vault the barbed wire. The post he grabbed for support broke off as he was in mid-air; one foot caught the topmost strand of wire. Falling, he felt the sickening impact as his head clubbed against an outcrop of stone and everything exploded into darkness.

They had him in the car and the car was moving. He heard someone moan, not realising it was himself. In the dim beginnings of revival he struggled, fighting the hands that seemed to be holding him down. Through swelling pain he babbled defiantly: 'I got him, anyway . . . I got him!' – kicking, straining against whoever was there.

'What d'you think?' someone asked a million miles away, but not of him, and someone else replied: 'Perhaps you'd better.'

He felt his jacket being dragged off, his left sleeve being pulled up, then the prick and deep slide of a needle in his flesh. Almost immediately the blackness started to lump and tumble into the featureless landscape of renewed unconsciousness.

'You should have told him about his son,' another voice was protesting. 'You should have told him that.'

It was the last thing to register and he took it under with him, bewildered even then. For it was Karen who had spoken.

CHAPTER 17

He floated in the darkness, sometimes totally unaware, sometimes with his mind beset with problems which had been with him since childhood, sometimes swept by eddies of weakness that seemed to suck him down to where it was darker still. In the delirium of this darkness people touched him, shifted him, talked to him and about him and several times a whisper echoed round the resonant cave of his skull – 'Patrick's all right. Can you hear? . . . Patrick's all right.'

How long he floated he pieced together afterwards. But a moment came when he felt himself once more being lifted, cradled, borne slowly upwards towards actuality. In a daze of vagueness he opened his eyes, then clamped them shut, stabbed by a blaze of light that seemed to start his head hammering as if a switch had been thrown. For an incalculable period his thoughts streamed away in ribbons of jumbled pictures, the thudding in his temples like a pile-driver. Then, fearfully, he began to blink, his hands to wander.

He was in a bed. A shaded light on a glossy wall beyond the hump made by his feet, a chintz-covered window, a silver-grey door, a silver-grey cupboard, a table . . . Gingerly he felt his head, discovering bandages; dully, he noticed that he was wearing his own pyjamas. The fevered condition of his mind prevented him from guessing where he might be, or even reflecting that it was different from what he ought to have expected. He called out, a hoarse croak, but no one came. His watch had been taken from his wrist, so he had no idea of the time. He felt sick and closed his eyes, yielding to the heavy drag on his senses, remembering the autobahn, the Moskvitch, Hartmann in his sights and Hartmann inert, sprawled like a rag-doll on the tarmac; remembering the narrow road and the Volga and the shock of who was in it, remembering running, knowing that something had gone horribly wrong – all that part very clear. And then remembering the darkness in which, impossibly, Karen Gisevius had existed and another voice had gently whispered lies to him about Patrick.

He slept again before the chaotic wandering took hold.

Now the curtains had been pulled aside and daylight was furring the edges of the window. He stared at it for what seemed a long time without fully realising he was awake. The pile-driver had been replaced by a lazy throbbing and he sat up cautiously, surveying the room, mystified. A vase of bronze chrysanthemums stood on the bedside table and his watch was there beside it.

Eight-fifteen . . . Monday? An enormous effort was required: his mind was sore, as if it had been kicked. Impulsively he started towards the window, but he swayed when he got to his feet and sank back, dizzy.

From the bed he could see the top of some trees. He pressed against the pillows, struggling to make sense of the neat room, the flowers, the comfort. A flask of water was also on the table and he started pouring some into a tumbler. As he was doing so the door opened and a dark-haired nurse looked in. The crisp headgear, the white crossbands over the lilac blouse, the starched cuffs and apron – none of it rang a bell with him.

'Where am I?'

He spoke in German. She hesitated fractionally, then entered, closing the door behind her.

'Where is this place?'

To his astonishment she answered in English. 'I haven't passed my colloquial yet, but if you're asking what I think you're asking the answer is the British Military Hospital in Hanover.'

'*Where?*'

'Hanover, Germany. And I'm from London, England.' She smiled pertly, Looking down at him. 'Have you been awake long?'

Hanover: it wouldn't sink in. 'How in the hell did I get here?'

'I wouldn't know,' the nurse said. 'I only came on duty at eight.'

'What's today?'

'Monday.' She was feeling his pulse. 'How's the head?'

'Spinning.'

'You've got six stitches in it, so no wonder. D'you feel you can cope with a visitor?'

'Who?'

'I wouldn't know that either. I'm just responsible for your well-being. What d'you think? Yes or no?'

'Yes,' he said.

'It's up to you.' She studied him clinically. 'Are you sure?'

He nodded.

'Very well. I'll get him.'

She went away with a starchy rustle. A minute or two elapsed before the door opened again, and in that time Laker's mind moved sufficiently fast through its labyrinth of bewilderment not to be entirely surprised to see who came in.

'Sam.'

Slattery tiptoed across to the bed as if he were in church.

'How are you, Sam?' The brick-red complexion, the smooth-as-glass manner.

Laker spurned his offered handshake. 'Where the blazes have you sprung from?'

'I've been waiting along the corridor. They gave me a cubby-hole in which to park myself. I wanted to be with you the moment you surfaced.'

'Is that so?'

'There's something you must know, Sam – right away.'

'Go on.'

'I talked to you during the night, and you answered after a fashion. D'you remember?'

'No.'

'About Patrick.' Slattery couldn't seem to manage it first time. 'He's come to no harm, Sam. He's safe and well, here in Hanover.'

All his life Laker was to remember that tremendous leap in his heart.

The delirious whispers echoed – 'Patrick's all right . . . All right . . .' Yet, staring at Slattery, he heard himself say: 'I don't believe you.'

'It's true. As true as we're together.'

'It can't be. *Neues Deutschland* – '

'It is, Sam.'

'Prove it.' Oh my God, he thought. Oh Jesus.

'I shall. But take it easy, take it easy.'

'Where is he?'

'With friends, on the other side of town.'

'Bring him over. Let me see him.'

'Just as soon as I can. But give him a chance, Sam.' A tentative smile. 'He probably hasn't had his breakfast yet.'

'Let me talk to him, then.'

'Are you up to it?'

'My God,' Laker said 'Where's the telephone?'

He started to scramble out of bed, beside himself with wonder and excitement, but Slattery checked him and went to the door, opened it and called the nurse.

'She's fetching one,' he said, returning. 'You're in no state to be walking about.'

Laker closed his eyes. He was trembling. His voice had thickened. 'There was a paragraph about him in *Neues Deutschland*. It said he'd been killed in a street accident.'

'It was false, Sam. A lie. You'll see.'

Laker sucked in air. He needed time. Time. 'How did you manage it?'

'Manage what?'

'Getting him out.' Incredibly, they were talking about the living.

'I'll put you in the picture presently.'

'Now.'

'Presently.'

'And me . . . What about me? I was picked up by a couple of – '

'Let it wait, Sam. First things first.'

Slattery raised a finger to his lips as the nurse entered to plug in a telephone. Only when he'd thanked her and she'd gone did he speak again.

'There's just one thing before you have a word with Patrick. He's swallowed the business-trip story, and as far as your being *hors de combat* is concerned the line is that you had an argument with a door at the airport last night. There shouldn't be any awkward questions, but play it by ear.'

Laker nodded. His mind was being asked to make too many somersaults all at once, but he was too relieved to be thinking clearly, too muddled, too grateful. A miracle had happened; at the moment he could forgive everything. He ran his hands over his face while Slattery gave the operator a number.

'There's quite a tale to tell, Sam.' The smile was still a shade uncertain. 'But this is what matters now.'

Slattery hung on, twisting the telephone cord in his fingers, blinking away behind his spectacles.

Laker exclaimed: 'Why did *Neues Deutschland* carry a false report, for God's sake? I shot Hartmann on the strength of it.' He looked sharply at Slattery. The nightmare wasn't done with yet. 'Hartmann's dead. I shot him with the rifle he supplied me with to kill Frenzel.'

But Slattery had turned aside. 'Yes?' he was saying. 'Is Patrick there, please? . . . It's his father.' And whatever reaction Laker had looked for in Slattery was forgotten as he grabbed the telephone.

'Patrick?'

'Hallo, dad. I hear you've been in the wars again.'

'It's nothing.'

'I was expecting you last night. I wasn't told until first thing this morning that you'd been carted off to hospital . . . How are you?'

'Some stitches in the head, that's all.'

'Did you have a good trip?'

'Fine, thanks . . . I'm sorry about Leipzig. It couldn't be helped.'

'That's okay, dad. Mr. Rauter explained.'

'Rauter?'

'Your associate. He fixed it for me to come over to Hanover.'

'Who've you been staying with?'

'Erich Meyer.'

'Erich?'

'You know, dad – Erich Meyer, one of my pen-friends.'

'Yes, yes; of course. Stupid of me, but I'm still a bit woolly . . . Have you had a good time?'

'Great. Mr. Rauter said you'd settle with him about the money and all that.'

'Of course . . . When are you coming over here?'

'Just as soon as I can.'

'A colleague of mine will send transport for you.'

'Oh, good.'

'In about an hour, probably . . . All right?'

How he controlled his voice he never knew. He was sweating when he hung up. Joy quivered through him, a kind of weariness in its wake. Slattery was at the window, gazing out, and Laker asked him for a cigarette.

As the smoke swirled Laker said: 'I don't understand. Rauter was the person . . .' Then: 'Christ, I'm so confused. So bloody confused. When did you get him over? And how? He spoke as if – '

'We'll start unravelling it, Sam.' Slattery pulled a chair across to the bed. 'When you're ready we'll unwind the whole thing.'

'The last I can remember is being in a car after I'd tried to jump some wire. Two of Hartmann's men were there, the same two who'd arrested me previously, the two who'd given me the firing-squad treatment . . . When I went back to Leipzig I made use of that last-ditch number of yours. It was the fellow at the house there who produced the *Neues Deutschland* cutting – and he believed it, too . . .'

Haltingly Laker attempted to feel his way.

'Hartmann was travelling south on the Berlin-Leipzig autobahn. Afterwards I went west to a side road as arranged. Then something went wrong . . .' He frowned, trapped by another memory, another echo. 'I was sure Partick was dead, d'you understand? I got a message from Hartmann in Copenhagen which said as much, and then there was this *Neues Deutschland* confirmation . . .'

He shook his head. 'That car,' he said suspiciously. 'Karen was in that car.'

'Slattery's lips began to curl.

'Karen Gisevius,' Laker insisted. 'Wasn't she?'

'Yes.'

'How the devil –?'

'She came over with you. You crossed near Duderstadt. And it wasn't easy, the state you were in.'

'But what about Hartmann's pair? Who squared them?'

'No one. They laid the crossing on.'

Disbelief narrowed Laker's eyes.

Slattery leaned forward. 'I told you the other day that Karen was one of the best contacts we had. Well, she'd be the first to admit that Hartmann knocks her into a cocked hat.'

'*Hartmann?*'

Slattery nodded.

'You're not serious?'

'Very much so.'

Stunned, Laker ejaculated: 'He's dead. I shot him.'

'No, Sam.'

'I got him twice. He was in a green Moskvitch – '

'Not Hartmann. Not Hartmann, Sam . . . You got the one we wanted you to get.'

And with the sudden hindsight of one too long deceived Laker began to see the rough outline of the whole appalling fraud.

It didn't matter to him at the moment who the other person was. All he could grasp was that he had been terrorised, debased, manipulated, led with a ring through his nose from beginning to end, forced to grieve, made to hate, sited to kill . . . All to order.

His brain seemed to writhe. Shaking, he pressed back on the pillows. A full minute must have passed. And then, in a low voice, he said: 'Who was he?'

'A very elusive gentleman.'

'Tell me,' he flared.

'Matthew Albright.'

'Who?'

'Matthew Albright.'

He hadn't needed the reminder. *Sino-Soviet expert missing from the U.S. State Department . . . Known since May to have defected . . . ALBRIGHT HERE, MOSCOW SAYS* . . . A key turned sharply in his mind, but there had been too many shocks for another to register. And that it was Albright wasn't the awful thing.

Woodenly he said: 'He was in Hartmann's car.'

'Hartmann switched him when he took over the escort role at the Leipzig district border. For safety's sake, d'you see? Ostensibly there was a rumour of an attempt on Albright's life.'

Slattery beamed without restraint.

'Albright was the Russians' prize piece. More precious to them than half a dozen nuclear physicists. He was *the* outstanding expert on Sino-Soviet relations and virtually the whole of the West's economic and military strategy in the Far East is based on his prognosis. Moscow was a long way from picking him clean, even after three months or so; he'd have been invaluable for plenty of time yet, particularly with the see-saw rocking as it is now. We had to get him, and the sooner the better. The Americans asked what we could do to help, and – thanks to you – our scheme paid off.' Slattery lit himself a cigarette. 'We knew where Albright was, but he couldn't be touched while he remained tucked up inside Russia. But directly we heard of this trip of his to satellite Party centres there was just a chance. I'm not a Kremlinologist, so why he was making the grand tour I couldn't say; perhaps Moscow has a *nouveau riche* compulsion to show off its assets. It's happened before – Burgess, Pontecorvo; they and others made the rounds. But in Albright's case the Russians were certain to be ultra careful – and so it proved. In Warsaw, for instance, they hardly let a chink of natural light fall on him. About the only time he was going to be at all vulnerable was when he was being shunted, and even then . . .'

Slattery went on, engrossed with the background, Slattery who had once had the gall to say: 'No hard feelings I hope, now or at any time.' And when he next paused Laker found his tongue.

'You bastard.' He dragged it out. 'You bloody bastard.'

Slattery blinked as if to ward off Laker's murderous glare. 'There wasn't any other way, Sam.'

'No one has the right to do what you've done.'

'A duty, though.'

'Balls. Oh balls to that.'

'I could give you precedents, chapter and verse.'

'To hell with precedents. I want an explanation.'

'You're getting it.'

'Am I?'

'I had you listed for this days before you got your name in the *Evening Standard*; that was a coincidence, pure and simple, though it couldn't have happened at a more convenient time as far as I was concerned.' Slattery blew smoke and tried another tack. 'Look at it my way. If I'd asked you to dispose of Albright, d'you think you'd have agreed? Of course not. But I especially needed you. In the first place you were the finest marksman I've ever known. And whoever took on this job would have to be a whole lot better than good.'

'I undertook to deliver a message – no more, no less.'

'And you finished by killing a man.'

'Thanks to you.'

'Not entirely. Nobody made you.'

'Oh no?'

'Nobody made you, Sam.'

'I was put against a tree with a bag over my head. I was told Patrick was dead . . . And you sit there and split hairs about who's responsible –'

'Listen. There's a second reason why I needed you. I haven't forgotten what you were like in Green Park that night during the war or the way you were when you got back from Gardelegen. No one who knew you in those days could ever forget. And we don't change, Sam – not underneath, not where it matters. Given the circumstances the chances are we'll conform. So' – he spread his hands – 'we set a sprat to catch a mackerel. And Hartmann couldn't be mealy-mouthed if he was to bring out what I knew was in you.'

Coldly, Laker said: 'Is this the way you work?'

'If need be.'

'Without thought for those you exploit – not caring what it costs them?'

'Albright had to be removed. It was vital.'

'You didn't answer the question.'

'The circumstances were exceptional. We put you through the hoop, I don't deny, but you qualified on that score, too. You're as tough as nails, Sam. You always were.' Slattery beamed again, and his look implied: but not the smartest, not the most cerebral. 'Fear and hatred are the best tools in the trade. It was a gamble, even so. You might easily have let us down.'

'*You* down!' Laker roller his head, seething. 'I wish to God I had.'

'At the moment, perhaps. But not at the time, not while you were waiting for Hartmann's car. You wanted him then as badly as we wanted Albright. And you made sure you got him, as I guessed you would.'

There was silence. Laker took a deep, shuddering breath and put his hands to his throbbing temples. He still hadn't grasped how completely he had been stage-managed.

Slattery said: 'I expect you've tumbled to it – Frenzel never existed. A dozen things could have gone wrong, but not that.' With a kind of relish, as if he were explaining a sequence of chess moves, he began to reconstruct the pattern of events. 'It was all relatively straightforward as far as Copenhagen. We tried to keep the pressure on you there, though Ritchie Jackson tells me the tailing was a bit too erratic. You were hardly expected to land up with the police, of course, though that was a minor matter – and it helped in a way. After Ritchie telephoned the Hartmann message to the Metropol it was a question then of wait and see. That was *the* crucial period, and later it was also touch and go whether you'd bite on that Leipzig number. What made everyone grey, though, was your going back with the rifle. We hadn't reckoned on that. Your friend with the macaw would have equipped you, d'you see?' He stubbed his cigarette. 'He was in a quandary about telling you who would pick you up on the side road for the getaway. We certainly hadn't anticipated your knocking yourself out and having to be bundled across the frontier like a sack of coals . . . However, by and large it all worked very well.'

He was speaking about a certain operation which had been carried out in a certain way, for all the world as though Laker hadn't been involved and there had been no private agonies. Laker studied him, amazed and contemptuous. Even Hartmann had been unable to contain a fleeting show of feeling.

'That cutting from *Neues Deutschland* – '

'We had it specially set, Sam.'

'Your idea?'

'After a fashion, yes.'

'Then sod you.'

'We have to do these things.'

'Don't try to justify yourself. For Christ's sake don't start that – not to me.'

'There's a war on, Sam. No one likes to admit it, but there is. For some of us it never ended. We fight it out how and where we can.' Slattery looked almost pained. 'I thought you'd understand, I really did.'

'Say I'd failed?'

'We'd have tried something else.'

'Used someone else, you mean.'

'If necessary. We'd have found a way.'

'God forgive you.'

Slattery got to his feet. 'You're tired,' he said. 'But all's well that ends well. Ease off, Sam. A lousy trick – all right. A lousy, shabby, underhand trick, and I apologise for it.' He was still smiling. 'But only you went through the hoop. Patrick was never in the least danger and we had your own safety at heart all along the line. For instance, there was no message in that watch-strap of yours.'

Near the door he turned. 'By the way, I gather you'll be fit enough to travel tomorrow. A word from you in the office downstairs and they'll see that you and Patrick are whisked off to Heidelburg or wherever you decide.' He paused, as if to receive thanks. 'There are just two other matters, then we can call it a day. Hartmann's stayed on. He's sticking it out, and he might get away with it. But Karen's been wanting to cry off for a longish while now, and finally she has. It's too hot for her there anyhow. Remember this, though, when you see her. She was almost as much in the dark about what was afoot as you were. All she was told was that someone would call at Kromadecka. She had no idea who it would be and she had no idea why – though when she did she hated every part of it. In fact you could say that we used her, too.'

Slattery cleared his throat.

'And – lastly – there's the fact that you're in a privileged position. You know too much, but that's the price I had to pay. I can't gag you. You can blow your top if you like. We'd deny everything, naturally – though that wouldn't prevent a few heads rolling over there in Leipzig. I can also appeal to you, though in your present mood I doubt if doing so would cut much ice. So I can only stress one unpalatable truth. You're a killer, Sam. Given the circumstances you're a killer. That, *inter alia*, is what's on the files, but don't brand yourself publicly as such; people wouldn't understand, not in the midst of their peace and plenty. Let's keep it between you and me.'

'Go away,' Laker grated.

'I'm going, Sam. Good-bye. Look after yourself.'

Ten minutes before Patrick arrived the door opened again. It was Karen.

'Sammy?'

She moved swiftly across to the bed. Laker held out his hands, taking hers. Tears, bright and shining, filled her eyes, and as he drew her towards him he knew that she wasn't crying for him, or for herself, or even out of happiness, but for what men had always done to one another in the endless collision of their dreams and would go on doing by way of lies and violence and dedicated cruelty until the world burned itself to a cinder.

Dr No

Ian
Fleming

CHAPTER 1

HEAR YOU LOUD AND CLEAR

Punctually at six o'clock the sun set with a last yellow flash behind the Blue Mountains, a wave of violet shadow poured down Richmond Road, and the crickets and tree frogs in the fine gardens began to zing and tinkle.

Apart from the background noise of the insects, the wide empty street was quiet. The wealthy owners of the big, withdrawn houses – the bank managers, company directors and top civil servants – had been home since five o'clock and they would be discussing the day with their wives or taking a shower and changing their clothes. In half an hour the street would come to life again with the cocktail traffic, but now this very superior half mile of 'Rich Road', as it was known to the tradesmen of Kingston, held nothing but the suspense of an empty stage and the heavy perfume of night-scented jasmine.

Richmond Road is the 'best' road in all Jamaica. It is Jamaica's Park Avenue, its Kensington Palace Gardens, its Avenue D'Iéna. The 'best' people live in its big old-fashioned houses, each in an acre or two of beautiful lawn set, too trimly, with the finest trees and flowers from the Botanical Gardens at Hope. The long, straight road is cool and quiet and withdrawn from the hot, vulgar sprawl of Kingston where its residents earn their money, and, on the other side of the T-intersection at its top, lie the grounds of King's House, where the Governor and Commander-in-Chief of Jamaica lives with his family. In Jamaica, no road could have a finer ending.

On the eastern corner of the top intersection stands No 1 Richmond Road, a substantial two-storey house with broad white-painted verandas running round both floors. From the road a gravel path leads up to the pillared entrance through wide lawns marked out with tennis courts on which this evening, as on all evenings, the sprinklers are at work. This mansion is the social Mecca of Kingston. It is Queen's Club, which, for fifty years, has boasted the power and frequency of its blackballs.

Such stubborn retreats will not long survive in modern Jamaica. One day Queen's Club will have its windows smashed and perhaps be burned to the ground, but for the time being it is a useful place to find in a sub-tropical island – well run, well staffed and with the finest cuisine and cellar in the Caribbean.

At that time of day, on most evenings of the year, you would find the same four motor cars standing in the road outside the club. They were the cars belonging to the high bridge game that assembled punctually at five and played until around midnight. You could almost set your watch by these cars. They belonged, reading from the order in which they now stood against the kerb, to the Brigadier in command of the Caribbean Defence Force, to Kingston's leading criminal lawyer, and to the Mathematics Professor from Kingston University. At the tail of the line stood the black Sunbeam Alpine of Commander John Strangways, RN (Ret.), Regional Control Officer for the Caribbean – or, less discreetly, the local representative of the British Secret Service.

Just before six-fifteen, the silence of Richmond Road was softly broken. Three blind beggars came round the corner of the intersection and moved slowly down the pavement towards the four cars. They were Chigroes – Chinese Negroes – bulky men, but bowed as they shuffled along, tapping at the kerb with their white sticks. They walked in file. The first man, who wore blue glasses and could presumably see better than the others, walked in front holding a tin cup against the crook of the stick in his left hand. The right hand of the second man rested on his shoulder and the right hand of the third on the shoulder of the second. The eyes of the second and third men were shut. The three men were dressed in rags and wore dirty jippa-jappa baseball caps with long peaks. They said nothing and no noise came from them except the soft tapping of their sticks as they came slowly down the shadowed pavement towards the group of cars.

The three blind men would not have been incongruous in Kingston, where there are many diseased people on the streets, but, in this quiet rich empty street, they made an unpleasant impression. And it was odd that they should all be Chinese Negroes. This is not a common mixture of bloods.

In the cardroom, the sunburned hand reached out into the green pool of the centre table and gathered up the four cards. There was a quiet snap as the trick went to join the rest. 'Hundred honours,' said Strangways, 'and ninety below!' He looked at his watch and stood up. 'Back in twenty minutes. Your deal, Bill. Order some drinks. Usual for me. Don't bother to cook a hand for me while I'm gone. I always spot them.'

Bill Templar, the Brigadier, laughed shortly. He pinged the bell by his side and raked the cards in towards him. He said, 'Hurry up, blast you.

You always let the cards go cold just as your partner's in the money.'

Strangways was already out of the chair. The three men sat back resignedly in their chairs. The coloured steward came in and they ordered drinks for themselves and a whisky and water for Strangways.

There was this maddening interruption every evening at six-fifteen, about halfway through their second rubber. At this time precisely, even if they were in the middle of a hand, Strangways had to go to his 'office' and 'make a call'. It was a damned nuisance. But Strangways was a vital part of their four and they put up with it. It was never explained what 'the call' was, and no one asked. Strangways's job was 'hush' and that was that. He was rarely away for more than twenty minutes and it was understood that he paid for his absence with a round of drinks.

The drinks came and the three men began to talk racing.

In fact, this was the most important moment in Strangways's day – the time of his duty radio contact with a powerful transmitter on the roof of the building in Regent's Park that is the headquarters of the Secret Service. Every day, at eighteen-thirty local time, unless he gave warning the day before that he would not be on the air – when he had business on one of the other islands in his territory, for instance, or was seriously ill – he would transmit his daily report and receive his orders. If he failed to come on the air precisely at six-thirty, there would be a second call, the 'Blue' call, at seven, and, finally, the 'Red' call at seven-thirty. After this, if his transmitter remained silent, it was 'Emergency', and Section III, his controlling authority in London, would urgently get on the job of finding out what had happened to him.

Even a 'Blue' call means a bad mark for an agent unless his 'Reasons in Writing' are unanswerable. London's radio schedules round the world are desperately tight and their minute disruption by even one extra call is a dangerous nuisance. Strangways had never suffered the ignominy of a 'Blue' call, let alone a 'Red', and was as certain as could be that he never would do so. Every morning, at precisely six-fifteen, he left Queen's Club, got into his car and drove for ten minutes up into the foothills of the Blue Mountains to his neat bungalow with the fabulous view over Kingston harbour. At six twenty-five he walked through the hall to the office at the back. He unlocked the door and locked it again behind him. Miss Trueblood, who passed as his secretary, but was in fact his No. 2 and a former Chief Officer WRNS, would already be sitting in front of the dials inside the dummy filing cabinet. She would have the earphones on and would be making first contact, tapping out his call-sign, WXN, on 14 megacycles. There would be a shorthand pad on her elegant knees. Strangways would drop into the chair beside her and pick up the other pair of headphones and, at exactly six twenty-eight, he would take over from her and wait for the sudden hollowness in the ether that meant that WWW in London was coming in to acknowledge.

It was an iron routine. Strangways was a man of iron routine. Unfortunately, strict patterns of behaviour can be deadly if they are read by an enemy.

Strangways, a tall lean man with a black patch over the right eye and the sort of aquiline good looks you associate with the bridge of a destroyer, walked quickly across the mahogany panelled hallway of Queen's Club and pushed through the light mosquito-wired doors and ran down the three steps to the path.

There was nothing very much on his mind except the sensual pleasure of the clean fresh evening air and the memory of the finesse that had given him his three spades. There was this case, of course, the case he was working on, a curious and complicated affair that M had rather nonchalantly tossed over the air at him two weeks earlier. But it was going well. A chance lead into the Chinese community had paid off. Some odd angles had come to light – for the present the merest shadows of angles – but if they jelled, thought Strangways as he strode down the gravel path and into Richmond Road, he might find himself involved in something very odd indeed.

Strangways shrugged his shoulders. Of course it wouldn't turn out like that. The fantastic never materialized in his line of business. There would be some drab solution that had been embroidered by overheated imaginations and the usual hysteria of the Chinese.

Automatically, another part of Strangways's mind took in the three blind men. They were tapping slowly towards him down the sidewalk. They were about twenty yards away. He calculated that they would pass him a second or two before he reached his car. Out of shame for his own health and gratitude for it, Strangways felt for a coin. He ran his thumb-nail down its edge to make sure it was a florin and not a penny. He took it out. He was parallel with the beggars. How odd, they were all Chigroes! How very odd! Strangways's hand went out. The coin clanged in the tin cup.

'Bless you, Master,' said the leading man. 'Bless you,' echoed the other two.

The car key was in Strangways's hand. Vaguely he registered the moment of silence as the tapping of the white sticks ceased. It was too late.

As Strangways had passed the last man, all three had swivelled. The back two had fanned out a step to have a clear field of fire. Three revolvers, ungainly with their sausage-shaped silencers, whipped out of holsters concealed among the rags. With disciplined precision the three men aimed at different points down Strangways's spine – one between the shoulders, one in the small of the back, one at the pelvis.

The three heavy coughs were almost one. Strangways's body was hurled forward as if it had been kicked. It lay absolutely still in the small puff of dust from the sidewalk.

It was six-seventeen. With a squeal of tyres, a dingy motor hearse with black plumes flying from the four corners of its roof took the T-intersection into Richmond Road and shot down towards the group on the pavement. The three men had just had time to pick up Strangways's body when the hearse slid to a stop abreast of them. The double doors at the back were open. So was the plain deal coffin inside. The three men manhandled the body through the doors and into the coffin. They climbed in. The lid was put on and the doors pulled shut. The three Negroes sat down on three of the four little seats at the corners of the coffin and unhurriedly laid their white sticks beside them. Roomy black alpaca coats hung over the backs of the seats. They put the coats on over their rags. Then they took off their baseball caps and reached down to the floor and picked up black top hats and put them on their heads.

The driver, who also was a Chinese Negro, looked nervously over his shoulder.

'Go, man. Go!' said the biggest of the killers. He glanced down at the luminous dial of his wrist watch. It said six-twenty. Just three minutes for the job. Dead on time.

The hearse made a decorous U-turn and moved at a sedate speed up to the intersection. There it turned right and at thirty miles an hour it cruised genteelly up the tarmac highway towards the hills, its black plumes streaming the doleful signal of its burden, and the three mourners sitting bolt upright with their arms crossed respectfully over their hearts.

'WXN calling WWW. . . . WXN calling WWW. . . . WXN . . . WXN . . .WXN. . . .'

The centre finger of Mary Trueblood's right hand stabbed softly, elegantly, at the key. She lifted her left wrist. Six twenty-eight. He was a minute late. Mary Trueblood smiled at the thought of the little open Sunbeam tearing up the road towards her. Now, in a second, she would hear the quick step, then the key in the lock and he would be sitting beside her. There would be the apologetic smile as he reached for the earphones. 'Sorry, Mary. Damned car wouldn't start.' Or, 'You'd think the blasted police knew my number by now. Stopped me at Halfway Tree.' Mary Trueblood took the second pair of earphones off their hook and put them on his chair to save him half a second.

'. . . WXN calling WWW. . . . WXN calling WWW. . . .' She tuned the dial a hair's breadth and tried again. Her watch said six-twenty-nine. She began to worry. In a matter of seconds, London would be coming in. Suddenly she thought, God, what could she do if Strangways wasn't on time! It was useless for her to acknowledge London and pretend she was him – useless and dangerous. Radio Security would be monitoring the call, as they monitored every call from an agent. Those instruments which measured the minute peculiarities in an operator's 'fist' would at once detect it wasn't Strangways at the key. Mary Trueblood had been shown the forest of dials in the quiet room on the top floor at headquarters, had watched as the dancing hands registered the weight of each pulse, the speed of each cipher group, the stumble over a particular letter. The Controller had explained it all to her when she had joined the Caribbean station five years before – how a buzzer would sound and the contact be automatically broken if the wrong operator had come on the air. It was the basic protection against a Secret Service transmitter falling into enemy hands. And if an agent had been captured and was being forced to contact London under torture, he had only to add a few hairbreadth peculiarities to his usual 'fist' and they would tell the story of his capture as clearly as if he had announced it *en clair*.

Now it had come! Now she was hearing the hollowness in the ether that meant London was coming in. Mary Trueblood glanced at her watch. Six-thirty. Panic! But now, at last, there were the footsteps in the hall. Thank God! In a second he would come in. She *must* protect him! Desperately she decided to take a chance and keep the circuit open.

'WWW calling WXN. . . . WWW calling WXN. . . . Can you hear me? . . . can you hear me?' London was coming over strong, searching for the Jamaica station.

The footsteps were at the door.

Coolly, confidently, she tapped back: 'Hear you loud and clear. . . . Hear you loud and clear. . . . Hear you . . .'

Behind her there was an explosion. Something hit her on the ankle. She looked down. It was the lock of the door.

Mary Trueblood swivelled sharply on her chair. A man stood in the doorway. It wasn't Strangways. It was a big Negro with yellowish skin and slanting eyes. There was a gun in his hand. It ended in a thick black cylinder.

Mary Trueblood opened her mouth to scream.

The man smiled broadly. Slowly, lovingly, he lifted the gun and shot her three times in and around the left breast.

The girl slumped sideways off her chair. The earphones slipped off her golden hair on to the floor. For perhaps a second the tiny chirrup of London sounded out into the room. Then it stopped. The buzzer at the Controller's desk in Radio Security had signalled that something was wrong on WXN.

The killer walked out of the door. He came back carrying a box with a coloured label on it that said PRESTO FIRE, and a big sugar sack marked TATE & LYLE. He put the box down on the floor and went to the body and roughly forced the sack over the head and down to the ankles. The feet stuck out. He bent them and crammed them in. He dragged the bulky sack out into the hall and came back. In the corner of the room the safe stood open, as he had been told it would, and the cipher books had been taken out and laid on the desk ready for work on the London signals. The man threw these and all the papers in the safe into the centre of the room. He tore down the curtains and added them to the pile. He topped it up with a couple of chairs. He opened the box of Presto fire-lighters and took out a handful and tucked them into the pile and lit them. Then he went out into the hall and lit similar bonfires in appropriate places. The tinder-dry furniture caught quickly and the flames began to lick up the panelling. The man went to the front door and opened it. Through the hibiscus hedge he could see the glint of the hearse. There was no noise except the zing of crickets and the soft tick-over of the car's engine. Up and down the road there was no other sign of life. The man went back into the smoke-filled hall and easily shouldered the sack and came out again, leaving the door open to make a draught. He walked swiftly down the path to the road. The back doors of the hearse were open. He handed in the sack and watched the two men force it into the coffin on top of Strangways's body. Then he climbed in and shut the doors and sat down and put on his top hat.

As the first flames showed in the upper windows of the bungalow, the hearse moved quietly from the sidewalk and went on its way up towards the Mona Reservoir. There the weighted coffin would slip down into its fifty-fathom grave and, in just forty-five minutes, the personnel and records of the Caribbean station of the Secret Service would have been utterly destroyed.

CHAPTER 2

CHOICE OF WEAPONS

Three weeks later, in London, March came in like a rattlesnake.

From first light on March 1st, hail and icy sleet, with a Force 8 gale behind them, lashed at the city and went on lashing as the people streamed miserably to work, their legs whipped by the wet hems of their macintoshes and their faces blotching with the cold.

It was a filthy day and everybody said so – even M, who rarely admitted the existence of weather even in its extreme forms. When the old black Silver Wraith Rolls with the nondescript number-plate stopped outside the tall building in Regent's Park and he climbed stiffly out on to the pavement, hail hit him in the face like a whiff of small-shot. Instead of hurrying inside the building, he walked deliberately round the car to the window beside the chauffeur.

'Won't be needing the car again today, Smith. Take it away and go home. I'll use the tube this evening. No weather for driving a car. Worse than one of those PQ convoys.'

Ex-Leading Stoker Smith grinned gratefully. 'Aye-aye, sir. And thanks.' He watched the elderly erect figure walk round the bonnet of the Rolls and across the pavement and into the building. Just like the old boy. He'd always see the men right first. Smith clicked the gear lever into first and moved off, peering forward through the steaming windscreen. They didn't come like that any more.

M went up in the lift to the eighth floor and along the thick-carpeted corridor to his office. He shut the door behind him, took off his overcoat and scarf and hung them behind the door. He took out a large blue silk bandanna handkerchief and brusquely wiped it over his face. It was odd, but he wouldn't have done this in front of the porters or the liftman. He went over to his desk and sat down and bent towards the intercom. He pressed the switch. 'I'm in, Miss Moneypenny. The signals, please, and anything else you've got. Then get me Sir James Molony. He'll be doing his rounds at St Mary's about now. Tell the Chief of Staff I'll see 007 in half an hour. And let me have the Strangways file.' M waited for the metallic 'Yes, sir' and released the switch.

He sat back and reached for his pipe and began filling it thoughtfully. He didn't look up when his secretary came in with the stack of papers and he even ignored the half dozen pink Most Immediates on top of the signal file. If they had been vital he would have been called during the night.

A yellow light winked on the intercom. M picked up the black telephone from the row of four. 'That you, Sir James? Have you got five minutes?'

'Six for you.' At the other end of the line the famous neurologist chuckled. 'Want me to certify one of Her Majesty's Ministers?'

'Not today.' M frowned irritably. The old Navy had respected governments. 'It's about that man of mine you've been handling. We won't bother about the name. This is an open line. I gather you let him out yesterday. Is he fit for duty?'

There was a pause on the other end. Now the voice was professional, judicious. 'Physically he's as fit as a fiddle. Leg's healed up. Shouldn't be any after-effects. Yes, he's all right.' There was another pause. 'Just one thing, M. There's a lot of tension there, you know. You work these men of yours pretty hard. Can you give him something easy to start with? From what you've told me he's been having a tough time for some years now.'

M said gruffly. 'That's what he's paid for. It'll soon show if he's not up to the work. Won't be the first one that's cracked. From what you say, he sounds in perfectly good shape. It isn't as if he'd really been damaged like some of the patients I've sent you – men who've been properly put through the mangle.'

'Of course, if you put it like that. But pain's an odd thing. We know very little about it. You can't measure it – the difference in suffering between a woman having a baby and a man having a renal colic. And, thank God, the body seems to forget fairly quickly. But this man of yours has been in *real* pain, M. Don't think that just because nothing's been broken . . .'

'Quite, quite.' Bond had made a mistake and he had suffered for it. In any case M didn't like being lectured, even by one of the most famous doctors in the world, on how he should handle his agents. There had been a note of criticism in Sir James Molony's voice. M said abruptly, 'Ever hear of a man called Steincrohn – Dr Peter Steincrohn?'

'No, who's he?'

'American doctor. Written a book my Washington people sent over for our library. This man talks about how much punishment the human body can put up with. Gives a list of the bits of the body an average man can do without. Matter of fact, I copied it out for future reference. Care to hear the list?' M dug into his coat pocket and put some letters and scraps of paper on the desk in front of him. With his left hand he selected a piece of paper and unfolded it. He wasn't put out by the silence on the other end of the line, 'Hullo, Sir James! Well, here they are: "Gall bladder, spleen, tonsils, appendix, one of his two kidneys, one of his two lungs, two of his four or five quarts of blood, two-fifths of his liver, most of his stomach, four of his twenty-three feet of intestines and half of his brain."' M paused. When the silence continued at the other end, he said, 'Any comments, Sir James?'

There was a reluctant grunt at the other end of the telephone. 'I wonder he didn't add an arm and a leg, or all of them. I don't see quite what you're trying to prove.'

M gave a curt laugh. 'I'm not trying to prove anything, Sir James. It just struck me as an interesting list. All I'm trying to say is that my man seems to have got off pretty lightly compared with that sort of punishment. But,' M relented, 'don't let's argue about it.' He said in a milder voice, 'As a matter of fact I did have it in mind to let him have a bit of a breather. Something's come up in Jamaica.' M glanced at the streaming windows. 'It'll be more of a rest cure than anything. Two of my people, a man and a girl, have gone off together. Or that's what it looks like. Our friend can have a spell at being an inquiry agent – in the sunshine too. How's that?'

'Just the ticket. I wouldn't mind the job myself on a day like this.' But Sir James Molony was determined to get his message through. He persisted mildly. 'Don't think I wanted to interfere, M, but there are limits to a man's courage. I know you have to treat these men as if they were expendable, but presumably you don't want them to crack at the wrong moment. This one I've had here is tough. I'd say you'll get plenty more work out of him. But you know what Moran has to say about courage in that book of his.'

'Don't recall.'

'He says that courage is a capital sum reduced by expenditure. I agree with him. All I'm trying to say is that this particular man seems to have been spending pretty hard since before the war. I wouldn't say he's overdrawn – not yet, but there are limits.'

'Just so.' M decided that was quite enough of that. Nowadays, softness was everywhere. 'That's why I'm sending him abroad. Holiday in Jamaica. Don't worry, Sir James. I'll take care of him. By the way, did you ever discover what the stuff was that Russian woman put into him?'

'Got the answer yesterday.' Sir James Molony also was glad the subject had been changed. The old man was as raw as the weather. Was there any chance that he had got his message across into what he described to himself as M's thick skull? 'Taken us three months. It was a bright chap at the School of Tropical Medicine who came up with it. The drug was *fugu* poison. The Japanese use it for committing suicide. It comes from the sex organs of the Japanese globe-fish. Trust the Russians to use something no one's ever heard of. They might just as well have used curare. It has much the same effect – paralysis of the central nervous system. *Fugu's* scientific name is Tetrodotoxin. It's terrible stuff and very quick. One shot of it like your man got and in a matter of seconds the motor and respiratory muscles are paralysed. At first the chap sees double and then he can't keep his eyes open. Next he can't swallow. His head falls and he can't raise it. Dies of respiratory paralysis.'

'Lucky he got away with it.'

'Miracle. Thanks entirely to that Frenchman who was with him. Got your man on the floor and gave him artificial respiration as if he was drowning. Somehow kept his lungs going until the doctor came. Luckily the doctor had worked in South America. Diagnosed curare and treated him accordingly. But it was a chance in a million. By the same token, what happened to the Russian woman?'

M said shortly, 'Oh, she died. Well, many thanks, Sir James. And don't worry about your patient. I'll see he has an easy time of it. Goodbye.'

M hung up. His face was cold and blank. He pulled over the signal file and went quickly through it. On some of the signals he scribbled a comment. Occasionally he made a brief telephone call to one of the Sections. When he had finished he tossed the pile into his *Out* basket and reached for his pipe and the tobacco jar made out of the base of a fourteen-pounder shell. Nothing remained in front of him except a buff folder marked with the Top Secret red star. Across the centre of the folder was written in block capitals: CARIBBEAN STATION, and underneath, in italics, *Strangways and Trueblood*.

A light winked on the intercom. M pressed down the switch. 'Yes?'

'007's here, sir.'

'Send him in. And tell the Armourer to come up in five minutes.'

M sat back. He put his pipe in his mouth and set a match to it. Through the smoke he watched the door to his secretary's office. His eyes were very bright and watchful.

James Bond came through the door and shut it behind him. He walked over to the chair across the desk from M and sat down.

''Morning, 007.'

'Good morning, sir.'

There was silence in the room except for the rasping of M's pipe. It

seemed to be taking a lot of matches to get it going. In the background
the fingernails of the sleet slashed against the two broad windows.

It was all just as Bond had remembered it through the months of being
shunted from hospital to hospital, the weeks of dreary convalescence, the
hard work of getting his body back into shape. To him this represented
stepping back into life. Sitting here in this room opposite M was the
symbol of normality he had longed for. He looked across through the
smoke clouds into the shrewd grey eyes. They were watching him. What
was coming? A post-mortem on the shambles which had been his last
case? A curt relegation to one of the home sections for a spell of desk
work? Or some splendid new assignment M had been keeping on ice
while waiting for Bond to get back to duty?

M threw the box of matches down on the red leather desk. He leant
back and clasped his hands behind his head.

'How do you feel? Glad to be back?'

'Very glad, sir. And I feel fine.'

'Any final thoughts about your last case? Haven't bothered you with
it till you got well. You heard I ordered an inquiry. I believe the Chief of
Staff took some evidence from you. Anything to add?' M's voice was
businesslike, cold. Bond didn't like it. Something unpleasant was
coming. He said, 'No, sir. It was a mess. I blame myself for letting that
woman get me. Shouldn't have happened.'

M took his hands from behind his neck and slowly leant forward and
place them flat on the desk in front of him. His eyes were hard. 'Just so.'
The voice was velvet, dangerous. 'Your gun got stuck, if I recall. This
Beretta of yours with the silencer. Something wrong there, 007. Can't
afford that sort of mistake if you're to carry an 00 number. Would you
prefer to drop it and go back to normal duties?'

Bond stiffened. His eyes looked resentfully into M's. The licence to kill
for the Secret Service, the double-0 prefix, was a great honour. It had
been earned hardly. It brought Bond the only assignments he enjoyed,
the dangerous ones. 'No, I wouldn't, sir.'

'Then we'll have to change your equipment. That was one of the
findings of the Court of Inquiry. I agree with it. D'you understand?'

Bond said obstinately, 'I'm used to that gun, sir. I like working with it.
What happened could have happened to anyone. With any kind of gun.'

'I don't agree. Nor does the Court of Inquiry. So that's final. The only
question is what you're to use instead.' M bent forward to the intercom.
'Is the Armourer there? Send him in.'

M sat back. 'You may not know it, 007, but Major Boothroyd's the
greatest small-arms expert in the world. He wouldn't be here if he

wasn't. We'll hear what he has to say.'

The door opened. A short slim man with sandy hair came in and walked over to the desk and stood beside Bond's chair. Bond looked up into his face. He hadn't often seen the man before, but he remembered the very wide apart clear grey eyes that never seemed to flicker. With a non-committal glance down at Bond, the man stood relaxed, looking across at M. He said 'Good morning, sir,' in a flat, unemotional voice.

''Morning, Armourer. Now I want to ask you some questions.' M's voice was casual. 'First of all, what do you think of the Beretta, the ·25?'

'Ladies' gun, sir.'

M raised ironic eyebrows at Bond. Bond smiled thinly.

'Really! And why do you say that?'

'No stopping power, sir. But it's easy to operate. A bit fancy looking too, if you know what I mean, sir. Appeals to the ladies.'

'How would it be with a silencer?'

'Still less stopping power, sir. And I don't like silencers. They're heavy and get stuck in your clothing when you're in a hurry. I wouldn't recommend anyone to try a combination like that, sir. Not if they were meaning business.'

M said pleasanty to Bond, 'Any comment, 007?'

Bond shrugged his shoulders. 'I don't agree. I've used the ·25 Beretta for fifteen years. Never had a stoppage and I haven't missed with it yet. Not a bad record for a gun. It just happens that I'm use to it and I can point it straight. I've used bigger guns when I've had to – the ·45 Colt with the long barrel, for instance. But for close-up work and conceal-ment I like the Beretta.' Bond paused. He felt he should give way somewhere. 'I'd agree about the silencer, sir. They're a nuisance. But sometimes you have to use them.'

'We've seen what happens when you do,' said M drily. 'And as for changing your gun, it's only a question of practice. You'll soon get the feel of a new one.' M allowed a trace of sympathy to enter his voice. 'Sorry, 007. But I've decided. Just stand up a moment. I want the Armourer to get a look at your build.'

Bond stood up and faced the other man. There was no warmth in the two pairs of eyes. Bond's showed irritation. Major Boothroyd's were indifferent, clinical. He walked round Bond. He said 'Excuse me' and felt Bond's biceps and forearms. He came back in front of him and said, 'Might I see your gun?'

Bond's hand went slowly into his coat. He handed over the taped Beretta with the sawn barrel. Boothroyd examined the gun and weighed it in his hand. He put it down on the desk. 'And your holster?'

Bond took off his coat and slipped off the chamois leather holster and harness. He put his coat on again.

With a glance at the lips of the holster, perhaps to see if they showed traces of snagging. Boothroyd tossed the holster down beside the gun with a motion that sneered. He looked across at M. 'I think we can do better than this, sir.' It was the sort of voice Bond's first expensive tailor had used.

Bond sat down. He just stopped himself gazing rudely at the ceiling. Instead he look impassively across at M.

'Well, Armourer, what do you recommend?'

Major Boothroyd put on the expert's voice. 'As a matter of fact, sir,' he said modestly, 'I've just been testing most of the small automatics. Five thousand rounds each at twenty-five yards. Of all of them, I'd choose the Walther PPK 7·65 mm. It only came fourth after the Japanese M-14, the Russian Tokarev and the Sauer M-38. But I like its light trigger pull and the extension spur of the magazine gives a grip that should suit 007. It's a real stopping gun. Of course it's about a ·32 calibre as compared with the Beretta's ·25, but I wouldn't recommend anything lighter. And you can get ammunition for the Walther anywhere in the world. That gives it an edge on the Japanese and the Russian guns.'

M turned to Bond. 'Any comments?'

'It's a good gun, sir,' Bond admitted. 'But more bulky than the Beretta. How does the Armourer suggest I carry it?'

'Berns Martin Triple-draw holster,' said Major Boothroyd succinctly. 'Best worn inside the trouser band to the left. But it's all right below the shoulder. Stiff saddle leather. Holds the gun in with a spring. Should make for a quicker draw than that,' he gestured towards the desk. 'Three-fifths of a second to hit a man at twenty feet would be about right.'

'That's settled then.' M's voice was final. 'And what about something bigger?'

'There's only one gun for that, sir,' said Major Boothroyd stolidly. 'Smith & Wesson Centennial Airweight. Revolver. ·38 calibre. Hammerless, so it won't catch in clothing. Overall length of six and a half inches and it only weighs thirteen ounces. To keep down the weight, the cylinder holds only five cartridges. But by the time they're gone,' Major Boothroyd allowed himself a wintry smile, 'somebody's been killed. Fires the ·38 S & W Special. Very accurate cartridge indeed. With standard loading it has a muzzle velocity of eight hundred and sixty feet per second and muzzle energy of two hundred and sixty foot-pounds. There are various barrel lengths, three and a half inch, five inch . . .'

'All right, all right.' M's voice was testy. 'Take it as read. If you say it's the best I'll believe you. So it's the Walther and the Smith & Wesson. Send up one of each to 007. With the harness. And arrange for him to fire them in. Starting today. He's got to be expert in a week. All right? Then thank you very much, Armourer. I won't detain you.'

'Thank you, sir,' said Major Boothroyd. He turned and marched stiffly out of the room.

There was a moment's silence. The sleet tore at the windows. M swivelled his chair and watched the streaming panes. Bond took the opportunity to glance at his watch. Ten o'clock. His eyes slid to the gun and holster on the desk. He thought of his fifteen years' marriage to the ugly bit of metal. He remembered the times its single word had saved his life – and the times when its threat alone had been enough. He thought of the days when he had literally dressed to kill – when he had dismantled the gun and oiled it and packed the bullets carefully into the springloaded magazine and tried the action once or twice, pumping the cartridges out on to the bedspread in some hotel bedroom somewhere round the world. Then the last wipe of a dry rag and the gun into the little holster and a pause in front of the mirror to see that nothing showed. And then out of the door and on his way to the rendezvous that was to end with either darkness or light. How many times had it saved his life? How many death sentences had is signed? Bond felt unreasonably sad. How could one have such ties with an inanimate object, an ugly one at that, and, he had to admit it, with a weapon that was not in the same class as the ones chosen by the Armourer? But he had the ties and M was going to cut them.

M swivelled back to face him. 'Sorry, James,' he said, and there was no sympathy in his voice. 'I know how you like that bit of iron. But I'm afraid it's got to go. Never give a weapon a second chance – any more than a man. I can't afford to gamble with the double-0 section. They've got to be properly equipped. You understand that? A gun's more important that a hand or a foot in your job.'

Bond smiled thinly. 'I know, sir. I shan't argue. I'm just sorry to see it go.'

'All right then. We'll say no more about it. Now I've got some more news for you. There's a job come up. In Jamaica. Personnel problem. Or that's what it looks like. Routine investigation and report. The sunshine'll do you good and you can practise your new guns on the turtles or whatever they have down there. You can do with a bit of holiday. Like to take it on?'

Bond thought: He's got it in for me over the last job. Feels I let him

down. Won't trust me with anything tough. Wants to see. Oh well! He
said: 'Sounds rather like the soft life, sir. I've had almost too much of that
lately. But if it's got to be done . . . If you say so, sir . . .'

'Yes,' said M. 'I say so.'

CHAPTER 3

HOLIDAY TASK

It was getting dark. Outside the weather was thickening. M reached
over and switched on the green-shaded desklight. The centre of the
room became a warm yellow pool in which the leather top of the desk
glowed blood-red.

M pulled the thick file towards him. Bond noticed it for the first time.
He read the reversed lettering without difficulty. What had Strangways
been up to? Who was Trueblood?

M pressed a button on his desk. 'I'll get the Chief of Staff in on this,' he
said. 'I know the bones of the case, but he can fill in the flesh. It's a drab
little story, I'm afraid.'

The Chief of Staff came in. He was a colonel in the Sappers, a man of
about Bond's age, but his hair was prematurely grey at the temples from
the endless grind of work and responsibility. He was saved from a
nervous breakdown by physical toughness and a sense of humour. He
was Bond's best friend at headquarters. They smiled at each other.

'Bring up a chair, Chief of Staff. I've given 007 the Strangways case.
Got to get the mess cleared up before we make a new appointment there.
007 can be acting Head of Station in the meantime. I want him to leave
in a week. Would you fix that with the Colonial Office and the
Governor? And now let's go over the case.' He turned to Bond. 'I think
you knew Strangways, 007. See you worked with him on that treasure
business about five years ago. What did you think of him?'

'Good man, sir. Bit highly strung. I'd have thought he'd have been
relieved by now. Five years is a long time in the tropics.'

M ignored the comment. 'And his number two, this girl Trueblood,
Mary Trueblood. Ever come across her?'

'No, sir.'

'I see she's got a good record. Chief Officer WRNS and then came to
us. Nothing against her on her Confidential Record. Good-looker to

judge from her photographs. That probably explains it. Would you say Strangways was a bit of a womanizer?'

'Could have been,' said Bond carefully, not wanting to say anything against Strangways, but remembering the dashing good looks. 'But what's happened to them, sir?'

'That's what we want to find out,' said M. 'They've gone, vanished into thin air. Both went on the same evening about three weeks ago. Left Strangways bungalow burned to the ground – radio, codebooks, files. Nothing left but a few charred scraps. The girl left all her things intact. Must have taken only what she stood up in. Even her passport was in her room. But it would have been easy for Strangways to cook up two passports. He had plenty of blanks. He was Passport Control Officer for the island. Any number of planes they could have taken – to Florida or South America or one of the other islands in his area. Police are still checking the passenger lists. Nothing's come up yet, but they could always have gone to ground for a day or two and then done a bunk. Dyed the girl's hair and so forth. Airport security doesn't amount to much in that part of the world. Isn't that so, Chief of Staff?'

'Yes, sir.' The Chief of Staff sounded dubious. 'But I still can't understand that last radio contact.' He turned to Bond. 'You see, they began to make their routine contact at eighteen-thirty Jamaican time. Someone, Radio Security thinks it was the girl, acknowledged our WWW and then went off the air. We tried to regain contact but there was obviously something fishy and we broke off. No answer to the Blue Call, or to the Red. So that was that. Next day Section III sent 258 down from Washington. By that time the police had taken over and the Governor had already made up his mind and was trying to get the case hushed up. It all seemed pretty obvious to him. Strangways has had occasional girl trouble down there. Can't blame the chap myself. It's a quiet station. Not much to occupy his time. The Governor jumped to the obvious conclusions. So, of course, did the local police. Sex and machete fights are about all they understand. 258 spent a week down there and couldn't turn up a scrap of contrary evidence. He reported accordingly and we sent him back to Washington. Since then the police have been scraping around rather ineffectually and getting nowhere.' The Chief of Staff paused. He looked apologetically at M. 'I know you're inclined to agree with the Governor, sir, but that radio contact sticks in my throat. I just can't see where it fits into the runaway-couple picture. And Strangways's friend at the club say he was perfectly normal. Left in the middle of a rubber of bridge – always did, when he was getting close to his deadline. Said he'd be back in twenty minutes. Ordered drinks all round – again just as he always did – and left the club on six-fifteen, exactly to schedule. Then he vanished into thin air. Even left his car in front of the club. Now, why should he set the rest of his bridge four looking for him if he wanted to skip with the girl? Why not leave in the morning, or better still, late at night, after they'd made their radio call and tidied up their lives? It just doesn't make sense to me.'

M grunted non-committally. 'People in—er—love do stupid things,' he said gruffly. 'Act like lunatics sometimes. And anyway, what other explanation is there? Absolutely no trace of foul play – no reason for it that anyone can see. It's a quiet station down there. Same routines every month – an occasional communist trying to get into the island from Cuba, crooks from England thinking they can hide away just because Jamaica's so far from London. I don't suppose Strangways has had a big case since 007 was there.' He turned to Bond. 'On what you've heard, what do you think, 007? There's not much else to tell you.'

Bond was definite. 'I just can't see Strangways flying off the handle like that, sir. I daresay he was having an affair with the girl, though I wouldn't have thought he was a man to mix business with pleasure. But the Service was his whole life. He'd never have let it down. I can see him handing in his papers, and the girl doing the same, and then going off with her after you'd sent out reliefs. But I don't believe it was in him to leave us in the air like this. And from what you say of the girl, I'd say it would be much the same with her. Chief Officers WRNS don't go out of their senses.'

'Thank you, 007.' M's voice was controlled. 'These considerations had also crossed my mind. No one's been jumping to conclusions without weighing all the possibilities. Perhaps you can suggest another solution.'

M sat back and waited. He reached for his pipe and began filling it. The case bored him. He didn't like personnel problems, least of all messy ones like this. There were plenty of other worries waiting to be coped with round the world. It was only to give Bond the pretence of a job, mixed with a good rest, that he had decided to send him out to Jamaica to close the case. He put the pipe in his mouth and reached for the matches. 'Well?'

Bond wasn't going to be put off his stride. He had liked Strangways and he was impressed by the points the Chief of Staff had made. He said: 'Well, sir. For instance, what was the last case Strangways was working on? Had he reported anything, or was there anything Section III had asked him to look into. Anything at all in the last few months?'

'Nothing whatsoever.' M was definite. He took the pipe out of his mouth and cocked it at the Chief of Staff. 'Right?'

'Right, sir,' said the Chief of Staff. 'Only that damned business about the birds.'

'Oh that,' said M contemptuously. 'Some rot from the Zoo or somebody. Got wished on us by the Colonial Office. About six weeks ago, wasn't it?'

'That's right, sir. But it wasn't the Zoo. It was some people in America called the Audubon Society. They protect rare birds from extinction or something like that. Got on to our Ambassador in Washington, and the FO passed the buck to the Colonial Office. They shoved it on to us. Seems these bird people are pretty powerful in America. They even got an atom bombing range shifted on the West Coast because it interfered with some birds' nests.'

M snorted. 'Damned thing called a Whooping Crane. Read about in the papers.'

Bond persisted. 'Could you tell me about it, sir? What did the Audubon people want us to do?'

M waved his pipe impatiently. He picked up the Strangways file and tossed it down in front of the Chief of Staff. 'You tell him, Chief of Staff,' he said wearily. 'It's all in there.'

The Chief of Staff took the file and rifled through the pages towards the back. He found what he wanted and bent the file in half. There was silence in the room while he ran his eye over three pages of typescript which Bond could see were headed with the blue and white cipher of the Colonial Office. Bond sat quietly, trying not to feel M's coiled impatience radiating across the desk.

The Chief of Staff slapped the file shut. He said, 'Well, this is the story as we passed it to Strangways on January 20th. He acknowledged receipt, but after that we heard nothing from him.' The Chief of Staff sat back in his chair. He looked at Bond. 'It seems there's a bird called a Roseate Spoonbill. There's a coloured photograph of it in here. Looks like a sort of pink stork with an ugly flat bill which it uses for digging for food in the mud. Not many years ago these birds were dying out. Just before the war there were only a few hundred left in the world, mostly in Florida and thereabouts. Then somebody reported a colony of them on an island called Crab Key between Jamaica and Cuba. It's British territory – a dependency of Jamaica. Used to be a guano island, but the quality of the guano was too low for the cost of digging it. When the birds were found there, it had been uninhabited for about fifty years. The Audubon people went there and ended up by leasing a corner as a sanctuary for these spoonbills. Put two wardens in charge and persuaded the airlines to stop flying over the island and disturbing the birds. The birds flourished and at the last count there were about five thousand of them on the island. Then came the war. The price of guano went up and some bright chap had the idea of buying the island and starting to work it again. He negotiated with the Jamaican Government and bought the place for ten thousand pounds with the condition that he didn't disturb the lease of the sanctuary. That was in 1943. Well, this man imported plenty of cheap labour and soon had the place working at a profit and it's gone on making a profit until recently. Then the price of guano took a dip and it's thought that he must be having a hard time making both ends meet.'

'Who is this man?'

'Chinaman, or rather half Chinese and half German. Got a daft name. Calls himself Doctor No – Doctor Julius No.'

'No? Spelt like Yes?'

'That's right.'

'Any facts about him?'

'Nothing except that he keeps very much to himself. Hasn't been seen since he made his deal with the Jamaican Government. And there's no traffic with the island. It's his and he keeps it private. Says he doesn't want people disturbing the guanay birds who turn out his guano. Seems reasonable. Well, nothing happened until just before Christmas when one of the Audubon wardens, a Barbadian, good solid chap apparently, arrived on the north shore of Jamaica in a canoe. He was very sick. He was terribly burned – died in a few days. Before he died he told some crazy story about their camp having been attacked by a dragon with flames coming out of its mouth. This dragon had killed his pal and burned up the camp and gone roaring off into the bird sanctuary belching fire among the birds and scaring them off to God knows where. He had been badly burned but he'd escaped to the coast and stolen a canoe and sailed all one night to Jamaica. Poor chap was obviously off his rocker. And that was that, except that a routine report had to be sent off to the Audubon Society. And they weren't satisfied. Sent down two of their big brass in a Beechcraft from Miami to investigate. There's an airstrip on the island. This Chinaman's got a Grumman Amphibian for bringing in supplies . . .'

M interjected sourly. 'All these people seem to have a hell of a lot of money to throw about on their damned birds.'

Bond and the Chief of Staff exchanged smiles. M had been trying for years to get the Treasury to give him an Auster for the Caribbean Station.

The Chief of Staff continued: 'And the Beechcraft crashed on landing and killed the two Audubon men. Well, that aroused these bird people to a fury. They got a corvette from the US Training Squadron in the Caribbean to make a call on Doctor No. That's how powerful these people are. Seems they've got quite a lobby in Washington. The captain of the corvette reported that he was received very civilly by Doctor No but was kept well away from the guano workings. He was taken to the airstrip and examined the remains of the plane. Smashed to pieces, but nothing suspicious – came in to land too fast probably. The bodies of the two men and the pilot had been reverently embalmed and packed in handsome coffins which were handed over with quite a ceremony. The captain was very impressed by Doctor No's courtesy. He asked to see the wardens' camp and he was taken out there and shown the remains of it. Doctor No's theory was that the two men had gone mad because of the heat and the loneliness, or at any rate one of them had gone mad and burned down the camp with the other inside it. This seemed possible to the captain when he'd seen what a godforsaken bit of marsh the men had been living in for ten years or more. There was nothing else to see and he was politely steered back to his ship and sailed away.' The Chief of Staff spread his hands. 'And that's the lot except that the captain reported that he saw only a handful of roseate spoonbills. When his report got back to the Audubon Society it was apparently the loss of their blasted birds that infuriated these people most of all, and ever since then they've been nagging at us to have an inquiry into the whole business. Of course nobody at the Colonial Office or in Jamaica's in the least interested. So in the end the whole fairy story was dumped in our lap.' The Chief of Staff shrugged his shoulders with finality. 'And that's how this pile of bumf,' he waved the file, 'or at any rate the guts of it, got landed on Strangways.'

M looked morosely at Bond. 'See what I mean, 007? Just the sort of mares' nest these old women's societies are always stirring up. People start preserving something – churches, old houses, decaying pictures, birds – and there's always a hullabaloo of some sort. The trouble is these sort of people get really worked up about their damned birds or whatever it is. They get the politicians involved. And somehow they all seem to have stacks of money. God knows where it comes from. Other old women, I suppose. And then there comes a point when someone has to do something to keep them quiet. Like this case. It gets shunted off on to me because the place is British territory. At the same time it's private land. Nobody wants to interfere officially. So I'm supposed to do what? Send a submarine to the island? For what? To find out what's happened to a covey of pink storks.' M snorted. 'Anyway, you asked about

Strangways's last case and that's it.' M leant forward belligerently. 'Any questions? I've got a busy day ahead.'

Bond grinned. He couldn't help it. M's occasional outbursts of rage were so splendid. And nothing set him going so well as any attempt to waste the time and energies and slim funds of the Secret Service. Bond got to his feet. 'Perhaps if I could have the file, sir,' he said placatingly. 'It just strike me that four people seem to have died more or less because of these birds. Perhaps two more did – Strangways and the Trueblood girl. I agree it sounds ridiculous, but we've got nothing else to go on.'

'Take it, take it,' said M impatiently. 'And hurry up and get your holiday over. You may not have noticed it, but the rest of the world happens to be in a bit of a mess.'

Bond reached across and picked up the file. He also made to pick up his Beretta and the holster. 'No,' said M sharply. 'Leave that. And mind you've got the hang of the other two guns by the time I see you again.'

Bond looked across into M's eyes. For the first time in his life he hated the man. He knew perfectly well why M was being tough and mean. It was deferred punishment for having nearly got killed on his last job. Plus getting away from this filthy weather into the sunshine. M couldn't bear his men to have an easy time. In a way Bond felt sure he was being sent on this cushy assignment to humiliate him. The old bastard.

With the anger balling up inside him like cats' fur, Bond said, 'I'll see to it sir,' and turned and walked out of the room.

CHAPTER 4

RECEPTION COMMITTEE

The sixty-eight tons deadweight of the Super-Constellation hurtled high above the green and brown chequerboard of Cuba and, with only another hundred miles to go, started its slow declining flight towards Jamaica.

Bond watched the big green turtle-backed island grow on the horizon and the water below him turn from the dark blue of the Cuba Deep to the azure and milk of the inshore shoals. Then they were over the North Shore, over its rash of millionaire hotels, and crossing the high mountains of the interior. The scattered dice of small-holdings showed on the slopes and in clearings in the jungle, and the setting sun flashed gold on the bright worms of tumbling rivers and streams. 'Xaymaca' the Arawak Indians had called it – 'The Land of Hills and Rivers'. Bond's heart lifted with the beauty of one of the most fertile islands in the world.

The other side of the mountains was in deep violet shadow. Lights were already twinkling in the foothills and spangling the streets of Kingston, but, beyond, the far arm of the harbour and the airport were still touched with the sun against which the Port Royal lighthouse blinked ineffectually. Now the Constellation was getting its nose down into a wide sweep beyond the harbour. There was a slight thump as the tricycle landing gear extended under the aircraft and locked into position, and a shrill hydraulic whine as the brake flaps slid out of the trailing edge of the wings. Slowly the great aircraft turned in again towards the land and for a moment the setting sun poured gold into the cabin. Then, the plane had dipped below the level of the Blue Mountains and was skimming down towards the single north-south runway. There was a glimpse of a road and telephone wires. Then the concrete, scarred with black skid-marks, was under the belly of the plane and there was the soft double thump of a perfect landing and the roar of reversing props as they taxied in towards the low white airport buildings.

The sticky fingers of the tropics brushed Bond's face as he left the aircraft and walked over to Health and Immigration. He knew that by the time he had got through Customs he would be sweating. He didn't mind. After the rasping cold of London, the stuffy, velvet heat was easily bearable.

Bond's passport described him as 'Import and Export Merchant'.

'What company, sir?'

'Universal Export.'

'Are you here on business or pleasure, sir?'

'Pleasure.'

'I hope you enjoy your stay, sir.' The Negro immigration officer handed Bond his passport with indifference.

'Thank you.'

Bond walked out into the Customs hall. At once he saw the tall brown-skinned man against the barrier. He was wearing the same old faded blue shirt and probably the same khaki twill trousers he had been wearing when Bond first met him five years before.

'Quarrel!'

From behind the barrier the Cayman Islander gave a broad grin. He lifted his right forearm across his eyes in the old salute of the West

Indians. 'How you, cap'n?' he called delightedly.

'I'm fine,' said Bond. 'Just wait till I get my bag through. Got the car?'

'Sure, cap'n.'

The Customs officer who, like most men from the waterfront, knew Quarrel, chalked Bond's bag without opening it and Bond picked it up and went out through the barrier. Quarrel took it from him and held out his right hand. Bond took the warm dry calloused paw and looked into the dark grey eyes that showed descent from a Cromwellian soldier or a pirate of Morgan's time. 'You haven't changed, Quarrel,' he said affectionately. 'How's the turtle fishing?'

'Not so bad, cap'n, an' not so good. Much de same as always.' He looked critically at Bond. 'Yo been sick, or somepun?'

Bond was surprised. 'As a matter of fact I have. But I've been fit for weeks. What made you say that?'

Quarrel was embarrassed. 'Sorry, cap'n,' he said, thinking he might have offended Bond. 'Dere some pain lines in yo face since de las' time.'

'Oh well,' said Bond. 'It was nothing much. But I could do with a spell of your training. I'm not as fit as I ought to be.'

'Shooting, cap'n.'

They were moving towards the exit when there came the sharp crack and flash of a Press camera. A pretty Chinese girl in Jamaican dress was lowering her Speed Graphic. She came up to them. She said with synthetic charm, 'Thank you, gentlemen. I am from the *Daily Gleaner*.' She glanced down at a list in her hand. 'Mister Bond, isn't it? And how long will you be with us, Mister Bond?'

Bond was offhand. This was a bad start. 'In transit,' he said shortly. 'I think you'll find there were more interesting people on the plane.'

'Oh no, I'm sure not, Mister Bond. You look very important. And what hotel will you be staying at?'

Damn, thought Bond. He said 'Myrtle Bank' and moved on.

'Thank you, Mister Bond,' said the tinkling voice. 'I hope you'll enjoy . . .'

They were outside. As they walked towards the parking place Bond said, 'Ever see that girl at the airport before?'

Quarrel reflected. 'Reck'n not, cap'n. But de *Gleaner* have plenty camera gals.'

Bond was vaguely worried. There was no earthly reason why his picture should be wanted by the Press. It was five years since his last adventures on the island, and anyway his name had been kept out of the papers.

They got to the car. It was a black Sunbeam Alpine. Bond looked sharply at it and then at the number plate. Strangways's car. What the hell?' 'Where did you get this, Quarrel?'

'ADC tell me fe to take him, cap'n. Him say hit de only spare car dey have. Why, cap'n? Him no good?'

'Oh, it's all right, Quarrel,' said Bond resignedly. 'Come on, let's get going.'

Bond got into the passenger seat. It was entirely his fault. He might have guessed at the chance of getting this car. But it would certainly put the finger on him and on what he was doing in Jamaica if anyone happened to be interested.

They moved off down the long cactus-fringed road towards the distant lights of Kingston. Normally, Bond would have sat and enjoyed the beauty of it all – the steady zing of the crickets, the rush of warm, scented air, the ceiling of stars, the necklace of yellow light shimmering across the harbour – but now he was cursing his carelessness and knowing what he shouldn't have done.

What he *had* done was to send one signal through the Colonial Office to the Governor. In it he had first asked that the ADC should get Quarrel over from the Cayman Islands for an indefinite period on a salary of ten pounds a week. Quarrel had been with Bond on his last adventure in Jamaica. He was an invaluable handyman with all the fine seaman's qualities of the Cayman Islander, and he was a passport into the lower strata of coloured life which would otherwise be closed to Bond. Everybody loved him and he was a splendid companion. Bond knew that Quarrel was vital if he was to get anywhere on the Strangways case – whether it was a case or just a scandal. Then Bond had asked for a single room and shower at the Blue Hills Hotel, for the loan of a car and for Quarrel to meet him with the car at the airport. Most of this had been wrong. In particular Bond should have taken a taxi to his hotel and made contact with Quarrel later. Then he would have seen the car and had a chance to change it.

As it was, reflected Bond, he might just as well have advertised his visit and its purpose in the *Gleaner*. He sighed. It was the mistakes one made at the beginning of a case that were the worst. They were the irretrievable ones, the ones that got you off on the wrong foot, that gave the enemy the first game. But was there an enemy? Wasn't he being over-cautious? On an impulse Bond turned in his seat. A hundred yards behind were two dim headlights. Most Jamaicans drive with their headlights full on. Bond turned back. He said, 'Quarrel. At the end of the Palisadoes, where the left fork goes to Kingston and right to Morant, I want you to turn quickly down the Morant road and stop at once and turn your lights off. Right? And now go like hell.'

'Okay, cap'n.' Quarrel's voice sounded pleased. He put his foot down to the floorboards. The little car gave a deep growl and tore off down the white road.

Now they were at the end of the straight. The car skidded round the curve where the corner of the harbour bit into the land. Another five hundred yards and they would be at the intersection. Bond looked back. There was no sign of the other car. Here was the signpost. Quarrel did a racing change and hurled the car round on a tight lock. He pulled in to the side and dowsed his lights. Bond turned and waited. At once he heard the roar of a big car at speed. Lights blazed on, looking for them. Then the car was past and tearing on towards Kingston. Bond had time to notice that it was a big American type taxicab and that there was no one in it but the driver. Then it was gone.

The dust settled slowly. They sat for ten minutes saying nothing. Then Bond told Quarrel to turn the car and take the Kingston road. He said, 'I think that car was interested in us, Quarrel. You don't drive an empty taxi back from the airport. It's an expensive run. Keep a watch out. He may find we've fooled him and be waiting for us.'

'Sho ting, cap'n,' said Quarrel happily. This was just the sort of life he had hoped for when he got Bond's message.

They came into the stream of Kingston traffic – buses, cars, horse-drawn carts, pannier-laden donkeys down from the hills, and the hand-drawn barrows selling violent coloured drinks. In the crush it was impossible to say if they were being followed. They turned off to the right and up towards the hills. There were many cars behind them. Any one of them could have been the American taxi. They drove for a quarter of an hour up to Halfway Tree and then on to the Junction Road, the main road across the island. Soon there was a neon sign of a green palm tree and underneath 'Blue Hills. THE hotel'. They drove in and up the drive lined with neatly rounded bushes of bougainvillaea.

A hundred yards higher up the road the black taxi waved the following drivers on and pulled in to the left. It made a U-turn in a break in the traffic and swept back down the hill towards Kingston.

The Blue Hills was a comfortable old-fashioned hotel with modern trimmings. Bond was welcomed with deference because his reservation had been made by King's House. He was shown to a fine corner room with a balcony looking out over the distant sweep of Kingston harbour. Thankfully he took off his London clothes, now moist with perspiration, and went into the glass-fronted shower and turned the cold water full on and stood under it for five minutes during which he washed his hair to remove the last dirt of big-city life. Then he pulled on a pair of Sea Island cotton shorts and, with sensual pleasure at the warm soft air on his nakedness, unpacked his things and rang for the waiter.

Bond ordered a double gin and tonic and one whole green lime. When the drink came he cut the lime in half, dropped the two squeezed halves into the long glass, almost filled the glass with ice cubes and then poured in the tonic. He took the drink out on to the balcony, and sat and looked out across the spectacular view. He thought how wonderful it was to be away from headquarters, and from London, and from hospitals, and to be here, at this moment, doing what he was doing and knowing, as all his senses told him, that he was on a good tough case again.

He sat for a while, luxuriously, letting the gin relax him. He ordered another and drank it down. It was seven-fifteen. He had arranged for Quarrel to pick him up at seven-thirty. They were going to have dinner together. Bond had asked Quarrel to suggest a place. After a moment of embarrassment, Quarrel had said that whenever he wanted to enjoy himself in Kingston he went to a waterfront nightspot called the Joy Boat. 'Hit no great shakes, cap'n,' he had said apologetically, 'but da food an' drinks an' music is good and I got a good fren' dere. Him owns de joint. Dey calls him 'Pus-Feller' seein' how him once fought wit' a big hoctopus.'

Bond smiled to himself at the way Quarrel, like most West Indians, added an 'h' where it wasn't needed and took it off when it was. He went into his room and dressed in his old dark blue tropical worsted suit, a sleeveless white cotton shirt and a black knitted tie, looked in the glass to see that the Walther didn't show under his armpit and went down and out to where the car was waiting.

They swooped down quietly through the soft singing dusk into Kingston and turned to the left along the harbour side. They passed one or two smart restaurants and night clubs from which came the throb and twang of calypso music. There was a stretch of private houses that dwindled into a poor-class shopping centre and then into shacks. Then, where the road curved away from the sea, there was a blaze of golden neon in the shape of a Spanish galleon above green lettering that said 'The Joy Boat'. They pulled into a parking place and Bond followed Quarrel through the gate into a small garden of palm trees growing out of lawn. At the end was the beach and the sea. Tables were dotted about under the palms, and in the centre was a small deserted cement dance floor to one side of which a calypso trio in sequined scarlet shirts was softly improvising on 'Take her to Jamaica where the rum comes from'.

Only half the tables were filled, mostly by coloured people. There was a sprinkling of British and American sailors with their girls. An immensely fat Negro in a smart white dinner jacket left one of the tables and came to meet them.

'Hi, Mister Q. Long time no see. Nice table for two?'

'That's right, Pus-Feller. Closer to da kitchen dan da music.'

The big man chuckled. He led them down towards the sea and placed them at a quiet table under a palm tree that grew out of the base of the restaurant building. 'Drinks gemmun?'

Bond ordered his gin and tonic with a lime, and Quarrel a Red Stripe beer. They scanned the menu and both decided on broiled lobster followed by a rare steak with native vegetables.

The drinks came. The glasses were dripping with condensation. The small fact reminded Bond of other times in hot climates. A few yards away the sea lisped on the flat sand. The three-piece began playing 'Kitch'. Above them the palm fronds clashed softly in the night breeze. A gecko chuckled somewhere in the garden. Bond thought of the London he had left the day before. He said, 'I like this place, Quarrel.'

Quarrel was pleased. 'Him a good fren of mine, da Pus-Feller. Him knows mostly what goes hon hin Kingston case you got hany questions, cap'n. Him come from da Caymans. Him an' me once share a boat. Then him go hoff one day catching boobies' heggs hat Crab Key. Went swimmin' to a rock for more heggs an' dis big hoctopus get him. Dey mos'ly small fellers roun' here but dey come bigger at da Crab seein' how its alongside de Cuba Deep, da deepest waters roun' dese parts. Pus-Feller have himself a bad time wit dis hanimal. Bust one lung cuttin' hisself free. Dat scare him an' him sell me his half of da boat an' come to Kingston. Dat were 'fore da war. Now him rich man whiles I go hon fishin'.' Quarrel chuckled at the quirk of fate.

'Crab Key,' said Bond. 'What sort of a place is that?'

Quarrel looked at him sharply. 'Dat a bad luck place now, cap'n,' he said shortly. 'Chinee gemmun buy hit durin' da war and bring in men and dig bird-dirt. Don's let nobody land dere and don' let no one get hoff. We gives it a wide bert'.'

'Why's that?'

'Him have plenty watchmen. An' guns – machine guns. An' a radar. An' a spottin' plane. Frens o' mine have landed dere and him never been seen again. Dat Chinee keep him island plenty private. Tell da trut', cap'n,' Quarrel was apologetic, 'dat Crab Key scare me plenty.'

Bond said thoughtfully, 'Well, well.'

The food came. They ordered another round of drinks and ate. While they ate, Bond gave Quarrel an outline of the Strangways case. Quarrel listened carefully, occasionally asking questions. He was particularly interested in the birds on Crab Key, and what the watchmen had said, and how the plane was supposed to have crashed. Finally he pushed his plate away. He wiped the back of his hand across his mouth. He took out a cigarette and lit it. He leant forward. 'Cap'n,' he said softly, 'I no mind if hit was birds or butterflies or bees. If dey was on Crab Key and da Commander was stickin' his nose into da business, yo kin bet yo bottom dollar him been mashed. Him and him girl. Da Chinee mash dem for sho.'

Bond looked carefully into the urgent grey eyes. 'What makes you so certain?'

Quarrel spread his hands. To him the answer was simple. 'Dat Chinee love him privacy. Him want to be left alone. I know him kill ma frens order keep folk away from da Crab. Him a mos' powerful man. Him kill hanyone what hinterfere with him.'

'Why?'

'Don' rightly know, cap'n,' said Quarrel indifferently. 'People dem want different tings in dis world. An' what dem want sufficient dem gits.'

A glint of light caught the corner of Bond's eye. He turned quickly. The Chinese girl from the airport was standing in the nearby shadows. Now she was dressed in a tight-fitting sheath of black satin slashed up one side almost to her hip. She had a Leica with a flash attachment in one hand. The other was in a leather case at her side. The hand came out holding a flashbulb. The girl slipped the base into her mouth to wet it and improve the contact and made to screw it into the reflector.

'Get that girl,' said Bond quickly.

In two strides Quarrel was up with her. He held out his hand. 'Evenin', missy,' he said softly.

The girl smiled. She let the Leica hang on the thin strap round her neck. She took Quarrel's hand. Quarrel swung her round like a ballet dancer. Now he had her hand behind her back and she was in the crook of his arm.

She looked up at him angrily. 'Don't. You're hurting.'

Quarrel smiled down into the flashing dark eyes in the pale, almond-shaped face. 'Cap'n like you take a drink wit' we,' he said soothingly. He came back to the table, moving the girl along with him. He hooked a chair out with his foot and sat her down beside him, keeping the grip on her wrist behind her back. They sat bolt upright, like quarrelling lovers.

Bond looked into the pretty, angry little face. 'Good evening. What are you doing here? Why do you want another picture of me?'

'I'm doing the night spots,' the Cupid's bow of a mouth parted persuasively. 'The first picture of you didn't come out. Tell this man to leave me alone.'

'So you work for the *Gleaner*? What's your name?'

'I won't tell you.'

Bond cocked an eyebrow at Quarrel.

Quarrel's eyes narrowed. His hand behind the girl's back turned slowly. The girl struggled like an eel, her teeth clenched on her lower lip. Quarrel went on twisting. Suddenly she said 'Ow!' sharply and gasped, 'I'll tell!' Quarrel eased his grip. The girl looked furiously at Bond: 'Annabel Chung.'

Bond said to Quarrel, 'Call the Pus-Feller.'

Quarrel picked up a fork with his free hand and clanged it against a glass. The big Negro hurried up.

Bond look up at him. 'Ever seen this girl before?'

'Yes, boss. She come here sometimes. She bein' a nuisance? Want for me to send her away?'

'No. We like her,' said Bond amiably, 'but she wants to take a studio portrait of me and I don't know if she's worth the money. Would you call up the *Gleaner* and ask if they've got a photographer called Annabel Chung? If she really is one of their people she ought to be good enough.'

'Sure, boss.' The man hurried away.

Bond smiled at the girl. 'Why didn't you ask that man to rescue you?'

The girl glowered at him.

'I'm sorry to have to exert pressure,' said Bond, 'but my export manager in London said that Kingston was full of shady characters. I'm sure you're not one of them, but I really can't understand why you're so anxious to get my picture. Tell me why.'

'What I told you,' said the girl sulkily. 'It's my job.'

Bond tried other questions. She didn't answer them.

The Pus-Feller came up. 'That's right, boss. Annabel Chung. One of their freelance girls. They say she takes fine pictures. You'll be okay with her.' He looked bland. Studio portrait! Studio bed, more like.

'Thanks,' said Bond. The Negro went away. Bond turned back to the girls. 'Freelance,' he said softly. 'That still doesn't explain who wanted my picture.' His face went cold. 'Now give!'

'No,' said the girl sullenly.

'All right, Quarrel. Go ahead.' Bond sat back. His instincts told him that this was the sixty-four thousand dollar question. If he could get the answer out the girl he might be saved weeks of legwork.

Quarrel's right shoulder started to dip downwards. The girl squirmed towards him to ease the pressure, but he held her body away with his free hand. The girl's face strained towards Quarrel's. Suddenly she spat full in his eyes. Quarrel grinned and increased the twist. The girl's feet kicked wildly under the table. She hissed out words in Chinese. Sweat beaded on her forehead.

'Tell,' said Bond softly. 'Tell and it will stop and we'll be friends and have a drink.' He was getting worried. The girl's arm must be on the verge of breaking.

'—— you.' Suddenly the girl's left hand flew up and into Quarrel's face. Bond was too slow to stop her. Something glinted and there was a sharp explosion. Bond snatched at her arm and dragged it back. Blood was streaming down Quarrel's cheek. Glass and metal tinkled on to the table. She had smashed the flashbulb on Quarrel's face. If she had been able to reach an eye it would have been blinded.

Quarrel's free hand went up and felt his cheek. He put it in front of his eyes and looked at the blood. 'Aha!' There was nothing but admiration and a feline pleasure in his voice. He said equably to Bond. 'We get nuthen out of dis gal, cap'n. She plenty tough. You want fe me to break she's arm?'

'Good God, no.' Bond let go the arm he was holding. 'Let her go.' He felt angry with himself for having hurt the girl and still failed. But he had learned something. Whoever was behind her held his people by a steel chain.

Quarrel brought the girl's right arm from behind her back. He still held on to the wrist. Now he opened the girls' hand. He looked into her eyes. His own were cruel. 'You mark me, Missy. Now I mark you.' He brought up his other hand and took the Mount of Venus, the soft lozenge of flesh in the palm below her thumb, between his thumb and forefinger. He began to squeeze it. Bond could see his knuckle's go white with the pressure. The girl gave a yelp. She hammered at Quarrel's hand and then at his face. Quarrel grinned and squeezed harder. Suddenly he let go. The girl shot to her feet and backed away from the table, her bruised hand at her mouth. She took her hand down and hissed furiously. 'He'll get you, you bastards!' Then, her Leica dangling, she ran off through the trees.

Quarrel laughed shortly. He took a napkin and wiped it down his cheek and threw it on the ground and took up another. He said to Bond, 'She's Love Moun' be sore long after ma face done get healed. Dat a fine piece of a woman, de Love Moun'. When him fat like wit' dat girl you kin tell her'll be good in bed. You know dat, cap'n?'

'No,' said Bond. 'That'e new to me.'

'Sho ting. Dat piece of da han' most hindicative. Don' you worry 'bout she,' he added, noticing the dubious expression on Bond's face. 'Hers got nuttin but a big bruise on she's Love Moun'. But boy, was dat a fat Love Moun'! I come back after dat girl sometime, see if ma teory is troof.'

Appropriately the band started playing 'Don' touch me tomato'. Bond said 'Quarrel, it's time you married and settled down. And you leave that girl alone or you'll get a knife between your ribs. Now come on. We'll get the check and go. It's three o'clock in the morning in London where I was yesterday. I need a night's sleep. You've got to start getting me into training. I think I'm going to need it. And it's about time you put some plaster on that cheek of yours. She's written her name and address on it.'

Quarrel grunted reminiscently. He said with quiet pleasure, 'Dat were some tough baby.' He picked up a fork and clanged it against his glass.

CHAPTER 5

FACTS AND FIGURES

'He'll get you. . . . He'll get you. . . . He'll get you, you bastards.'

The words were still ringing in Bond's brain the next day as he sat on his balcony and ate a delicious breakfast and gazed out across the riot of tropical gardens to Kingston, five miles below him.

Now he was sure that Strangways and the girl had been killed. Someone had needed to stop them looking any further into his business, so he had killed them. The same person knew or suspected that the Secret Service would follow up Strangways's disappearance. Somehow he had known that Bond had been given the job. He had wanted a picture of Bond and he had wanted to know where Bond was staying. He would be keeping an eye on Bond to see if Bond picked up any of the leads that had led to Strangways's death. If Bond did so, Bond would also have to be eliminated. There would be a car smash or a street fight or some other innocent death. And how, Bond wondered, would this person react to their treatment of the Chung girl? If he was as ruthless as Bond supposed, that would be enough. It showed that Bond was on to something. Perhaps Strangways had made a preliminary report to London before he was killed. Perhaps someone had leaked. The enemy would be foolish to take chances. If he had any sense, after the Chung incident, he would deal with Bond and perhaps also with Quarrel without delay.

Bond lit his first cigarette of the day – the first Royal Blend he had smoked for five years – and let the smoke come out between his teeth in a luxurious hiss. That was his 'Enemy Appreciation'. Now, who was his enemy?

Well, there was only one candidate, and a pretty insubstantial one at that, Doctor No, Doctor Julius No, the German Chinese who owned Crab Key and made his money out of guano. There had been nothing on this man in Records and a signal to the FBI had been negative. The affair of the roseate spoonbills and the trouble with the Audubon Society meant precisely nothing except, as M had said, that a lot of old women had got excited about some pink storks. All the same, four people had died because of these storks and, most significant of all to Bond, Quarrel was scared of Doctor No and his island. That was very odd indeed. Cayman Islanders, least of all Quarrel, did not scare easily. And why had Doctor No got this mania for privacy? Why did he go to such expense and trouble to keep people away from his guano island? Guano – bird dung. Who wanted the stuff? How valuable was it? Bond was due to call on the Governor at ten o'clock. After he had made his number he would get hold of the Colonial Secretary and try and find out all about the damned stuff and about Crab Key and, if possible, about Doctor No.

There was a double knock on the door. Bond got up and unlocked it. It was Quarrel, his left cheek decorated with a piratical cross of sticking-plaster. 'Mornin', cap'n. Yo said eight-tirty.'

'Yes, come on in, Quarrel. We've got a busy day. Had some breakfast?'

'Yes, tank you, cap'n. Salt fish an' ackee an' a tot of rum.'

'Good God,' said Bond. 'That's tough stuff to start the day on.'

'Mos' refreshin',' said Quarrel stolidly.

They sat down outside on the balcony. Bond offered Quarrel a cigarette and lit one himself. 'Now then,' he said. 'I'll be spending most of the day at King's House and perhaps at the Jamaica Institute. I shan't need you till tomorrow morning, but there are some things for you to do downtown. All right?'

'Okay, cap'n. Jes' yo say.'

'First of all, that car of ours is hot. We've got to get rid of it. Go down to Motta's or one of the other hire people and pick up the newest and best little self-drive car you can find, the one with the least mileage. Saloon. Take it for a month. Right? Then hunt around the waterfront and find two men who look as near as possible like us. One must be able to drive a car. Buy them both clothes, at least for their top halves, that look like ours. And the sort of hats we might wear. Say we want a car taken over to Montego tomorrow morning – by the Spanish Town, Ocho Rios road. To be left at Levy's garage there. Ring up Levy and tell him to expect it and keep it for us. Right?'

Quarrel grinned. 'Yo want fox someone?'

'That's right. They'll get ten pounds each. Say I'm a rich American and I want my car to arrive in Montego Bay driven by a respectable couple of men. Make me out a bit mad. They must be here at six o'clock tomorrow morning. You'll be here with the other car. See they look the part and send them off in the Sunbeam with the roof down. Right?'

'Okay, cap'n.'

'What's happened to that house we had on the North Shore last time – Beau Desert at Morgan's Harbour? Do you know if it's let?'

'Couldn't say, cap'n. Hit's well away from de tourist places and dey askin' a big rent for it.'

'Well, go to Graham Associates and see if you can rent it for a month, or another bungalow near by. I don't mind what you pay. Say it's for a rich American, Mr James. Get the keys and pay the rent and say I'll write and confirm. I can telephone them if they want more details.' Bond reached into his hip pocket and brought out a thick wad of notes. He handed half of it to Quarrel. 'Here's two hundred pounds. That should cover all this. Get in touch if you want some more. You know where I'll be.'

'Tanks, cap'n,' said Quarrel, awestruck by the big sum. He stowed it away inside his blue shirt and buttoned the shirt up to his neck. 'Anyting helse?'

'No, but take a lot of trouble about not being followed. Leave the car somewhere downtown and walk to these places. And watch out particularly for any Chinese near you.' Bond got up and they went to the door. 'See you tomorrow morning at six-fifteen and we'll get over to the North Coast. As far as I can see that's going to be our base for a while.'

Quarrel nodded. His face was enigmatic. He said 'Okay, cap'n' and went off down the corridor.

Half an hour later Bond went downstairs and took a taxi to King's House. He didn't sign the Governor's book in the cool hall. He was put in a waiting room for the quarter of an hour necessary to show him that he was unimportant. Then the ADC came for him and took him up to the Governor's study on the first floor.

It was a large cool room smelling of cigar smoke. The Acting

Governor, in a cream tussore suit and an appropriate wing collar and spotted bow tie, was sitting at a broad mahogany desk on which there was nothing but the *Daily Gleaner*, the *Times Weekly* and a bowl of hibiscus blossoms. His hands lay flat on the desk in front of him. He was sixtyish with a red, rather petulant face and bright, bitter blue eyes. He didn't smile or get up. He said, 'Good morning, Mr—er—Bond. Please sit down.'

Bond took the chair across the desk from the Governor and sat down. He said, 'Good morning, sir,' and waited. A friend at the Colonial Office had told him his reception would be frigid. 'He's nearly at retiring age. Only an interim appointment. We had to find an Acting Governor to take over at short notice when Sir Hugh Foot was promoted. Foot was a great success. This man's not even trying to compete. He knows he's only got the job for a few months while we find someone to replace Foot. This man's been passed over for the Governor Generalship of Rhodesia. Now all he wants is to retire and get some directorships in the City. Last thing he wants is any trouble in Jamaica. He keeps on trying to close this Strangways case of yours. Won't like you ferreting about.'

The Governor cleared his throat. He recognized that Bond wasn't one of the servile ones. 'You wanted to see me?'

'Just to make my number sir,' said Bond equably. 'I'm here on the Strangways case. I think you had a signal from the Secretary of State.' This was a reminder that the people behind Bond were powerful people. Bond didn't like attempts to squash him or his Service.

'I recall the signal. And what can I do for you? So far as we're concerned here the case is closed.'

'In what way "closed", sir?'

The Governor said roughly, 'Strangways obviously did a bunk with the girl. Unbalanced sort of fellow at the best of times. Some of your—er—colleagues don't seem to be able to leave women alone.' The Governor clearly included Bond. 'Had to bail the chap out of various scandals before now. Doesn't do the Colony any good, Mr—er—Bond. Hope your people will be sending us a rather better type of man to take his place. That is,' he added coldly, 'if a Regional Control man is really needed here. Personally I have every confidence in our police.'

Bond smiled sympathetically. 'I'll report your views, sir. I expect my Chief will like to discuss them with the Minister of Defence and the Secretary of State. Naturally, if you would like to take over these extra duties it will be a saving in manpower so far as my Service is concerned. I'm sure the Jamaican Constabulary is more efficient.'

The Governor looked at Bond suspiciously. Perhaps he had better handle this man a bit more carefully. 'This is an informal discussion, Mr Bond. When I have decided on my views I will communicate them myself to the Secretary of State. In the meantime, is there anyone you wish to see on my staff?'

'I'd like to have a word with the Colonial Secretary, sir.'

'Really? And why, pray?'

'There's been some trouble on Crab Key. Something about a bird sanctuary. The case was passed to us by the Colonial Office. My Chief asked me to look into it while I'm here.'

The Governor looked relieved. 'Certainly, certainly. I'll see that Mr Pleydell-Smith receives you straight away. So you feel we can leave the Strangways case to sort itself out? They'll turn up before long, never fear.' He reached over and rang a bell. The ADC came in. 'This gentleman would like to see the Colonial Secretary, ADC. Take him along, would you? I'll call Mr Pleydell-Smith myself and ask him to make himself available.' He got up and came round the desk. He held out his hand. 'Goodbye, then Mr Bond. And I'm so glad we see eye to eye. Crab Key, eh? Never been there myself, but I'm sure it would repay a visit.'

Bond shook hands. 'That was what I was thinking. Goodbye, sir.'

'Goodbye, goodbye.' The Governor watched Bond's back retreating out of the door and himself returned well satisfied to his desk. 'Young whippersnapper,' he said to the empty room. He sat down and said a few peremptory words down the telephone to the Colonial Secretary. Then he picked up the *Times Weekly* and turned to the Stock Exchange prices.

The Colonial Secretary was a youngish shaggy-haired man with bright, boyish eyes. He was one of those nervous pipe smokers who are constantly patting their pockets for matches, shaking the box to see how many are left in it, or knocking the dottle out of their pipes. After he had gone through this routine two or three times in his first ten minutes with Bond, Bond wondered if he ever got any smoke into his lungs at all.

After pumping energetically at Bond's hand and waving vaguely at a chair, Pleydell-Smith walked up and down the room scratching his temple with the stem of his pipe. 'Bond. Bond. Bond! Rings a bell. Now let me see. Yes, by jove! You were the chap who was mixed up in that treasure business here. By jove, yes! Four, five years ago. Found the file lying around only the other day. Splendid show. What a lark! I say, wish you'd start another bonfire like that here. Stir the place up a bit. All they think of nowadays is Federation and their bloody self-importance. Self-determination indeed! They can't even run a bus service. And the colour problem! My dear chap, there's far more colour problem between the straight-haired and the crinkly-haired Jamaicans than there is between me and my black cook. However—' Pleydell-Smith came to rest beside his desk. He sat down opposite Bond and draped one leg over the arm of his chair. Reaching for a tobacco jar with the arms of King's College, Cambridge, on it, he dug into it and started filling his pipe – 'I mean to say I don't want to bore you with all that. You go ahead and bore me. What's your problem? Glad to help. I bet it's more interesting than this muck,' he waved at the pile of papers in his *In* tray.

Bond grinned at him. This was more like it. He had found an ally, and an intelligent one at that. 'Well,' he said seriously, 'I'm here on the Strangways case. But first of all I want to ask you a question that may sound odd. Exactly how did you come to be looking at that other case of mine? You say you found the file lying about. How was that? Had someone asked for it? I don't want to be indiscreet, so don't answer if you don't want to. I'm just inquisitive.'

Pleydell-Smith cocked an eye at him. 'I suppose that's your job.' He reflected, gazing at the ceiling. 'Well, now I come to think of it I saw it on my secretary's desk. She's a new girl. Said she was trying to get up to date with the files. Mark you,' the Colonial Secretary hastened to exonerate his girl, 'there were plenty of other files on her desk. It was just this one that caught my eye.'

'Oh, I see,' said Bond. 'It was like that.' He smiled apologetically. 'Sorry, but various people seem to be rather interested in me being here. What I really wanted to talk to you about was Crab Key. Anything you know about the place. And about this Chinaman, Doctor No, who bought it. And anything you can tell me about his guano business. Rather a tall order, I'm afraid, but any scraps will help.'

Pleydell-Smith laughed shortly through the stem of his pipe. He jerked the pipe out of his mouth and talked while he tamped down the burning tobacco with his matchbox. 'Bitten off a bit more than you can chew on guano. Talk to you for hours about it. Started in the Consular before I transferred to the Colonial Office. First job was in Peru. Had a lot to do with their people who administer the whole trade – *Compania Aministradora del Guano*. Nice people.' The pipe was going now and Pleydell-Smith threw his matchbox down on the table. 'As for the rest, it's just a question of getting the file.' He rang a bell. In a minute the door opened behind Bond. 'Miss Taro, the file on Crab Key, please. The one on the sale of the place and the other one on that warden fellow who turned up before Christmas. Miss Longfellow will know where to find them.'

A soft voice said, 'Yes, sir.' Bond heard the door close.

'Now then, guano.' Pleydell-Smith tilted his chair back. Bond prepared to be bored. 'As you know, it's bird dung. Comes from the rear end of two birds, the masked booby and the guanay. So far as Crab Key is concerned, it's only the guanay, otherwise known as the green cormorant, same bird as you find in England. The guanay is a machine for converting fish into guano. They eat mostly anchovies. Just to show you how much fish they eat, they've found up to seventy anchovies inside one bird!' Pleydell-Smith took out his pipe and pointed it impressively at Bond. 'The whole population of Peru eats four thousand tons of fish a year. The sea birds of the country eat five hundred thousand tons!'

Bond pursed his lips to show he was impressed. 'Really.'

'Well, now,' continued the Colonial Secretary, 'every day each one of these hundreds of thousands of guarays eat a pound or so of fish and deposit an ounce of guano on the guanera – that's the guano island.'

Bond interrupted, 'Why don't they do it in the sea?'

'Don't know.' Pleydell-Smith took the question and turned it over in his mind. 'Never occurred to me. Anyway they don't. They do it on the land and they've been doing it since before Genesis. That makes the hell of a lot of bird dung – millions of tons of it on the Pescadores and the other guanera. Then, around 1850 someone discovered it was the greatest natural fertilizer in the world – stuffed with nitrates and phosphates and what have you. And the ships and the men came to the guaneras and simply ravaged them for twenty years or more. It's a time known as the "Saturnalia" in Peru. It was like the Klondyke. People fought over the muck, hi-jacked each other's ships, shot the workers, sold phoney maps of secret guano islands – anything you like. And people made fortunes out of the stuff.'

'Where does Crab Key come in?' Bond wanted to get down to cases.

'That was the only worthwhile guanera so far north. It was worked too, God knows who by. But the stuff had a low nitrate content. Water's not as rich round here as it is down along the Humboldt Current. So the fish aren't so rich in chemicals. So the guano isn't so rich either. Crab Key got worked on and off when the price was high enough, but the whole industry went bust, with Crab Key and the other poor-quality deposits in the van, when the Germans invented artificial chemical manure. By this time Peru had realized that she had squandered a fantastic capital asset and she set about organizing the remains of the industry and protecting the guanera. She nationalized the industry and protected the birds, and slowly, very slowly, the supplies built up again. Then people found that there were snags about the German stuff, it impoverishes the soil, which guano doesn't do, and gradually the price of guano improved and the industry staggered back to its feet. Now it's going fine, except that Peru keeps most of the guano to herself, for her own agriculture. And that was where Crab Key came in again.'

'Ah.'

'Yes,' said Pleydell-Smith, patting his pockets for the matches, finding them on the desk, shaking them against his ear, and starting his pipe-filling routine, 'at the beginning of the war, this Chinaman, who must be a wily devil, by the way, got the idea that he could make a good thing out of the old guanera on Crab Key. The price was about fifty dollars a ton on this side of the Atlantic and he bought the island from us, for about ten thousand pounds as I recall it, brought in labour and got to work. Been working it ever since. Must have made a fortune. He ships direct to Europe, to Antwerp. They send him a ship once a month. He's installed the latest crushers and separators. Sweats his labour, I daresay. To make a decent profit, he'd have to. Particularly now. Last year I heard he was only getting about thirty-eight to forty dollars a ton c.i.f. Antwerp. God knows what he must pay his labour to make a profit at that price. I've never been able to find out. He runs that place like a fortress – sort of forced labour camp. No one ever gets off it. I've heard some funny rumours, but no one's ever complained. It's his island, of course, and he can do what he likes on it.'

Bond hunted for clues. 'Would it really be so valuable to him, this place? What do you suppose it's worth?'

Pleydell-Smith said, 'The guanay is the most valuable bird in the world. Each pair produces about two dollars' worth of guano in a year without any expense to the owner. Each female lays an average of three eggs and raises two young. Two broods a year. Say they're worth fifteen dollars a pair, and say there are one hundred thousand birds on Crab Key, which is a reasonable guess on the old figures we have. That makes his birds worth a million and a half dollars. Pretty valuable property. Add the value of the installations, say another million, and you've got a small fortune on that hideous little place. Which reminds me,' Pleydell-Smith pressed the bell, 'what the hell has happened to those files? You'll find all the dope you want in them.'

The door opened behind Bond.

Pleydell-Smith said irritably, 'Really, Miss Taro. What about those files?'

'Very sorry, sir,' said the soft voice. 'But we can't find them anywhere.'

'What do you mean "can't find them"? Who had them last?'

'Commander Strangways, sir.'

'Well, I remember distinctly him bringing them back to this room. What happened to them then?'

'Can't say, sir,' the voice was unemotional. 'The covers are there but there's nothing inside them.'

Bond turned in his chair. He glanced at the girl and turned back. He smiled grimly to himself. He knew where the files had gone. He also knew why the old file on himself had been out on the Secretary's desk. He also guessed how the particular significance of 'James Bond, Import and Export Merchant' seemed to have leaked out of King's House, the only place where the significance was known.

Like Doctor No, like Miss Annabel Chung, the demure, efficient-looking little secretary in the horn-rimmed glasses was a Chinese.

CHAPTER 6

THE FINGER ON THE TRIGGER

The Colonial Secretary gave Bond lunch at Queen's Club. They sat in a corner of the elegant mahogany-panelled dining-room with its four big ceiling fans and gossiped about Jamaica. By the time coffee came, Pleydell-Smith was delving well below the surface of the prosperous, peaceful island the world knows.

'It's like this.' He began his antics with the pipe. 'The Jamaican is a kindly lazy man with the virtues and vices of a child. He lives on a very rich island but he doesn't get rich from it. He doesn't know how to and he's too lazy. The British come and go and take the easy pickings, but for about two hundred years no Englishman has made a fortune out here. He doesn't stay long enough. He takes a fat cut and leaves. It's the Portuguese Jews who make the most. They came here with the British and they've stayed. But they're snobs and they spend too much of their fortunes on building fine houses and giving dances. They're the names that fill the social column in the *Gleaner* when the tourists have gone. They're in rum and tobacco and they represent the big British firms over here – motor cars, insurance and so forth. Then come the Syrians, very rich too, but not such good businessmen. They have most of the stores and some of the best hotels. They're not a very good risk. Get over-stocked and have to have an occasional fire to get liquid again. Then there are the Indians with their usual flashy trade in soft goods and the like. They're not much of a lot. Finally there are the Chinese, solid, compact, discreet – the most powerful clique in Jamaica. They've got the bakeries and the laundries and the best food stores. They keep to themselves and keep their strain pure.' Pleydell-Smith laughed. 'Not that they don't take the black girls when they want them. You can see the result all over Kingston – Chigroes – Chinese Negroes and Negresses. The Chigroes are a tough, forgotten race. They look down on the Negroes and the Chinese look down on them. One day they may become a nuisance. They've got some of the intelligence of the Chinese and most of the vices of the black man. The police have a lot of trouble with them.'

Bond said, 'That secretary of yours. Would she be one of them?'

'That's right. Bright girl and very efficient. Had her for about six months. She was far the best of the ones that answered our advertisement.'

'She looks bright,' said Bond non-committally. 'Are they organized, these people? Is there some head of the Chinese Negro community?'

'Not yet. But someone'll get hold of them one of these days. They'd be a useful little pressure group.' Pleydell-Smith glanced at his watch. 'That reminds me. Must be getting along. Got to go and read the riot act about those files. Can't think what happened to them. I distinctly remember . . .' He broke off. 'However, main point is that I haven't been able to give you much dope about Crab Key and this doctor fellow. But I can tell you there wasn't much you'd have found out from the files. He seems to have been a pleasant spoken chap. Very businesslike. Then there was that argument with the Audubon Society. I gather you know all about that. As for the place itself, there was nothing on the files but one or two pre-war reports and a copy of the last ordnance survey. God-forsaken bloody place it sounds. Nothing but miles of mangrove swamps and a huge mountain of bird dung at one end. But you said you were going down to the Institute. Why don't I take you there and introduce you to the fellow who runs the map section?'

An hour later Bond was ensconced in a corner of a sombre room with the ordnance survey map of Crab Key, dated 1910, spread out on a table in front of him. He had a sheet of the Institute's writing-paper and had made a rough sketch-map and was jotting down the salient points.

The overall area of the island was about fifty square miles. Three-quarters of this, to the east, was swamp and shallow lake. From the lake a flat river meandered down to the sea and came out halfway along the south coast into a small sandy bay. Bond guessed that somewhere at the headwaters of the river would be a likely spot for the Audubon wardens to have chosen for their camp. To the west, the island rose steeply to a hill stated to be five hundred feet high and ended abruptly with what appeared to be a sheer drop to the sea. A dotted line led from this hill to a box in the corner of the map which contained the words *Guano deposits. Last workings 1880.*

There was no sign of a road, or even of a track on the island, and no sign of a house. The relief map showed that the island looked rather like a swimming water rat – a flat spine rising sharply to the head – heading west. It appeared to be about thirty miles due north of Galina Point on the north shore of Jamaica and about sixty miles south of Cuba.

Little else could be gleaned from the map. Crab Key was surrounded by shoal water except below the western cliff where the nearest marking was five hundred fathoms. After that came the plunge into the Cuba Deep. Bond folded the map and handed it in to the librarian.

Suddenly he felt exhausted. It was only four o'clock, but it was roasting in Kingston and his shirt was sticking to him. Bond walked out of the Institute and found a taxi and went back up into the cool hills to his hotel. He was well satisfied with his day, but nothing else could be done on this side of the island. He would spend a quiet evening at his hotel and be ready to get up early next morning and be away.

Bond went to the reception desk to see if there was a message from Quarrel. 'No messages, sir,' said the girl. 'But a basket of fruit came from King's House. Just after lunch. The messenger took it up to your room.'

'What sort of messenger?'

'Coloured man, sir. Said he was from the ADC's office.'

'Thank you.' Bond took his key and went up the stairs to the first floor. It was ridiculously improbable. His hand on the gun under his coat, Bond softly approached the door. He turned the key and kicked the door open. The empty room yawned at him. Bond shut and locked the door. On his dressing table was a large, ornate basket of fruit – tangerines, grapefruit, pink bananas, soursop, star-apples and even a couple of hot-house nectarines. Attached to a broad ribbon on the handle was a white envelope. Bond removed it and held it up to the light. He opened it. On a plain sheet of expensive white writing paper was typed 'With the Compliments of His Excellency the Governor'.

Bond snorted. He stood looking at the fruit. He bent his ear to it and listened. He then took the basket by the handle and tipped its contents out on to the floor. The fruit bounced and rolled over the coconut matting. There was nothing but fruit in the basket. Bond grinned at his precautions. There was a last possibility. He picked up one of the nectarines, the most likely for a greedy man to choose first, and took it into the bathroom. He dropped it in the washbasin and went back to the bedroom and, after inspecting the lock, unlocked the wardrobe. Gingerly he lifted out his suitcase and stood it in the middle of the room. He knelt down and looked for the traces of talcum powder he had dusted round the two locks. They were smeared and there was minute scratches round the keyholes. Bond sourly examined the marks. These people were not as careful as some others he had had to deal with. He unlocked the case and stood it up on end. There were four innocent copper studs in the welting at the front right-hand corner of the lid. Bond prised at the top one of these studs with his nail and eased it out. He took hold of it and pulled out three feet of stick steel wire and put it on the floor beside him. This wire threaded through small wire loops inside the lid and sewed the case shut. Bond lifted the lid and verified that nothing had been disturbed. From his 'tool case' he took out a jeweller's glass and went back into the bathroom and switched on the light over the shaving mirror. He screwed the glass into his eye and gingerly picked the nectarine out of the washbasin and revolved it slowly between finger and thumb.

Bond stopped turning the nectarine. He had come to a minute pinhole, its edges faintly discoloured brown. It was in the crevice of the fruit, invisible except under a magnifying glass. Bond put the nectarine down in the washbasin. He stood for a moment and looked thoughtfully into his eyes in the mirror.

So it *was* war. Well, well. How very interesting. Bond felt the slight tautening of the skin at the base of his stomach. He smiled thinly at his reflection in the mirror. So his instincts and his reasoning had been correct. Strangways and the girl had been murdered and their records destroyed because they had got too hot on the trail. Then Bond had come on the scene and, thanks to Miss Taro, they had been waiting for him. Miss Chung, and perhaps the taxi driver, had picked up the scent. He had been traced to the Blue Hills hotel. The first shot had been fired. There would be others. And whose finger was on the trigger? Who had got him so accurately in his sights? Bond's mind was made up. The evidence was nil. But he was certain of it. This was long range fire, from Crab Key. The man behind the gun was Doctor No.

Bond walked back into the bedroom. One by one he picked up the fruit and took each piece back to the bathroom and examined it through his glass. The pin-prick was always there, concealed in the stalk-hole or a crevice. Bond rang down and asked for a cardboard box and paper and string. He packed the fruit carefully in the box and picked up the telephone and called King's House. He asked for the Colonial Secretary.

'That you, Pleydell-Smith? James Bond speaking. Sorry to bother you. Got a bit of a problem. Is there a public analyst in Kingston? I see. Well, I've got something I want analysed. If I sent the box down to you, would you be very kind and pass it on to this chap? I don't want my name to come into this. All right? I'll explain later. When you get this report would you send me a short telegram telling me the answer? I'll be at Beau Desert, over at Morgan's Harbour, for the next week or so. Be glad if you'd keep that to yourself too. Sorry to be so damned mysterious. I'll explain everything when I see you next. I expect you'll get a clue when you see what the analyst has to say. And by the way, tell him to handle the specimens carefully, would you. Warn him there's more in them than meets the eye. Very many thanks. Lucky I met you this morning. Goodbye.'

Bond addressed the parcel and went down and paid a taxi to deliver it at once to King's House. It was six o'clock. He went back to his room and had a shower and changed and ordered his first drink. He was about to take it out on the balcony when the telephone rang. It was Quarrel.

'Everyting fixed, cap'n.'

'Everything? That's wonderful. That house all right?'

'Everyting okay.' Quarrel repeated, his voice careful. 'See yo as yo done said, cap'n.'

'Fine,' said Bond. He was impressed with Quarrel's efficiency and a sense of security. He put down the telephone and went out on to the balcony.

The sun was just setting. The wave of violet shadow was creeping down towards the town and the harbour. When it hits the town, thought Bond, the lights will go on. It happened as he had expected. Above him there was the noise of a plane. It came into sight, a Super Constellation, the same flight that Bond had been on the night before. Bond watched it sweep out over the sea and then turn and come in to land at the Palisadoes airport. What a long way he had come since that moment, only twenty-four hours before, when the door of the plane had clanged open and the loudspeaker had said, 'This is Kingston, Jamaica. Will passengers please remain seated until the aircraft has been cleared by the Health Authorities.'

Should he tell M how the picture had changed? Should he make a report to the Governor? Bond thought of the Governor and dismissed the idea. But what about M? Bond had his own cipher. He could easily send M a signal through the Colonial Office. What would he say to M? That Doctor No had sent him some poisoned fruit? But he didn't even know that it was poisoned, or, for the matter of that, that it had come from Doctor No. Bond could see M's face as he read the signal. He saw him press down the lever on the intercom: 'Chief of Staff, 007's gone round the bend. Says someone's been trying to feed him a poisoned banana. Fellow's lost his nerve. Been in hospital too long. Better call him home.'

Bond smiled to himself. He got up and rang down for another drink. It wouldn't be quite like that, of course. But still . . . No, he'd wait until he had something more to show. Of course if something went badly wrong, and he hadn't sent a warning, he'd be in trouble. It was up to him to see that nothing did go wrong.

Bond drank his second drink and thought over the details of his plan. Then he went down and had dinner in the half-deserted dining-room and read the *Handbook of the West Indies*. By nine o'clock he was half asleep. He went back to his room and packed his bag ready for the morning. He telephoned down and arranged to be called at five-thirty. Then he bolted the door on the inside, and also shut and bolted the slatted jalousies across the windows. It would mean a hot, stuffy night. That couldn't be helped. Bond climbed naked under the single cotton sheet and turned over on his left side and slipped his right hand on to the butt of the Walther PPK under the pillow. In five minutes he was asleep.

The next thing Bond knew was that it was three o'clock in the morning. He knew it was three o'clock because the luminous dial of his watch was close to his face. He lay absolutely still. There was not a sound in the room. He strained his ears. Outside, too, it was deathly quiet. Far in the distance a dog started to bark. Other dogs joined in and there was a brief hysterical chorus which stopped as suddenly as it had begun. Then it was quite quiet again. The moon coming through the slats in the jalousies threw black and white bars across the corner of the room next to his bed. It was as if he was lying in a cage. What had woken him up? Bond moved softly, preparing to slip out of bed.

Bond stopped moving. He stopped as dead as a live man can.

Something had stirred on his right ankle. Now it was moving up the inside of his shin. Bond could feel the hairs on his leg being parted. It was an insect of some sort. A very big one. It was long, five or six inches – as long as his hand. He could feel dozens of tiny feet lightly touching his skin. What was it?

Then Bond heard something he had never heard before – the sound of the hair on his head rasping up on the pillow. Bond analysed the noise. It couldn't be! It simply couldn't! Yes, his hair was standing on end. Bond could even feel the cool air reaching his scalp between the hairs. How extraordinary! How very extraordinary! He had always thought it was a figure of speech. But why? Why was it happening to him?

The thing on his leg moved. Suddenly Bond realized that he was afraid, terrified. His instincts, even before they had communicated with his brain, had told his body that he had a centipede on him.

Bond lay frozen. He had once seen a tropical centipede in a bottle of spirit on the shelf in a museum. It had been pale brown and very flat and five or six inches long – about the length of this one. On either side of the blunt head there had been curved poison claws. The label on the bottle had said that its poison was mortal if it hit an artery. Bond had looked curiously at the corkscrew of dead cuticle and had moved on.

The centipede had reached his knee. It was starting up his thigh. Whatever happened he mustn't move, mustn't even tremble. Bond's whole consciousness had drained down to the two rows of softly creeping feet. Now they had reached his flank. God, it was turning down towards his groin! Bond set his teeth! Supposing it liked the warmth there! Supposing it tried to crawl into the crevices! Could he stand it? Supposing it chose that place to bite? Bond could feel it questing amongst the first hairs. It tickled. The skin on Bond's belly fluttered. There was nothing he could do to control it. But now the thing was turning up and along his stomach. Its feet were gripping tighter to prevent it falling. Now it was at his heart. If it bit there, surely it would kill him. The centipede trampled steadily on through the thin hairs on Bond's right breast up to his collar bone. It stopped. What was it doing? Bond could feel the blunt head questing blindly to and fro. What was it looking for? Was there room between his skin and the sheet for it to get through? Dare he lift the sheet an inch to help it. No. Never! The animal was at the base of his jugular. Perhaps it was intrigued by the heavy pulse there. Christ, if only he could control the pumping of his blood. Damn you! Bond tried to communicate with the centipede. It's nothing. It's not dangerous, that pulse. It means you no harm. Get on out into the the fresh air!

As if the beast had heard, it moved on up the column of the neck and into the stubble on Bond's chin. Now it was at the corner of his mouth, tickling madly. On it went, up along the nose. Now he could feel its whole weight and length. Softly Bond closed his eyes. Two by two the pairs of feet, moving alternately, trampled across his right eyelid. When it got off his eye, should he take a chance and shake it off – rely on its feet slipping in his sweat? No, for God's sake! The grip of the feet was endless. He might shake one lot off, but not the rest.

With incredible deliberation the huge insect ambled across Bond's forehead. It stopped below the hair. What the hell was it doing now?

Bond could feel it nuzzling at his skin. It was drinking! Drinking the beads of salt sweat. Bond was sure of it. For minutes it hardly moved. Bond felt weak with the tension. He could feel the sweat pouring off the rest of his body on to the sheet. In a second his limbs would start to tremble. He could feel it coming on. He would start to shake with an ague of fear. Could he control it, could he? Bond lay and waited, the breath coming softly through his open, snarling mouth.

The centipede started to move again. It walked into the forest of hair. Bond could feel the roots being pushed aside as it forced its way along. Would it like it there? Would it settle down? How did centipedes sleep? Curled up, or at full length? The tiny centipedes he had known as a child, the ones that always seemed to find their way up the plughole into the empty bath, curled up when you touched them. Now it had come to where his head lay against the sheet. Would it walk out on to the pillow or would it stay on in the warm forest? The centipede stopped. Out! OUT! Bond's nerves screamed at it.

The centipede stirred. Slowly it walked out of his hair on to the pillow.

Bond waited a second. Now he could hear the rows of feet picking softly at the cotton. It was a tiny scraping noise, like soft fingernails.

With a crash that shook the room Bond's body jackknifed out of bed and on to the floor.

At once Bond was on his feet and at the door. He turned on the light. He found he was shaking uncontrollably. He staggered to the bed. There it was crawling out of sight over the edge of the pillow. Bond's first instinct was to twitch the pillow on to the floor. He controlled himself, waiting for his nerves to quieten. Then softly, deliberately, he picked up the pillow by one corner and walked into the middle of the room and dropped it. The centipede came out from under the pillow. It started to snake swiftly across the matting. Now Bond was uninterested. He looked round for something to kill it with. Slowly he went and picked up a shoe and came back. The danger was past. His mind was now wondering how the centipede had got into his bed. He lifted the shoe and slowly, almost carelessly, smashed it down. He heard the crack of the hard carapace.

Bond lifted the shoe.

The centipede was whipping from side to side in its agony – five inches of grey-brown, shiny death. Bond hit it again. It burst open, yellowly.

Bond dropped the shoe and ran for the bathroom and was violently sick.

CHAPTER 7

NIGHT PASSAGE

'By the way, Quarrel—' Bond dared a bus with 'Brown Bomber' painted above its windshield. The bus pulled over and roared on down the hill towards Kingston sounding a furious chord on its triple windhorn to restore the driver's ego, '—what do you know about centipedes?'

'Centipedes, cap'n?' Quarrel squinted sideways for a clue to the question. Bond's expression was casual. 'Well, we got some bad ones here in Jamaica. Tree, fo, five inches long. Dey kills folks. Dey mos'ly lives in de old houses in Kingston. Dey loves de rotten wood an' de mouldy places. Dey hoperates mos'ly at night. Why, cap'n? Yo seen one?'

Bond dodged the question. He had also not told Quarrel about the fruit. Quarrel was a tough man, but there was no reason to sow the seeds of fear. 'Would you expect to find one in a modern house, for instance? In your shoe, or in a drawer, or in your bed?'

'Nossir.' Quarrel's voice was definite. 'Not hunless dem put dere a purpose. Dese hinsecks love de holes and de crannies. Dey not love de clean places. Dey dirty-livin' hinsecks. Mebbe yo find dem in de bush, under logs an' stones. But never in de bright places.'

'I see.' Bond changed the subject. 'By the way, did those two men get off all right in the Sunbeam?'

'Sho ting, cap'n. Dey plenty happy wid de job. An' dey look plenty like yo an' me, cap'n.' Quarrel chuckled. He glanced at Bond and said hesitantly, 'I fears dey weren't very good citizens, cap'n. Had to find de two men wheres I could. Me, I'm a beggarman, cap'n. An' fo you, cap'n, I get a miserable no-good whiteman from Betsy's.'

'Who's Betsy?'

'She done run de lousiest brothel in town, cap'n,' Quarrel spat emphatically out of the window. 'Dis whiteman, he does de book-keepin'.'

Bond laughed. 'So long as he can drive a car. I only hope they get to Montego all right.'

'Don' yo worry,' Quarrel misunderstood Bond's concern. 'I say I tell de police dey stole de car if dey don'.'

They were at the saddleback at Stony Hill where the Junction Road dives down through fifty S-bends towards the North Coast. Bond put the little Austin A.30 into second gear and let it coast. The sun was coming up over the Blue Mountain peak and dusty shafts of gold lanced into the plunging valley. There were few people on the road – an occasional man going off to his precipitous smallholding on the flank of a hill, his three-foot cutlass dangling from his right hand, chewing at his breakfast, a foot of raw sugar cane held in his left, or a woman sauntering up the road with a covered basket of fruit or vegetables for Stony Hill market, her shoes on her head, to be donned when she got near the village. It was a savage, peaceful scene that had hardly changed, except for the surface of the road, for two hundred years or more. Bond almost smelled the dung of the mule train in which he would have been riding over from Port Royal to visit the garrison at Morgan's Harbour in 1750.

Quarrel interrupted his thoughts. 'Cap'n,' he said apologetically, 'beggin' yo pardon, but kin yo tell me what yo have in mind for we? I'se bin puzzlin' an' Ah caint seem to figger hout yo game.'

'I've hardly figured it out myself, Quarrel.' Bond changed up into top and dawdled through the cool, beautiful glades of Castleton Gardens. 'I told you I'm here because Commander Strangways and his secretary have disappeared. Most people think they've gone off together. I think they've been murdered.'

'Dat so?' said Quarrel unemotionally. 'Who yo tink done hit?'

'I've come to agree with you. I think Doctor No, that Chinaman on Crab Key, had it done. Strangways was poking his nose into this man's affairs – something to do with the bird sanctuary. Doctor No has this mania for privacy. You were telling me so yourself. Seems he'll do anything to stop people climbing over his wall. Mark you, it's not more than a guess about Doctor No. But some funny things happened in the last twenty-four hours. That's why I sent the Sunbeam over to Montego, to lay a false scent. And that's why we're going to hide out at the Beau Desert for a few days.'

'Den what, cap'n?'

'First of all I want you to get me absolutely fit – the way you trained me the last time I was here. Remember?'

'Sho, cap'n. Ah kin do dat ting.'

'And then I was thinking you and me might go and take a look at Crab Key.'

Quarrel whistled. The whistle ended on a downward note.

'Just sniff around. We needn't get too close to Doctor No's end. I want to take a look at this bird sanctuary. See for myself what happened to the wardens' camp. If we find anything wrong, we'll get away again and come back by the front door – with some soldiers to help. Have a full-dress inquiry. Can't do that until we've got something to go on. What do you think?'

Quarrel dug into his hip pocket for a cigarette. He made a fuss about lighting it. He blew a cloud of smoke through his nostrils and watched it whip out of the window. He said, 'Cap'n, Ah tink yo'se plumb crazy to trespass hon dat island.' Quarrel had wound himself up. He paused. There was no comment. He looked sideways at the quiet profile. He said more quietly, in an embarrassed voice, 'Jess one ting, cap'n. Ah have some folks back in da Caymans. Would yo consider takin' hout a life hinsurance hon me afore we sail?'

Bond glanced affectionately at the strong brown face. It had a deep cleft of worry between the eyes. 'Of course, Quarrel. I'll fix it at Port Maria tomorrow. We'll make it big, say five thousand pounds. Now then, how shall we go? Canoe?'

'Dat's right, cap'n.' Quarrel's voice was reluctant. 'We need a calm sea an' a light wind. Come hin on de Nor-easterly Trades. Mus' be a dark night. Dey startin' right now. By end of da week we git da secon' moon quarter. Where yo reckon to land, cap'n?'

'South shore near the mouth of the river. Then we'll go up the river to the lake. I'm sure that's where the wardens' camp was. So as to have fresh water and be able to get down to the sea to fish.

Quarrel grunted without enthusiasm. 'How long we stayin', cap'n? Caint take a whole lot of food wit us. Bread, cheese, salt pork. No tobacco – caint risk da smoke an' light. Dat's mighty rough country, cap'n. Marsh an' mangrove.'

Bond said: 'Better plan for three days. Weather may break and stop us getting off for a night or two. Couple of good hunting knives. I'll take a gun. You never can tell.'

'No, sir,' said Quarrel emphatically. He relapsed into a brooding silence which lasted until they got to Port Maria.

They went through the little town and on round the headland to Morgan's Harbour. It was just as Bond remembered – the sugar-loaf of the Isle of Surprise rising out of the calm bay, the canoes drawn up beside the mounds of empty conch shells, the distant boom of the surf on the reef which had so nearly been his grave. Bond, his mind full of memories, took the car down the little side road and through the cane fields in the middle of which the gaunt ruin of the old Great House of Beau Desert Plantation stood up like a stranded galleon.

They came to the gate leading to the bungalow. Quarrel got out and opened the gate, and Bond drove through and pulled up in the yard behind the white single-storeyed house. It was very quiet. Bond walked round the house and across the lawn to the edge of the sea. Yes, there it was, the stretch of deep, silent water – the submarine path he had taken to the Isle of Surprise. It sometimes came back to him in nightmares. Bond stood looking at it and thinking of Solitaire, the girl he had brought back, torn and bleeding, from that sea. He had carried her across the lawn to the house. What had happened to her? Where was she? Brusquely Bond turned and walked back into the house, driving the phantoms away from him.

It was eight-thirty. Bond unpacked his few things and changed into sandals and shorts. Soon there was the delicious smell of coffee and frying bacon. They ate their breakfast while Bond fixed his training routine – up at seven, swim a quarter of a mile, breakfast, an hour's sunbathing, run a mile, swim again, lunch, sleep, sunbathe, swim a mile, hot bath and massage, dinner and asleep by nine.

After breakfast the routine began.

Nothing interrupted the grinding week except a brief story in the *Daily Gleaner* and a telegram from Pleydell-Smith. The *Gleaner* said that a Sunbeam Talbot, H. 2473, had been involved in a fatal accident on the Devil's Racecourse, a stretch of winding road between Spanish Town and Ochos Rio – on the Kingston-Montego route. A runaway lorry, whose driver was being traced, had crashed into the Sunbeam as it came round a bend. Both vehicles had left the road and hurtled into the ravine below. The two occupants of the Sunbeam, Ben Gibbons of Harbour Street, and Josiah Smith, no address, had been killed. A Mr Bond, an English visitor, who had been lent the car, was asked to contact the nearest police station.

Bond burned that copy of the *Gleaner*. He didn't want to upset Quarrel.

With only one day to go, the telegram came from Pleydell-Smith. It said:

EACH OBJECT CONTAINED ENOUGH CYANIDE TO KILL A HORSE STOP
SUGGEST YOU CHANGE YOUR GROCER STOP GOOD LUCK SMITH

Bond also burned the telegram.

Quarrel hired a canoe and they spent three days sailing it. It was a clumsy shell cut out of a single giant cotton tree. It had two thin thwarts, two heavy paddles and a small sail of dirty canvas. It was a blunt instrument. Quarrel was pleased with it.

'Seven, eight hours, cap'n,' he said. 'Den we bring down de sail an' use de paddles. Less target for de radar to see.'

The weather held. The forecast from Kingston radio was good. The nights were as black as sin. The two men got in their stores. Bond fitted himself out with cheap black canvas jeans and a dark blue shirt and rope-soled shoes.

The last evening came. Bond was glad he was on his way. He had only once been out of the training camp – to get the stores and arrange Quarrel's insurance – and he was chafing to get out of the stable and on to the track. He admitted to himself that this adventure excited him. It had the right ingredients – physical exertion, mystery, and a ruthless enemy. He had a good companion. His cause was just. There might also be the satisfaction of throwing the 'holiday in the sun' back in M's teeth. That had rankled. Bond didn't like being coddled.

The sun blazed beautifully into its grave.

Bond went into his bedroom and took out his two guns and looked at them. Neither was a part of him as the Beretta had been – an extension of his right hand – but he already knew them as better weapons. Which should he take? Bond picked up each in turn, hefting them in his hand. It had to be the heavier Smith & Wesson. There would be no close shooting, if there was any shooting, on Crab Key. Heavy, long-range stuff – if anything. The brutal, stumpy revolver had an extra twenty-five yards over the Walther. Bond fitted the holster into the waistband of his jeans and clipped in the gun. He put twenty spare rounds in his pocket. Was it over-insurance to take all this metal on what might only be a tropical picnic?

Bond went to the icebox and took a pint of Canadian Club Blended Rye and some ice and soda-water and went and sat in the garden and watched the last light flame and die.

The shadows crept from behind the house and marched across the lawn and developed him. The Undertaker's Wind that blows at night from the centre of the island, clattered softly in the tops of the palm trees. The frogs began to tinkle among the shrubs. The fireflies, the 'blink-a-blinks', as Quarrel called them, came out and began flashing their sexual morse. For a moment the melancholy of the tropical dusk caught at Bond's heart. He picked up the bottle and looked at it. He had drunk a quarter of it. He poured another big slug into his glass and added some ice. What was he drinking for? Because of the thirty miles of black sea he had to cross tonight? Because he was going into the unknown? Because of Doctor No?

Quarrel came up from the beach. 'Time, cap'n.'

Bond swallowed his drink and followed the Cayman Islander down to the canoe. It was rocking quietly in the water, its bows on the sand.

Quarrel went aft and Bond climbed into the space between the forrard thwart and the bows. The sail, wrapped round the short mast, was at his back. Bond took up his paddle and pushed off, and they turned slowly and headed out for the break in the softly creaming waves that was the passage through the reef. They paddled easily, in unison, the paddles turning in their hands so that they did not leave the water on the forward stroke. The small waves slapped softly against the bows. Otherwise they made no noise. It was dark. Nobody saw them go. They just left the land and went off across the sea.

Bond's only duty was to keep paddling. Quarrel did the steering. At the opening through the reef there was a swirl and suck of conflicting currents and they were in amongst the jagged niggerheads and coral trees, bared like fangs by the swell. Bond could feel the strength of Quarrel's great sweeps with the paddle as the heavy craft wallowed and plunged. Again and again Bond's own paddle thudded against rock, and once he had to hold on as the canoe hit a buried mass of brain coral and slid off again. Then they were through, and far below the boat there were indigo patches of sand and around them the solid oily feel of deep water.

'Okay, cap'n,' said Quarrel softly. Bond shipped his paddle and got down off one knee and sat with his back to the thwart. He heard the scratching of Quarrel's nails against canvas as he unwrapped the sail and then the sharp flap as it caught the breeze. The canoe straightened and began to move. It tilted slowly. There was a soft hiss under the bows. A handful of spray tossed up into Bond's face. The wind of their movement was cool and would soon get cold. Bond hunched up his knees and put his arms round them. The wood was already beginning to bite into his buttocks and his back. It crossed his mind that it was going to be the hell of a long and uncomfortable night.

In the darkness ahead Bond could just make out the rim of the world. Then came a layer of black haze above which the stars began, first sparsely and then merging into a dense bright carpet. The Milky Way soared overhead. How many stars? Bond tried counting a finger's length and was soon past the hundred. The stars lit the sea into a faint grey road and then arched away over the tip of the mast towards the black silhouette of Jamaica. Bond looked back. Behind the hunched figure of Quarrel there was a faraway cluster of lights which would be Port Maria. Already they were a couple of miles out. Soon they would be a tenth of the way, then a quarter, then half. That would be around midnight when Bond would take over. Bond sighed and put his head down to his knees and closed his eyes.

He must have slept because he was awakened by the clonk of a paddle against the boat. He lifted his arm to show that he had heard and glanced at the luminous blaze of his watch. Twelve-fifteen. Stiffly he unbent his legs and turned and scrambled over the thwart.

'Sorry, Quarrel,' he said, and it was odd to hear his voice. 'You ought to have shaken me up before.'

'Hit don signify, cap'n,' said Quarrel with a grey glint of teeth. 'Do yo good to sleep.'

Gingerly they slipped past each other and Bond settled in the stern and picked up the paddle. The sail was secured to a bent nail beside him. It was flapping. Bond brought the bows into the wind and edged them round so that the North Star was directly over Quarrel's bent head in the bows'. For a time this would be fun. There was something to do.

There was no change in the night except that it seemed darker and emptier. The pulse of the sleeping sea seemed slower. The heavy swell was longer and the troughs deeper. They were running through a patch of phosphorus that winked at the bows and dripped jewels when Bond lifted the paddle out of the water. How safe it was, slipping through the night in this ridiculously vulnerable little boat. How kind and soft the sea could be. A covey of flying fish broke the surface in front of the bows and scattered like shrapnel. Some kept going for a time beside the canoe, flying as much as twenty yards before they dived into the wall of the swell. Was some bigger fish after them or did they think the canoe was a fish, or were they just playing? Bond thought of what was going on in the hundreds of fathoms below the boat, the big fish, the shark and barracuda and tarpon and sailfish quietly cruising, the shoals of kingfish and mackerel and bonito and, far below in the grey twilight of the great depths, the phosphorous jellied boneless things that were never seen, the fifty-foot squids, with eyes a foot wide, that streamed along like zeppelins, the last real monsters of the sea, whose size was only known from the fragments found inside whales. What would happen if a wave caught the canoe broadside and capsized them? How long would they last? Bond took an ounce more pains with his steering and put the thought aside.

One o'clock, two o'clock, three, four. Quarrel awoke and stretched. He called softly to Bond. 'Ah smells land, cap'n.' Soon there was a thickening of the darkness ahead. The low shadow slowly took on the shape of a huge swimming rat. A pale moon rose slowly behind them. Now the island showed distinctly, a couple of miles away, and there was the distant grumble of surf.

They changed places. Quarrel brought down the sail and they took up the paddles. For at least another mile, thought Bond, they would be invisible in the troughs of the waves. Not even radar would distinguish them from the crests. It was the last mile they would have to hurry over with the dawn not far off.

Now he too could smell the land. It had no particular scent. It was just something new in the nose after hours of clean sea. He could make out the white fringe of surf. The swell subsided and the waves became choppier. 'Now, cap'n,' called Quarrel, and Bond, the sweat already dropping off his chin, dug deeper and more often. God, it was hard work! The hulking log of wood which had sped along so well under the sail now seemed hardly to move. The wave at the bows was only a ripple. Bond's shoulders were aching like fire. The one knee he was resting on was beginning to bruise. His hands were cramped on the clumsy shaft of a paddle made of lead.

It was incredible, but they were coming up with the reef. Patches of sand showed deep under the boat. Now the surf was a roar. They followed along the edge of the reef, looking for an opening. A hundred yards inside the reef, breaking the sandline, was the shimmer of water running inland. The river! So the landfall had been all right. The wall of surf broke up. There was a patch of black oily current swelling over hidden coral heads. The nose of the canoe turned towards it and into it. There was a turmoil of water and a series of grating thuds, and then a sudden rush forward into peace and the canoe was moving slowly across a smooth mirror towards the shore.

Quarrel steered the boat towards the lee of a rocky promontory where the beach ended. Bond wondered why the beach didn't shine white under the thin moon. When they grounded and Bond climbed stiffly out he understood why. The beach was black. The sand was soft and wonderful to the feet but it must have been formed out of volcanic rock, pounded over the centuries, and Bond's naked feet on it looked like white crabs.

They made haste. Quarrel took three short lengths of thick bamboo out of the boat and laid them up the flat beach. They heaved the nose of the canoe on to the first and pushed the boat up the rollers. After each yard of progress, Bond picked up the back roller and brought it to the front. Slowly the canoe moved up the sand until at last it was over the back tideline and among the rocks and turtle grass and low sea-grape bushes. They pushed it another twenty yards inland into the beginning of the mangrove. There they covered it with dried seaweed and bits of driftwood from the tideline. Then Quarrel cut lengths of screwpalm and went back over their tracks, sweeping and tidying.

It was still dark, but the breath of grey in the east would soon be turning to pearl. It was five o'clock. They were dead tired. They exchanged a few words and Quarrel went off among the rocks on the promontory. Bond scooped out a depression in the fine dry sand under a thick bush of sea-grape. There were a few hermit crabs beside his bed. He picked up as many as he could find and hurled them into the mangrove. Then, not caring what other animals or insects might come to his smell and his warmth, he lay down full length in the sand and rested his head on his arm.

He was at once asleep.

CHAPTER 8

THE ELEGANT VENUS

Bond awoke lazily. The feel of the sand reminded him where he was. He glanced at his watch. Ten o'clock. The sun through the round thick leaves of the sea-grape was already hot. A larger shadow moved across the dappled sand in front of his face. Quarrel? Bond shifted his head and peered through the fringe of leaves and grass that concealed him from the beach. He stiffened. His heart missed a beat and then began pounding so that he had to breathe deeply to quieten it. His eyes, as he stared through the blades of grass, were fierce slits.

It was a naked girl, with her back to him. She was not quite naked. She wore a broad leather belt round her waist with a hunting knife in a leather sheath at her right hip. The belt made her nakedness extraordinarily erotic. She stood not more than five yards away on the tideline looking down at something in her hand. She stood in the classical relaxed pose of the nude, all the weight on the right leg and the left knee bent and turning slightly inwards, the head to one side as she examined the things in her hand.

It was a beautiful back. The skin was a very light uniform *café au lait* with the sheen of dull satin. The gentle curve of the backbone was deeply indented, suggesting more powerful muscles than is usual in a woman, and the behind was almost as firm and rounded as a boy's. The legs were straight and beautiful and no pinkness showed under the slightly lifted left heel. She was not a coloured girl.

Her hair was ash blonde. It was cut to the shoulders and hung there and along the side of her bent cheek in thick wet strands. A green diving mask was pushed back above her forehead, and the green rubber thong bound hair hair at the back.

The whole scene, the empty beach, the green and blue sea, the naked girl with the strands of hair, reminded Bond of something. He searched his mind. Yes, she was Botticelli's Venus, seen from behind.

How had she got there? What was she doing? Bond looked up and down the beach. It was not black, he now saw, but a deep chocolate brown. To the right he could see as far as the river mouth, perhaps five hundred yards away. The beach was empty and featureless except for a scattering of small pinkish objects. There were a lot of them, shells of some sort Bond supposed, and they looked decorative against the dark brown background. He looked to the left, to where, twenty yards away, the rocks of the small headland began. Yes, there was a yard or two of groove in the sand where a canoe had been drawn up into the shelter of the rocks. It must have been a light one or she couldn't have drawn it up alone. Perhaps the girl wasn't alone. But there was only one set of footprints leading down from the rocks to the sea and another set coming out of the sea and up the beach to where she now stood on the tideline. Did she live here, or had she too sailed over from Jamaica that night? Hell of a thing for a girl to do. Anyway, what in God's name *was* she doing here?

As if to answer him, the girl made a throwaway gesture of the right hand and scattered a dozen shells on the sand beside her. They were violent pink and seemed to Bond to be the same as he had noticed on the beach. The girl looked down into her left hand and began to whistle softly to herself. There was a happy note of triumph in the whistle. She was whistling 'Marion', a plaintive little calypso that has now been cleaned up and made famous outside Jamaica. It had always been one of Bond's favourites. It went:

All day, all night, Marion,
Sittin' by the seaside siftin' sand . . .

The girl broke off to stretch her arms out in a deep yawn. Bond smiled to himself. He wetted his lips and took up the refrain:

'The water from her eyes could sail a boat,
The hair on her head could tie a goat . . .'

The hands flew down and across her chest. The muscles of her behind bunched with tension. She was listening, her head, still hidden by the curtain of hair, cocked to one side.

Hesitantly she began again. The whistle trembled and died. At the first note of Bond's echo, the girl whirled round. She didn't cover her body with the two classical gestures. One hand flew downwards, but the other, instead of hiding her breasts, went up to her face, covering it below the eyes, now wide with fear. 'Who's that?' The words came out in a terrified whisper.

Bond got to his feet and stepped out through the sea-grape. He stopped on the edge of the grass. He held his hands open at his sides to show they were empty. He smiled cheerfully at her. 'It's only me. I'm another trespasser. Don't be frightened.'

The girl dropped her hand down from her face. It went to the knife at her belt. Bond watched the fingers curl round the hilt. He looked up at her face. Now he realized why her hand had instinctively gone to it. It was a beautiful face, with wide-apart deep blue eyes under lashes paled by the sun. The mouth was wide and when she stopped pursing the lips with tension they would be full. It was a serious face and the jawline was determined – the face of a girl who fends for herself. And once, reflected Bond, she had failed to fend. For the nose was badly broken, smashed crooked like a boxer's. Bond stiffened with revolt at what had happened to this supremely beautiful girl. No wonder this was her shame and not the beautiful firm breasts that now jutted towards him without concealment.

The eyes examined him fiercely. 'Who are you? What are you doing here?' There was the slight lilt of a Jamaican accent. The voice was sharp and accustomed to being obeyed.

'I'm an Englishman. I'm interested in birds.'

'Oh,' the voice was doubtful. The hand still rested on the knife. 'How long have you been watching me? How did you get here?'

'Ten minutes, but no more answers until you tell me who *you* are.'

'I'm no one in particular. I come from Jamaica. I collect shells.'

'I came in a canoe. Did you?'

'Yes. Where is your canoe?'

'I've got a friend with me. We've hidden it in the mangroves.'

'There are no marks of a canoe landing.'

'We're careful. We covered them up. Not like you.' Bond gestured towards the rocks. 'You ought to take more trouble. Did you use a sail? Right up to the reef?'

'Of course. Why not? I always do.'

'Then they'll know you're here. They've got radar.'

'They've never caught me yet.' The girl took her hand away from her knife. She reached up and stripped off the diving mask and stood swinging it. She seemed to think she had the measure of Bond. She said, with some of the sharpness gone from her voice, 'What's your name?'

'Bond. James Bond. What's yours?'

She reflected. 'Rider.'

'What Rider?'

'Honeychile.'

Bond smiled.

'What's so funny about it?'

'Nothing. Honeychile Rider. It's a pretty name.'

She unbent. 'People call me "Honey".'

'Well, I'm glad to meet you?'

The prosaic phrase seemed to remind her of her nakedness. She blushed. She said uncertainly, 'I must get dressed.' She looked down at the scattered shells around her feet. She obviously wanted to pick them up. Perhaps she realized that the movement might be still more revealing than her present pose. She said sharply, 'You're not to touch those while I'm gone.'

Bond smiled at the childish challenge. 'Don't worry, I'll look after them.'

The girl looked at him doubtfully and then turned and walked stiff-legged over to the rocks and disappeared behind them.

Bond walked the few steps down the beach and bent and picked up one of the shells. It was alive and the two halves were shut tight. It appeared to be some kind of a cockle, rather deeply ribbed and coloured a mauve-pink. Along both edges of the hinge, thin horns stood out, about half a dozen to each side. It didn't seem to Bond a very distinguished shell. He replaced it carefully with the others.

He stood looking down at the shells and wondering. Was she really collecting them? It certainly looked like it. But what a risk to take to get them – the voyage over alone in the canoe and then back again. And she seemed to realize that this was a dangerous place. 'They've never caught me yet.' What an extraordinary girl. Bond's heart warmed and his senses stirred as he thought of her. Already, as he had found so often when people had deformities, he had almost forgotten her broken nose. It had somehow slipped away behind his memory of her eyes and her mouth and her amazingly beautiful body. Her imperious attitude and her quality of attack were exciting. The way she had reached for her knife to defend herself! She was like an animal whose cubs are threatened. Where did she live? Who were her parents? There was something uncared for about her – a dog that nobody wants to pet. Who was she?

Bond heard her footsteps riffling the sand. He turned to look at her.

She was dressed almost in rags – a faded brown shirt with torn sleeves and a knee-length patched brown cotton skirt held in place by the leather belt with the knife. She had a canvas knapsack slung over one shoulder. She looked like a principal girl dressed as Man Friday.

She came up with him and at once went down on one knee and began picking up the live shells and stowing them in the knapsack.

Bond said, 'Are those rare?'

She sat back on her haunches and looked up at him. She surveyed his face. Apparently she was satisfied. 'You promise you won't tell anybody? Swear?'

'I promise,' said Bond.

'Well then, yes, they are rare. Very. You can get five dollars for a perfect specimen. In Miami. That's where I deal with. They're called *Venus Elegans* – The Elegant Venus.' Her eyes sparkled up at him with excitement. 'This morning I found what I wanted. The bed where they live,' she waved towards the sea. 'You wouldn't find them though,' she added with sudden carefulness. 'It's very deep and hidden away. I doubt if you could dive that deep. And anyway,' she looked happy, 'I'm going to clear the whole bed today. You'd only get the imperfect ones if you came back here.'

Bond laughed. 'I promise I won't steal any. I really don't know anything about shells. Cross my heart.'

She stood up, her work completed. 'What about these birds of yours? What sort are they? Are they valuable too? I won't tell either if you tell me. I only collect shells.'

'They're called roseate spoonbills,' said Bond. 'Sort of pink stork with a flat beak. Ever seen any?'

'Oh, *those*,' she said scornfully. 'There used to be thousands of them here. But you won't find many now. They scared them all away.' She sat down on the sand and put her arms round her knees, proud of her superior knowledge and now certain that she had nothing to fear from this man.

Bond sat down a yard away. He stretched out and turned towards her, resting on his elbow. He wanted to preserve the picnic atmosphere and try to find out more about this queer, beautiful girl. He said, easily, 'Oh, really. What happened? Who did it?'

She shrugged impatiently. 'The people here did it. I don't know who they are. There's a Chinaman. He doesn't like birds or something. He's got a dragon. He sent the dragon after the birds and scared them away. The dragon burned up their nesting places. There used to be two men who lived with the birds and looked after them. They got scared away too, or killed or something.'

It all seemed quite natural to her. She gave the facts indifferently, staring out to sea.

Bond said, 'This dragon. What kind is he? Have you ever seen him?'

'Yes, I've seen him.' She screwed up her eyes and made a wry face as if she was swallowing bitter medicine. She looked earnestly at Bond to make him share her feelings. 'I've been coming here for about a year, looking for shells and exploring. I only found these,' she waved at the beach, 'about a month ago. On my last trip. But I've found plenty of other good ones. Just before Christmas I thought I'd explore the river. I went up it to the top, where the birdmen had their camp. It was all broken up. It was getting late and I decided to spend the night there. In the middle of the night I woke up. The dragon was coming by only a few chains away from me. It had two great glaring eyes and a long snout. It had sort of short wings and a pointed tail. It was all black and gold.' She frowned at the expression on Bond's face. 'There was a full moon. I could see it quite clearly. It went by me. It was making a sort of roaring noise. It went over the marsh and came to some thick mangrove and it simply climbed over the bushes and went on. A whole flock of birds got up in front of it and suddenly a lot of fire came out of its mouth and it burned a lot of them up and all the trees they'd been roosting in. It was horrible. The most horrible thing I've ever seen.'

The girl leant sideways and peered at Bond's face. She sat up straight again and stared obstinately out to sea. 'I can see you don't believe me,' said said in a furious, tense voice. 'You're one of these city people. You don't believe anything. Ugh,' she shuddered with dislike of him.

Bond said reasonably, 'Honey, there just aren't such things as dragons in the world. You saw something that looked very like a dragon. I'm just wondering what it was.'

'How do you know there aren't such things as dragons?' Now he had made her really angry. 'Nobody lives on this end of the island. One could easily have survived here. Anyway, what do you think you know about animals and things? I've lived with snakes and things since I was a child. Alone. Have you ever seen a praying mantis eat her husband after they've made love? Have you ever seen the mongoose dance? Or an octopus dance? How long is a humming bird's tongue? Have you ever had a pet snake that wore a bell round its neck and rang it to wake you? Have you seen a scorpion get sunstroke and kill itself with its own sting? Have you seen the carpet of flowers under the sea at night? Do you know that a John Crow can smell a dead lizard a mile away . . .?' The girl had fired these questions like scornful jabs with a rapier. Now she stopped, out of breath. She said hopelessly, 'Oh, you're just city folk like all the rest.'

Bond said, 'Honey, now look here. You know these things. I can't help it that I live in towns. I'd like to know about your things too. I just haven't had that sort of life. I know other things instead. Like . . .' Bond searched his mind. He couldn't think of anything as interesting as hers. He finished lamely, 'Like for instance that this Chinaman is going to be more interested in your visit this time. This time he's going to try and stop you getting away.' He paused and added. 'And me for the matter of that.'

She turned and looked at him with interest. 'Oh. Why? But then it doesn't really matter. One just hides during the day and gets away at night. He's sent dogs after me and even a plane. He hasn't got me yet.' She examined Bond with a new interest. 'Is it you he's after?'

'Well, yes,' admitted Bond. 'I'm afraid it it. You see we dropped the sail about two miles out so that their radar wouldn't pick us up. I think the Chinaman may have been expecting a visit from me. Your sail will have been reported and I'd bet anything he'll think your canoe was mine. I'd better go and wake my friend up and we'll talk it over. You'll like him. He's a Cayman Islander, name of Quarrel.'

The girl said, 'Well, I'm sorry if . . .' The sentence trailed away. Apologies wouldn't come easy to someone so much on the defensive. 'But after all I couldn't know, could I?' She searched his face.

Bond smiled into the questing blue eyes. He said reassuringly, 'Of course you couldn't. It's just bad luck – bad luck for you too. I don't suppose he minds too much about a solitary girl who collects shells. You can be sure they've had a good look at your footprints and found clues like that' – he waved the scattered shells on the beach. 'But I'm afraid he'd take a different view of me. Now he'll try and hunt me down with everything he's got. I'm only afraid he may get you into the net in the process. Anyway,' Bond grinned reassuringly, 'we'll see what Quarrel has to say. You stay here.'

Bond got to his feet. He walked along the promontory and cast about him. Quarrel had hidden himself well. It took Bond five minutes to find him. He was lying in a grassy depression between two big rocks, half covered by a board of grey drift-wood. He was still fast asleep, the brown head, stern in sleep, cradled on his forearm. Bond whistled softly and smiled as the eyes sprang wide open like an animal's. Quarrel saw Bond and scrambled to his feet, almost guiltily. He rubbed his big hands over his face as if he was washing it.

'Mornin', cap'n.' he said. 'Guess Ah been down deep. Dat China girl come to me.'

Bond smiled. 'I got something different,' he said. They sat down and Bond told him about Honeychile Rider and her shells and the fix they were in. 'And now it's eleven o'clock,' Bond added. 'And we've got to make a new plan.'

Quarrel scratched his head. He looked sideways at Bond. 'Yo don' plan we jess ditch dis girl?' he asked hopefully. 'Ain't nuttin to do wit we . . .' Suddenly he stopped. His head swivelled round and pointed like a dog's. He held up a hand for silence, listening intently.

Bond held his breath. In the distance, to the eastwards, there was a faint droning.

Quarrel jumped to his feet. 'Quick, cap'n,' he said urgently. 'Dey's a comin'.'

CHAPTER 9

CLOSE SHAVES

Ten minutes later the bay was empty and immaculate. Small waves curled lazily in across the mirrored water inside the reef and flopped exhausted on the dark sand where the mauve shells glittered like shed toenails. The heap of discarded shells had gone and there was no longer any trace of footprints. Quarrel had cut branches of mangrove and had walked backwards sweeping carefully as he went. Where he had swept, the sand was of a different texture from the rest of the beach, but not too different as to be noticed from outside the reef. The girl's canoe had been pulled deeper among the rocks and covered with seaweed and driftwood.

Quarrel had gone back to the headland. Bond and the girl lay a few feet apart under the bush of sea-grape where Bond had slept, and gazed silently out across the water to the corner of the headland round which the boat would come.

The boat was perhaps a quarter of a mile away. From the slow pulse of the twin diesels Bond guessed that every cranny of the coastline was being searched for signs of them. It sounded a powerful boat. A big cabin cruiser, perhaps. What crew would it have? Who would be in command of the search? Doctor No? Unlikely. He would not trouble himself with this kind of police work.

From the west a wedge of cormorants appeared, flying low over the

sea beyond the roof. Bond watched them. They were the first evidence
he had seen of the guanay colony at the other end of the island. These,
according to Pleydell-Smith's description, would be scouts for the silver
flash of the anchovy near the surface. Sure enough, as he watched, they
began to back-pedal in the air and then go into shallow dives, hitting the
water like shrapnel. Almost at once a fresh file appeared from the west,
then another and another that merged into a long stream and then into a
solid black river of birds. For minutes they darkened the skyline and
then they were down on the water, covering several acres of it,
screeching and fighting and plunging their heads below the surface,
cropping at the solid field of anchovy like piranha fish feasting on a
drowned horse.

Bond felt a gentle nudge from the girl. She gestured with her head.
'The Chinaman's hens getting their corn.'

Bond examined the happy, beautiful face. She had seemed quite
unconcerned by the arrival of the search party. To her it was only the
game of hide-and-seek she had played before. Bond hoped she wasn't
going to get a shock.

The iron thud of the diesels was getting louder. The boat must be just
behind the headland. Bond took a last look round the peaceful bay and
then fixed his eyes, through the leaves and grass, on the point of the
headland inside the reef.

The knife of white bows appeared. It was followed by ten yards of
empty polished deck, glass windshields, a low raked cabin with a siren
and a blunt radio mast, the glimpse of a man inside at the wheel, then the
long flat well of the stern and a drooping red ensign. Converted MTB,
British Government surplus?

Bond's eyes went to the two men standing in the stern. They were
pale-skinned Negroes. They wore neat khaki ducks and shirts, broad
belts, and deep visored baseball caps of yellow straw. They were
standing side by side, bracing themselves against the slow swell. One of
them was holding a long black loud-hailer with a wire attached. The
other was manning a machine gun on a tripod. It looked to Bond like a
Spandau.

The man with the loud-hailer let it fall so that it swung on a strap
round his neck. He picked up a pair of binoculars and began inching
them along the beach. The low murmur of his comments just reached
Bond above the glutinous flutter of the diesels.

Bond watched the eyes of the binoculars begin with the headland and
then sweep the sand. The twin eyes paused among the rocks and moved
on. They came back. The murmur of comment rose to a jabber. The

man handed the glasses to the machine gunner who took a quick glance through them and gave them back. The scanner shouted something to the helmsman. The cabin cruiser stopped and backed up. Now she lay outside the reef exactly opposite Bond and the girl. The scanner again levelled the binoculars at the rocks where the girl's canoe lay hidden. Again the excited jabber came across the water. Again the glasses were passed to the machine gunner who glanced through. This time he nodded decisively.

Bond thought: now we've had it. These men know their job.

Bond watched the machine gunner pull the bolt back to load. The double click came to him over the bubbling of the diesels.

The scanner lifted his loud-hailer and switched it on. The twanging echo of the amplifier moaned and screeched across the water. The man brought it up to his lips. The voice roared across the bay.

'Okay, folks! Come on out and you won't get hurt.'

It was an educated voice. There was a trace of American accent.

'Now then, folks,' the voice thundered, 'make it quick! We've seen where you came ashore. We've spotted the boat under the driftwood. We ain't fools an' we ain't fooling. Take it easy. Just walk out with your hands up. You'll be okay.'

Silence fell. The waves lapped softly on the beach. Bond could hear the girl breathing. The thin screeching of the cormorants came to them muted across the mile of sea. The diesels bubbled unevenly as the swell covered the exhaust pipe and then opened it again.

Softly Bond reached over to the girl and tugged at her sleeve. 'Come close,' he whispered. 'Smaller target.' He felt her warmth nearer to him. Her cheek brushed against his forearm. He whispered, 'Burrow into the sand. Wriggle. Every inch'll help.' He began to worm his body carefully deeper into the depression they had scooped out for themselves. He felt her do the same. He peered out. Now his eyes were only just above the skyline of the top of the beach.

The man was lifting his loud-hailer. The voice roared. 'Okay, folks! Just so as you'll know this thing isn't for show.' He lifted his thumb. The machine gunner trained his gun into the tops of the mangroves behind the beach. There came the swift rattling roar Bond had last heard coming from the German lines in the Ardennes. The bullets made the same old sound of frightened pigeons whistling overhead. Then there was silence.

In the distance Bond watched the black cloud of cormorants take to the air and begin circling. His eyes went back to the boat. The machine gunner was feeling the barrel of his gun to see if it had warmed. The two men exchanged some words. The scanner picked up his loud-hailer.

"Kay, folks,' he said harshly. 'You've been warned. This is it.'

Bond watched the snout of the Spandau swing and depress. The man was going to start with the canoe among the rocks. Bond whispered to the girl, 'All right, Honey. Stick it. Keep right down. It won't last long.' He felt her hand squeeze his arm. He thought: poor little bitch, she's in this because of me. He leant to the right to cover her head and pushed his face deep into the sand.

This time the crash of noise was terrific. The bullets howled into the corner of the headland. Fragments of splintered rock whined over the beach like hornets. Ricochets twanged and buzzed off into the hinterland. Behind it all there was the steady road-drill hammer of the gun.

There was a pause. New magazine, thought Bond. Now it's us. He could feel the girl clutching at him. Her body was trembling along his flank. Bond reached out an arm and pressed her to him.

The roar of the gun began again. The bullets came zipping along the tideline towards them. There was a succession of quick close thuds. The bush above them was being torn to shreds. 'Zwip. Zwip. Zwip.' It was as if the thong of a steel whip was cutting the bush to pieces. Bits scattered around them, slowly covering them. Bond could smell the cooler air that meant they were now lying in the open. Were they hidden by the leaves and debris? The bullets marched away along the shoreline. In less than a minute the racket stopped.

The silence sang. The girl whimpered softly. Bond hushed her and held her tighter.

The loud-hailer boomed. 'Okay, folks. If you still got ears, we'll be along soon to pick up the bits. And we'll be bringing the dogs. 'Bye for now.'

The slow thud of the diesel quickened. The engine accelerated into a hasty roar and through the fallen leaves Bond watched the stern of the launch settle lower in the water as it made off to the west. Within minutes it was out of earshot.

Bond cautiously raised his head. The bay was serene, the beach unmarked. All was as before except for the stench of cordite and the sour smell of blasted rock. Bond pulled the girl to her feet. There were tear streaks down her face. She looked at him aghast. She said solemnly, 'That was horrible. What did they do it for? We might have been killed.'

Bond thought, this girl has always had to fend for herself, but only against nature. She knows the world of animals and insects and fishes and she's got the better of it. But it's been a small world, bounded by the sun and the moon and the seasons. She doesn't know the big world of the smoke-filled room, of the bullion broker's parlour, of the corridors and waiting-rooms of government offices, of careful meetings on park seats – she doesn't know about the struggle for big power and big money by the big men. She doesn't know that she's been swept out of her rock pool into the dirty waters.

He said, 'It's all right, Honey. They're just a lot of bad men who are frightened of us. We can manage them.' Bond put his arm round her shoulders. 'And you were wonderful. As brave as anything. Come on now, we'll look for Quarrel and make some plans. Anyway, it's time we had something to eat. What do you eat on these expeditions?'

They turned and walked up the beach to the headland. After a minute she said in a controlled voice, 'Oh, there's stacks of food about. Sea urchins mostly. And there are wild bananas and things. I eat and sleep for two days before I come out here. I don't need anything.'

Bond held her more closely. He dropped his arm as Quarrel appeared on the skyline. Quarrel scrambled down among the rocks. He stopped, looking down. They came up with him. The girl's canoe was sawn almost in half by the bullets. The girl gave a cry. She looked desperately at Bond, 'My boat! How am I to get back?'

'Don't you worry, missy.' Quarrel appreciated the loss of a canoe better than Bond. He guessed it might be most of the girl's capital. 'Cap'n fix you up wit' anudder. An' yo come back wit' we. Us got a fine boat in de mangrove. Hit not get broke. Ah's bin to see him.' Quarrel looked at Bond. Now his face was worried. 'But cap'n, yo sees what I means about dese folk. Dey mighty tough men an' dey means business. Dese dogs dey speak of. Dose is police-houns – Pinschers dey's called. Big bastards. Mah frens tell me as der's a pack of twenty or moh. We better make plans quick – an' good.'

'All right, Quarrel. But first we must have something to eat. And I'm damned if I'm going to be scared off the island before I've had a good look. We'll take Honey with us.' He turned to the girl. 'Is that all right with you, Honey? You'll be all right with us. Then we sail home together.'

The girl looked doubtfully at him. 'I guess there's no alternative. I mean. I'd love to go with you if I won't be in the way. I really don't want anything to eat. But will you take me home as soon as you can? I don't want to see any more of those people. How long are you going to be looking at these birds?'

Bond said evasively, 'Not long. I've got to find out what happened to them and why. Then we'll be off.' He looked at his watch. 'It's twelve now. You wait here. Have a bathe or something. Don't walk about leaving footprints. Come on, Quarrel, we'd better get that boat hidden.'

It was one o'clock before they were ready. Bond and Quarrel filled the canoe with stones and sand until it sank in a pool among the mangroves. They smeared over their footprints. The bullets had left so much litter behind the shoreline that they could do most of their walking on broken leaves and twigs. They ate some of their rations – avidly, the girl reluctantly – and climbed across the rocks and into the shallow water off-shore. Then they trudged along the shallows towards the river mouth three hundred yards away down the beach.

It was very hot. A harsh, baking wind had sprung up from the north-east. Quarrel said this wind blew daily the year round. It was vital to the guanera. It dried the guano. The glare from the sea and from the shiny green leaves of the mangroves was dazzling. Bond was glad he had taken trouble to get his skin hardened to the sun.

There was a sandy bar at the river mouth and a long deep stagnant pool. They could either get wet or strip. Bond said to the girl, 'Honey, we can't be shy on this trip. We'll keep our shirts on because of the sun. Wear what's sensible and walk behind us.' Without waiting for her reply the two men took off their trousers. Quarrel rolled them and packed them in the knapsack with the provisions and Bond's gun. They waded into the pool. Quarrel in front, then Bond, then the girl. The water came up to Bond's waist. A big silver fish leaped out of the pool and fell back with a splash. There were arrows on the surface where others fled out of their way. 'Tarpon,' commented Quarrel.

The pool converged into a narrow neck over which the mangroves touched. For a time they waded through a cool tunnel, and then the river broadened into a deep sluggish channel that meandered ahead among the giant spider-legs of the mangroves. The bottom was muddy and at each step their feet sank inches into slime. Small fish or shrimps wriggled and fled from under their feet, and every now and then they had to stoop to brush away leeches before they got hold. But otherwise it was easy going and quiet and cool among the bushes and, at least to Bond, it was a blessing to be out of the sun.

Soon, as they got away from the sea, it began to smell bad with the bad egg, sulphuretted hydrogen smell of marsh gas. The mosquitoes and sandflies began to find them. They liked Bond's fresh body. Quarrel told him to dip himself in the river water. 'Dem like dere meat wid salt on him,' he explained cheerfully. Bond took off his shirt and did as he was told. Then it was better and after a while Bond's nostrils even got used to the marsh gas, except when Quarrel's feet disturbed some aged pocket in the mud and a vintage bubble wobbled up from the bottom and burst stinking under his nose.

The mangroves became fewer and sparser and the river slowly opened out. The water grew shallower and the bottom firmer. Soon they came round a bend and into the open. Honey said, 'Better watch out now. We'll be easier to see. It goes on like this for about a mile. Then the river gets narrower until the lake. Then there's the sandspit the birdmen lived on.'

They stopped in the shadow of the mangrove tunnel and looked out. The river meandered sluggishly away from them towards the centre of the island. Its banks, fringed with low bamboo and sea-grape, would give only half shelter. From its western bank the ground rose slowly and then sharply up to the sugar-loaf about two miles away which was the guanera. Round the base of the mountain there was a scattering of Quonset huts. A zigzag of silver ran down the hillside to the huts – a Decauville Track, Bond guessed, to bring the guano from the diggings down to the crusher and separator. The summit of the sugar-loaf was white, as if with snow. From the peak flew a smoky flag of guano dust. Bond could see the black dots of cormorants against the white background. They were landing and taking off like bees at a hive.

Bond stood and gazed at the distant glittering mountain of bird dung. So this was the kingdom of Doctor No! Bond thought he had never seen a more godforsaken landscape in his life.

He examined the ground between the river and the mountain. It seemed to be the usual grey dead coral broken, where there was a pocket of earth, by low scrub and screwpalm. No doubt a road or a track led down the mountainside to the central lake and the marshes. It looked bad stuff to cross unless there was. Bond noticed that all the vegetation was bent to the westwards. He imagined living the year round with that hot wind constantly scouring the island, the smell of the marsh gas and the guano. No penal colony could have a worse site than this.

Bond looked to the east. There the mangroves in the marshland seemed more hospitable. They marched away in a solid green carpet until they lost their outline in the dancing heat haze on the horizon. Over them a thick froth of birds tossed and settled and tossed again. Their steady scream carried over on the harsh wind.

Quarrel's voice broke in on Bond's thoughts. 'Dey's a comin', cap'n.'

Bond followed Quarrel's eyes. A big lorry was racing down from the huts, dust streaming from its wheels. Bond followed it for ten minutes until it disappeared amongst the mangroves at the head of the river. He listened. The baying of dogs came down on the wind.

Quarrel said, 'Dey'll come down de ribber, cap'n. Dem'll know we caint move 'cept up de ribber, assumin' we ain't dead. Dey'll surely come down de ribber to de beach and look for de pieces. Den mos' likely de boat come wit' a dinghy an' take de men and dogs off. Leastways, dat's what Ah'd do in dere place.'

Honey said, 'That's what they do when they look for me. It's quite all right. You cut a piece of bamboo and when they get near you go under the water and breathe through the bamboo till they've gone by.'

Bond smiled at Quarrel. He said, 'Supposing you get the bamboo while I find a good mangrove clump.'

Quarrel nodded dubiously. He started off upstream towards the bamboo thickets. Bond turned back into the mangrove tunnel.

Bond had avoided looking at the girl. She said impatiently, 'You needn't be so careful of looking at me. It's no good minding those things at a time like this. You said so yourself.'

Bond turned and looked at her. Her tattered shirt came down to the waterline. There was a glimpse of pale wavering limbs below. The beautiful face smiled at him. In the mangroves the broken nose seemed appropriate in its animalness.

Bond looked at her slowly. She understood. He turned and went on downstream and she followed him.

Bond found what he wanted, a crack in the wall of mangrove that seemed to go deeper. He said, 'Don't break a branch.' He bent his head and waded in. The channel went in ten yards. The mud under their feet became deeper and softer. Then there was a solid wall of roots and they could go no farther. The brown water flowed slowly through a wide, quiet pool. Bond stopped. The girl came close to him. 'This is real hide and seek,' she said tremulously.

'Yes, isn't it.' Bond was thinking of his gun. He was wondering how well it would shoot after a bath in the river – how many dogs and men he could get if they were found. He felt a wave of disquiet. It had been a bad break coming across this girl. In combat, like it or not, a girl is your extra heart. The enemy has two targets against your one.

Bond remembered his thirst. He scooped up some water. It was brackish and tasted of earth. It was all right. He drank some more. The girl put out her hand and stopped him. 'Don't drink too much. Wash your mouth and spit. You could get fever.'

Bond looked at her quietly. He did as she told him.

Quarrel whistled from somewhere in the main stream. Bond answered and waded out towards him. They came back along the channel. Quarrel splashed the mangrove roots with water where their bodies might have brushed against them. 'Kill da smell of us,' he explained briefly. He produced his handful of bamboo lengths and began whittling and cutting them. Bond looked to his gun and the spare ammunition. They stood still in the pool so as not to stir up more mud.

The sunlight dappled down through the thick roof of leaves. The shrimps nibbled softly at their feet. Tension built up in the hot, crouching silence.

It was almost a relief to hear the baying of the dogs.

CHAPTER 10

DRAGON SPOOR

The search party was coming fast down the river. The two men in bathing trunks and tall waders were having to run to keep up with the dogs. They were big Chinese Negroes wearing shoulder holsters across their naked sweating chests. Occasionally they exchanged shouts that were mostly swear-words. Ahead of them the pack of big Dobermann Pinschers swam and floundered through the water, baying excitedly. They had a scent and they quested frenziedly, the diamond-shaped ears erect on the smooth, serpentine heads.

'May be a —ing crocodile,' yelled the leading man through the hubbub. He was carrying a short whip which he occasionally cracked like a whipper-in on the hunting field.

The other man converged towards him. He shouted excitedly, 'For my money it's the —ing limey! Bet ya he's lying up in the mangrove. Mind he doesn't give us a —ing ambush.' The man took the gun out of its holster and put it under his armpit and kept his hand on the butt.

They were coming out of the open river into the mangrove tunnel. The first man had a whistle. It stuck out of his broad face like a cigar butt. He blew a shrill blast. When the dogs swept on he laid about him with the whip. The dogs checked, whimpering as the slow current forced them to disobey orders. The two men took their guns and waded slowly downstream through the straggly legs of the mangroves.

The leading man came to the narrow break that Bond had found. He grasped a dog by the collar and swung it into the channel. The dog snorted eagerly and paddled forward. The man's eyes squinted at the mangrove roots on either side of the channel to see if they were scratched.

The dog and the man came into the small enclosed pool at the end of the channel. The man looked round disgustedly. He caught the dog by the collar and pulled him back. The dog was reluctant to leave the place. The man lashed down into the water with his whip. The second man had been waiting at the entrance to the little channel. The first man came out. He shook his head and they went on downstream, the dogs, now less excited, streaming ahead.

Slowly the noise of the hunt grew less and vanished.

For another five minutes nothing moved in the mangrove pool, then, in one corner among the roots, a thin periscope of bamboo rose slowly out of the water. Bond's face emerged, the forehead streaked with wet hair, like the face of a surfacing corpse. In his right hand under the water the gun was ready. He listened intently. There was dead silence, not a sound. Or was there? What was that soft swish out in the main stream? Was someone wading very quietly along in the wake of the hunt? Bond reached out on either side of him and softly touched the other two bodies that lay among the roots on the edge of the pool. As the two faces surfaced he put his finger to his lips. It was too late. Quarrel had coughed and spat. Bond made a grimace and nodded urgently towards the main stream. They all listened. There was dead silence. Then the soft swishing began again. Whoever it was was coming into the side-channel. The tubes of bamboo went back into the three mouths and the heads softly submerged again.

Underwater, Bond rested his head in the mud, pinched his nostrils with his left hand and pursed his lips round the tube. He knew the pool had been examined once already. He had felt the disturbance of the swimming dog. That time they had not been found. Would they get away with it again? This time there would have been less chance for the stirred mud to seep away out of the pool. If this searcher saw the darker brown stain, would he shoot into it or stab into it? What weapons would he have? Bond decided that he wouldn't take chances. At the first movement in the water near him he would get to his feet and shoot and hope for the best.

Bond lay and focused all his senses. What hell this controlled breathing was and how maddening the soft nibbling of the shrimps! It was lucky none of them had a sore on their bodies or the damned things would have eaten into it. But it had been a bright idea of the girl's. Without it the dogs would have got to them wherever they had hidden.

Suddenly Bond cringed. A rubber boot had stepped on his shin and slid off. Would the man think it was a branch? Bond couldn't chance it. With one surge of motion he hurled himself upwards, spitting out the length of bamboo.

Bond caught a quick impression of a huge body standing almost on top of him and of a swirling rifle butt. He lifted his left arm to protect his head and felt the jarring blow on his forearm. At the same time his right hand lunged forward and as the muzzle of his gun touched the glistening right breast below the hairless aureole he pulled the trigger.

The kick of the explosion, pent up against the man's body, almost broke Bond's wrist, but the man crashed back like a chopped tree into the water. Bond caught a glimpse of a huge rent in his side as he went under. The rubber waders thrashed once and the head, a Chinese Negroid head, broke the surface, its eyes turned up and water pouring from its silently yelling mouth. Then the head went under again and there was nothing but muddy froth and a slowly widening red stain that began to seep away downstream.

Bond shook himself. He turned. Quarrel and the girl were standing behind him, water streaming from their bodies. Quarrel was grinning from ear to ear, but the girl's knuckles were at her mouth and her eyes were staring horror-struck at the reddened water.

Bond said curtly, 'I'm sorry, Honey. It had to be done. He was right on top of us. Come on, let's get going.' He took her roughly by the arm and thrust her away from the place and out into the main stream, only stopping when they had reached the open river at the beginning of the mangrove tunnel.

The landscape was empty again. Bond glanced at his watch. It had stopped at three o'clock. He looked at the westering sun. It might be four o'clock now. How much farther had they to go? Bond suddenly felt tired. Now he'd torn it. Even if the shot hadn't been heard – and it would have been well muffled by the man's body and by the mangroves – the man would be missed when the others rendezvoused, if Quarrel's guess was right, at the river mouth to be taken off to the launch. Would they come back up the river to look for the missing man? Probably not. It would be getting dark before they knew for certain that he was missing. They'd send out a search party in the morning. The dogs would soon get the body. Then what?

The girl tugged at his sleeve. She said angrily, 'It's time you told me what all this is about! Why's everybody trying to kill each other? And who are you? I don't believe all this story about birds. You don't take a revolver after birds.'

Bond looked down into the angry, wide-apart eyes. 'I'm sorry,

Honey. I'm afraid I've got you into a bit of a mess. I'll tell you all about it this evening when we get to the camp. It's just bad luck you being mixed up with me like this. I've got a bit of a war on with these people. They seem to want to kill me. Now I'm only interested in seeing us all off the island without anyone else getting hurt. I've got enough to go on now so that next time I can come back by the front door.'

'What do you mean? Are you some sort of a policeman? Are you trying to send this Chinaman to prison?'

'That's about it,' Bond smiled down at her. 'At least you're on the side of the angels. And now you tell me something. How much farther to the camp?'

'Oh, about an hour.'

'Is it a good place to hide? Could they find us there easily?'

'They'd have to come across the lake or up the river. It'll be all right so long as they don't send their dragon after us. He can go through the water. I've seen him do it.'

'Oh well,' said Bond diplomatically, 'let's hope he's got a sore tail or something.'

The girl snorted. 'All right, Mr Know-all,' she said angrily. 'Just you wait.'

Quarrel splashed out of the mangroves. He was carrying a rifle. He said apologetically. 'No harm 'n havin' anudder gun, cap'n. Looks like us may need hit.'

Bond took it. It was a U.S. Army Remington Carbine, ·300. These people certainly had the right equipment. He handed it back.

Quarrel echoed his thoughts. 'Dese is sly folks, cap'n. Dat man mus' of come sneakin' down soffly behind de udders to ketch us comin' out after de dawgs had passed. He sho is a sly mongoose, dat Doctor feller.'

Bond said thoughtfully, 'He must be quite a man.' He shrugged away his thoughts. 'Now let's get going. Honey says there's another hour to the camp. Better keep to the left bank so as to get what cover we can from the hill. For all we know they've got glasses trained on the river.' Bond handed his gun to Quarrel who stowed it in the sodden knapsack. They moved off again with Quarrel in the lead and Bond and the girl walking together.

They got some shade from the bamboo and bushes along the western bank, but now they had to face the full force of the scorching wind. They splashed water over their arms and faces to cool the burns. Bond's eyes were bloodshot with the glare and his arm ached intolerably where the gun butt had struck. And he was not looking forward to his dinner of soaking bread and cheese and salt pork. How long would they be able to sleep? He hadn't had much last night? It looked like the same ration again. And what about the girl? She had had none. He and Quarrel would have to keep watch and watch. And then tomorrow. Off into the mangrove again and work their way slowly back to the canoe across the eastern end of the island. It looked like that. And sail the following night. Bond thought of hacking a way for five miles through solid mangroves. What a prospect! Bond trudged on, thinking of M's 'holiday in the sunshine'. He'd certainly give something for M to be sharing it with him now.

The river grew narrower until it was only a stream between the bamboo clumps. Then it widened out into a flat marshy estuary beyond which the five square miles of shallow lake swept away to the other side of the island in a ruffled blue-grey mirror. Beyond, there was the shimmer of the airstrip and the glint of the sun on a single hangar. The girl told them to keep to the east and they worked their way slowly along inside the fringe of bushes.

Suddenly Quarrel stopped, his face pointing like a gun-dog's at the marshy ground in front of them. Two deep parallel grooves were cut into the mud, with a fainter groove in the centre. They were the tracks of something that had come down from the hill and gone across the marsh towards the lake.

The girl said indifferently. 'That's where the dragon's been.'

Quarrel turned the whites of his eyes towards her.

Bond walked slowly along the tracks. The outside ones were quite smooth with an indented curve. They could have been made by wheels, but they were vast – at least two feet across. The centre track was of the same shape but only three inches across, about the width of a motor tyre. The tracks were without a trace of tread, and they were fairly fresh. They marched along in a dead straight line and the bushes they crossed were squashed flat as if a tank had gone over them.

Bond couldn't imagine what kind of vehicle, if it was a vehicle, had made them. When the girl nudged him and whispered fiercely 'I told you so', he could only say thoughtfully, 'Well, Honey, if it isn't a dragon, it's something else I've never seen before.'

Farther on, she tugged urgently at his sleeve. 'Look,' she whispered. She pointed forward to a big clump of bushes beside which the tracks ran. They were leafless and blackened. In the centre there showed the remains of birds' nests. 'He breathed on them,' she said excitedly.

Bond walked up to the bushes and examined them. 'He certainly did,' he admitted. Why had this particular clump been burned? It was all very odd.

The tracks swerved out towards the lake and disappeared into the water. Bond would have liked to follow them but there was no question of leaving cover. They trudged on, wrapped in their different thoughts.

Slowly the day began to die behind the sugar-loaf, and at last the girl pointed ahead through the bushes and Bond could see a long spit of sand running out into the lake. There were thick bushes of sea-grape along its spine and, halfway, perhaps a hundred yards from the shore, the remains of a thatched hut. It looked a reasonably attractive place to spend the night and it was well protected by the water on both sides. The wind had died and the water was soft and inviting. How heavenly it was going to be to take off their filthy shirts and wash in the lake, and, after the hours of squelching through the mud and stench of the river and the marsh, be able to lie down on the hard dry sand!

The sun blazed yellowly and sank behind the mountain. The day was still alive at the eastern tip of the island, but the black shadow of the sugar-loaf was slowly marching across the lake and would soon reach out and kill that too. The frogs started up, louder than in Jamaica, until the thick dusk was shrill with them. Across the lake a giant bull frog began to drum. The eerie sound was something between a tom-tom and an ape's roar. It sent out short messages that were suddenly throttled. Soon it fell silent. It had found what it had sent for.

They reached the neck of the sandspit and filed out along a narrow track. They came to the clearing with the smashed remains of the wattle hut. The big mysterious tracks led out of the water on both sides and through the clearing and over the nearby bushes as if the thing, whatever it was, had stampeded the place. Many of the bushes were burned or charred. There were the remains of a fireplace made of lumps of coral and a few scattered cooking pots and empty tins. They searched in the debris and Quarrel unearthed a couple of unopened tins of Heinz pork and beans. The girl found a crumpled sleeping-bag. Bond found a small leather purse containing five one-dollar notes, three Jamaica pounds and some silver. The two men had certainly left in a hurry.

They left the place and moved farther along to a small sandy clearing. Through the bushes they could see lights winking across the water from the mountain, perhaps two miles away. To the eastward there was nothing but the soft black sheen of water under the darkening sky.

Bond said, 'As long as we don't show a light we should be fine here. The first thing is to have a good wash. Honey, you take the rest of the sandspit and we'll have the landward end. See you for dinner in about half an hour.'

The girl laughed. 'Will you be dressing?'

'Certainly,' said Bond. 'Trousers.'

Quarrel said, 'Cap'n, while dere's henough light I'll get dese tins open and get tings fixed for de night.' He rummaged in the knapsack. 'Here's yo trousers and yo gun. De bread don't feel so good but hit only wet. Hit eat okay an' mebbe hit dry hout come de mornin'. Guess we'd better eat de tins tonight an' keep de cheese an' pork. Dose tins is heavy an' we got plenty footin' tomorrow.

Bond said, 'All right, Quarrel. I'll leave the menu to you.' He took the gun and the damp trousers and walked down into the shallow water and back the way they had come. He found a hard dry stretch of sand and took off his shirt and stepped back into the water and lay down. The water was soft but disgustingly warm. He dug up handfuls of sand and scrubbed himself with it, using it as soap. Then he lay and luxuriated in the silence and the loneliness.

The stars began to shine palely, the stars that had brought them to the island last night, a year ago, the stars that would take them away again tomorrow night, a year away. What a trip! But at least it had already paid off. Now he had enough evidence, and witnesses, to go back to the Governor and get a full-dress inquiry going into the activities of Doctor No. One didn't use machine guns on people, even on trespassers. And, by the same token, what was this thing of Doctor No's that had trespassed on the leasehold of the Audubon Society, the thing that had smashed their property and had possibly killed one of their wardens? That would have to be investigated too. And what would he find when he came back to the island through the front door, in a destroyer, perhaps, and with a detachment of marines? What would be the answer to the riddle of Doctor No? What was he hiding? What did he fear? Why was privacy so important to him that he would murder, again and again, for it? Who *was* Doctor No?

Bond heard splashing away to his right. He thought of the girl. And who, for the matter of that, was Honeychile Rider? That, he decided, as he climbed out on to dry land, was at least something that he ought to be able to find out before the night was over.

Bond pulled on his clammy trousers and sat down on the sand and dismantled his gun. He did it by touch, using his shirt to dry each part and each cartridge. Then he reassembled the gun and clicked the trigger round the empty cylinder. The sound was healthy. It would be days before it rusted. He loaded it and tucked it into the holster inside the waistband of his trousers and got up and walked back to the clearing.

The shadow of Honey reached up and pulled him down beside her. 'Come on,' she said, 'we're starving. I got one of the cooking pots and

cleaned it out and we poured the beans into it. There's about two full
handfuls each and a cricket ball of bread. And I'm not feeling guilty
about eating your food because you made me work far harder than I
would if I'd been alone. Here, hold out your hand.'

Bond smiled at the authority in her voice. He could just make out her
silhouette in the dusk. Her head looked sleeker. He wondered what her
hair looked like when it was combed and dry. What would she be like
when she was wearing clean clothes over that beautiful golden body? He
could see her coming into a room or across the lawn at Beau Desert. She
would be a beautiful, ravishing, Ugly Duckling. Why had she never had
the broken nose mended? It was an easy operation. Then she would be
the most beautiful girl in Jamaica.

Her shoulder brushed against him. Bond reached out and put his
hand down in her lap, open. She picked up his hand and Bond felt the
cold mess of beans being poured into it.

Suddenly he smelled her warm animal smell. It was so sensually
thrilling that his body swayed against her and for a moment his eyes
closed.

She gave a short laugh in which there was shyness and satisfaction and
tenderness. She said 'There,' maternally, and carried his laden hand
away from her and back to him.

CHAPTER 11

AMIDST THE ALIEN CANE

It would be around eight o'clock, Bond thought. Apart from the
background tinkle of the frogs it was very quiet. In the far corner of the
clearing he could see the dark outline of Quarrel. There was the soft
clink of metal as he dismantled and dried the Remington.

Through the bushes the distant yellow lights from the guanera made
festive pathways across the dark surface of the lake. The ugly wind had
gone and the hideous scenery lay drowned in darkness. It was cool.
Bond's clothes had dried on him. The three big handfuls of food had
warmed his stomach. He felt comfortable and drowsy and at peace.
Tomorrow was a long way off and presented no problems except a great
deal of physical exercise. Life suddenly felt easy and good.

The girl lay beside him in the sleeping-bag. She was lying on her back with her head cradled in her hands, looking up at the roof of stars. He could just make out the pale pool of her face. She said, 'James. You promised to tell me what this is all about. Come on. I shan't go to sleep until you do.'

Bond laughed. 'I'll tell if you'll tell. I want to know what you're all about.'

'I don't mind. I've got no secrets. But you first.'

'All right then.' Bond pulled his knees up to his chin and put his arms round them. 'It's like this. I'm a sort of policeman. They send me out from London when there's something odd going on somewhere in the world that isn't anybody else's business. Well, not so long ago one of the Governor's staff in Kingston, a man called Strangways, friend of mine, disappeared. His secretary, who was a pretty girl, did too. Most people thought they'd run away together. I didn't. I . . .'

Bond told the story in simple terms, with good men and bad men, like an adventure story out of a book. He ended, 'So you see, Honey, it's just a question of getting back to Jamaica tomorrow night, all three of us in the canoe, and then the Governor will listen to us and send over a lot of soldiers to get this Chinaman to own up. I expect that'll mean he'll go to prison. He'll know that too and that's why he's trying to stop us. That's all. Now it's your turn.'

The girl said, 'You seem to live a very exciting life. Your wife can't like you being away so much. Doesn't she worry about you getting hurt?'

'I'm not married. The only people who worry about me getting hurt are my insurance company.'

She probed, 'But I suppose you have girls.'

'Not permanent ones.'

'Oh.'

There was a pause. Quarrel came over to them. 'Cap'n, Ah'll take de fust watch if dat suits. Be out on de point of de sandspit. Ah'll come call yo around midnight. Den mebbe yo take on till five and den we all git goin'. Need to get well away from dis place afore it's light.'

'Suits me,' said Bond. 'Wake me if you see anything. Gun all right?'

'Him's jess fine,' said Quarrel happily. He said, 'Sleep well, missy,' with a hint of meaning, and melted noiselessly away into the shadows.

'I like Quarrel,' said the girl. She paused, then, 'Do you really want to know about me? It's not as exciting as your story.'

'Of course I do. And don't leave anything out.'

'There's nothing to leave out. You could get my whole life on to the back of a postcard. To begin with I've never been out of Jamaica. I've lived all my life at a place called Beau Desert on the North Coast near Morgan's Harbour.'

Bond laughed. 'That's odd. So do I. At least for the moment. I didn't
notice you about. Do you live up a tree?'

'Oh, I suppose you've taken the beach house. I never go near the
place. I live in the Great House.'

'But there's nothing left of it. It's a ruin in the middle of the cane
fields.'

'I live in the cellars. I've lived there since I was five. It was burned
down then and my parents were killed. I can't remember anything
about them so you needn't say you're sorry. At first I lived there with my
black nanny. She died when I was fifteen. For the last five years I've
lived there alone.'

'Good heavens.' Bond was appalled. 'But wasn't there anyone else to
look after you? Didn't your parents leave any money?'

'Not a penny.' There was no bitterness in the girls voice – pride if
anything. 'You see the Riders were one of the old Jamaican families. The
first one had been given the Beau Desert lands by Cromwell for having
been one of the people who signed King Charles's death warrant. He
built the Great House and my family lived in it on and off ever since. But
then sugar collapsed and I suppose the place was badly run, and by the
time my father inherited it there was nothing but debts – mortgages and
things like that. So when my father and mother died the property was
sold up. I didn't mind. I was too young. Nanny must have been
wonderful. They wanted people to adopt me, the clergyman and the
legal people did, but Nanny collected the sticks of furniture that hadn't
been burned and we settled down in the ruins and after a bit no one
came and interfered with us. She did a bit of sewing and laundry in the
village and grew a few plantains and bananas and things and there was a
big breadfruit tree up against the old house. We ate what the Jamaicans
eat. And there was the sugar cane all round us and she made a fishpot
which we used to go and take up every day. It was all right. We had
enough to eat. Somehow she taught me to read and write. There was a
pile of old books left from the fire. There was an encyclopedia. I started
with A when I was about eight. I've got as far as the middle of T.' She
said defensively. 'I bet I know more than you do about a lot of things.'

'I bet you do.' Bond was lost in the picture of the little flaxen-haired
girl pattering about the ruins with the obstinate old Negress watching
over her and calling her in to do the lessons that must have been just as
much a riddle to the old woman. 'Your nanny must have been a
wonderful person.'

'She was a darling.' It was a flat statement. 'I thought I'd die when
she did. It wasn't such fun after that. Before, I'd led a child's life; then I

suddenly had to grow up and do everything for myself. And men tried to catch me and hurt me. They said they wanted to make love to me.' She paused. 'I used to be pretty then.'

Bond said seriously, 'You're one of the most beautiful girls I've ever seen.'

'With this nose? Don't be silly.'

'You don't understand.' Bond tried to find words that she would believe. 'Of course anyone can see your nose is broken. But since this morning I've hardly noticed it. When you look at a person you look into their eyes or at their mouth. That's where the expressions are. A broken nose isn't any more significant than a crooked ear. Noses and ears are bits of face-furniture. Some are prettier than others, but they're not nearly as important as the rest. They're part of the background of the face. If you had a beautiful nose as well as the rest of you you'd be the most beautiful girl in Jamaica.'

'Do you mean that?' her voice was urgent. 'Do you think I could be beautiful? I know some of me's all right, but when I look in the glass I hardly see anything except my broken nose. I'm sure it's like that with other people who are, who are – well – sort of deformed.'

Bond said impatiently, 'You're not deformed! Don't talk such nonsense. And anyway you can have it put right by a simple operation. You've only got to get over to America and it would be done in a week.'

She said angrily, 'How do you expect me to do that? I've got about fifteen pounds under a stone in my cellar. I've got three skirts and three shirts and a knife and a fishpot. I know all about these operations. The doctor at Port Maria found out for me. He's a nice man. He wrote to America. Do you know, to have it properly done it would cost me about five hundred pounds, what with the fare to New York and the hospital and everything?' Her voice became hopeless. 'How do you expect me to find that amount of money?'

Bond had already made up his mind what would have to be done about that. Now he merely said tenderly, 'Well, I expect there are ways. But anyway, go on with your story. It's very exciting – far more interesting than mine. You'd got to where your Nanny died. What happened then?'

The girl began again reluctantly.

'Well, it's your fault for interrupting. And you mustn't talk about things you don't understand. I suppose people tell you you're good-looking. I expect you get all the girls you want. Well you wouldn't if you had a squint or a hare-lip or something. As a matter of fact,' he could hear the smile in her voice, 'I think I shall go to the obeahman when we get back and get him to put a spell on you and give you something like that.' She added lamely, 'Then we should be more alike.'

Bond reached out. His hand brushed against her. 'I've got other plans,' he said. 'But come on. I want to hear the rest of the story.'

'Oh well,' the girl sighed, 'I'll have to go back a bit. You see all the property is in cane and the old house stands in the middle of it. Well, about twice a year they cut the cane and send it off to the mill. And when they do that all the animals and insects and so on that live in the cane fields go into a panic and most of them have their houses destroyed and get killed. At cutting time some of them took to coming to the ruins of the house and hiding. My Nanny was terrified of them to begin with, the mongooses and the snakes and the scorpions and so on, but I made a couple of the cellar rooms into sort of homes for them. I wasn't frightened of them and they never hurt me. They seemed to understand that I was looking after them. They must have told their friends or something because after a bit it was quite natural for them all to come trooping into their rooms and settling down there until the young cane had started to grow again. Then they all filed out and went back to living in the fields. I gave them what food we could spare when they were staying with us and they behaved very well except for making a bit of a smell and sometimes fighting amongst each other. But they all got quite tame with me, and their children did, too, and I could do anything with them. Of course the cane-cutters found out about this and saw me walking about with snakes round my neck and so forth, and they got frightened of me and thought I was obeah. So they left us absolutely alone.' She paused. 'That's where I found out so much about animals and insects. I used to spend a lot of time in the sea finding out about those people too. It was the same with birds. If you find out what all these people like to eat and what they're afraid of, and if you spend all your time with them you can make friends.' She looked up at him. 'You miss a lot not knowing about these things.'

'I'm afraid I do,' said Bond truthfully. 'I expect they're much nicer and more interesting than humans.'

'I don't know about that,' said the girl thoughtfully. 'I don't know many human people. Most of the ones I have met have been hateful. But I suppose they can be interesting too.' She paused. 'I hadn't ever really thought of liking them like I like the animals. Except for Nanny, of course. Until . . .' She broke off with a shy laugh. 'Well, anyway we all lived happily together until I was fifteen and Nanny died and then things got difficult. There was a man called Mander. A horrible man. He was the white overseer for the people who own the property. He kept coming to see me. He wanted me to move up to his house near Port Maria. I hated him and I used to hide when I heard his horse coming through the cane. One night he came on foot and I didn't hear him. He was drunk. He came into the cellar and fought with me because I wouldn't do what he wanted me to do. You know, the things people in love do.'

'Yes, I know.'

'I tried to kill him with my knife, but he was very strong and he hit me as hard as he could in the face and broke my nose. He knocked me unconscious and then I think he did things to me. I mean I know he did. Next day I wanted to kill myself when I saw my face and when I found what he had done. I thought I would have a baby. I would certainly have killed myself if I'd had a baby by that man. Anyway, I didn't, so that was that. I went to the doctor and he did what he could for my nose and didn't charge me anything. I didn't tell him about the rest. I was too ashamed. The man didn't come back. I waited and did nothing until the next cane-cutting. I'd got my plan. I was waiting for the Black Widow spiders to come in for shelter. One day they came. I caught the biggest of the females and shut her in a box with nothing to eat. They're the bad ones, the females. Then I waited for a dark night without any moon. I took the box with the spider in it and walked and walked until I came to the man's house. It was very dark and I was frightened of the duppies I might meet on the road but I didn't see any. I waited in his garden in the bushes and watched him go up to bed. Then I climbed a tree and got on to his balcony. I waited there until I heard him snoring and then I crept through the window. He was lying naked on the bed under the mosquito net. I lifted the edge and opened the box and shook the spider out on to his stomach. Then I went away and came home.'

'God Almighty!' said Bond reverently. 'What happened to him?'

She said happily, 'He took a week to die. It must have hurt terribly. They do, you know. The obeahmen say there's nothing like it.' She paused. When Bond made no comment, she said anxiously, 'You don't think I did wrong, do you?'

'It's not a thing to make a habit of,' said Bond mildly. 'But I can't say I blame you the way it was. So what happened then?'

'Well then I just settled down again,' her voice was matter-of-fact. 'I had to concentrate on getting enough food, and of course all I wanted to do was save up money to get my nose made good again.' She said persuasively, 'It really was quite a pretty nose before. Do you think the doctors can put it back to how it was?'

'They can make it any shape you like,' said Bond definitely. 'What did you make money at?'

'It was the encyclopedia. It told me that people collect sea-shells. That one could sell the rare ones. I talked to the local schoolmaster, without telling him my secret of course, and he found out that there's an American magazine called *Nautilus* for shell collectors. I had just enough money to subscribe to it and I began looking for the shells that people said they wanted in the advertisements. I wrote to a dealer in Miami and he started buying from me. It was thrilling. Of course I made some awful mistakes to begin with. I thought people would like the prettiest shells, but they don't. Very often they want the ugliest. And then when I found rare ones I cleaned them and polished them to make them look better. That's wrong too. They want shells just as they come out of the sea, with the animal in and all. So I got some formalin from the doctor and put it into the live shells to stop them smelling and sent them off to this man in Miami. I only got it right about a year ago and I've already made fifteen pounds. I'd worked out that now I knew how they wanted them, and if I was lucky, I ought to make at least fifty pounds a year. Then in ten years I would be able to go to America and have the operation. And then,' she giggled delightedly, 'I had a terrific stroke of luck. I went over to Crab Key. I'd been there before, but this was just before Christmas, and I found these purple shells. They didn't look very exciting, but I sent one or two to Miami and the man wrote back at once and said he could take as many as I could get at five dollars each for the whole ones. He said that I must keep the place where they live a dead secret as otherwise we'd what he called "spoil the market" and the price would get cheaper. It's just like having one's private gold mine. Now I may be able to save up the money in five years. That's why I was so suspicious of you when I found you on my beach. I thought you'd come to steal my shells.'

'You gave me a bit of a shock. I thought you must be Doctor No's girl friend.'

'Thanks very much.'

'But when you've had the operation, what are you going to do then? You can't go on living alone in a cellar all your life.'

'I thought I'd be a call girl.' She said it as she might have said 'nurse' or 'secretary'.

'Oh, what do you mean by that?' Perhaps she had picked up the expression without understanding it.

'One of those girls who has a beautiful flat and lovely clothes. You know what I mean,' she said impatiently. 'People ring them up and come and make love to them and pay them for it. They get a hundred dollars for each time in New York. That's where I thought I'd start. Of course,' she admitted, 'I might have to do it for less to begin with. Until I learned to do it really well. How much do you pay the untrained ones?'

Bond laughed. 'I really can't remember. It's quite a long time since I had one.'

She sighed. 'Yes, I suppose you can have as many women as you want for nothing. I suppose it's only the ugly men that pay. But that can't be helped. Any kind of job in the big towns must be dreadful. At least you can earn much more being a call girl. Then I can come back to Jamaica and buy Beau Desert. I'd be rich enough to find a nice husband and have some children. Now that I've found these Venus shells I've worked out that I might be back in Jamaica by the time I'm thirty. Won't that be lovely?'

'I like the last part of the plan. But I'm not so sure of the first. Anyway, where did you find out about these call girls? Were they under C in the encyclopedia?'

'Of course not. Don't be silly. There was a big case about them in New York about two years ago. There was a rich playboy called Jelke. He had a whole string of girls. There was a lot about the case in the *Gleaner*. They gave all the prices and everything. And anyway, there are thousands of those sort of girls in Kingston, only of course not such good ones. They only get about five shillings and they have nowhere to go and do it except the bush. My Nanny told me about them. She said I mustn't grow up like them or I'd be very unhappy. I can see that for only five shillings. But for a hundred dollars . . . !'

Bond said, 'You wouldn't be able to keep all of that. You'd have to have a sort of manager to get the men, and then you'd have to bribe the police to leave you alone. And you could easily go to prison if something went wrong. I really don't think you'd like the work. I'll tell you what, with all you know about animals and insects and so on you could get a wonderful job looking after them in one of the American zoos. Or what about the Jamaica Institute? I'm sure you'd like that better. You'd be just as likely to meet a nice husband. Anyway you mustn't think of being a call girl any more. You've got a beautiful body. You must keep it for the men you love.'

'That's what people say in books,' she said doubtfully. 'The trouble is there aren't any men to love at Beau Desert.' She said shyly, 'You're the first Englishman I've ever talked to. I liked you from the beginning. I don't mind telling you these things at all. I suppose there are plenty of other people I should like if I could get away.'

'Of course there are. Hundreds. And you're a wonderful girl. I thought so directly I saw you.'

'Saw my behind, you mean.' The voice was getting drowsy, but it was full of pleasure.

Bond laughed. 'Well, it was a wonderful behind. And the other side was wonderful too.' Bond's body began to stir with the memory of how she had been. He said gruffly, 'Now come on, Honey. It's time to go to sleep. There'll be plenty of time to talk when we get back to Jamaica.'

'Will there?' she said sleepily. 'Promise?'

'Promise.'

He heard her stir in the sleeping-bag. He looked down. He could just make out the pale profile turned towards him. She gave the deep sigh of a child before it falls asleep.

There was silence in the clearing. It was getting cold. Bond put his head down on his hunched knees. He knew it was no good trying to get to sleep. His mind was full of the day and of this extraordinary Girl Tarzan who had come into his life. It was as if some beautiful animal had attached itself to him. There would be no dropping the leash until he had solved her problems for her. He knew it. Of course there would be no difficulty about most of them. He could fix the operation – even, with the help of friends, find a proper job and a home for her. He had the money. He would buy her dresses, have her hair done, get her started in the big world. It would be fun. But what about the other side? What about the physical desire he felt for her? One could not make love to a child. But was she a child? There was nothing childish about her body or her personality. She was fully grown and highly intelligent in her fashion, and far more capable of taking care of herself than any girl of twenty Bond had ever met.

Bond's thought were interrupted by a tug at his sleeve. The small voice said, 'Why don't you go to sleep? Are you cold?'

'No, I'm fine.'

'It's nice and warm in the sleeping-bag. Would you like to come in? There's plenty of room.'

'No thank you, Honey. I'll be all right.'

There was a pause, then, almost in a whisper, 'If you're thinking . . . I mean – you don't have to make love to me . . . We could go to sleep back to front, you know, like spoons.'

'Honey, darling, you go to sleep. It'd be lovely to be like that, but not tonight. Anyway I'll have to take over from Quarrel soon.'

'Yes, I see.' The voice was grudging. 'Perhaps when we get back to Jamaica.'

'Perhaps.'

'Promise. I won't go to sleep until you promise.'

Bond said desperately. 'Of course I promise. Now go to sleep, Honeychile.'

The voice whispered triumphantly, 'Now you owe me slave-time. You've promised. Good night, darling James.'

'Good night, darling Honey.'

CHAPTER 12

THE THING

The grip on Bond's shoulder was urgent. He was instantly on his feet.

Quarrel whispered fiercely, 'Somepn comin' across de water, cap'n! It de dragon fo sho!'

The girl woke up. She said anxiously, 'What's happened?'

Bond said, 'Stay here, Honey! Don't move. I'll be back.' He broke through the bushes on the side away from the mountain and ran along the sand with Quarrel at his elbow.

They came to the tip of the sandspit, twenty yards from the clearing. They stopped under cover of the final bushes. Bond parted them and looked through.

What was it? Half a mile away, coming across the lake, was a shapeless thing with two glaring orange eyes with black pupils. From between these, where the mouth might be, fluttered a yard of blue flame. The grey luminescence of the stars showed some kind of domed head above two short batlike wings. The thing was making a low moaning roar that overlaid another noise, a deep rhythmic thud. It was coming towards them at about ten miles an hour, throwing up a creamy wake.

Quarrel whispered, 'Gawd, cap'n! What's dat fearful ting?'

Bond stood up. He said shortly, 'Don't know exactly. Some sort of tractor affair dressed up to frighten. It's running on a diesel engine, so you can forget about dragons. Now let's see.' Bond spoke half to himself. 'No good running away. The thing's too fast for us and we know it can go over mangroves and swamps. Have to fight it here. What'll its weak spots be? The drivers. Of course they'll have protection. We don't know how much. Quarrel, you start firing at that dome on top when it gets to two hundred yards. Aim carefully and keep on firing. I'll go for its headlights when it gets to fifty yards. It's not running on tracks. Must have some kind of giant tyres, aeroplane tyres probably. I'll go for them too. Stay here. I'll go ten yards along. They may start firing back and we've got to keep the bullets away from the girl. Okay?' Bond reached out and squeezed the big shoulder. 'And don't worry too much. Forget about dragons. It's just some gadget of Doctor No's. We'll kill the drivers and capture the damn thing and ride it down to the coast. Save us shoe-leather. Right?'

Quarrel laughed shortly. 'Okay, cap'n. Since you says so. But Ah sho hopes de Almighty knows he's no dragon too!'

Bond ran down the sand. He broke through the bushes until he had a clear field of fire. He called softly, 'Honey!'

'Yes, James.' There was a relief in the nearby voice.

'Make a hole in the sand like we did on the beach. Behind the thickest roots. Get into it and lie down. There may be some shooting. Don't worry about dragons. This is just a painted up motor car with some of Doctor No's men in it. Don't be frightened. I'm quite close.'

'All right, James. Be careful.' The voice was high with fright.

Bond knelt on one knee in the leaves and sand and peered out.

Now the thing was only about three hundred yards away and its yellow headlights were lighting up the sandspit. Blue flames were still fluttering from the mouth. They were coming from a long snout mocked-up with gaping jaws and gold paint to look like a dragon's mouth. Flame-thrower! That would explain the burned bushes and the warden's story. The blue flames would be coming from some kind of an after-burner. The apparatus was now in neutral. What would its range be when the compression was unleashed?

Bond had to admit that the thing was an awesome sight as it moaned forward through the shallow lake. It was obviously designed to terrify. It would have frightened him but for the earthy thud of the diesel. Against native intruders it would be devastating. But how vulnerable would it be to people with guns who didn't panic?

He was answered at once. There came the crack of Quarrel's Remington. A spark flew off the domed cabin and there was a dull clang. Quarrel fired another single shot and then a burst. The bullets hammered ineffectually against the cabin. There was not even a check in speed. The thing rolled on, swerving slightly to make for the source of the gunfire. Bond cradled the Smith & Wesson on his forearm and took careful aim. The deep cough of his gun sounded above the rattle of the Remington. One of the headlamps shattered and went out. He fired four shots at the other and got it with the fifth and last round in the cylinder. The thing didn't care. It rolled straight on towards Quarrel's hiding place. Bond reloaded and began firing at the huge bulge of the tyres under the bogus black and gold wings. The range was now only thirty yards and he could have sworn that he hit the nearest wheel again and again. No effect. Solid rubber? The first breath of fear stirred Bond's skin.

He reloaded. Was the damn thing vulnerable from the rear? Should he dash out into the lake and try and board it? He took a step forward through the bushes. Then he froze, incapable of movement.

Suddenly, from the dribbling snout, a yellow-tipped bolt of blue flame had howled out toward's Quarrel's hiding place. There was a single puff of orange and red flame from the bushes to Bond's right and one unearthly scream, immediately choked. Satisfied, the searing tongue of fire licked back into the snout. The thing turned on its axis and stopped dead. Now the blue hole of its mouth aimed straight at Bond.

Bond stood and waited for his unspeakable end. He looked into the blue jaws of death and saw the glowing red filament of the firer deep inside the big tube. He thought of Quarrel's body – there was no time to think of Quarrel – and imagined the blackened, smoking figure lying in the melted sand. Soon he, too, would flame like a torch. The single scream would be wrung from him and his limbs would jerk into the dancing pose of burned bodies. Then it would be Honey's turn. Christ, what had he led them into! Why had he been so insane as to take on this man with his devastating armoury. Why hadn't he been warned by the long finger that had pointed at him in Jamaica? Bond set his teeth. Hurry up, you bastards. Get it over.

There came the twang of a loud-hailer. A voice howled metallically, 'Come on out, Limey. And the doll. Quick, or you'll fry in hell like your pal.' To rub in the command, the bolt of flame spat briefly towards him. Bond stepped back from the searing heat. He felt the girl's body against his back. She said hysterically, 'I had to come. I had to come.'

Bond said, 'It's all right, Honey. Keep behind me.'

He had made up his mind. There was no alternative. Even if death was to come later it couldn't be worse than this kind of death. Bond reached for the girl's hand and drew her after him out on to the sand.

The voice howled. 'Stop there. Good boy. And drop the pea-shooter. No tricks or the crabs'll be getting a cooked breakfast.'

Bond dropped his gun. So much for the Smith & Wesson. The Beretta would have been just as good against this thing. The girl whimpered. Bond squeezed her hand. 'Stick it, Honey,' he said. 'We'll get out of this somehow.' Bond sneered at himself for the lie.

There was the clang of an iron door being opened. From the back of the dome a man dropped into the water and walked towards them.

There was a gun in his hand. He kept out of the line of fire of the flame-thrower. The fluttering blue flame lit up his sweating face. He was a Chinese Negro, a big man, clad only in trousers. Something dangled from his left hand. When he came closer, Bond saw it was handcuffs.

The man stopped a few yards away. He said, 'Hold out your hands. Wrists together. Then walk towards me. You first, Limey. Slowly or you get an extra navel.'

Bond did as he was told. When he was within sweat-smell of the man, the man put his gun between his teeth and reached out and snapped the handcuffs on Bond's wrists. Bond looked into the face, gunmetal-coloured from the blue flames. It was a brutal, squinting face. It sneered at him. 'Dumb bastard,' said the man.

Bond turned his back on the man and started walking away. He was going to see Quarrel's body. He had to say goodbye to it. There was the roar of a gun. A bullet kicked up sand close to his feet. Bond stopped and turned slowly round. 'Don't be nervous,' he said. 'I'm going to take a look at the man you've just murdered. I'll be back.'

The man lowered his gun. He laughed harshly. 'Okay. Enjoy yourself. Sorry we ain't got a wreath. Come back quick or we give the doll a toastin'. Two minutes.'

Bond walked on towards the smoking clump of bushes. He got there and looked down. His eyes and mouth winced. Yes, it had been just as he had visualized. Worse. He said softly, 'I'm sorry, Quarrel.' He kicked into the ground and scooped up a handful of cool sand between his manacled hands and poured it over the remains of the eyes. Then he walked slowly back and stood beside the girl.

The man waved them forward with his gun. They walked round the back of the machine. There was a small square door. A voice from inside said, 'Get in and sit on the floor. Don't touch anything or you get your fingers broke.'

They scrambled into the iron box. It stank of sweat and oil. There was just room for them to sit with their knees hunched up. The man with the gun followed them in and banged the door. He switched on a light and sat down on an iron tractor seat beside the driver. He said, 'Okay, Sam. Let's get goin'. You can put out the fire. It's light enough to steer by.'

There was a row of dials and switches on the instrument panel. The driver reached forward and pulled down a couple of the switches. He put the machine into gear and peered out through a narrow slit in the iron wall in front of him. Bond felt the machine turn. There came a faster beat from the engine and they moved off.

The girl's shoulder pressed against his. 'Where are they taking us?' The whisper trembled.

Bond turned his head and looked at her. It was the first time he had been able to see her hair when it was dry. Now it was disarrayed by sleep, but it was no longer a bunch of rats' tails. It hung heavily straight down to her shoulders, where it curled softly inwards. It was of the palest ash blonde and shone almost silver under the electric light. She looked up at him. The skin round her eyes and at the corners of her mouth was white with fear.

Bond shrugged with an indifference he didn't feel. He whispered, 'Oh, I expect we're going to see Doctor No. Don't worry too much, Honey. These men are just little gangsters. It'll be different with him. When we get to him don't you say anything, I'll talk for both of us.' He pressed her shoulder. 'I like the way you do your hair. I'm glad you don't cut it too short.'

Some of the tension went out of her face. 'How can you think of things like that?' She half smiled at him. 'But I'm glad you like it. I wash it in coconut oil once a week.' At the memory of her other life her eyes grew bright with tears. She bent her head down to her manacled hands to hide her tears. She whispered almost to herself, 'I'll try to be brave. It'll be all right as long as you're there.'

Bond shifted so that he was right up against her. He brought his handcuffed hands close up to his eyes and examined them. They were the American police model. He contracted his left hand, the thinner of the two, and tried to pull it through the squat ring of steel. Even the sweat on his skin was no help. It was hopeless.

The two men sat on their iron seats with their backs to them, indifferent. They knew they had total command. There wasn't room for Bond to give any trouble. Bond couldn't stand up or get enough momentum into his hands to do any damage to the backs of their heads with his handcuffs. If Bond somehow managed to open the hatch and drop into the water, where would that get him? They would at once feel the fresh air on their backs and stop the machine, and either burn him in the water or pick him up. It annoyed Bond that they didn't worry about him, that they knew he was utterly in their power. He also didn't like the idea that these men were intelligent enough to know that he presented no threat. Stupider men would have sat over him with a gun out, would have trussed him and the girl with inexpert thoroughness, might even have knocked them unconscious. These two knew their business. They were professionals, or had been trained to be professionals.

The two men didn't talk to each other. There was no nervous chatter about how clever they had been, about their destination, about how tired they were. They just drove the machine quietly, efficiently along, finishing their competent job.

Bond still had no idea what this contraption was. Under the black and gold paint and the rest of the fancy dress it was some sort of a tractor, but of a kind he had never seen or heard of. The wheels, with their vast smooth rubber tyres, were nearly twice as tall as himself. He had seen no trade name on the tyres, it had been too dark, but they were certainly either solid or filled with porous rubber. At the rear there had been a small training wheel for stability. An iron fin, painted black and gold, had been added to help the dragon effect. The high mudguards had been extended into short backswept wings. A long metal dragon's head had been added to the front of the radiator and the headlamps had been given black centres to make 'eyes'. That was all there was to it, except that the cabin had been covered with an armoured dome and the flame-thrower added. It was, as Bond had thought, a tractor dressed up to frighten and burn – though why it had a flame-thrower instead of a machine gun he couldn't imagine. It was clearly the only sort of vehicle that could travel the island. Its huge wide wheels would ride over mangrove and swamp and across the shallow lake. It would negotiate the rough coral uplands and, since its threat would be at night, the heat in the iron cabin would remain at least tolerable.

Bond was impressed. He was always impressed by professionalism. Doctor No was obviously a man who took immense pains. Soon Bond would be meeting him. Soon he would be up against the secret of Doctor No. And then what? Bond smiled grimly to himself. He wouln't be allowed to get away with his knowledge. He would certainly be killed unless he could escape or talk his way out. And what about the girl? Could Bond prove her innocence and have her spared? Conceivably, but she would never be let off the island. She would have to stay there for the rest of her life, as the mistress or wife of one of the men, or Doctor No himself if she appealed to him.

Bond's thoughts were interrupted by rougher going under the wheels. They had crossed the lake and were on the track that led up the mountain to the huts. The cabin tilted and the machine began to climb. In five minutes they would be there.

The co-driver glanced over his shoulder at Bond and the girl. Bond smiled cheerfully up at him. He said, 'You'll get a medal for this.'

The brown and yellow eyes looked impassively into his. The purple, blubbery lips parted in a sneer in which there was slow hate: 'Shut your —ing mouth.' The man turned back.

The girl nudged him and whispered, 'Why are they so rude? Why do they hate us so much?'

Bond grinned down at her, 'I expect it's because we made them afraid. Perhaps they're still afraid. That's because we don't seem to be frightened of them. We must keep them that way.'

The girl pressed against him. 'I'll try.'

Now the climb was getting steeper. Grey light showed through the slots in the armour. Dawn was coming up. Outside, another day of brazen heat and ugly wind and the smell of marsh gas would be beginning. Bond thought of Quarrel, the brave giant who would not be seeing it, with whom they should now be setting off for the long trek through the mangrove swamps. He remembered the life insurance. Quarrel had smelled his death. Yet he had followed Bond unquestioningly. His faith in Bond had been stronger than his fear. And Bond had let him down. Would Bond also be the death of the girl?

The driver reached forward to the dashboard. From the front of the machine there sounded the brief howl of a police siren. It meandered into a dying moan. After a minute the machine stopped, idling in neutral. The man pressed a switch and took a microphone off a hook beside him. He spoke into it and Bond could hear the echoing voice of the loud-hailer outside. 'Okay. Got the Limey and the girl. Other man's dead. That's the lot. Open up.'

Bond heard a door being pulled sideways on iron rollers. The driver put in the clutch and they rolled slowly forward a few yards and stopped. The man switched off the engine. There was a clang as the iron hatch was opened from the outside. A gush of fresh air and a flood of brighter light came into the cabin. Hands took hold of Bond and dragged him roughly out backwards on to a cement floor. Bond stood up. He felt the prod of a gun in his side. A voice said, 'Stay where you are. No tricks.' Bond looked at the man. He was another Chinese Negro, from the same stable as the others. The yellow eyes examined him curiously. Bond turned away indifferently. Another man was prodding the girl with his gun. Bond said sharply, 'Leave the girl alone.' He walked over and stood beside her. The two men seemed surprised. They stood, pointing their guns indecisively.

Bond looked around him. They were in one of the Quonset huts he had seen from the river. It was a garage and workshop. The 'dragon' had been halted over an examination pit in the concrete. A dismantled outboard motor lay on one of the benches. Strips of white sodium lighting ran along the ceiling. There was a smell of oil and exhaust smoke. The driver and his mate were examining the machine. Now they sauntered up.

One of the guards said, 'Passed the message along. The word is to send them through. Everything go okay?'

The co-driver, who seemed to be the senior man present, said, 'Sure. Bit of gunfire. Lights gone. May be some holes in the tyres. Get the boys crackin' – full overhaul. I'll put these two through and go get myself some shuteye.' He turned to Bond. 'Okay, git moving,' he gestured down the long hut.

Bond said, 'Get moving yourself. Mind your manners. And tell those apes to take their guns off us. They might let one off by mistake. They look dumb enough.'

The man came closer. The other three closed up behind him. Hate shone redly in their eyes. The leading man lifted a clenched fist as big as a small ham and held it under Bond's nose. He was controlling himself with an effort. He said tensely, 'Listen, mister. Sometimes us boys is allowed to join in the fun at the end. I'm just praying this'll be one of those times. Once we made it last a whole week. An' Jees, if I get you . . .' He broke off. His eyes were alight with cruelty. He looked past Bond at the girl. The eyes became mouths that licked their lips. He wiped his hands down the sides of his trousers. The tip of his tongue showed pinkly between the purple lips. He turned to the other three. 'What say, fellers?'

The three men were also looking at the girl. They nodded dumbly, like children in front of a Christmas tree.

Bond longed to run berserk among them, laying into their faces with his manacled wrists, accepting their bloody revenge. But for the girl he would have done it. Now all he achieved with his brave words was to get her frightened. He said, 'All right, all right. You're four and we're two and we've got our hands tied. Come on. We won't hurt you. Just don't push us around too much. Doctor No might not be pleased.'

At the name, the men's faces changed. Three pairs of eyes looked whitely from Bond to the leader. For a minute the leader stared suspiciously at Bond, wondering, trying to fathom whether perhaps Bond had got some edge on their boss. His mouth opened to say something. He thought better of it. He said lamely, 'Okay, okay. We was just kiddin'.' He turned to the men for confirmation. 'Right?'

'Sure. Sure thing.' It was a ragged mumble. The men looked away.

The leader said gruffly, 'This way, mister.' He walked off down the long hut.

Bond took the girl's wrist and followed. He was impressed with the weight of Doctor No's name. That was something to remember if they had any more dealings with the staff.

The man came to a rough wooden door at the end of the hut. There was a bellpush beside it. He rang twice and waited. There came a click and the door opened to reveal ten yards of carpeted rock passage with another door, smarter and cream-painted, at the end.

The man stood aside. 'Straight ahead, mister. Knock on the door. The receptionist'll take over.' There was no irony in his voice and his eyes were impassive.

Bond led the girl into the passage. He heard the door shut behind them. He stopped and looked down at her. He said, 'Now what?'

She smiled tremulously. 'It's nice to feel carpet under one's feet.'

Bond squeezed her wrist. He walked forward to the cream-painted door and knocked.

The door opened. Bond went through with the girl at his heels. When he stopped dead in his tracks, he didn't feel the girl bump into him. He just stood and stared.

CHAPTER 13

MINK-LINED PRISON

It was the sort of reception room the largest American corporations have on the President's floor in their New York skyscrapers. It was of pleasant proportions, about twenty feet square. The floor was close-carpeted in the thickest wine-red Wilton and the walls and ceiling were painted a soft dove grey. Colour lithograph reproductions of Degas ballet sketches were well hung in groups on the walls and the lighting was by tall modern standard lamps with dark green silk shades in a fashionable barrel design.

To Bond's right was a broad mahogany desk with a green leather top, handsome matching desk furniture and the most expensive type of intercom. Two tall antique chairs waited for visitors. On the other side of the room was a refectory-type table with shiny magazines and two more chairs. On both the desk and the table were tall vases of freshly cut hibiscus. The air was fresh and cool and held a slight, expensive fragrance.

There were two women in the room. Behind the desk, with pen poised over a printed form, sat an efficient-looking Chinese girl with horn-rimmed spectacles below a bang of black hair cut short. Her eyes and mouth wore the standard receptionist's smile of welcome – bright, helpful, inquisitive.

Holding the door through which they had come, and waiting for them to move farther into the room so that she could close it, stood an older, rather matronly woman of about forty-five. She also had Chinese blood. Her appearance, wholesome, bosomy, eager, was almost excessively gracious. Her square cut pince-nez gleamed with the hostess's desire to make them feel at home.

Both women were dressed in spotless white, with white stockings and white suede brogues, like assistants in the most expensive American beauty-parlours. There was something soft and colourless about their skins as if they rarely went out of doors.

While Bond took in the scene, the woman at the door twittered conventional phrases of welcome as if they had been caught in a storm and had arrived late at a party.

'You poor dears. We simply didn't know when to expect you. We kept on being told you were on your way. First it was teatime yesterday, then dinner, and it was only half an hour ago we heard you would only be here in time for breakfast. You must be famished. Come along now and help Sister Rose fill in your forms and then I'll pack you both straight off to bed. You must be tired out.'

Clucking softly, she closed the door and ushered them forward to the desk. She got them seated in the chairs and rattled on. 'Now I'm Sister Lily and this is Sister Rose. She just wants to ask you a few questions. Now, let me see, a cigarette?' She picked up a tooled leather box. She opened it and put it on the desk in front of them. It had three compartments. She pointed with a little finger. 'Those are American, and those are Players, and those are Turkish.' She picked up an expensive desk-lighter and waited.

Bond reached out his manacled hands to take a Turkish cigarette.

Sister Lily gave a squeak of dismay. 'Oh, but really.' She sounded genuinely embarrassed. 'Sister Rose, the key, quickly. I've said again and again that patients are never to be brought in like that.' There was impatience and distaste in her voice. 'Really, that outside staff! It's time they had a talking to.'

Sister Rose was just as much put out. Hastily, she scrabbled in a drawer and handed a key across to Sister Lily who, with much cooing and tut-tutting, unlocked the two pairs of handcuffs and walked behind the desk and dropped them as if they were dirty bandages into the wastepaper basket.

'Thank you.' Bond was unable to think of any way to handle the situation except to fall in with what was happening on the stage. He reached out and took a cigarette and lit it. He glanced at Honeychile

Rider who sat looking dazed and nervously clutching the arms of her chair. Bond gave her a reassuring smile.

'Now, if you please.' Sister Rose bent over a long printed form on expensive paper. 'I promise to be as quick as I can. Your name please Mister—er . . .'

'Bryce, John Bryce.'

She wrote busily. 'Permanent address?'

'Care of the Royal Zoological Society, Regent's Park, London, England.'

'Profession.'

'Ornithologist.'

'Oh dear,' she dimpled at him, 'could you please spell that?'

Bond did so.

'Thank you so much. Now, let me see, Purpose of Visit?'

'Birds,' said Bond. 'I am also a representative of the Audubon Society of New York. They have a lease of part of this island.'

'Oh, really.' Bond watched the pen writing down exactly what he had said. After the last word she put a neat query in brackets.

'And,' Sister Rose smiled politely in the direction of Honeychile, 'your wife? Is she also interested in birds?'

'Yes, indeed.'

'And her first name?'

'Honeychile.'

Sister Rose was delighted. 'What a pretty name.' She wrote busily. 'And now just your next of kin and then we're finished.'

Bond gave M's real name as next of kin for both of them. He described him as 'uncle' and gave his address as 'Managing Director, Universal Export, Regent's Park, London'.

Sister Rose finished writing and said, 'There, that's done. Thank you so much, Mr Bryce, and I do hope you both enjoy your stay.'

'Thank you very much. I'm sure we will.' Bond got up. Honeychile Rider did the same, her face still expressionless.

Sister Lily said, 'Now come along with me, you poor dears.' She walked to a door in the far wall. She stopped with her hand on the cut-glass doorknob. 'Oh deary me, now I've gone and forgotten the number of their rooms! It's the Cream Suite, isn't it, Sister?'

'Yes, that's right. Fourteen and fifteen.'

'Thank you, my dear. And now,' she opened the door, 'if you'll just follow me. I'm afraid it's a terribly long walk.' She shut the door behind them and led the way. 'The Doctor's often talked of putting in one of those moving stairway things, but you know how it is with a busy man,' she laughed gaily. 'So many other things to think of.'

'Yes, I expect so,' said Bond politely.

Bond took the girl's hand and they followed the motherly bustling figure down a hundred yards of lofty corridor in the same style as the reception room but lit at frequent intervals by discreetly expensive wall-brackets.

Bond answered with polite monosyllables the occasional twittering comments Sister Lily threw over her shoulder. His whole mind was focused on the extraordinary circumstances of their reception. He was quite certain the two women had been genuine. Not a look or word had been dropped that was out of place. It was obviously a front of some kind, but a solid one, meticulously supported by the decor and the cast. The lack of resonance in the room, and now in the corridor, suggested that they had stepped from the Quonset hut into the side of the mountain and that they were now walking through its base. At a guess they would be walking towards the west – towards the cliff-face with which the island ended. There was no moisture on the walls and the air was cool and pure with a strongish breeze coming towards them. A lot of money and good engineering had gone into the job. The pallor of the two women suggested that they spent all their time inside the mountain. From what Sister Lily had said it sounded as if they were part of an inside staff that had nothing to do with the strong-arm squad outside and perhaps didn't even understand what sort of men they were.

It was grotesque, concluded Bond as they came nearer to a door at the end of the corridor, dangerously grotesque, but it was no good wondering about it. He could only follow the lines of the gracious script. At least this was better than the backstage of the island outside.

At the door, Sister Lily rang. They had been expected. The door opened at once. An enchanting Chinese girl in a mauve and white flowered kimono stood smiling and bowing as Chinese girls are supposed to do. Again there was nothing but warmth and welcome in the pale, flowerlike face. Sister Lily cried, 'Here they are at last, May! Mr and Mrs John Bryce. And I know they must be exhausted so we must take them straight to their rooms for some breakfast and a sleep.' She turned to Bond. 'This is May. Such a dear girl. She will be looking after you both. Anything you want, just ring for May. She's a favourite with all our patients.'

Patients, thought Bond. That's the second time she's used the word. He smiled politely at the girl. 'How do you do. Yes, we'd certainly both of us like to get to our rooms.'

May embraced them both with a warm smile. She said in a low, attractive voice, 'I do hope you'll both be comfortable, Mr Bryce. I took the liberty of ordering breakfast as soon as I heard you had come in. Shall we . . .?' Corridors branched off to left and right of double lift-doors set in the wall opposite. The girl led the way to the right. Bond and Honeychile followed with Sister Lily taking up the rear.

Numbered doors led off the corridor on either side. Now the decor was in the lightest pink with a dove grey carpet. The numbers on the doors were in the tens. The corridor came to an abrupt end with two doors side by side, 14 and 15. May opened the door of 14, and they followed her in.

It was a charming double bedroom in modern Miami style with dark green walls, dark polished mahogany floor with occasional thick white rugs, and well-designed bamboo furniture with a chintz of large red roses on a white background. There was a communicating door into a more masculine dressing-room and another that led into an extremely luxurious modern bathroom with a step-down bath and a bidet.

It was like being shown into the very latest Florida hotel suite – except for two details which Bond noticed. There were no windows and no inside handles to the doors.

May looked hopefully from one to the other.

Bond turned to Honeychile. He smiled at her. 'It looks very comfortable, don't you think, darling?'

The girl played with the edge of her skirt. She nodded, not looking at him.

There was a timid knock on the door and another girl, as pretty as May, tripped in with a loaded tray balanced on her upturned hand. She put it down on the centre table and pulled up two chairs. She whisked off the speckless linen cloth that covered the dishes and pattered out of the room. There was a delicious smell of bacon and coffee.

May and Sister Lily backed to the door. The older woman stopped on the threshold. 'And now we'll leave you two dear people in peace. If you want anything, just ring. The bells are by the bed. Oh, and by the way, you'll find plenty of fresh clothes in the cupboards. Chinese style, I'm afraid,' she twinkled apologetically, 'but I hope they're the right sizes. The wardrobe room only got the measurements yesterday evening. The Doctor has given strict orders that you're not to be disturbed. He'd be delighted if you'd join him for dinner this evening. He wants you to have the whole of the rest of the day to yourselves – to get settled down, you know.' She paused and looked from one to the other smiling inquiry. 'Shall I say you . . . ?'

'Yes, please,' said Bond. 'Tell the Doctor we shall be delighted to join him for dinner.'

'Oh, I know he'll be so pleased.' With a last twitter the two women softly withdrew and closed the door behind them.

Bond turned towards Honeychile. She looked embarrassed. She still avoided his eyes. It occurred to Bond that she could never have met such soft treatment or seen such luxury in her life. To her, all this must be far more strange and terrifying than what they had gone through outside. She stood and fiddled at the hem of her Man Friday skirt. There were streaks of dried sweat and salt and dust on her face. Her bare legs were filthy and Bond noticed that her toes were moving softly as they gripped nervously into the wonderful thick pile carpet.

Bond laughed. He laughed with real pleasure that her fear had been drowned in the basic predicament of clothes and how to behave, and he laughed at the picture they made – she in her rags and he in his dirty blue shirt and black jeans and muddy canvas shoes.

He went to her and took her hands. They were cold. He said, 'Honey, we're a couple of scarecrows. There's only one problem. Shall we have breakfast first while it's hot, or shall we get out of these rags and have a bath and eat the breakfast when it's cold? Don't worry about anything else. We're here in this wonderful little house and that's all that matters. Now then, what shall we do?'

She smiled uncertainly. The blue eyes searched his face for reassurance. 'You're not worried about what's going to happen to us?' She nodded at the room. 'Don't you think this is all a trap?'

'If it's a trap we're in it. There's nothing we can do now but eat the cheese. The only question is whether we eat it hot or cold.' He pressed her hands. 'Really, Honey. Leave the worrying to me. Just think where we were an hour ago. Isn't this better? Now come on and decide the really important things. Bath or breakfast?'

She said reluctantly, 'Well, if you think . . . I mean – I'd rather get clean first.' She added quickly, 'But you've got to help me.' She jerked her head towards the bathroom door. 'I don't know how to work one of those places. What do you do?'

Bond said seriously, 'It's quite easy. I'll fit it all ready for you. While you're having your bath, I'll have my breakfast. I'll keep yours warm.' Bond went to one of the built-in clothes cupboards and ran the door back. There were half a dozen kimonos, some silk and some linen. He took out a linen one at random. 'You take off your clothes and get into this and I'll get the bath ready. Later on you can choose the things you want to wear for bed and dinner.'

She said gratefully, 'Oh yes, James. If you'll just show me . . .' She started to unbutton her shirt.

Bond wanted to take her in his arms and kiss her. Instead he said abruptly, 'That's fine, Honey,' and went into the bathroom and turned on the taps.

There was everything in the bathroom – Floris Lime bath essence for men and Guerlain bathcubes for women. He crushed a cube into the water and at once the room smelled like an orchid house. The soap was Guerlain's Sapoceti, *Fleurs des Alpes*. In a medicine cupboard behind the mirror over the washbasin were toothbrushes and toothpaste, Steradent toothpicks, Rose mouthwash, dental floss, Aspirin and Milk of Magnesia. There was also an electric razor, Lentheric aftershave lotion, and two nylon hairbrushes and combs. Everything was brand new and untouched.

Bond looked at his filthy unshaven face in the mirror and smiled grimly into the grey, sunburned castaway's eyes. The coating on the pill was certainly of the very finest sugar. It would be wise to expect that the medicine inside would be of the bitterest.

He turned back to the bath and felt the water. It would be too hot for someone who presumably had never had a hot bath before. He let in some cold. As he bent over, two arms were thrown round his neck. He stood up. The golden body blazed in the white tiled bathroom. She kissed him hard and clumsily on the lips. He put his arms round her and crushed her to him, his heart pounding. She said breathlessly at his ear. 'The Chinese dress felt strange. Anyway, you told that woman we were married.'

Bond's hand was on her left breast. Its peak was hard with passion. Her stomach pressed against his. Why not? Why not? Don't be a fool! This is a crazy time for it. You're both in deadly danger. You must stay cold as ice to have any chance of getting out of this mess. Later! Later! Don't be weak.

Bond took his hand away from her breast and put it round he neck. He rubbed his face against hers and then brought his mouth round to hers and gave her one long kiss.

He stood away and held her at arm's length. For a moment they looked at each other, their eyes bright with desire. She was breathing fast, her lips parted so that he could see the glint of teeth. He said unsteadily, 'Honey, get into that bath before I spank you.'

She smiled. Without saying anything she stepped down into the bath and lay at full length. She looked up. The fair hair on her body glittered up through the water like golden sovereigns. She said provocatively, 'You've got to wash me. I don't know what to do. You've got to show me.'

Bond said desperately, 'Shut up, Honey. And stop flirting. Just take the soap and the sponge and start scrubbing. Damn you! This isn't the time for making love. I'm going to have breakfast.' He reached for the door handle and opened the door. She said softly, 'James!' He looked back. She was sticking her tongue out at him. He grinned savagely back at her and slammed the door.

Bond went into the dressing-room and stood in the middle of the floor and waited for his heart to stop pounding. He rubbed his hands over his face and shook his head to get rid of the thought of her.

To clear his mind he went carefully over both rooms looking for exits, possible weapons, microphones – anything that would add to his knowledge. There were none of these things. There was an electric clock on the wall which said eight-thirty and a row of bells beside the double bed. They said, Room Service, Coiffeur, Manicurist, Maid. There was no telephone. High up in a corner of both rooms was a small ventilator grille. Each was about two feet square. Useless. The doors appeared to be of some light metal, painted to match the walls. Bond threw the whole weight of his body against one of them. It didn't give a millimetre. Bond rubbed his shoulder. The place was a prison – an exquisite prison. It was no good arguing. The trap had shut tight on them. Now the only thing for the mice to do was to make the most of the cheese.

Bond sat down at the breakfast table. There was a large tumbler of pineapple juice in a silver-plated bowl of crushed ice. He swallowed it down and lifted the cover off his individual hot-plate. Scrambled eggs on toast, four rashers of bacon, a grilled kidney and what looked like an English pork sausage. There were also two kinds of hot toast, rolls inside a napkin, marmalade, honey and strawberry jam. The coffee was boiling hot in a large Thermos decanter. The cream smelled fresh.

From the bathroom came the sound of the girl crooning 'Marion'. Bond closed his ears to the sound and started on the eggs.

Ten minutes later, Bond heard the bathroom door open. He put down his toast and marmalade and covered his eyes with his hands. She laughed. She said, 'He's a coward. He's frightened of a simple girl.' Bond hear her rummaging in the cupboards. She went on talking, half to herself. 'I wonder why he's frightened. Of course if I wrestled with him I'd win easily. Perhaps he's frightened of that. Perhaps he's really not very strong. His arms and his chest look strong enough. I haven't seen the rest yet. Perhaps it's weak. Yes, that must be it. That's why he doesn't dare take his clothes off in front of me. H'm, now let's see, would he like me in this?' She raised her voice. 'Darling James, would you like me in white with pale blue birds flying all over me?'

'Yes, damn you,' said Bond through his hands. 'Now stop chattering to yourself and come and have breakfast. I'm getting sleepy.'

She gave a cry. 'Oh, if you mean it's time for us to go to bed, of course, I'll hurry.'

There was a flurry of feet and Bond heard her sit down opposite. He took his hands down. She was smiling at him. She looked ravishing. Her hair was dressed and combed and brushed to kill, with one side falling down the side of the cheek and the other slicked back behind her ear. Her skin sparkled with freshness and the big blue eyes were alight with happiness. Now Bond loved the broken nose. It had become part of his thoughts of her and it suddenly occurred to him that he would be sad when she was just an immaculately beautiful girl like other beautiful girls. But he knew it would be no good trying to persuade her of that. She sat demurely, with her hands in her lap below the end of a cleavage which showed half her breasts and a deep vee of her stomach.

Bond said severely, 'Now, listen, Honey. You look wonderful, but that isn't the way to wear a kimono. Pull it up right across your body and tie it tight and stop trying to look like a call girl. It just isn't good manners at breakfast.'

'Oh, you are a stuffy old beast.' She pulled her kimono an inch or two closer. 'Why don't you like playing? I want to play at being married.'

'Not at breakfast time,' said Bond firmly. 'Come on and eat up. It's delicious. And anyway, I'm filthy. I'm going to shave and have a bath.' He got up and walked round the table and kissed the top of her head. 'And as for playing, as you call it, I'd rather play with you than anyone in the world. But not now.' Without waiting for her answer he walked into the bathroom and shut the door.

Bond shaved and had a bath and a shower. He felt desperately sleepy. Sleep came to him in waves so that from time to time he had to stop what he was doing and bend his head down between his knees. When he came to brush his teeth he could hardly do it. Now he recognized the signs. He had been drugged. In the coffee or in the pineapple juice? It didn't matter. Nothing mattered. All he wanted to do was lie down on the tiled floor and shut his eyes. Bond weaved drunkenly to the door. He forgot that he was naked. That didn't matter either. Anyway the girl had finished her breakfast. She was in bed. He staggered over to her, holding on to the furniture. The kimono was lying in a pile on the floor. She was fast asleep, naked under a single sheet.

Bond gazed dreamily at the empty pillow beside her head. No! He found the switches and turned out the lights. Now he had to crawl across the floor and into his room. He got to his bed and pulled himself on to it.

He reached out an arm of lead and jabbed at the switch on the bed-light. He missed it. The lamp crashed to the floor and the bulb burst. With a last effort Bond turned on his side and let the waves sweep over his head.

The luminous figures on the electric clock in the double room said nine-thirty.

At ten o'clock the door of the double room opened softly. A very tall thin figure was silhouetted against the lighted corridor. It was a man. He must have been six feet six tall. He stood on the threshold with his arms folded, listening. Satisfied, he moved slowly into the room and up to the bed. He knew the way exactly. He bent down and listened to the quiet breathing of the girl. After a moment he reached up to his chest and pressed a switch. A flashlight was attached to him by a belt that held it above the breast bone. He bent forward so that the soft light shone on the girl's face.

The intruder examined the girl's face for several minutes. One of his hands came up and took the sheet at her chin and softly drew the sheet down to the end of the bed. The hand that drew down the sheet was not a hand. It was a pair of articulated steel pincers at the end of a metal stalk that disappeared into a black silk sleeve. It was a mechanical hand.

The man gazed for a long time at the naked body, moving his chest to and fro so that every corner of the body came under the light. Then the claw came out again and delicately lifted a corner of the sheet from the bottom of the bed and drew it back over the girl. The man stood for another moment gazing down at the sleeping face, then he switched off the torch on his chest and moved quietly away across the room to the open door through which Bond was sleeping.

The man spent longer beside Bond's bed. He scrutinized every line, every shadow on the dark, rather cruel face that lay drowned, almost extinct, on the pillow. He watched the pulse in the neck and counted it and, when he had pulled down the sheet, he did the same with the area round the heart. He gauged the curve of the muscles on Bond's arms and thighs and looked thoughtfully at the hidden strength in the flat stomach. He even bent down close over the outflung open right hand and examined its life and fate lines.

Finally, with infinite care, the steel claw drew the sheet back up to Bond's neck. For another minute the tall figure stood over the sleeping man, then it swished softly away and out into the corridor and the door closed with a click.

CHAPTER 14

COME INTO MY PARLOUR

The electric clock in the cool dark room in the heart of the mountain showed four-thirty.

Outside the mountain, Crab Key had sweltered and stunk its way through another day. At the eastern end of the island, the mass of birds, Louisiana herons, pelicans, avocets, sandpipers, egrets, flamingoes and the few roseate spoonbills, went on with building their nests or fished in the shallow waters of the lake. Most of the birds had been disturbed so often that year that they had given up any idea of building. In the past few months they had been raided at regular intervals by the monster that came at night and burned their roosting places and the beginnings of their nests. This year many would not breed. There would be vague movements to migrate and many would die of the nervous hysteria that seizes bird colonies when they no longer have peace and privacy.

At the other end of the island, on the guanera that gave the mountain its snow-covered look, the vast swarm of cormorants had passed their usual day of gorging themselves with fish and paying back the ounce of precious manure to their owner and protector. Nothing had interfered with *their* nesting season. Now they were noisily fiddling with the untidy piles of sticks that would be their nests – each pile at exactly sixty centimetres from the next, for the guanay is a quarrelsome bird and this sixty-centimetre ring represents their sparring space. Soon the females would be laying the three eggs from which their master's flock would be increased by an average of two young cormorants.

Below the peak, where the diggings began, the hundred or so Negro men and women who were the labour force were coming to the end of the day's shift. Another fifty cubic yards of guano had been dug out of the mountainside and another twenty yards of terrace had been added to the working level. Below, the mountainside looked like terraced vineyards in Upper Italy, except that here there were no vines, only deep barren shelves cut in the mountainside. And here, instead of the stink of marsh gas on the rest of the island, there was a strong ammoniac smell, and the ugly hot wind that kept the diggings dry blew the freshly turned whitish-brown dust into the eyes and ears and noses of the diggers. But the workers were used to the smell and the dust, and it was easy, healthy work. They had no complaints.

The last iron truck of the day started off on the Decauville Track that snaked down the mountainside to the crusher and separator. A whistle blew and the workers shouldered their clumsy picks and moved lazily down towards the high-wired group of Quonset huts that was their compound. Tomorrow, on the other side of the mountain, the monthly ship would be coming in to the deep-water quay they had helped to build ten years before, but which, since then, they had never seen. That would mean fresh stores and fresh goods and cheap jewellery at the canteen. It would be a holiday. There would be rum and dancing and a few fights. Life was good.

Life was good, too, for the senior outside staff – all Chinese Negroes like the men who had hunted Bond and Quarrel and the girl. They also stopped work in the garage and the machine shops and at the guard posts and filtered off to the 'officers'' quarters. Apart from watch and loading duties, tomorrow would also be a holiday for most of them. They too would have their drinking and dancing, and there would be a new monthly batch of girls from 'inside'. Some 'marriages' from the last lot would continue for further months or weeks according to the taste of the 'husband', but for the others there would be a fresh choice. There would be some of the older girls who had had their babies in the creche and were coming back for a fresh spell of duty 'outside', and there would be a sprinkling of young ones who had come of age and would be 'coming out' for the first time. There would be fights over these and blood would be shed, but in the end the officers' quarters would settle down for another month of communal life, each officer with his woman to look after his needs.

Deep down in the cool heart of the mountain, far below this well-disciplined surface life, Bond awoke in his comfortable bed. Apart from a slight nembutal headache he felt fit and rested. Lights were on in the girl's room and he could hear her moving about. He swung his feet to the ground and, avoiding the fragment of glass from the broken lamp, walked softly over to the clothes cupboard and put on the first kimono that came to his hand. He went to the door. The girl had a pile of kimonos out on the bed and was trying them on in front of the wall mirror. She had on a very smart one in sky-blue silk. It looked wonderful against the gold of her skin. Bond said, 'That's the one.'

She whirled round, her hand at her mouth. She took it down. 'Oh, it's you!' She smiled at him. 'I thought you'd never wake up. I've been to look at you several times. I'd made up my mind to wake you at five. It's half-past four and I'm hungry. Can you get us something to eat?'

'Why not,' Bond walked across to her bed. As he passed her he put his arm round her waist and took her with him. He examined the bells. He pressed the one marked 'Room Service'. He said, 'What about the others? Let's have the full treatment.'

She giggled. 'But what's a manicurist?'

'Someone who does your nails. We must look our best for Doctor No.' At the back of Bond's mind was the urgent necessity to get his hands on some kind of weapon – a pair of scissors would be better than nothing. Anything would do.

He pressed two more bells. He let her go and looked round the room. Someone had come while they were asleep and taken away the breakfast things. There was a drink tray on a sideboard against the wall. Bond went over and examined it. It had everything. Propped among the bottles were two menus, huge double-folio pages covered with print. They might have been from the Savoy Grill, or the '21', or the Tour d'Argent. Bond ran his eye down one of them. It began with *Caviar double de Beluga* and ended with *Sorbet à la Champagne*. In between was every dish whose constituents would not be ruined by a deep freeze. Bond tossed it down. One certainly couldn't grumble about the quality of the cheese in the trap!

There was a knock on the door and the exquisite May came in. She was followed by two other twittering Chinese girls. Bond brushed aside their amiabilities, ordered tea and buttered toast for Honeychile and told them to look after her hair and nails. Then he went into the bathroom and had a couple of Aspirins and a cold shower. He put on his kimono again, reflected that he looked idiotic in it, and went back into the room. A beaming May asked if he would be good enough to select what he and Mrs Bryce could care to have for dinner. Without enthusiasm, Bond ordered caviar, grilled lamb cutlets and salad, and angels on horseback for himself. When Honeychile refused to make any suggestions, he chose melon, roast chicken à l'Anglaise and vanilla icecream with hot chocolate sauce for her.

May dimpled her enthusiasm and approval. 'The Doctor asks if seven forty-five for eight would be convenient.'

Bond said curtly that it would.

'Thank you so much, Mr Bryce, I will call for you at seven forty-four.'

Bond walked over to where Honeychile was being ministered to at the dressing table. He watched the busy delicate fingers at work on her hair and her nails. She smiled at him excitedly in the mirror. He said gruffly, 'Don't let them make too much of a monkey out of you,' and went to the drink tray. He poured himself out a stiff Bourbon and soda and took it into his own room. So much for his idea of getting hold of a weapon. The

scissors and files and probes were attached to the manicurist's waist by a
chain. So were the scissors of the hairdresser. Bond sat down on his
rumpled bed and lost himself in drink and gloomy reflections.

The women went. The girl looked in at him. When he didn't lift his
head she went back into her room and left him alone. In due course Bond
came into her room to get himself another drink. He said perfunctorily,
'Honey, you look wonderful.' He glanced at the clock on the wall and
went back and drank his drink and put on another of the idiotic
kimonos, a plain black one.

In due course there came the soft knock on the door and the two of
them went silently out of the room and along the empty, gracious
corridor. May stopped at the lift. Its doors were held open by another
eager Chinese girl. They walked in and the doors shut. Bond noticed
that the lift was made by Waygood Otis. Everything in the prison was de
luxe. He gave an inward shudder of distaste. He noticed the reaction. He
turned to the girl. 'I'm sorry, Honey. Got a bit of a headache.' He didn't
want to tell her that all this luxury play-acting was getting him down,
that he hadn't the smallest idea what it was all about, that he knew it was
bad news, and that he hadn't an inkling of a plan of how to get them out
of whatever situation they were in. That was the worst of it. There was
nothing that depressed Bond's spirit so much as the knowledge that he
hadn't one line of either attack or defence.

The girl moved closer to him. She said, 'I'm sorry, James. I hope it
will go away. You're not angry with me about anything?'

Bond dredged up a smile. He said, 'No darling. I'm only angry with
myself.' He lowered his voice: 'Now, about this evening. Just leave the
talking to me. Be natural and don't be worried by Doctor No. He may be
a bit mad.'

She nodded solemnly. 'I'll do my best.'

The lift sighed to a stop. Bond had no idea how far down they had
gone – a hundred feet, two hundred? The automatic doors hissed back
and Bond and the girl stepped out into a large room.

It was empty. It was a high-ceilinged room about sixty feet long, lined
on three sides with books to the ceiling. At first glance, the fourth wall
seemed to be made of solid blue-black glass. The room appeared to be a
combined study and library. There was a big paper-strewn desk in one
corner and a central table with periodicals and newspapers. Comfortable club chairs, upholstered in red leather, were dotted about. The
carpet was dark green, and the lighting, from standard lamps, was
subdued. The only odd feature was that the drink tray and sideboard
were up against the middle of the long glass wall, and chairs and

occasional tables with ashtrays were arranged in a semi-circle round it so that the room was centred in front of the empty wall.

Bond's eye caught a swirl of movement in the dark glass. He walked across the room. A silvery spray of small fish with a bigger fish in pursuit fled across the dark blue. They disappeared, so to speak, off the edge of the screen. What was this? An aquarium? Bond looked upwards. A yard below the ceiling, small waves were lapping at the glass. Above the waves was a strip of greyer blue-black, dotted with sparks of light. The outlines of Orion were the clue. This was not an aquarium. This was the sea itself and the night sky. The whole of one side of the room was made of armoured glass. They were under the sea, looking straight into its heart, twenty feet down.

Bond and the girl stood transfixed. As they watched, there was the glimpse of two great goggling orbs. A golden sheen of head and deep flank showed for an instant and was gone. A big grouper? A silver swarm of anchovies stopped and hovered and sped away. The twenty-foot tendrils of a Portuguese man-o'-war drifted slowly across the window, glinting violet as they caught the light. Up above there was the dark mass of its underbelly and the outline of its inflated bladder, steering with the breeze.

Bond walked along the wall, fascinated by the idea of living with this slow, endlessly changing moving picture. A big tulip shell was progressing slowly up the window from the floor level, a frisk of demoiselles and angel fish and a ruby-red moonlight snapper were nudging and rubbing themselves against a corner of the glass and a sea centipede quested along, nibbling at the minute algae that must grow every day on the outside of the window. A long dark shadow paused in the centre of the window and then moved slowly away. If only one could see more!

Obediently, two great shafts of light, from off the 'screen', lanced out into the water. For an instant they searched independently. Then they converged on the departing shadow and the dull grey torpedo of a twelve-foot shark showed up in all its detail. Bond could even see the piglike pink eyes roll inquisitively in the light and the slow pulse of the slanting gill-rakers. For an instant the shark turned straight into the converged beam and the white half-moon mouth showed below the reptile's flat head. It stood poised for a second and then, with an elegant, disdainful swirl, the great swept-back tail came round and with a lightning quiver the shark had gone.

The searchlights went out. Bond turned slowly. He expected to see Doctor No, but still the room was empty. It looked static and lifeless compared with the pulsing mysteries outside the window. Bond looked back. What must this be like in the colours of day, when one could see everything perhaps for twenty yards or more? What must it be like in a storm when the waves crashed noiselessly against the glass, delving almost to the floor and then sweeping up and out of sight. What must it be like in the evening when the last golden shafts of the sun shone into the upper half of the room and the waters below were full of dancing motes and tiny water insects? What an amazing man this must be who had thought of this fantastically beautiful conception, and what an extraordinary engineering feat to have carried it out! How had he done it? There could only be one way. He must have built the glass wall deep inside the cliff and then delicately removed layer after layer of the outside rock until the divers could prise off the last skin of coral. But how thick was the glass? Who had rolled it for him? How had he got it to the island? How many divers had he used? How much, God in heaven, could it have cost?

'One million dollars.'

It was a cavernous, echoing voice, with a trace of American accent.

Bond turned slowly, almost reluctantly, away from the window.

Doctor No had come through a door behind his desk. He stood looking at them benignly, with a thin smile on his lips.

'I expect you were wondering about the cost. My guests usually think about the material side after about fifteen minutes. Were you?'

'I was.'

Still smiling (Bond was to get used to that thin smile), Doctor No came slowly out from behind the desk and moved towards them. He seemed to glide rather than take steps. His knees did not dent the matt, gunmetal sheen of his kimono and no shoes showed below the sweeping hem.

Bond's impression was of thinness and erectness and height. Doctor No was at least six inches taller than Bond, but the straight immovable poise of his body made him seem still taller. The head also was elongated and tapered from a round, completely bald skull down to a sharp chin so that the impression was of a reversed raindrop – or rather oildrop, for the skin was of a deep almost translucent yellow.

It was impossible to tell Doctor No's age: as far as Bond could see, there were no lines on the face. It was odd to see a forehead as smooth as the top of the polished skull. Even the cavernous indrawn cheeks below the prominent cheekbones looked as smooth as fine ivory. There was something Dali-esque about the eyebrows, which were fine and black and sharply upswept as if they had been painted on a make-up for a conjurer. Below them, slanting jet black eyes stared out of the skull. They were without eyelashes. They looked like the mouths of two small revolvers, direct and unblinking and totally devoid of expression. The thin fine nose ended very close above a wide compressed wound of a mouth which, despite its almost permanent sketch of a smile, showed only cruelty and authority. The chin was indrawn towards the neck. Later Bond was to notice that it rarely moved more than slightly away from centre, giving the impression that the head and the vertebra were in one piece.

The bizarre, gliding figure looked like a giant venomous worm wrapped in grey tin-foil, and Bond would not have been surprised to see the rest of it trailing slimly along the carpet behind.

Doctor No came within three steps of them and stopped. The wound in the tall face opened. 'Forgive me for not shaking hands with you,' the deep voice was flat and even. 'I am unable to.' Slowly the sleeves parted and opened. 'I have no hands.'

The two pairs of steel pincers came out on their gleaming stalks and were held up for inspection like the hands of a praying mantis. Then the two sleeves joined again.

Bond felt the girl at his side gave a start.

The black apertures turned towards her. They slid down to her nose. The voice said flatly, 'It is a misfortune.' The eyes came back to Bond. 'You were admiring my aquarium.' It was a statement, not a question. 'Man enjoys the beasts and the birds. I decided to enjoy also the fish. I find them far more varied and interesting. I am sure you both share my enthusiasm.'

Bond said, I congratulate you. I shall never forget this room.'

'No.' Again a statement perhaps with a sardonic inflection, of fact. 'But we have much to talk about. And so little time. Please sit down. You will have a drink? Cigarettes are beside your chairs.'

Doctor No moved to a high leather chair and folded himself down on to the seat. Bond took the chair opposite. The girl sat between them and slightly back.

Bond felt a movement behind him. He looked over his shoulder. A short man, a Chinese Negro, with the build of a wrestler, stood at the drink tray. He was dressed in black trousers and a smart white jacket. Black almond eyes in a wide moon face met his and slid incuriously away.

Doctor No said, 'This is my bodyguard. He is expert in many things. There is no mystery about his sudden appearance. I always carry what is known as a walkie-talkie here,' he inclined his chin towards the bosom of his kimono. 'Thus I can summon him when he is needed. What will the girl have?'

Not 'Your Wife'. Bond turned to Honeychile. Her eyes were wide and staring. She said quietly, 'A Coca-Cola, please.'

Bond felt a moment of relief. At least she was not being got down by the performance. Bond said, 'And I would like a medium Vodka dry Martini – with a slice of lemon peel. Shaken and not stirred, please. I would prefer Russian or Polish vodka.'

Doctor No gave his thin smile an extra crease. 'I see you are also a man who knows what he wants. On this occasion your desires will be satisfied. Do you not find that it is generally so? When one wants a thing one gets it? That is my experience.'

'The small things.'

'If you fail at the large things it means you have not large ambitions. Concentration, focus – that is all. The aptitudes come, the tools forge themselves. 'Give me a fulcrum and I will move the world' – but only if the desire to move the world is there.' The thin lips bent minutely downwards in deprecation. 'But this is chatter. We are making conversation. Instead, let us talk. Both of us, I am sure, prefer talk to conversation. Is the Martini to your liking? You have cigarettes – enough and the right sort to cosset your cancer? So be it. Sam-sam, put the shaker beside the man and another bottle of Coca-Cola beside the girl. It should now be eight-ten. We will have dinner at nine o'clock precisely.'

Doctor No sat slightly more upright in his chair. He inclined himself forward, staring at Bond. There was a moment's silence in the room. Then Doctor No said, 'And now Mister James Bond of the Secret Service, let us tell each other our secrets. First, to show you that I hide nothing, I will tell you mine. Then you will tell me yours.' Doctor No's eyes blazed darkly. 'But let us tell each other the truth.' He drew one steel claw out of the wide sleeve and held it upwards. He paused, 'I shall do so. But you must do the same. If you do not, these,' he pointed the claw at his eyes, 'will know that you are lying.'

Doctor No brought the steel claw delicately in front of each eye and tapped the centre of each eyeball.

Each eyeball in turn emitted a dull ting. 'These,' said Doctor No, 'see everything.'

CHAPTER 15

PANDORA'S BOX

James Bond picked up his glass and sipped at it thoughtfully. It seemed pointless to go on bluffing. His story of representing the Audubon Society was anyway a thin one which could be punctured by anyone who knew about birds. It was obvious that his own cover was in shreds. He must concentrate on protecting the girl. To begin with he must reassure her.

Bond smiled at Doctor No. He said, 'I know about your contact in King's House, Miss Taro. She is your agent. I have recorded the fact and it will be divulged in certain circumstances' – Doctor No's expression showed no interest – 'as will other facts. But, if we are to have a talk, let us have it without any more stage effects. You are an interesting man. But it is not necessary to make yourself more interesting than you are. You have suffered the misfortune of losing your hands. You wear mechanical hands. Many men wounded in the war wear them. You wear contact lenses instead of spectacles. You use a walkie-talkie instead of a bell to summon your servant. No doubt you have other tricks. But, Doctor No, you are still a man who sleeps and eats and defecates like the rest of us. So no more conjuring tricks, please. I am not one of your guano diggers and I am not impressed by them.'

Doctor No inclined his head a fraction. 'Bravely spoken, Mister Bond. I accept the rebuke. I have no doubt developed annoying mannerisms from living too long in the company of apes. But do not mistake these mannerisms for bluff. I am a technician. I suit the tool to the material. I possess also a range of tools for working with refractory materials. However,' Doctor No raised his joined sleeves an inch and let them fall back in his lap, 'let us proceed with our talk. It is a rare pleasure to have an intelligent listener and I shall enjoy telling you the story of one of the most remarkable men in the world. You are the first person to hear it. I have not told it before. You are the only person I have ever met who will appreciate my story and also—' Doctor No paused for the significance of the last words to make itself felt – 'keep it to himself.' He continued, 'The second of these considerations also applies to the girl.'

So that was it. There had been little doubt in Bond's mind ever since the Spandau had opened up on them, and since, even before then, in Jamaica, where the attempts on him had not been half-hearted. Bond had assumed from the first that this man was a killer, that it would be a duel to the death. He had had his usual blind faith that he would win the deal – all the way until the moment when the flame-thrower had pointed at him. Then he had begun to doubt. Now he knew. This man was too strong, too well equipped.

Bond said, 'There is no point in the girl hearing this. She has nothing to do with me. I found her yesterday on the beach. She is a Jamaican from Morgan's Harbour. She collects shells. Your men destroyed her canoe so I had to bring her with me. Send her away now and then back home. She won't talk. She will swear not to.'

The girl interrupted fiercely. 'I *will* talk! I shall tell everything. I'm not going to move. I'm going to stay with you.'

Bond looked at her. He said icily, 'I don't want you.'

Doctor No said softly, 'Do not waste your breath on these heroics. Nobody who comes to this island has ever left it. Do you understand? Nobody – not even the simplest fisherman. It is not my policy. Do not argue with me or attempt to bluff me. It is entirely useless.'

Bond examined the face. There was no anger in it, no obstinacy – nothing but a supreme indifference. He shrugged his shoulders. He looked at the girl and smiled. He said, 'All right, Honey. And I didn't mean it. I'd hate you to go away. We'll stay together and listen to what the maniac has to say.'

The girl nodded happily. It was as if her lover had threatened to send her out of the cinema and now had relented.

Doctor No said, in the same soft resonant voice, 'you are right, Mister Bond. That is just what I am, a maniac. All the greatest men are maniacs. They are possessed by a mania which drives them forward towards their goal. The great scientists, the philosophers, the religious leaders – all maniacs. What else but a blind singleness of purpose could have given focus to their genius, would have kept them in the groove of their purpose? Mania, my dear Mister Bond, is as priceless as genius. Dissipation of energy, fragmentation of vision, loss of momentum, the lack of follow-through – these are the vices of the herd.' Doctor No sat slightly back in his chair. 'I do not possess these vices. I am, as you correctly say, a maniac – a maniac, Mister Bond, with a mania for power. That' – the black holes glittered blankly at Bond through the contact lenses – 'is the meaning of my life. That is why I am here. That is why you are here. That is why here exists.'

Bond picked up his glass and drained it. He filled it again from the shaker. He said, 'I'm not surprised. It's the old business of thinking you're the King of England, or the President of the United States, or

God. The asylums are full of them. The only difference is that instead of being shut up, you've built your own asylum and shut yourself up in it. But why did you do it? Why does sitting shut up in this cell give you the illusion of power?'

Irritation flickered at the corner of the thin mouth. 'Mister Bond, power is sovereignty. Clausewitz's first principle was to have a secure base. From there one proceeds to freedom of action. Together, that is sovereignty. I have secured these things and much besides. No one else in the world possesses them to the same degree. They *cannot* have them. The world is too public. These things can only be secured in privacy. You talk of kings and presidents. How much power do they possess? As much as their people will allow them. Who in the world had the power of life or death over his people? Now that Stalin is dead, can you name any man except myself? And how do I possess that power, that sovereignty? Through privacy. Through the fact that nobody *knows*. Through the fact that I have to account to no one.'

Bond shrugged. 'That is only the illusion of power, Doctor No. Any man with a loaded revolver has the power of life and death over his neighbour. Other people besides you have murdered in secret and got away with it. In the end they generally get their deserts. A greater power than they possess is exerted upon them by the community. That will happen to you, Doctor No. I tell you, your search for power is an illusion because power itself is an illusion.'

Doctor No said equably, 'So is beauty, Mister Bond. So is art, so is money, so is death. And so, probably is life. These concepts are relative. Your play upon words does not shake me. I know philosophy, I know ethics, and I know logic – better than you do, I daresay. But let us move away from this sterile debate. Let us return to where I began, with my mania for power, or, if you wish it, for the illusion of power. And please, Mister Bond,' again the extra crease in the fixed smile, 'please do not imagine that half an hour's conversation with you will alter the pattern of my life. Interest yourself rather in the history of my pursuit, let us put it, of an illusion.'

'Go ahead.' Bond glanced at the girl. She caught his eyes. She put her hand up to her mouth as if to conceal a yawn. Bond grinned at her. He wondered when it would amuse Doctor No to crack her pose of indifference.

Doctor No said benignly, 'I shall endeavour not to bore you. Facts are so much more interesting than theories, don't you agree?' Doctor No was not expecting a reply. He fixed his eye on the elegant tulip shell that had now wandered half way up the outside of the dark window. Some small silver fish squirted across the black void. A bluish prickle of phosphorescence meandered vaguely. Up by the ceiling, the stars shone more brightly through the glass.

The artificiality of the scene inside the room – the three people sitting in the comfortable chairs, the drinks on the sideboard, the rich carpet, the shaded lights, suddenly seemed ludicrous to Bond. Even the drama of it, the danger, were fragile things compared with the progress of the tulip shell up the glass outside. Supposing the glass burst. Supposing the stresses had been badly calculated, the workmanship faulty. Supposing the sea decided to lean a little more heavily against the window.

Doctor No said, 'I was the only son of a German Methodist missionary and a Chinese girl of good family. I was born in Pekin, but on what is known as 'the wrong side of the blanket'. I was an encumbrance. An aunt of my mother was paid to bring me up.' Doctor No paused. 'No love, you see, Mister Bond. Lack of parental care.' He went on, 'The seed was sown. I went to work in Shanghai. I became involved with the Tongs, with their illicit proceedings. I enjoyed the conspiracies, the burglaries, the murders, the arson of insured properties. They represented revolt against the father figure who had betrayed me. I loved the death and destruction of people and things. I became adept in the technique of criminality – if you wish to call it that. Then there was trouble. I had to be got out of the way. The Tongs considered me too valuable to kill. I was smuggled to the United States. I settled in New York. I had been given a letter of introduction, in code, to one of the two most powerful Tongs in America – the Hip Sings. I never knew what the letter said, but they took me on at once as a confidential clerk. In due course, at the age of thirty, I was made the equivalent of treasurer. The treasury contained over a million dollars. I coveted this money. Then began the great Tong wars of the late 'twenties. The two great New York Tongs, my own, the Hip Sings, and our rival, the On Lee Ongs, joined in combat. Over the weeks hundreds on both sides were killed and their houses and properties burned to the ground. It was a time of torture and murder and arson in which I joined with delight. Then the riot squads came. Almost the whole police force of New York was mobilized. The two underground armies were prised apart and the headquarters of the two Tongs were raided and the ringleaders sent to jail. I was tipped off about the raid on my own Tong, the Hip Sings. A few hours before it was due, I got to the safe and rifled the million dollars in gold and disappeared into Harlem and went to ground. I was foolish. I should have left America, gone to the farthest corner of the earth. Even from the condemned cells in Sing Sing the heads of my Tong reached out for me.

They found me. The killers came in the night. They tortured me. I would not say where the gold was. They tortured me all through the night. Then, when they could not break me, they cut off my hands to show that the corpse was that of a thief, and they shot me through the heart and went away. But they did not know something about me. I am the one man in a million who has his heart on the right side of his body. Those are the odds against it, one in a million. I lived. By sheer willpower I survived the operation and the months in hospital. And all the time I planned and planned how to get away with the money – how to keep it, what to do with it.'

Doctor No paused. There was a slight flush at his temples. His body fidgeted inside his kimono. His memories had excited him. For a moment he closed his eyes, composing himself. Bond thought, now! Shall I leap at him and kill him? Break off my glass and do it with the jagged stem?

The eyes opened. 'I am not boring you? You are sure? For an instant I felt your attention wandering.'

'No.' The moment had passed. Would there be others? Bond measured the inches of the leap: noted that the jugular vein was in full view above the neck of the kimono.

The thin purple lips parted and the story went on. 'It was, Mister Bond, a time for clear, firm decisions. When they let me out of the hospital I went to Silberstein, the greatest stamp dealer in New York. I bought an envelope, just one envelope, full of the rarest postage stamps in the world. I took weeks to get them together. But I didn't mind what I paid – in New York, London, Paris, Zurich. I wanted my gold to be mobile. I invested it all in these stamps. I had foreseen the World War. I knew there would be inflation. I knew the best would appreciate, or at least hold its value. And meanwhile I was changing my appearance. I had all my hair taken out by the roots, my thick nose made thin, my mouth widened, my lips sliced. I could not get smaller, so I made myself taller. I wore built up shoes. I had weeks of traction on my spine. I held myself differently. I put away my mechanical hands and wore hands of wax inside gloves. I changed my name to Julius No – the Julius after my father and the No for my rejection of him and of all authority. I threw away my spectacles and wore contact lenses – one of the first pairs ever built. Then I went to Milwaukee, where there are no Chinamen, and enrolled myself in the faculty of medicine. I hid myself in the academic world, the world of libraries and laboratories and classrooms and campuses. And there, Mister Bond, I lost myself in the study of the human body and the human mind. Why? Because I wished to know what this clay is capable of. I had to learn what my tools were before I put them to use on my next goal – total security from physical weaknesses, from material dangers and from the hazards of living. Then, Mister Bond, from that secure base, armoured even against the casual slings and arrows of the world, I would proceed to the achievement of power – the power, Mister Bond, to do unto others what had been done unto me, the power of life and death, the power to decide, to judge, the power of absolute independence from outside authority. For that, Mister Bond, whether you like it or not, is the essence of temporal power.'

Bond reached for the shaker and poured himself a third drink. He looked at Honeychile. She seemed composed and indifferent – as if her mind was on other things. She smiled at him.

Doctor No said benignly. 'I expect you are both hungry. Pray be patient. I will be brief. So, if you recall, there I was, in Milwaukee. In due course, I completed my studies and I left America and went by easy stages round the world. I called myself "doctor" because doctors receive confidences and they can ask questions without arousing suspicion. I was looking for my headquarters. It had to be safe from the coming war, it had to be an island, it had to be entirely private, and it had to be capable of industrial development. In the end I purchased Crab Key. And here I have remained for fourteen years. They have been secure and fruitful years, without a cloud on the horizon. I was entertained by the idea of converting bird dung into gold, and I attacked the problem with passion. It seemed to me the ideal industry. There was a constant demand for the product. The birds require no care except to be left in peace. Each one is a simple factory for turning fish into dung. The digging of the guano is only a question of not spoiling the crop by digging too much. The sole problem is the cost of the labour. It was 1942. The simple Cuban and Jamaican labourer was earning ten shillings a week cutting cane. I tempted a hundred of them over to the island by paying them twelve shillings a week. With guano at fifty dollars a ton I was well placed. But on one condition – that the wages remained constant. I ensured that by isolating my community from world inflation. Harsh methods have had to be used from time to time, but the result is that my men are content with their wages because they are the highest wages they have ever known. I brought in a dozen Chinese Negroes with their families to act as overseers. They receive a pound a week per man. They are tough and reliable. On occasion I had to be ruthless with them, but they soon learned. Automatically my people increased in numbers. I added some engineers and some builders. We set to work on the mountain. Occasionally I brought in teams of specialists on high wages.

They were kept apart from the others. They lived inside the mountain until their work was done and then left by ship. They put in the lighting and ventilation and the lift. They built this room. Stores and furnishings came in from all over the world. These people built the sanatorium façade which will cover my operations in case one day there is a shipwreck or the Governor of Jamaica decides to pay me a call.' The lips glazed into a smile. 'You must admit that I am able, if I wish, to accord visitors a most fragrant reception – a wise precaution for the future! And gradually, methodically, my fortress was built while the birds defecated on top of it. It has been hard, Mister Bond.' The black eyes did not look for sympathy or praise. 'But by the end of last year the work was done. A secure, well-camouflaged base had been achieved. I was ready to proceed to the next step – an extension of my power to the outside world.'

Doctor No paused. He lifted his arms an inch and dropped them again resignedly in his lap. 'Mister Bond, I said that there was not a cloud in the sky during all these fourteen years. But one was there, all the time, below the horizon. And do you know what it was? It was a bird, a ridiculous bird called a roseate spoonbill! I will not weary you with the details, Mister Bond. You are already aware of the circumstances. The two wardens, miles away in the middle of the lake, were provisioned by launch from Cuba. They sent out their reports by the launch. Occasionally, ornithologists from America came by the launch and spent some days at the camp. I did not mind. The area is out of bounds to my men. The wardens were not allowed near my compounds. There was no contact. From the first I made it clear to the Audubon Society that I would not meet their representatives. And then what happens? One day, out of a clear sky, I get a letter by the monthly boat. The roseate spoonbills have become one of the bird wonders of the world. The Society gives me formal notification that they intend to build a hotel on their leasehold, near the river up which you came. Bird lovers from all over the world will come to observe the birds. Films will be taken. Crab Key, they told me in their flattering, persuasive letter, would become famous.

'Mister Bond,' the arms were raised and dropped back. Irony gathered at the edges of the set smile. 'Can you believe it? This privacy I had achieved! The plans I had for the future! To be swept aside because of a lot of old women and their birds! I examined the lease. I wrote offering a huge sum to buy it. They refused. So I studied these birds. I found out about their habits. And suddenly the solution was there. And it was easy. Man had always been the worst predator on these birds.

Spoonbills are extremely shy. They frighten easily. I sent to Florida for a marsh buggy – the vehicle that is used for oil prospecting, that will cover any kind of terrain. I adapted it to frighten and to burn – not only birds, but humans as well, for the wardens would have to go too. And, one night in December, my marsh buggy howled off across the lake. It smashed the camp, both wardens were reported killed – though one, it turned out, escaped to die in Jamaica – it burned the nesting places, it spread terror among the birds. Complete success! Hysteria spread among the spoonbills. They died in thousands. But then I get a demand for a plane to land on my airstrip. There was to be an investigation. I decide to agree. It seemed wiser. An accident is arranged. A lorry goes out of control down the airstrip as the plane is coming in. The plane is destroyed. All signs of the lorry are removed. The bodies are reverently placed in coffins and I report the tragedy. As I expected, there is further investigation. A destroyer arrives. I receive the captain courteously. He and his officers are brought round by sea and then led inland. They are shown the remains of the camp. My men suggest that the wardens went mad with loneliness and fought each other. The survivor set fire to the camp and escaped in his fishing canoe. The airstrip is examined. My men report that the plane was coming in too fast. The tyres must have burst in impact. The bodies are handed over. It is very sad. The officers are satisfied. The ship leaves. Peace reigns again.'

Doctor No coughed delicately. He looked from Bond to the girl and back again, 'And that, my friends, is my story – or rather the first chapter of what I am confident will be a long and interesting tale. Privacy has been re-established. There are now no roseate spoonbills, so there will be no wardens. No doubt the Audubon Society will decide to accept my offer for the rest of their lease. No matter. If they start their puny operations again, other misfortunes will befall them. This has been a warning to me. There will be no more interference.'

'Interesting,' said Bond. 'An interesting case history. So that was why Strangways had to be removed. What did you do with him and his girl?'

'They are at the bottom of the Mona Reservoir. I sent three of my best men. I have a small but efficient machine in Jamaica. I need it. I have established a watch on the intelligence services in Jamaica and Cuba. It is necessary for my further operations. Your Mister Strangways became suspicious and started ferreting about. Fortunately, by this time, the routines of this man were known to me. His death and the girl's were a simple matter of timing. I had hoped to deal with you with similar expedition. You were fortunate. But I knew what type of a man you were from the files at King's House. I guessed that the fly would come to the spider. I was ready for you, and when the canoe showed up on the radar screen I knew you would not get away.'

Bond said, 'Your radar is not very efficient. There were two canoes. The one you saw was the girl's. I tell you she had nothing to do with me.'

'Then she is unfortunate. I happen to be needing a white woman for a small experiment. As agreed earlier, Mister Bond, one generally gets what one wants.'

Bond looked thoughtfully at Doctor No. He wondered if it was worth while even trying to make a dent in this impregnable man. Was it worth wasting breath by threatening or bluffing? Bond had nothing but a miserable two of clubs up his sleeve. The thought of playing it almost bored him. Casually, indifferently he threw it down.

'Then you're out of luck, Doctor No. You are now a file in London. My thoughts on this case, the evidence of the poisoned fruit and the centipede and the crashed motor car, are on record. So are the names of Miss Chung and Miss Taro. Instructions were left with someone in Jamaica that my report should be opened and acted upon if I failed to return from Crab Key within three days.'

Bond paused. The face of Doctor No was impassive. Neither the eyes nor the mouth had flickered. The jugular vein throbbed evenly. Bond bent forward. He said softly, 'But because of the girl, and only because of her, Doctor No, I will strike a bargain. In exchange for our safe return to Jamaica, you may have a week's start. You may take your aeroplane and your packet of stamps and try to get away.'

Bond sat back. 'Any interest, Doctor No?'

CHAPTER 16

HORIZONS OF AGONY

A voice behind Bond said quietly, 'Dinner is served.'

Bond swung round. It was the bodyguard. Beside him was another man who might have been his twin. They stood there, two stocky barrels of muscle, their hands buried in the sleeves of their kimonos, and looked over Bond's head at Doctor No.

'Ah, nine o'clock already.' Doctor No rose slowly to his feet. 'Come along. We can continue our conversation in more intimate surroundings. It is kind of you both to have listened to me with such exemplary patience. I hope the modesty of my cuisine and my cellar will not prove a further imposition.'

Double doors stood open in the wall behind the two white-jacketed men. Bond and the girl followed Doctor No through into a small octagonal mahogany panelled room lit by a central chandelier in silver with storm glasses round the candles. Beneath it was a round mahogany table laid for three. Silver and glass twinkled warmly. The plain dark blue carpet was luxuriously deep. Doctor No took the centre high-backed chair and bowed the girl into the chair on his right. They sat down and unfolded napkins of white silk.

The hollow ceremony and the charming room maddened Bond. He longed to break it up with his own hands – to wind his silk napkin round Doctor No's throat and squeeze until the contact lenses popped out of the black, damnable eyes.

The two guards wore white cotton gloves. They served the food with a suave efficiency that was prompted by an occasional word in Chinese from Doctor No.

At first, Doctor No seemed preoccupied. He slowly ate through three bowls of different soup, feeding himself with a spoon with a short handle that fitted neatly between the pincers. Bond concentrated on hiding his fears from the girl. He sat relaxed and ate and drank with a forced good appetite. He talked cheerfully to the girl about Jamaica – about the birds and the animals and the flowers which were an easy topic for her. Occasionally his feet felt for her under the table. She became almost gay. Bond thought they were putting on an excellent imitation of an engaged couple being given dinner by a detested uncle.

Bond had no idea if his thin bluff had worked. He didn't give much for

their chances. Doctor No, and Doctor No's story, exuded impregna-
bility. The incredible biography rang true. Not a word of it was
impossible. Perhaps there were other people in the world with their
private kingdoms – away from the beaten track, where there were no
witnesses, where they could do what they liked. And what did Doctor
No plan to do next, after he had squashed the flies that had come to
annoy him? And if – when – he killed Bond and the girl, would London
pick up the threads that Bond had picked up? Probably they would.
There would be Pleydell-Smith. The evidence of the poisoned fruit. But
where would Bond's replacement get with Doctor No? Not far. Doctor
No would shrug his shoulders over the disappearance of Bond and
Quarrel. Never heard of them. And there would be no link with the girl.
In Morgan's Harbour they would think she had been drowned on one of
her expeditions. It was hard to see what could interfere with Doctor No –
with the second chapter of his life, whatever it was.

Underneath his chatter with the girl, Bond prepared for the worst.
There were plenty of weapons beside his plate. When the cutlets came,
perfectly cooked, Bond fiddled indecisively with the knives and chose the
bread knife to eat them with. While he ate and talked, he edged the big
steel meat knife towards him. An expansive gesture of his right hand
knocked over his glass of champagne and in the split second of the crash
his left hand flicked the knife into the deep sleeve of his kimono. In the
midst of Bond's apologies and the confusion as he and the bodyguard
mopped up the spilled champagne, Bond raised his left arm and felt the
knife slip back to below his armpit and then fall inside the kimono
against his ribs. When he had finished his cutlets he tightened the silk
belt round his waist, shifting the knife across his stomach. The knife
rested comfortingly against his skin and gradually the steel grew warm.

Coffee came and the meal was ended. The two guards came and stood
close behind Bond's chair and the girl's. They stood with their arms
crossed on their chests, impassive, motionless, like executioners.

Doctor No put his cup softly down on his saucer. He laid his two steel
claws down on the table in front of him. He sat a fraction more upright.
He turned his body an inch in Bond's direction. Now there was no
preoccupation in his face. The eyes were hard and direct. The thin
mouth creased and opened. 'You have enjoyed your dinner, Mister
Bond?'

Bond took a cigarette from the silver-box in front of him and lit it. He
played with the silver table-lighter. He smelled bad news coming. He
must somehow pocket the lighter. Fire might perhaps be another
weapon. He said easily, 'Yes, It was excellent.' He looked across at the

girl. He leant forward in his chair and rested his forearms on the table. He crossed them, enveloping the lighter. He smiled at her. 'I hope I ordered what you like.'

'Oh yes, it was lovely.' For her the party was still going on.

Bond smoked busily, agitating his hands and forearms to create an atmosphere of movement. He turned to Doctor No. He stubbed out his cigarette and sat back in his chair. He folded his arms across his chest. The lighter was in his left armpit. He smiled cheerfully. 'And what happens now, Doctor No?'

'We can proceed to our after-dinner entertainment, Mister Bond.' The thin smile creased and vanished. 'I have examined your proposition from every angle. I do not accept it.'

Bond shrugged his shoulders. 'You are unwise.'

'No, Mister Bond. I suspect that your proposition is a gold brick. People in your trade do not behave as you suggest. They make routine reports to their headquarters. They keep their chief aware of the progress of their investigations. I know these things. Secret agents do not behave as you suggest you have done. You have been reading too many novels of suspense. Your little speech reeked of grease-paint and cardboard. No, Mister Bond, I do not accept your story. If it is true, I am prepared to face the consequences. I have too much at stake to be turned from my path. So the police come, the soldiers come. Where are a man and a girl? What man and what girl? I know nothing. Please go away. You are disturbing my guanera. Where is your evidence? Your search warrant? The English law is strict, gentlemen. Go home and leave me in peace with my beloved cormorants. You see, Mister Bond? And let us even say that the worst comes to the worst. That one of my agents talks, which is highly improbable (Bond remembered the fortitude of Miss Chung). What have I to lose? Two more deaths on the charge sheet. But, Mister Bond, a man can only be hanged once.' The tall pear-shaped head shook gently from side to side. 'Have you anything else to say? Any questions to ask? You both have a busy night ahead of you. Your time is getting short. And I must get my sleep. The monthly ship is putting in tomorrow and I have the loading to supervise. I shall have to spend the whole day down on the quay. Well, Mister Bond?'

Bond looked across at the girl. She had gone deathly pale. She was gazing at him, waiting for the miracle he would work. He looked down at his hands. He examined his nails carefully. He said, playing for time, 'And then what? After your busy day with the bird dung, what comes next on your programme? What is the next chapter you think you're going to write?'

Bond didn't look up. The deep quiet authoritative voice came to him as if it was coming down from the night sky.

'Ah, yes. You must have been wondering, Mister Bond. You have the habit of inquiry. It persists even to the last, even into the shadows. I admire such qualities in a man with only a few hours to live. So I will tell you. I will turn over the next page. It will console you. There is more to this place than bird dung. Your instincts did not betray you.' Doctor No paused for emphasis. 'This island, Mister Bond, is about to be developed into the most valuable technical intelligence centre of the world.'

'Really?' Bond kept his eyes bent on his hands.

'Doubtless you know that Turks Island, about three hundred miles from here through the Windward Passage, is the most important centre for testing the guided missiles of the United States?'

'It is an important centre, yes.'

'Perhaps you have read of the rockets that have been going astray recently? The multi-stage SNARK, for instance, that ended its flight in the forests of Brazil instead of the depths of the South Atlantic?'

'Yes.'

'You recall that it refused to obey the telemetred instructions to change its course, even to destroy itself. It developed a will of its own?'

'I remember.'

'There have been other failures, decisive failures, from the long list of prototypes – the ZUNI, MATADOR, PETREL, REGULUS, BOMARC – so many names, so many changes, I can't even remember them all. Well, Mister Bond,' Doctor No could not keep a note of pride out of his voice, 'it may interest you to know that the vast majority of those failures have been caused from Crab Key.'

'Is that so?'

'You do not believe me? No matter. Others do. Others who have seen the complete abandonment of one series, the MASTODON, because of its recurring navigational errors, its failure to obey the radio directions from Turks Island. Those others are the Russians. The Russians are my partners in this venture. They trained six of my men, Mister Bond. Two of those men are on watch at this moment, watching the radio frequencies, the beams on which these weapons travel. There is a million dollars' worth of equipment up above us in the rock galleries, Mister Bond, sending fingers up into the Heavyside Layer, waiting for the signals, jamming them, countering beams with other beams. And from time to time a rocket soars up on its way a hundred, five hundred miles into the Atlantic. And we track it, as accurately as they are tracking it in the Operations Rooms on Turks Island. Then, suddenly, our pulses go out to the rocket, its brain is confused, it goes mad, it plunges into the sea, it destroys itself, it roars off at a tangent. Another test has failed. The operators are blamed, the designers, the manufacturers. There is panic in the Pentagon. Something else must be tried, different frequencies, different metals, a different radio brain. Of course,' Doctor No was fair, 'we too have our difficulties. We track many practice shoots without being able to get through to the brain of the new rocket. But then we communicate urgently with Moscow. Yes, they have even given us a cipher machine with our frequencies and routines. And the Russians get thinking. They make suggestions. We try them out. And then, one day, Mister Bond, it is like catching the attention of a man in a crowd. Up in the stratosphere the rocket acknowledges our signal. We are recognized and we can speak to it and change its mind.' Doctor No paused. 'Do you not find that interesting, Mister Bond, this little sideline to my business in guano? It is, I assure you, most profitable. It might be still more so. Perhaps Communist China will pay more. Who knows? I already have my feelers out.'

Bond lifted his eyes. He looked thoughtfully at Doctor No. So he *had* been right. There *had* been more, much more, in all this than met the eye. This was a big game, a game that explained everything, a game that was certainly, in the international espionage market, well worth the candle. Well, well! Now the pieces in the puzzle fell firmly into place. For this it was certainly worth scaring away a few birds and wiping out a few people. Privacy? Of course Doctor No would have to kill him and the girl. Power? This was it. Doctor No had really got himself into business.

Bond looked into the two black holes with a new respect. He said, 'You'll have to kill a lot more to keep this thing in your hands, Doctor No. It's worth a lot of money. You've got a good property here – a better one than I thought. People are going to want to cut themselves a piece of this cake. I wonder who will get to you first and kill you. Those men up there,' he gestured towards the ceiling, 'who were trained in Moscow? They're the technicians. I wonder what Moscow is telling them to do? You wouldn't know that, would you?'

Doctor No said, 'You persist in underestimating me, Mister Bond. You are an obstinate man, and stupider than I had expected. I am aware of these possibilities. I have taken one of these men and made him into a private monitor. He has duplicates of the ciphers and of the cipher machine. He lives in another part of the mountain. The others think that he died. He watches on all the routine times. He gives me a second copy of all the traffic that passes. So far, the signals from Moscow have been innocent of any sign of conspiracy. I am thinking of these things constantly, Mister Bond. I take precautions and I shall take further precautions. As I said, you underestimate me.'

'I don't underestimate you, Doctor No. You're a very careful man, but you've got too many files open on you. In my line of business, the same thing applies to me. I know the feeling. But you've got some really bad ones. The Chinese one, for instance. I wouldn't like to have that one. The FBI should be the least painful – robbery and false identity. But do you know the Russians as well as I do? You're a 'best friend' at the moment. But the Russians don't have partners. They'll want to take you over – buy you out with a bullet. Then there's the file you've started with my Service. You really want me to make that one fatter? I shouldn't do it if I were you, Doctor No. They're a tenacious lot of people in my Service. If anything happens to me and the girl, you'll find Crab Key's a very small and naked little island.'

'You cannot play for high stakes without taking risks, Mister Bond. I accept the dangers and, so far as I can, I have equipped myself against them. You see, Mister Bond,' the deep voice held a hint of greed, 'I am on the edge of still greater things. The Chapter Two to which I referred holds the promise of prizes which no one but a fool would throw away because he was afraid. I have told you that I can bend the beams on which these rockets fly, Mister Bond. I can make them change course and ignore their radio control. What would you say, Mister Bond, if I could go further? If I could bring them down into the sea near this island and salvage the secrets of their construction. At present American destroyers, far out in the South Atlantic, salvage these missiles when they come to the end of their fuel and parachute down in the sea. Sometimes the parachutes fail to open. Sometimes the self-destruction devices fail to operate. No one on Turks Island would be surprised if every now and then the prototype of a new series broke off its flight and came down near Crab Key. To begin with, at least, it would be put down to mechanical failure. Later, perhaps, they would discover that other radio signals besides theirs were guiding their rockets. A jamming war would start. They would try and locate the origin of the false signals. Directly I found they were looking for me, I would have one last fling. Their rockets would go mad. They would land on Havana, on Kingston. They would turn round and home on Miami. Even without warheads, Mister Bond, five tons of metal arriving at a thousand miles an hour can cause plenty of damage in a crowded town. And then what? There would be panic, a public outcry. The experiments would have to cease. The Turks Island base would have to close down. And how much would Russia pay for that to happen, Mister Bond? And how much for each of the prototypes I captured for them? Shall we say ten million dollars for the whole operation? Twenty million? It would be a priceless victory in the armaments race. I could name my figure. Don't you agree, Mister Bond? And don't you agree that these considerations make your arguments and threats seem rather puny?'

Bond said nothing. There was nothing to say. Suddenly he was back in the quiet room high up above Regent's Park. He could hear the rain slashing softly against the window and M's voice, impatient, sarcastic, saying, 'Oh, some damned business about birds . . . holiday in the sun'll do you good . . . routine inquiry.' And he, Bond, had taken a canoe and a fisherman and a picnic lunch and had gone off – how many days, how many weeks ago? – 'to have a look'. Well, he had had his look into Pandora's Box. He had found out the answers, been told the secrets – and now? Now he was going to be politely shown the way to his grave, taking the secrets with him and the waif he had picked up and dragged along with him on his lunatic adventure. The bitterness inside Bond came up into his mouth so that for a moment he thought he was going to retch. He reached for his champagne and emptied the glass. He said harshly, 'All right, Doctor No. Now let's go on with the cabaret. What's the programme – knife, bullet, poison, rope? But make it quick, I've seen enough of you.'

Doctor No's lips compressed into a thin purple line. The eyes were hard as onyx under the billiard-ball forehead and skull. The polite mask had gone. The Grand Inquisitor sat in the high-backed chair. The hour had struck for the *peine forte et dure*.

Doctor No spoke a word and the two guards took a step forward and held the two victims above the elbows, forcing their arms back against the sides of their chairs. There was no resistance. Bond concentrated on holding the lighter in his armpit. The white-gloved hands on his biceps felt like steel bands. He smiled across at the girl. 'I'm sorry about this, Honey. I'm afraid we're not going to be able to play together after all.'

The girl's eyes in the pale face were blue-black with fear. Her lips trembled. She said, 'Will it hurt?'

'Silence!' Doctor No's voice was the crack of a whip. 'Enough of this foolery. Of course it will hurt. I am interested in pain. I am also interested in finding out how much the human body can endure. From time to time I make experiments on those of my people who have to be punished. And on trespassers like yourselves. You have both put me to a great deal of trouble. In exchange I intend to put you to a great deal of pain. I shall record the length of your endurance. The facts will be noted. One day my findings will be given to the world. Your deaths will have served the purpose of science. I never waste human material. The German experiments on live humans during the war were of great benefit to science. It is a year since I put a girl to death in the fashion I have chosen for you, woman. She was a Negress. She lasted three hours. She died of terror. I have wanted a white girl for comparison. I was not surprised when your arrival was reported. I get what I want.' Doctor No sat back in his chair. His eyes were now fixed on the girl, watching her reactions. She stared back at him, half hypnotized, like a bush mouse in front of a rattlesnake.

Bond set his teeth.

'You are a Jamaican, so you will know what I am talking about. This island is called Crab Key. It is called by that name because it is infested with crabs, land crabs – what they call in Jamaica 'black crabs'. You know them. They weigh about a pound each and they are as big as saucers. At this time of year they come up in thousands from their holes near the shore and climb up towards the mountain. There, in the coral uplands, they go to ground again in holes in the rock and spawn their broods. They march up in armies of hundreds at a time. They march through everything and over everything. In Jamaica they go through houses that are in their path. They are like the lemmings of Norway. It is a compulsive migration.' Doctor No paused. He said softly, 'But there is a difference. The crabs devour what they find in their path. And at present, woman, they are 'running'. They are coming up the mountain-side in their tens of thousands, great red and orange and black waves of them, scuttling and hurrying and scraping against the rock above us at this moment. And tonight, in the middle of their path, they are going to find the naked body of a woman pegged out – a banquet spread for them – and they will feel the warm body with their feeding pincers, and one will make the first incision with his fighting claws and then . . . and then . . .'

There was a moan from the girl. Her head fell forward slackly on to her chest. She had fainted. Bond's body heaved in his chair. A string of obscenities hissed out between his clenched teeth. The huge hands of the guard were like fire round his arms. He couldn't even move the chair-legs on the floor. After a moment he desisted. He waited for his voice to steady, then he said, with all the venom he could put into the words, 'You bastard. You'll fry in hell for this.'

Doctor No smiled thinly. 'Mister Bond. I do not admit the existence of hell. Console yourself. Perhaps they will start at the throat or the heart. The movement of the pulse will attract them. Then it will not be long.'

He spoke a sentence in Chinese. The guard behind the girl's chair leant forward and plucked her bodily out of the chair as if she had been a child and slung the inert body over his shoulder. Between the dangling arms the hair fell down in a golden shower. The guard went to the door and opened it and went out, closing it noiselessly behind him.

For a moment there was silence in the room. Bond thought only of the knife against his skin and of the lighter under his armpit. How much damage could he do with the two pieces of metal? Could he somehow get within range of Doctor No?

Doctor No said quietly. 'You said that power was an illusion, Mister Bond. Do you change your mind? My power to select this particular death for the girl is surely not an illusion. However, let us proceed to the method of your departure. That also has its novel aspects. You see, Mister Bond, I am interested in the anatomy of courage – in the power of the human body to endure. But how to measure human endurance? How to plot a graph of the will to survive, the tolerance of pain, the conquest of fear? I have given much thought to the problem, and I believe I have solved it. It is, of course, only a rough and ready method, and I shall learn by experience as more and more subjects are put to the test. I have prepared you for the experiment as best I could. I gave you a sedative so that your body should be rested and I have fed you well so that you may be at full strength. Future – what shall I call them – patients, will have the same advantages. All will start equal in that respect. After that it will be a question of the individual's courage and powers of endurance.' Doctor No paused, watching Bond's face. 'You see, Mister Bond, I have just finished constructing an obstacle race, an assault course against death. I will say no more about it because the element of surprise is one of the constituents of fear. It is the unknown dangers that are the worst, that bear most heavily on the reserves of courage. And I flatter myself that the gauntlet you will run contains a rich assortment of the unexpected. It will be particularly interesting, Mister Bond, that a man of your physical qualities is to be my first competitor. It will be most interesting to observe how far you get down the course I have devised. You should put up a worthy target figure for future runners. I have high expectations of you. You should go far, but when, as is inevitable, you have finally failed at an obstacle, your body will be recovered and I shall most meticulously examine the physical state of your remains. The data will be recorded. You will be the first dot on a graph. Something of an honour, is it not, Mister Bond?'

Bond said nothing. What the hell did all this mean? What could this test consist of? Would it be possible to survive it? Could he conceivably escape from it and get to the girl before it was too late, even if it was only to kill her and save her from her torture? Silently Bond gathered his reserves of courage, steeling his mind against the fear of the unknown that already had him by the throat, focusing his whole will on survival. Somehow, above all else, he must cling to his weapons.

Doctor No rose and stepped away from his chair. He walked slowly to the door and turned. The menacing black holes looked back at Bond from just below the lintel of the door. The head was inclined a fraction. The purple lips creased back. 'Run a good race for me, Mister Bond. My thoughts, as they say, will be with you.'

Doctor No turned away and the door closed softly behind the long thin gunmetal back.

CHAPTER 17

THE LONG SCREAM

There was a man on the lift. The doors were open, waiting. James Bond, his arms still locked to his sides, was marched in. Now the dining-room would be empty. How soon would the guards go back, start clearing away the dinner, notice the missing things? The doors hissed shut. The liftman stood in front of the buttons so that Bond could not see which he had pressed. They were going up. Bond tried to estimate the distance. The lift sighed to a stop. The time seemed rather less than when he had come down with the girl. The doors opened on to an uncarpeted corridor with rough grey paint on the stone walls. It ran about twenty yards straight ahead.

'Hold it, Joe,' said Bond's guard to the liftman. 'Be right with you.'

Bond was marched down the corridor past doors numbered with letters of the alphabet. There was a faint hum of machinery in the air and behind one door Bond thought he could catch the crackle of radio static. It sounded as if they might be in the engine-room of the mountain. They came to the end door. It was marked with a black Q. It was ajar and the guard pushed Bond into the door so that it swung open. Through the door was a grey painted stone cell about fifteen feet square. There was nothing in it except a wooden chair on which lay, laundered and neatly folded, Bond's black canvas jeans and his blue shirt.

The guard let go of Bond's arms. Bond turned and looked into the broad yellow face below the crinkly hair. There was a hint of curiosity and pleasure in the liquid brown eyes. The man stood holding the door handle. He said, 'Well, this is it, bud. You're at the starting gate. You can either sit here and rot or find your way out on to the course. Happy landings.'

Bond thought it was just worth trying. He glanced past the guard to where the liftman was standing beside his open doors, watching them. He said softly, 'How would you like to earn ten thousand dollars, guaranteed, and a ticket to anywhere in the world?' He watched the man's face. The mouth spread in a wide grin to show brownish teeth worn to uneven points by years of chewing sugar-cane.

'Thanks, Mister. I'd rather stay alive.' The man made to close the door. Bond whispered urgently. 'We could get out of here together.'

The thick lips sneered. The man said, 'Shove it!' The door shut with a solid click.

Bond shrugged his shoulders. He gave the door a cursory glance. It was made of metal and there was no handle on the inside. Bond didn't waste his shoulder on it. He went to the chair and sat down on the neat pile of his clothes and looked round the cell. The walls were entirely naked except for a ventilation grille of thick wire in one corner just below the ceiling. It was wider than his shoulders. It was obviously the way out into the assault course. The only other break in the walls was a thick glass porthole, no bigger than Bond's head, just above the door. Light from the corridor filtered through it into the cell. There was nothing else. It was no good wasting any more time. It would now be about ten-thirty. Outside, somewhere on the slope of the mountain, the girl would already be lying, waiting for the rattle of claws on the grey coral. Bond clenched his teeth at the thought of the pale body spread-eagled out there under the stars. Abruptly he stood up. What the hell was he doing sitting still. Whatever lay on the other side of the wire grille, it was time to go.

Bond took out his knife and the lighter and threw off the kimono. He dressed in the trousers and shirt and stowed the lighter in his hip pocket. He tried the edge of the knife with his thumb. It was very sharp. It would be better still if he could get a point on it. He knelt on the floor and began whittling the rounded end on the stone. After a precious quarter of an hour he was satisfied. It was no stiletto, but it would serve to stab as well a cut. Bond put the knife between his teeth and set the chair below the grille, and climbed on to it. The grille! Assuming he could tear it off its hinges, the frame of quarter-inch wire might straighten into a spear. That would make a third weapon. Bond reached up with crooked fingers.

The next thing he knew was a searing pain up his arm and the crack of his head hitting the stone floor. He lay, stunned, with only the memory of a blue flash and the hiss and crackle of electricity to tell him what had hit him.

Bond got to his knees and stayed there. He bent his head down and shook it slowly from side to side like a wounded animal. He noticed a smell of burning flesh. He lifted his right hand up to his eyes. There was the red smear of an open burn across the inside of his fingers. Seeing it brought the pain. Bond spat out a four-letter word. Slowly he got to his feet. He squinted up at the wire grille as if it might strike at him again, like a snake. Grimly he set the chair upright against the wall. He picked up his knife and cut a strip off the discarded kimono and tied it firmly across his fingers. Then he climbed up again on to the chair and looked at the grille. He was meant to get through it. The shock had been to soften him up – a taste of pain to come. Surely he had fused the blasted thing. Surely they would have switched off the current. He looked at it only for an instant, then the fingers of his left hand crooked and went straight up to the impersonal wire mesh. His fingers went through the wire rim and gripped.

Nothing! Nothing at all – just wire. Bond grunted. He felt his nerves slacken. He tugged at the wire. It gave an inch. He tugged again and it came away in his hand and dangled down from two strands of copper flex that disappeared into the wall. Bond pulled the grille loose from the flex and got down from the chair. Yes, there was a join in the frame. He set to work unravelling the mesh. Then using the chair as a hammer, he straightened the heavy wire.

After ten minutes, Bond had a crooked spear about four feet long. One end, where it had originally been cut by the pliers, was jagged. It would not pierce a man's clothes, but it would be good enough for the face and neck. By using all his strength and the crack at the bottom of the metal door, Bond turned the blunt end into a clumsy crook. He measured the wire against his leg. It was too long. He bent it double and slipped the spear down a trouser leg. Now it hung from his waistband to just above the knee. He went back to the chair and climbed up again and reached, nervously, for the edge of the ventilator shaft. There was no shock. Bond heaved up and through the opening and lay on his stomach looking along the shaft.

The shaft was about four inches wider than Bond's shoulders. It was circular and of polished metal. Bond reached for his lighter, blessing the inspiration that had made him take it, and flicked it on. Yes, zinc sheeting that looked new. The shaft stretched straight ahead, featureless except for the ridges where the sections of pipe joined. Bond put the lighter back in his pocket and snaked forward.

It was easy going. Cool air from the ventilating system blew strongly in Bond's face. The air held no smell of the sea – it was the canned stuff that comes from an air-conditioning plant. Doctor No must have adapted one of the shafts to his purpose. What hazards had he built into it to test out his victims? They would be ingenious and painful – designed to reduce the resistance of the victim. At the winning post, so to speak, there would be the *coup de grâce* – if the victim ever got that far. It would be something conclusive, something from which there would be no escape, for there would be no prizes in this race except oblivion – an oblivion, thought Bond, he might be glad to win. Unless of course Doctor No had been just a bit too clever. Unless he had underestimated the will to survive. That, thought Bond, was his only hope – to try to survive the intervening hazards, to get through at least to the last ditch.

There was a faint luminosity ahead. Bond approached it carefully, his senses questing in front of him like antennae. It grew brighter. It was the glint of light against the end of the lateral shaft. He went on until his head touched the metal. He twisted over on his back. Straight above him, at the top of fifty yards or so of vertical shaft, was a steady glimmer. It was like looking up a long gun barrel. Bond inched round the square bend and looked upright. So he was supposed to climb straight up this shining tube of metal without a foothold! Was it possible? Bond expanded his shoulders. Yes, they gripped the sides. His feet could also get a temporary purchase, though they would slip except where the ridges at the joints gave him an ounce of upward leverage. Bond shrugged his shoulders and kicked off his shoes. It was no good arguing. He would just have to try.

Six inches at a time, Bond's body began to worm up the shaft – expand shoulders to grip the sides, lift feet, lock knees, force the feet outwards against the metal and, as the feet slipped downwards with his weight, contract shoulders and raise them a few inches higher. Do it again, and again and again and again. Stop at each tiny bulge where the sections joined and use the millimetre of extra support to get some breath and measure the next lap. Otherwise don't look up, think only of the inches of metal that have to be conquered one by one. Don't worry about the glimmer of light that never grows brighter or nearer. Don't worry about losing your grip and falling to smash your ankles at the bottom of the shaft. Don't worry about cramp. Don't worry about your screaming muscles or the swelling bruises on your shoulders and the sides of your feet. Just take the silver inches as they come, one by one, and conquer them.

But then the feet began to sweat and slip. Twice Bond lost a yard before his shoulders, scalding with the friction, could put on the brake. Finally he had to stop altogether to let his sweat dry in the downward draught of air. He waited for a full ten minutes, staring at his faint reflection in the polished metal, the face split in half by the knife between the teeth. Still he refused to look up to see how much more there was. It might be too much to bear. Carefully Bond wiped each foot against a trouser-leg and began again.

Now half Bond's mind was dreaming while the other half fought the battle. He wasn't even conscious of the strengthening breeze or the slowly brightening light. He saw himself as a wounded caterpillar crawling up a waste pipe towards the plug-hole of a bath. What would he see when he got through the plug-hole? A naked girl drying herself? A man shaving? Sunlight streaming through an open window into an empty bathroom?

Bond's head bumped against something. The plug was in the plug-hole! The shock of disappointment made him slip a yard before his shoulders got a fresh grip. Then he realized. He was at the top! Now he noticed the bright light and the strong wind. Feverishly, but with a more desperate care, he heaved up again until his head touched. The wind was coming into his left ear. Cautiously he turned his head. It was another lateral shaft. Above him light was shining through a thick porthole. All he had to do was inch himself round and grip the edge of the new shaft and somehow gather enough strength to heave himself in. Then he would be able to lie down.

With an extra delicacy, born of panic that something might now go wrong, that he might make a mistake and plummet back down the shaft to land in a crackle of bone, Bond, his breath steaming against the metal, carried out the manoeuvre and, with his last ounce of strength, jackknifed into the opening and crumpled full length on his face.

Later – how much later? – Bond's eyes open and his body stirred. The cold had woken him from the fringe of total unconsciousness into which his body had plunged. Painfully he rolled over on his back, his feet and shoulders screaming at him, and lay gathering his wits and summoning more strength. He had no idea what time it was or whereabouts he was inside the mountain. He lifted his head and looked back at the porthole above the yawning tube out of which he had come. The light was yellowish and the glass looked thick. He remembered the porthole in Room Q. There had been nothing breakable about that one, nor he guessed, would there be here.

Suddenly, behind the glass, he saw movement. As he watched, a pair of eyes materialized from behind the electric light bulb. They stopped and looked at him, the bulb making the yellow glass nose between them. They gazed incuriously at him and then they were gone. Bond's lips snarled back from his teeth. So his progress was going to be observed, reported back to Doctor No!

Bond said out loud, viciously, '—— them all,' and turned sullenly back on his stomach. He raised his head and looked forward. The tunnel shimmered away into blackness. Come on! No good hanging about. He picked up his knife and put it back between his teeth and winced his way forward.

Soon there was no more light. Bond stopped from time to time and used the lighter, but there was nothing but blackness ahead. The air began to get warmer in the shaft, and perhaps fifty yards further, definitely hot. There was the smell of heat in the air, metallic heat. Bond began to sweat. Soon his body was soaked and he had to pause every few minutes to wipe his eyes. There came a right-hand turn in the shaft. Round it the metal of the big tube was hot against his skin. The smell of heat was very strong. There came another right-angled turn. As soon as Bond's head got round he quickly pulled out his lighter and lit it and then snaked back and lay panting. Bitterly he examined the new hazard, probing it, cursing it. His light had flickered on discoloured, oyster-hued zinc. The next hazard was to be heat!

Bond groaned aloud. How could his bruised flesh stand up to that? How could he protect his skin from the metal? But there wasn't anything he could do about it. He could either go back, or stay where he was, or go on. There was no other decision to make, no other shift or excuse. There was one, and only one, grain of consolation. This would not be heat that would kill, only maim. This would not be the final killing ground – only one more test of how much he could take.

Bond thought of the girl and of what she was going through. Oh well. Get on with it. Now, let's see. . . .

Bond took his knife and cut off the whole front of his shirt and sliced it into strips. The only hope that was to put some wrapping round the parts of his body that would have to bear the brunt – his hands and his feet. His knees and elbows would have to get along with their single covering of cotton fabric. Wearily he set to work, cursing softly.

Bond turned the corner and forged forward into the heat stench.

Keep your naked stomach off the ground! Contract your shoulders! Hands, knees, toes; hands, knees, toes. Faster, faster! Keep going fast so that each touch on the ground is quickly taken over by the next.

The knees were getting it worst, taking the bulk of Bond's weight.

Now the padded hands were beginning to smoulder. There was a spark, and another one, and then a worm of red as the sparks began to run. The smoke from the stuff smarted in Bond's sweating eyes. God, he couldn't do any more! There was no air. His lungs were bursting. Now his hands shed sparks as he thrust them forward. The stuff must be nearly gone. Then the flesh would burn. Bond lurched and his bruised shoulder hit the metal. He screamed. He went on screaming, regularly, with each contact of hand or knee or toes. Now he was finished. Now it was the end. Now he would fall flat and slowly fry to death. No! He must drive on, screaming, until his flesh was burned to the bone. The skin must have already gone from the knees. In a moment the balls of his hands would meet the metal. Only the sweat running down his arms could be keeping the pads of stuff damp. Scream, scream, scream! It helps the pain. It tells you you're alive. Go on! Go on! It can't be much longer. This isn't where you're supposed to die. You are still alive. Don't give up! You can't!

Bond's right hand hit something that gave before it. There was a stream of ice-cold air. His other hand hit, then his head. There was a tinny noise. Bond felt the lower edge of an asbestos baffle scrape down his back. He was through. He heard the baffle bang shut. His hands came up against solid wall. They quested to left and right. It was a right-angled bend. His body followed blindly round the corner. The cool air felt like daggers in his lungs. Gingerly he laid his fingers down on the metal. It was cold! With a groan Bond fell on his face and lay still.

Sometime later the pain revived him. Bond turned sluggishly over on his back. Vaguely he noticed the lighted porthole above him. Vaguely he took in the eyes gazing down on him. Then he let the black waves take him away again.

Slowly, in the darkness, the blisters formed across the skin and the bruised feet and shoulders stiffened. The sweat dried on the body and then on the rags of clothing, and the cool air soaked down into the overheated lungs and began its insidious work. But the heart beat on, strongly and regularly inside the tortured envelope, and the healing sorceries of oxygen and rest pumped life back into the arteries and veins and recharged the nerves.

Years later, Bond awoke. He stirred. As his eyes opened and met the other pair, inches away behind the glass, pain took him and shook him like a rat. He waited for the shock to die. He tried again, and then again, until he had measured the strength of his adversary. Then Bond, to hide himself away from the witness, turned over on his stomach and took the full blast of it. Again he waited, exploring his body for its reactions, testing the strength of the resolve that was left in the batteries. How much more could he take now? Bond's lips drew back from his teeth and he snarled into the darkness. It was an animal sound. He had come to the end of his human reactions to pain and adversity. Doctor No had got him cornered. But there were animal reserves of desperation left and, in a strong animal, those reserves are deep.

Slowly, agonizingly, Bond snaked a few yards away from the eyes and then reached for his lighter and lit it. Ahead there was only the black full moon, the yawning circular mouth that led into the stomach of death. Bond put back the lighter. He took a deep breath and got to his hands and knees. The pain was no greater, only different. Slowly, stiffly, he winced forward.

The cotton fabric at Bond's knees and elbows had burned away. Numbly his mind registered the moisture as his blisters burst against the cool metal. As he moved, he flexed his fingers and toes, testing the pain. Slowly he got the measure of what he could do, what hurt most. This pain is supportable, he argued to himself. If I had been in an aeroplane crash, they would only diagnose superficial contusions and burns. I would be out of hospital in a few days. There's nothing wrong with me. I'm a survivor from the crash. It hurts, but it's nothing. Think of the bits and pieces of the other passengers. Be thankful. Put it out of your mind. But, nagging behind these reflections, was the knowledge that he had not yet had the crash – that he was still on his way towards it, his resistance, his effectiveness reduced. When would it come? What shape would it take? How much more was he to be softened up before he reached the killing ground?

Ahead in the darkness the tiny red pinpoints might have been a hallucination, specks before the eyes as a result of exhaustion. Bond stopped and screwed up his eyes. He shook his head. No, they were still there. Slowly he snaked closer. Now they were moving. Bond stopped again. He listened. Above the quiet thumping of his heart there was a soft, delicate rustling. The pinpoints had increased in number. Now there were twenty or thirty, shifting to and fro, some quickly, some slowly, all over the circle of blackness ahead. Bond reached for his lighter. He held his breath as he lit the little yellow flame. The red pinpoints went out. Instead, a yard ahead of him, very narrow mesh wire, almost as fine as muslin, blocked the shaft.

Bond inched forward, the lighter held before him. It was some sort of a cage with small things living in it. He could hear them scuttling back, away from the light. A foot away from the mesh he dowsed the light and waited for his eyes to get used to the dark. As he waited, listening, he could hear the tiny scuttling back towards him, and gradually the forest of red pinpoints gathered again, peering at him through the mesh.

What was it? Bond listened to the pounding of his heart. Snakes? Scorpions? Centipedes?

Carefully he brought his eyes close up to the little glowing forest. He inched the lighter up beside his face and suddenly pressed the lever. He caught a glimpse of tiny claws hooked through the mesh and of dozens of thick furry feet and of furry sacklike stomachs topped by big insect heads that seemed to be covered with eyes. The things plopped hurriedly off the wire on to the tin and scurried back and huddled in a grey-brown furry mass at the end of the cage.

Bond squinted through the mesh, moving the light back and forward. Then he dowsed the light, to save fuel, and let the breath come through his teeth in a quiet sigh.

They were spiders, giant tarantulas, three or four inches long. There were twenty of them in the cage. And somehow he had to get past them.

Bond lay and rested and thought while the red eyes gathered again in front of his face.

How deadly were these things? How much of the tales about them were myth? They could certainly kill animals, but how mortal to men were these giant spiders with the long soft friendly fur of a borzoi? Bond shuddered. He remembered the centipede. The touch of the tarantulas would be much softer. They would be like tiny teddy bears' paws against one's skin— until they bit and emptied their poison sacs into you.

But again, would this be Doctor No's killing ground? A bite or two perhaps – to send one into a delirium of pain. The horror of having to burst through the mesh in the darkness – Doctor No would not have reckoned with Bond's lighter – and squash through the forest of eyes, crushing some soft bodies, but feeling the jaws of the others lance home. And then more bites from the ones that had caught in the clothing. And then the creeping agony of the poison. That would have been the way Doctor No's mind would have worked – to send one screaming on one's way. To what? To the final fence?

But Bond had the lighter and the knife and the wire spear. All he needed was the nerve, and infinite, infinite precision.

Bond softly opened the jaws of the lighter and pulled the wick out an inch with his thumb and fingernail to give a bigger flame. He lit it and, as the spiders scuttled back, he pierced the thin wire mesh with his knife. He made a hole near the frame and cut down sideways and round. Then he seized the flap of wire and wrenched it out of the frame. It tore like stiff calico and came away in one piece. He put the knife back between his teeth and snaked through the opening. The spiders cowered before the flame of the lighter and crowded back on top of each other. Bond slid the wire spear out of his trousers and jabbed the blunt, doubled wire into the middle of them. He jabbed again and again, fiercely pulping the bodies. When some of the spiders tried to escape towards him he waved the light at them and smashed the fugitives one by one. Now the living spiders were attacking the dead and wounded and all Bond had to do was bash and bash into the writhing, sickening mess of blood and fur.

Slowly all movement slackened and then ceased. Were they all dead? Were some shamming? The flame of the lighter was beginning to die. He would have to chance it. Bond reached forward and shovelled the dead mess to one side. Then he took his knife from between his teeth and reached out and slashed open the second curtain of wire, bending the flap down over the heap of pulped bodies. The light flickered and became a red glow. Bond gathered himself and shot his body over the bloody pile of corpses and through the jagged frame.

He had no idea what bits of metal he touched or whether he had put his knee or his foot among the spiders. All he knew was that he had got through. He heaved himself yards on along the shaft and stopped to gather his breath and his nerve.

Above him a dim light came on. Bond squinted sideways and upwards, knowing what he would see. The slanting yellow eyes behind the thick glass looked keenly down at him. Slowly, behind the bulb, the head moved from side to side. The eyelids dropped in mock pity. A closed fist, the thumb pointing downwards in farewell and dismissal, inserted itself between the bulb and the glass. Then it was withdrawn. The light went out. Bond turned his face back to the floor of the shaft and rested his forehead on the cool metal. The gesture said that he was coming into the last lap, that the observers had finished with him until they came for his remains. It took an extra ounce of heart out of Bond that there had been no gesture of praise, however small, that he had managed to survive so far. These Chigroes hated him. They only wanted him to die, and as miserably as possible.

Bond's teeth ground softly together. He thought of the girl and the thought gave him strength. He wasn't dead yet. Damn it, he wouldn't die! Not until the heart was torn from his body.

Bond tensed his muscles. It was time to go. With extra care he put his weapons back in their places and painfully began to drag himself on into the blackness.

The shaft was beginning to slope gently downwards. It made the going easier. Soon the slope grew steeper so that Bond could almost slide

along under the momentum of his weight. It was a blessed relief not to
have to make the effort with his muscles. There was a glimmer of grey
light ahead, nothing more than a lessening of the darkness, but it was a
change. The quality of the air seemed to be different. There was a new,
fresh smell to it. What was it? The sea?

Suddenly Bond realized that he was slipping down the shaft. He
opened his shoulders and spread his feet to slow himself. It hurt and the
braking effect was small. Now the shaft was widening. He could no
longer get a grip! He was going faster and faster. A bend was just ahead.
And it was a bend downwards!

Bond's body crashed into the bend and round it. Christ, he was diving
head downwards! Desperately Bond spread his feet and hands. The
metal flayed his skin. He was out of control, diving down a gun barrel.
Far below there was a circle of grey light. The open air? The sea? The
light was tearing up at him. He fought for breath. Stay alive, you fool!
Stay alive!

Head first, Bond's body shot out of the shaft and fell through the air,
slowly, slowly, down towards the gunmetal sea that waited for him a
hundred feet below.

CHAPTER 18

KILLING GROUND

Bond's body shattered the mirror of the dawn sea like a bomb.

As he had hurtled down the silver shaft towards the widening disc of
light, instinct had told him to get his knife from between his teeth, to get
his hands forward to break his fall, and to keep his head down and his
body rigid. And, at the last fraction of a second when he glimpsed the
up-rushing sea, he had managed to take a gulp of breath. So Bond hit the
water in the semblance of a dive, his outstretched clenched fists cleaving
a hole for his skull and shoulders, and though, by the time he had shot
twenty feet below the surface, he had lost consciousness, the forty-mile-
an-hour impact with the water failed to smash him.

Slowly the body rose to the surface and lay, head down, softly rocking
in the ripples of the dive. The water-choked lungs somehow contrived to
send a last message to the brain. The legs and arms thrashed clumsily.

The head turned up, water pouring from its open mouth. It sank. Again the legs jerked, instinctively trying to get the body upright in the water. This time, coughing horribly, the head jerked above the surface and stayed there. The arms and legs began to move feebly, paddling like a dog, and, through the red and black curtain, the bloodshot eyes saw the lifeline and told the sluggish brain to make for it.

The killing ground was a narrow deep water inlet at the base of the towering cliff. The lifeline towards which Bond struggled, hampered by the clumsy spear in his trouser-leg, was a strong wire fence, stretched from the rock walls of the inlet and caging it off from the open sea. The two-feet squares of thick wire were suspended from a cable six feet above the surface and disappeared, algae encrusted, into the depths.

Bond got to the wire and hung, crucified. For fifteen minutes he stayed like that, his body occasionally racked with vomiting, until he felt strong enough to turn his head and see where he was. Blearily his eyes took in the towering cliffs above him and the narrow vee of softly breathing water. The place was in deep grey shadow, cut off from the dawn by the mountain, but out at sea there was the pearly iridescence of first light that meant that for the rest of the world the day was dawning. Here it was dark and gloomy and brooding.

Sluggishly Bond's mind puzzled over the wire fence. What was its purpose, closing off this dark cleft of sea? Was it to keep things out, or keep them in? Bond gazed vaguely down into the black depths around him. The wire strands vanished into nothingness below his clinging feet. There were small fish round his legs below the waist. What were they doing? They seemed to be feeding, darting in towards him and then backing away, catching at black strands. Strands of what? Of cotton from his rags? Bond shook his head to clear it. He looked again. No, they were feeding off his blood.

Bond shivered. Yes, blood was seeping off his body, off the torn shoulders, the knees, the feet, into the water. Now for the first time he felt the pain of the sea water on his sores and burns. The pain revived him, quickened his mind. If these small fish liked it, what about barracuda and shark? Was that what the wire fence was for, to keep man-eating fish from escaping to sea? Then why hadn't they been after him already? To hell with it! The first thing was to crawl up the wire and get over to the other side. To put the fence between him and whatever lived in this black aquarium.

Weakly, foothold by foothold, Bond climbed up the wire and over the top and down again to where he could rest well above the water. He hooked the thick cable under his arms and hung, a bit of washing on a line, and gazed vaguely down at the fish that still fed from the blood that dripped off his feet.

Now there was nothing much left of Bond, not many reserves. The last dive down the tube, the crash of impact and the half-death from drowning had squeezed him like a sponge. He was on the verge of surrender, on the verge of giving one small sigh and then slipping back into the soft arms of the water. How beautiful it would be to give in at last and rest – to feel the sea softly take him to its bed and turn out the light.

It was the explosive flight of the fish from their feeding ground that shook Bond out of his death-dreaming. Something had moved far below the surface. There was a distant shimmer. Something was coming slowly up on the landward side of the fence.

Bond's body tautened. His hanging jaw slowly shut and the slackness cleared from his eyes. With the electric shock of danger, life flooded back into him, driving out the lethargy, pumping back the will to survive.

Bond uncramped the fingers that, a long time ago, his brain had ordered not to lose his knife. He flexed his fingers and took a fresh grip of the silver-plated handle. He reached down and touched the crook of the wire spear that still hung inside his trouser-leg. He shook his head sharply and focused his eyes. Now what?

Below him the water quivered. Something was stirring in the depths, something huge. A great length of luminescent greyness showed, poised far down in the darkness. Something snaked up from it, a whiplash as thick as Bond's arm. The tip of the thong was swollen to a narrow oval, with regular bud-like markings. It swirled through the water where the fish had been and was withdrawn. Now there was nothing but the huge grey shadow. What was it doing? Was it . . . ? Was it tasting the blood?

As if in answer, two eyes as big as footballs slowly swam up and into Bond's vision. They stopped, twenty feet below his own, and stared up through the quiet water at his face.

Bond's skin crawled on his back. Softly, wearily, his mouth uttered one bitter four-lettered word. So this was the last surprise of Doctor No, the end of the race!

Bond stared down, half hypnotized, into the wavering pools of eye far below. So this was the giant squid, the mythical kraken that could pull ships beneath the waves, the fifty-foot-long monster that battled with whales, that weighed a ton or more. What else did he know about them? That they had two long seizing tentacles and ten holding ones. That they had a huge blunt beak beneath eyes that were the only fishes' eyes that worked on the camera principle, like a man's. That their brains were efficient, that they could shoot backwards through the water at thirty knots, by jet propulsion. That explosive harpoons burst in their jellied mantle without damaging them. That . . . but the bulging black and white targets of the eyes were rising up towards him. The surface of the water shivered. Now Bond could see the forest of tentacles that flowered out of the face of the thing. They were weaving in front of the eyes like a bunch of thick snakes. Bond could see the dots of the suckers on their undersides. Behind the head, the great flap of the mantle softly opened and closed, and behind that the jellied sheen of the body disappeared into the depths. God, the thing was as a big as a railway engine!

Softly, discreetly, Bond snaked his feet and then his arms through the squares in the wire, lacing himself into them, anchoring himself so that the tentacles would have either to tear him to bits or wrench down the wire barrier with him. He squinted to right and left. Either way it was twenty yards along the wire to the land. And movement, even if he was capable of it, would be fatal. He must stay dead quiet and pray that the thing would lose interest. If it didn't . . . Softly Bond's fingers clenched on the puny knife.

The eyes watched him, coldly, patiently. Delicately, like the questing trunk of an elephant, one of the long seizing tentacles broke the surface and palped its way up the wire towards his leg. It reached his foot. Bond felt the hard kiss of the suckers. He didn't move. He dared not reach down and lose the grip of his arms through the wire. Softly the suckers tugged, testing the amount of yield. It was not enough. Like a huge slimy caterpillar, the tentacle walked slowly on up the leg. It got to the bloody blistered kneecap and stopped there, interested. Bond's teeth gritted with the pain. He could imagine the message going back down the thick tentacle to the brain: Yes, it's good to eat! And the brain signalling back: then get it! Bring it to me!

The suckers walked on up the thigh. The tip of the tentacle was pointed, then it splayed out so that it almost covered the width of Bond's thigh and then tapered off to a wrist. That was Bond's target. He would just have to take the pain and the horror and wait for the wrist to come within range.

A breeze, the first soft breeze of early morning, whispered across the metal surface of the inlet. It raised small waves that slapped gently against the sheer walls of the cliff. A wedge of cormorants took off from the guanera, five hundred feet above the inlet, and, cackling softly, made out to sea. As they swept over, the noise that had disturbed them reached Bond – the triple blast of a ship's siren that means it is ready to take on cargo. It came from Bond's left. The jetty must be round the corner from the northern arm of the inlet. The tanker from Antwerp had come in. Antwerp! Part of the world outside – the world that was a million miles away, out of Bond's reach – surely out of his reach for ever. Just around that corner, men would be in the galley, having breakfast. The radio would be playing. There would be the sizzle of bacon and eggs, the smell of coffee . . . breakfast cooking. . . .

The suckers were at his hip. Bond could see into the horny cups. A stagnant sea smell reached him as the hand slowly undulated upwards. How tough was the mottled grey-brown jelly behind the hand? Should he stab? No, it must be a quick hard slash, straight across, like cutting a rope. Never mind about cutting his own skin.

Now! Bond took a quick glance into the two football eyes, so patient, so incurious. As he did so the other seizing arm broke the surface and shot straight up at his face. Bond jerked back and the hand curled into a fist round the wire in front of his eyes. In a second it would shift to an arm or shoulder and he would be finished. Now!

The first hand was on his ribs. Almost without taking aim, Bond's knife-hand slashed down and across. He felt the blade bite into the puddingy flesh and then the knife was almost torn from his grip as the wounded tentacle whipped back into the water. For a moment the sea boiled around him. Now the other hand let go the wire and slapped across his stomach. The pointed hand stuck like a leech, all the power of the suckers furiously applied. Bond screamed as the suckers bit into his flesh. He slashed madly, again and again. God, his stomach was being torn out! The wire shook with the struggle. Below him the water boiled and foamed. He would have to give in. One more stab, this time into the back of the hand. It worked! The hand jerked free and snaked down and away leaving twenty red circles, edged with blood, across his skin.

Bond had not time to worry about them. Now the head of the squid had broken the surface and the sea was being thrashed into foam by the great heaving mantle round it. The eyes were glaring up at him, redly, venomously, and the forest of feeding arms was at his feet and legs, tearing the cotton fabric away and flailing back. Bond was being pulled down, inch by inch. The wire was biting into his armpits. He could even feel his spine being stretched. If he held on he would be torn in half. Now the eyes and the great triangular beak were right out of the water and the beak was reaching up for his feet. There was one hope, only one!

Bond thrust his knife between his teeth and his hand dived for the crook of the wire spear. He tore it out, got it between his two hands and wrenched the doubled wire almost straight. He would have to let go with one arm to stoop and get within range. If he missed, he would be torn to shreds on the fence.

Now, before he died of the pain! Now, now!

Bond let his whole body slip down the ladder of wire and lunged through and down with all his force.

He caught a glimpse of the tip of his spear lancing into the centre of a black eyeball and then the whole sea erupted up at him in a fountain of blackness and he fell and hung upside down by the knees, his head an inch from the surface of the water.

What had happened? Had he gone blind? He could see nothing. His eyes were stinging and there was a horrible fish taste in his mouth. But he could feel the wire cutting into tendons behind his knees. So he must be alive! Dazedly Bond let go the spear from his trailing hand and reached up and felt for the nearest strand of wire. He got a hold and reached up his other hand and slowly, agonizingly, pulled himself up so that he was sitting in the fence. Streaks of light came into his eyes. He wiped a hand across his face. Now he could see. He gazed at his hand. It was black and sticky. He looked down at his body. It was covered with black slime, and blackness stained the sea for twenty yards around. Then Bond realized. The wounded squid had emptied its ink sac at him.

But where was the squid? Would it come back? Bond searched the sea. Nothing, nothing but the spreading stain of black. Not a movement. Not a ripple. Then don't wait! Get away from here! Get away quick! Wildly Bond looked to right and left. Left was towards the ship, but also towards Doctor No. But right was towards nothing. To build the wire fence the men must have come from the left, from the direction of the jetty. There would be some sort of a path. Bond reached for the top cable and frantically began to edge along the swaying fence towards the rocky headland twenty yards away.

The stinking, bleeding, black scarecrow moved it arms and legs quite automatically. The thinking, feeling apparatus of Bond was no longer part of his body. It moved alongside his body, or floated above it, keeping enough contact to pull the strings that made the puppet work. Bond was like a cut worm, the two halves of which continue to jerk forward although life has gone and been replaced by the mock life of nervous impulses. Only, with Bond, the two halves were not yet dead. Life was only in abeyance in them. All he needed was an ounce of hope, an ounce of reassurance that it was still worth while trying to stay alive.

Bond got to the rock face. Slowly he let himself down to the bottom rung of wire. He gazed vaguely at the softly heaving sheen of water. It was black, impenetrable, as deep as the rest. Should he chance it? He must! He could do nothing until he had washed off the caking slime and blood, the horrible stale fish-smell. Moodily, fatalistically, he took off the rags of his shirt and trousers and hung them on the wire. He looked down at his brown and white body, striped and pock-marked with red. On an instinct he felt his pulse. It was slow but regular. The steady thump of life revived his spirits. What the hell was he worrying about? He was alive. The wounds and bruises on his body were nothing – absolutely nothing. They looked ugly, but nothing was broken. Inside the torn envelope, the machine was quietly, solidly ticking over. Superficial cuts and abrasions, bloody memories, deathly exhaustion – these were hurts that an accident ward would sneer at. Get on, you bastard! Get moving! Clean yourself and wake up. Count your blessings. Think of the girl. Think of the man you've somehow got to find and kill. Hang on to life like you've hung on to the knife between your teeth. Stop being sorry for yourself. To hell with what happened just now. Get down into the water and wash!

Ten minutes later, Bond, his wet rags clinging to his scrubbed, stinging body and his hair slicked back out of his eyes, climbed over the top of the headland.

Yes, it was as he had guessed. A narrow rocky track, made by the feet of the workers, led down the other side and round the bulge of the cliff.

From close by came various sounds and echoes. A crane was working. He could hear the changing beat of its engine. There were iron ship-noises and the sound of water splashing into the sea from a bilge pump.

Bond looked up at the sky. It was pale blue. Clouds tinged with golden pink were trailing away towards the horizon. Far above him the cormorants were wheeling round the guanera. Soon they would be going off to feed. Perhaps even now they were watching the scout groups far out at sea locating the fish. It would be about six o'clock, the dawn of a beautiful day.

Bond, leaving drops of blood behind him, picked his way carefully down the track and along the bottom of the shadowed cliff. Round the bend, the track filtered through a maze of giant, tumbled boulders. The noises grew louder. Bond crept softly forward, watching his footholds for loose stones. A voice called out, startlingly close, 'Okay to go?' There was a distant answer: 'Okay.' The crane engine accelerated. A few more yards. One more boulder. And another. Now!

Bond flattened himself against the rock and warily inched his head round the corner.

CHAPTER 19

A SHOWER OF DEATH

Bond took one long comprehensive look and pulled back. He leant against the cool face of rock and waited for his breathing to get back to normal. He lifted his knife close up to his eyes and carefully examined the blade. Satisfied, he slipped it behind him and down the waistband of his trousers up against his spine. There it would be handy but protected from hitting against anything. He wondered about the lighter. He took it out of his hip pocket. As a hunk of metal it might be useful, but it wouldn't light any more and it might scrape against the rock. He put it down on the ground away from his feet.

Then Bond sat down and meticulously went over the photograph that was in his brain.

Round the corner, not more than ten yards away, was the crane. There was no back to the cabin. Inside it a man sat at the controls. It was the Chinese Negro boss, the driver of the marsh buggy. In front of him the jetty ran twenty yards out into the sea and ended in a T. An aged tanker of around ten thousand tons deadweight was secured alongside the top of the T. It stood well out of the water, its deck perhaps twelve feet above the quay. The tanker was called *Blanche*, and the *Ant* of Antwerp showed at her stern. There was no sign of life on board except one figure lolling at the wheel in the enclosed bridge. The rest of the crew would be below, battened away from the guano dust. From just to the right of the crane, an overhead conveyor-belt in a corrugated-iron housing ran out from the cliff-face. It was carried on high stanchions above the jetty and stopped just short of the hold of the tanker. Its mouth ended in a huge canvas sock, perhaps six feet in diameter. The purpose of the crane was to lift the wire-framed mouth of the sock so that it hung directly over the hold of the tanker and to move it to right or left to give even distribution. From out of the mouth of the sock, in a solid downward jet, the scrambled-egg-coloured guano dust was pouring into the hold of the tanker at a rate of tons a minute.

Below, on the jetty, to the left and to leeward of the drifting smoke of the guano dust, stood the tall, watchful figure of Doctor No.

That was all. The morning breeze feathered the deep-water anchorage, still half in shadow beneath the towering cliffs, the conveyor-belt thudded quietly on its rollers, the crane's engine chuffed rhythmically.

There was no other sound, no other movement, no other life apart from the watch at the ship's wheel, the trusty working at the crane, and Doctor No, seeing that all went well. On the other side of the mountain men would be working, feeding the guano to the conveyor-belt that rumbled away through the bowels of the rock, but on this side no one was allowed and no one was necessary. Apart from aiming the canvas mouth of the conveyor, there was nothing else for anyone to do.

Bond sat and thought, measuring distances, guessing at angles, remembering exactly where the crane driver's hand and feet were on the levers and the pedals. Slowly, a thin, hard smile broke across the haggard, sunburned face. Yes! It was on! It could be done. But softly, gently, slowly! The prize was almost intolerably sweet.

Bond examined the soles of his feet and his hands. They would serve. They would have to serve. He reached back and felt the handle of the knife. Shifted it an inch. He stood up and took several slow deep breaths, ran his hands through his salt- and sweat-matted hair, rubbed them harshly up and down his face and then down the tattered side of his black jeans. He gave a final flex to his fingers. He was ready.

Bond stepped up to the rock and inched an eye round. Nothing had changed. His guess at the distances had been right. The crane driver was watchful, absorbed. The neck above the open khaki shirt was naked, offered, waiting. Twenty yards away, Doctor No, also with his back to Bond, stood sentry over the thick rich cataract of whity-yellow dust. On the bridge, the watch was lighting a cigarette.

Bond looked along the ten yards of path that led past the back of the crane. He picked out the places he would put each foot. Then he came out from behind the rock and ran.

Bond ran to the right of the crane, to a point he had chosen where the lateral side of the cabin would hide him from the driver and the jetty. He got there and stopped, crouching, listening. The engine hurried on, the conveyor-belt rumbled steadily out of the mountain above and behind him. There was no change.

The two iron footholds at the back of the cabin, inches away from Bond's face, looked solid. Anyway the noise of the engine would drown small sounds. But he would have to be quick to yank the man's body out of the seat and get his own hands and feet on the controls. The single stroke of the knife would have to be mortal. Bond felt along his own collarbone, felt the soft triangle of skin beneath which the jugular pumped, remembered the angle of approach behind the man's back, reminded himself to force the blade and hold it in.

For a final second he listened, then he reached behind his back for the

knife and went up the iron steps and into the cabin with the stealth and
speed of a panther.

At the last moment there was need to hurry. Bond stood behind the
man's back, smelling him. He had time to raise his knife hand almost to
the roof of the cabin, time to summon every ounce of strength, before he
swept the blade down and into the square inch of smooth, brownish-
yellow skin.

The man's hands and legs splayed away from the controls. His face
strained back towards Bond. It seemed to Bond that there was a flash of
recognition in the bulging eyes before the whites rolled upwards. Then a
strangled noise came from the open mouth and the big body rolled
sideways off its iron seat and crashed to the floor.

Bond's eyes didn't even follow it as far as the ground. He was already
in the seat and reaching for the pedals and levers. Everything was out of
control. The engine was running in neutral, the wire hawser was tearing
off the drum, the tip of the crane was bending slowly forwards like a
giraffe's neck, the canvas mouth of the conveyor-belt had wilted and was
now pouring its column of dust between the jetty and the ship. Doctor
No was staring upwards. His mouth was open. Perhaps he was shouting
something.

Coolly, Bond reined the machine in, slowly easing the levers and
pedals back to the angles at which the driver had been holding them.
The engine accelerated, the gears bit and began to work again. The
hawser slowed on the spinning drum and reversed, bringing the canvas
mouth up and over the ship. The tip of the crane lifted and stopped. The
scene was as before. Now!

Bond reached forward for the iron wheel which the driver had been
handling when Bond had caught his first glimpse of him. Which way to
turn it? Bond tried to the left. The tip of the crane veered slightly to the
right. So be it. Bond spun the wheel to the right. Yes, by God, it was
answering, moving across the sky, carrying the mouth of the conveyor
with it.

Bond's eyes flashed to the jetty. Doctor No had moved. He had moved
a few paces to a stanchion that Bond had missed. He had a telephone in
his hand. He was getting through to the other side of the mountain.
Bond could see his hand frantically jiggling the receiver arm, trying to
attract attention.

Bond whirled the director wheel. Christ, wouldn't it turn any faster?
In seconds Doctor No would get through and it would be too late.
Slowly the tip of the crane arced across the sky. Now the mouth of the
conveyor was spewing the dust column down over the side of the ship.

Now the yellow mound was marching silently across the jetty. Five yards, four, three, two! Don't look round, you bastard! Arrh, got you! Stop the wheel! Now, *you* take it, Doctor No!

At the first brush of the stinking dust column, Doctor No had turned. Bond saw the long arms fling wide as if to embrace the thudding mass. One knee rose to run. The mouth opened and a thin scream came up to Bond above the noise of the engine. Then there was a brief glimpse of a kind of dancing snowman. And then only a mound of yellow bird dung that grew higher and higher.

'God!' Bond's voice gave back an iron echo from the walls of the cabin. He thought of the screaming lungs stuffing with the filthy dust, the body bending and then falling under the weight, the last impotent kick of the heels, the last flash of thought – rage, horror, defeat? – and then the silence of the stinking tomb.

Now the yellow mountain was twenty feet high. The stuff was spilling off the sides of the jetty into the sea. Bond glanced at the ship. As he did so, there came three blasts on its siren. The noise crashed round the cliffs. There came a fourth blast which didn't stop. Bond could see the watch holding on to the lanyard as he craned out of the bridge window, looking down. Bond took his hands off the controls and let them rip. It was time to go.

He slipped off the iron seat and bent over the dead body. He took the revolver out of the holster and looked at it. He smiled grimly – Smith & Wesson ·38, the regular model. He slipped it down inside his waistband. It was fine to feel the heavy cold metal against his skin. He went to the door of the cabin and dropped down to the ground.

An iron ladder ran up the cliff behind the crane to where the conveyor-housing jutted out. There was a small door in the corrugated iron wall of the housing. Bond scrambled up the ladder. The door opened easily, letting out a puff of guano dust, and he clambered through.

Inside, the clanking of the conveyor-belt over its rollers was deafening, but there were dim inspection lights in the stone ceiling of the tunnel and a narrow catwalk that stretched away into the mountain alongside the hurrying river of dust. Bond moved quickly along it, breathing shallowly against the fishy ammoniac smell. At all costs he must get to the end before the significance of the ship's siren and of the unanswered telephone overcame the fear of the guards.

Bond half ran and half stumbled through the echoing stinking tunnel. How far would it be? Two hundred yards? And then what? Nothing for it but to break out of the tunnel mouth and start shooting – cause a panic and hope for the best. He would get hold of one of the men and wring out of him where the girl was. Then what? When he got to the place on the mountainside, what would he find? What would be left of her?

Bond ran on faster, his head down, watching the narrow breadth of planking, wondering what would happen if he missed his footing and slipped into the rushing river of guano dust. Would he be able to get off the belt again or would he be whirled away and down until he was finally spewed out on to the burial mound of Doctor No?

When Bond's head hit into the soft stomach and he felt the hands at his throat, it was too late to think of his revolver. His only reaction was to throw himself down and forward at the legs. The legs gave against his shoulder and there was a shrill scream as the body crashed down on his back.

Bond had started the heave that would hurl his attacker sideways and on to the conveyor-belt when the quality of the scream and something light and soft about the impact of the body froze his muscles.

It couldn't be!

As if in answer, sharp teeth bit deeply into the calf of his right leg and an elbow jabbed viciously, knowledgeably, backwards into his groin.

Bond yelled with the pain. He tried to squirm sideways to protect himself, but even as he shouted 'Honey!' the elbow thudded into him again.

The breath whistled through Bond's teeth with the agony. There was only one way to stop her without throwing her on to the conveyor-belt. He took a firm grip of one ankle and heaved himself to his knees. He stood upright, holding her slung over his shoulder by one leg. The other foot banged against his head, but half-heartedly, as if she too realised that something was wrong.

'Stop it, Honey! It's me!'

Through the din of the conveyor-belt, Bond's shout got through to her. He heard her cry 'James!' from somewhere near the floor. He felt her hands clutch at his legs. 'James, James!'

Bond slowly let her down. He turned and knelt and reached for her. He put his arms round her and held her tightly to him. 'Oh Honey, Honey. Are you all right?' Desperately, unbelieving, he strained her to him.

'Yes, James! Oh, Yes!' He felt her hands at his back and his hair. 'Oh, James, my darling!' she fell against him, sobbing.

'It's all right, Honey.' Bond smoothed her hair. 'And Doctor No's dead. But now we've got to run for it. We've got to get out of here. Come on! How can we get out of the tunnel? How did you get here? We've got to hurry!'

As if in comment, the conveyor-belt stopped with a jerk.

Bond pulled the girl to her feet. She was wearing a dirty suit of workmen's blue dungarees. The sleeves and legs were rolled up. The suit was far too big for her. She looked like a girl in a man's pyjamas. She was powdered white with the guano dust except where the tears had marked her cheeks. She said breathlessly, 'Just up there! There's a side tunnel that leads to the machine shops and the garage. Will they come after us?'

There was no time to talk. Bond said urgently, 'Follow me!' and started running. Behind him her feet padded softly in the hollow silence. They came to the fork where the side tunnel led off into the rock. Which way would the men come? Down the side tunnel or along the catwalk in the main tunnel? The sound of voices booming far up the side tunnel answered him. Bond drew the girl a few feet up the main tunnel. He brought her close to him and whispered, 'I'm sorry, Honey. I'm afraid I'm going to have to kill them.'

'Of course.' The answering whisper was matter of fact. She pressed his hand and stood back to give him room. She put her hands up to her ears.

Bond eased the gun out of his waistband. Softly he broke the cylinder sideways and verified with his thumb that all six chambers were loaded. Bond knew he wasn't going to like this, killing again in cold blood, but these men would be the Chinese Negro gangsters, the strong-arm guards who did the dirty work. They would certainly be murderers many times over. Perhaps they were the ones who had killed Strangways and the girl. But there was no point in trying to ease his conscience. It was kill or be killed. He must just do it efficiently.

The voices were coming closer. There were three men. They were talking loudly, nervously. Perhaps it was many years since they had even thought of going through the tunnel. Bond wondered if they would look round as they came out into the main tunnel. Or would he have to shoot them in the back?

Now they were very close. He could hear their shoes scuffing the ground.

'That makes ten bucks you owe me, Sam.'

'Not after tonight it won't be. Roll them bones, boy. Roll them bones.'

'No dice for me tonight, feller. I'm goin' to cut maself a slice of de white girl.'

'Haw, haw, haw.'

The first man came out, then the second, then the third. They were carrying their revolvers loosely in their right hands.

Bond said sharply, 'No, you won't.'

The three men whirled round. White teeth glinted in open mouths. Bond shot the rear man in the head and the second man in the stomach. The front man's gun was up. A bullet whistled past Bond and away up the main tunnel. Bond's gun crashed. The man clutched at his neck and spun slowly round and fell across the conveyor-belt. The echoes thundered slowly up and down the tunnel. A puff of fine dust rose in the air and settled. Two of the bodies lay still. The man with the stomach shot writhed and jerked.

Bond tucked his hot gun into the waistband of his trousers. He said roughly to the girl, 'Come on.' He reached for her hand and pulled her after him into the mouth of the side tunnel. He said, 'Sorry about that, Honey,' and started running, pulling her after him by the hand. She said, 'Don't be stupid.' Then there was no sound but the thud of their naked feet on the stone floor.

The air was clean in the side tunnel and it was easier going but, after the tension of the shooting, pain began to crowd in again and take possession of Bond's body. He ran automatically. He hardly thought of the girl. His whole mind was focused on taking the pain and on the problems that waited at the end of the tunnel.

He couldn't tell if the shots had been heard and he had no idea what opposition was left. His only plan was to shoot anyone who got in his way and somehow get to the garage and the marsh buggy. That was their only hope of getting away from the mountain and down to the coast.

The dim yellow bulbs in the ceiling flickered by overhead. Still the tunnel stretched on. Behind him, Honey stumbled. Bond stopped, cursing himself for not having thought of her. She reached for him and for a moment she leaned against him panting. 'I'm sorry, James. It's just that . . .'

Bond held her to him. He said anxiously, 'Are you hurt, Honey?'

'No, I'm all right. It's just that I'm so terribly tired. And my feet got rather cut on the mountain. I fell a lot in the dark. If we could walk a bit. We're nearly there. And there's a door into the garage before we get to the machine shop. Couldn't we go in there?'

Bond hugged her to him. He said, 'That's just what I'm looking for, Honey. That's our only hope of getting away. If you can stick it till we get there, we've got a real chance.'

Bond put his arm round her waist and took her weight. He didn't trust himself to look at her feet. He knew they must be bad. It was no good being sorry for each other. There wasn't time for it if they were to stay alive.

They started moving again, Bond's face grim with the extra effort, the girl's feet leaving bloody footsteps on the ground, and almost immediately she whispered urgently and there was a wooden door in the wall of the tunnel and it was ajar and no sound came from the other side. Bond took out his gun and gently eased the door open. The long garage was empty. Under the neon lights the black and gold painted dragon on wheels looked like a float waiting for the Lord Mayor's Show. It was pointing towards the sliding doors and the hatch of the armoured cabin stood open. Bond prayed that the tank was full and that the mechanic had carried out his orders to get the damage fixed.

Suddenly, from somewhere outside, there was the sound of voices. They came nearer, several of them, jabbering urgently.

Bond took the girl by the hand and ran forward. There was only one place to hide – in the marsh buggy. The girl scrambled in. Bond followed, softly pulling the door shut behind him. They crouched, waiting. Bond thought: only three rounds left in the gun. Too late he remembered the rack of weapons on the wall of the garage. Now the voices were outside. There came the clang of the door being slid back on its runners and a confusion of talk.

'How d'ya know they were shootin'?'

'Couldn't been nuthen else. I should know.'

'Better take rifles. Here, Joe! Take that one, Lemmy! An' some pineapples. Box under da table.'

There was the metallic noise of bolts being slid home and safety catches clicked.

'Some feller must a gone nuts. Couldn't ha' been da Limey. You ever seen da big pus-feller in da creek? Cheessus! An' da rest of da tricks da Doc fixed up in da tube? An' dat white gal. She cain't have been in much shape dis mornin'. Any of you men bin to have a look?'

'Nossir.'

'No.'

'No.'

'Haw, haw. I'se sho surprised at you fellers. Dat's a fine piece of ass out dere on de crab walk.'

More rattling and shuffling of feet, then, 'Okay let's go! Two abreast till we gets to da main tunnel. Shoot at da legs. Whoever's makin' trouble, da Doc'll sure want him to play wit.'

'Tee-hee.'

Feet echoed hollowly on the concrete. Bond held his breath as they filed by. Would they notice the shut door of the buggy? But they went on down the garage and into the tunnel and the noise of them slowly faded away.

Bond touched the girl's arm and put his finger to his lips. Softly he eased open the door and listened again. Nothing. He dropped to the ground and walked round the buggy and went to the half-open entrance. Cautiously he edged his head round. There was no one in sight. There was a smell of frying food in the air that brought the saliva to Bond's mouth. Dishes and pans clattered in the nearest building, about twenty yards away, and from one of the further Quonsets came the sound of a guitar and a man's voice singing a calypso. Dogs started to bark half-heartedly and then were silent. The Dobermann Pinschers.

Bond turned and ran back to the end of the garage. No sound came from the tunnel. Softly Bond closed the tunnel door and locked and bolted it. He went to the arms-rack on the wall and chose another Smith & Wesson and a Remington carbine. He verified that they were loaded and went to the door of the marsh buggy and handed them in to the girl. Now the entrance door. Bond put his shoulder to it and softly eased it wide open. The corrugated iron rumbled hollowly. Bond ran back and scrambled through the open hatch and into the driver's seat. 'Shut it, Honey,' he whispered urgently and bent and turned the ignition key.

The needle on the gauge swung to Full. Pray God the damned thing would start up quickly. Some diesels were slow. Bond stamped his foot down on the starter.

The grinding rattle was deafening. It must be audible all over the compound! Bond stopped and tried again. The engine fluttered and died. And again, and this time the blessed thing fired and the strong iron pulse hammered as Bond revved it up. Now, gently into gear. Which one? Try this. Yes, it bit. Brake off, you bloody fool! Christ, it had nearly stalled. But now they were out and on the track and Bond rammed his foot down to the floor.

'Anyone after us?' Bond had to shout above the noise of the diesel.

'No. Wait! Yes, there's a man come out of the huts! And another! They're waving and shouting as us. Now some more are coming out. One of them's run off to the right. Another's gone back into the hut. He's come out with a rifle. He's lying down. He's firing!'

'Close the slot! Lie down on the floor!' Bond glanced at the speedometer. Twenty. And they were on a slope. There was nothing more to get out of the machine. Bond concentrated on keeping the huge bucking wheels on the track. The cabin bounced and swayed on the springs. It was a job to keep his hands and feet on the controls. An iron fist clanged against the cabin. And another. What was the range? Four hundred? Good shooting! But that would be the lot. He shouted, 'Take a look, Honey! Open the slot an inch.'

'The man's got up. He's stopped firing. They're all looking after us – a whole crowd of them. Wait, there's something else. The dogs are coming! There's no one with them. They're just tearing down the track after us. Will they catch us?'

'Doesn't matter if they do. Come and sit by me, Honey. Hold tight. Mind your head against the roof.' Bond eased up the throttle. She was beside him. He grinned sideways at her. 'Hell, Honey. We've made it. When we get down to the lake I'll stop and shoot up the dogs. If I know those brutes I've only got to kill one and the whole pack'll stop to eat him.'

Bond felt her hand at his neck. She kept it there as they swayed and thundered down the track. At the lake, Bond went on fifty yards into the water and turned the machine round and put it in neutral. Through the oblong slot he could see the pack streaming round the last bend. He reached down for the rifle and pushed it through the aperture. Now the dogs were in the water and swimming. Bond kept his finger on the trigger and sprayed bullets into the middle of them. One floundered, kicking. Then another and another. He could hear their snarling screams above the clatter of the engine. There was blood in the water. A fight had started. He saw one dog leap on one of the wounded ones and sink its teeth into the back of its neck. Now they all seemed to have gone berserk. They were milling around in the frothing bloody water. Bond emptied his magazine among them and dropped the gun on the floor. He said, 'That's that, Honey,' and put the machine into gear and swung it round and began rolling at an easy speed across the shallow lake towards the distant gap in the mangroves that was the mouth of the river.

For five minutes they moved along in silence. Then Bond put a hand on the girl's knee and said, 'We should be all right now, Honey. When they find the boss is dead there'll be panic. I guess some of the brighter ones will try and get away to Cuba in the plane or the launch. They'll worry about their skins, not about us. All the same, we'll not take the canoe out until it's dark. I guess it's about ten by now. We should be at the coast in an hour. Then we'll rest up and try and get in shape for the trip. Weather looks all right and there'll be a bit more moon tonight. Think you can make it?'

Her hand squeezed his neck. 'Of course I can, James. But what about you? Your poor body! It's nothing but burns and bruises. And what are those red marks across your stomach?'

'Tell you later. I'll be okay. But you tell me what happened to you last night. How in hell did you manage to get away from the crabs? What went wrong with that bastard's plan? All night long I could only think of you out there being slowly eaten to death. God, what a thing to have dreamed up! What happened!

The girl was actually laughing. Bond looked sideways. The golden hair was tousled and the blue eyes were heavy with lack of sleep, but otherwise she might just be coming home from a midnight barbecue.

'That man thought he knew everything. Silly old fool.' She might have been talking about a stupid schoolteacher. 'He's much more impressed by the black crabs than I am. To begin with, I don't mind any animal touching me, and anyway those crabs wouldn't think of even nipping someone if they stay quite still and haven't got an open sore or anything. The whole point is that they don't really like meat. They live mostly on plants and things. If he was right and he did kill a black girl that way, either she had an open wound or she must have died of fright. He must have wanted to see if I'd stand it. Filthy old man. I only fainted down there at dinner because I knew he'd have something much worse for you.'

'Well, I'm damned. I wish to heaven I'd known that. I thought of you being picked to pieces.'

The girl snorted. 'Of course it wasn't very nice having my clothes taken off and being tied down to pegs in the ground. But those black men didn't dare touch me. They just made jokes and then went away. It wasn't very comfortable out there on the rock, but I was thinking of you and how I could get at Doctor No and kill him. Then I heard the crabs beginning to run – that's what we call it in Jamaica – and soon they came scurrying and rattling along – hundreds of them. I just lay still and thought of you. They walked round me and over me. I might have been a rock for all they cared. They tickled a bit. One annoyed me by trying to pull out a bit of my hair. But they don't smell or anything, and I just waited for the early morning when they crawl into holes and go to sleep. I got quite fond of them. They were company. Then they got fewer and fewer and finally stopped coming and I could move. I pulled at all the pegs in turn and then concentrated on my right-hand one. In the end I got it out of the crack in the rock and the rest was easy. I got back to the buildings and began scouting about. I got into the machine shop near the garage and found this filthy old suit. Then the conveyor thing started up not far away and I thought about it and I guessed it must be taking the guano through the mountain. I knew you must be dead by then,' the quiet voice was matter of fact, 'so I thought I'd get to the conveyor somehow and get through the mountain and kill Doctor No. I took a screwdriver to do it with.' She giggled. 'When we ran into each other, I'd have stuck it into you only it was in my pocket and I couldn't get to it.

I found the door in the back of the machine shop and walked through and into the main tunnel. That's all.' She caressed the back of his neck. 'I ran along watching my step and the next thing I knew was your head hitting me in the stomach.' She giggled again. 'Darling, I hope I didn't hurt you too much when we were fighting. My Nanny told me always to hit men there.'

Bond laughed. 'She did, did she?' He reached out and caught her by the air and pulled her face to him. Her mouth felt its way round his cheek and locked itself against his.

The machine gave a sideways lurch. The kiss ended. They had hit the first mangrove roots at the entrance to the river.

CHAPTER 20

SLAVE-TIME

'You're quite sure of all this?'

The Acting Governor's eyes were hunted, resentful. How could these things have been going on under his nose, in one of Jamaica's dependencies? What would the Colonial Office have to say about it? He already saw the long, pale blue enveloped marked 'Personal. For Addressee Only', and the foolscap page with those very wide margins: 'The Secretary of State for the Colonies has instructed me to express to you his surprise . . .'

'Yes, sir. Quite sure.' Bond had no sympathy for the man. He hadn't liked the reception he had had on his last visit to King's House, nor the mean comments on Strangways and the girl. He liked the memory of them even less now that he knew his friend and the girl were at the bottom of the Mona Reservoir.

'Er—well we musn't let any of this get out to the Press. You understand that? I'll send my report in to the Secretary of State by the next bag. I'm sure I can rely on your . . .'

'Excuse me, sir.' The Brigadier in command of the Caribbean Defence Force was a modern young soldier of thirty-five. His military record was good enough for him to be unimpressed by relics from the Edwardian era of Colonial Governors, whom he collectively referred to as 'feather-hatted fuddy duddies'. 'I think we can assume that Commander Bond is unlikely to communicate with anyone except his Department. And if

I may say so, sir, I submit that we should take steps to clear up Crab Key without waiting for approval from London. I can provide a platoon ready to embark by this evening. HMS *Narvik* came in yesterday. If the programme of receptions and cocktail parties for her could possibly be deferred for forty-eight hours or so . . .' The Brigadier let his sarcasm hang in the air.

'I agree with the Brigadier, sir.' The voice of the Police Superintendent was edgy. Quick action might save him from a reprimand, but it would have to be quick. 'And in any case I shall have to proceed immediately against the various Jamaicans who appear to be implicated. I'll have to get the divers working at Mona. If this case is to be cleaned up we can't afford to wait for London. As Mister—er—Commander Bond says, most of these Negro gangsters will probably be in Cuba by now. Have to get in touch with my opposite number in Havana and catch up with them before they take to the hills or go underground. I think we ought to move at once, sir.'

There was silence in the cool shadowy room where the meeting was being held. On the ceiling above the massive mahogany conference table there was an unexpected dapple of sunlight. Bond guessed that it shone up through the slats of the jalousies from a fountain or a lily pond in the garden outside the tall windows. Far away there was the sound of tennis balls being knocked about. Distantly a young girl's voice called, 'Smooth. Your serve, Gladys.' The Governor's children? Secretaries? From one end of the room King George VI, from the other end the Queen, looked down the table with grace and good humour.

'What do you think, Colonial Secretary?' The Governor's voice was hustled.

Bond listened to the first few words. He gathered that Pleydell-Smith agreed with the other two. He stopped listening. His mind drifted into a world of tennis courts and lily ponds and kings and queens, of London, of people being photographed with pigeons on their heads in Trafalgar Square, of the forsythia that would soon be blazing on the bypass roundabouts, of May, the treasured housekeeper in his flat off the King's Road, getting up to brew herself a cup of tea (here it was eleven o'clock. It would be four o'clock in London), of the first tube trains beginning to run, shaking the ground beneath his cool, dark bedroom. Of the douce weather of England: the soft airs, the heat waves, the cold spells – 'The only country where you can take a walk every day of the year' – Chesterfield's Letters? And then Bond thought of Crab Key, of the hot ugly wind beginning to blow, of the stink of the marsh gas from the mangrove swamps, the jagged grey, dead coral in whose eyes the black crabs were now squatting, the black and red eyes moving swiftly on their stalks as a shadow – a cloud, a bird – broke their small horizons. Down in the bird colony the brown and white and pink birds would be stalking in the shallows, or fighting or nesting, while up on the guanera the cormorants would be streaming back from their breakfast to deposit their milligramme of rent to the landlord who would no longer be collecting. And where would the landlord be? The men from the SS *Blanche* would have dug him out. The body would have been examined for signs of life and then put somewhere. Would they have washed the yellow dust off him and dressed him in his kimono while the Captain radioed Antwerp for instructions? And where had Doctor No's soul gone to? Had it been a bad soul or just a mad one? Bond thought of the burned twist down in the swamp that had been Quarrel. He remembered the soft ways of the big body, the innocence in the grey, horizon-seeking eyes, the simple lusts and desires, the reverence for superstitions and instincts, the childish faults, the loyalty and even love that Quarrel had given him – the warmth, there was only one word for it, of the man. Surely he hadn't gone to the same place as Doctor No. Whatever happened to dead people, there was surely one place for the warm and another for the cold. And which, when the time came, would he, Bond, go to?

The Colonial Secretary was mentioning Bond's name. Bond pulled himself together.

'. . . survived is quite extraordinary. I do think, sir, that we should show our gratitude to Commander Bond and to his Service by accepting his recommendations. It does seem, sir, that he has done at least three-quarters of the job. Surely the least we can do is look after the other quarter.'

The Governor grunted. He squinted down the table at Bond. The chap didn't seem to be paying much attention. But one couldn't be sure with these Secret Service fellows. Dangerous chaps to have around, sniffing and snooping. And their damned Chief carried a lot of guns in Whitehall. Didn't do to get on the wrong side of him. Of course there was something to be said for sending the *Narvik*. News would leak, of course. All the Press of the world would be coming down on his head. But then suddenly the Governor saw the headlines: 'GOVERNOR TAKES SWIFT ACTION . . . ISLAND'S STRONG MAN INTERVENES . . . THE NAVY'S THERE!' Perhaps after all it would be better to do it that way. Even go down and see the troops off himself. Yes, that was it, by jove. Cargill, of the *Gleaner*, was coming to lunch. He'd drop a hint or two to the chap and make sure the story got proper coverage. Yes, that was it. That was the way to play the hand.

The Governor raised his hands and let them fall flat on the table in a gesture of submission. He embraced the conference with a wry smile of surrender.

'So I am overruled, gentlemen. Well, then,' the voice was avuncular, telling the children that just this once . . . 'I accept your verdict. Colonial Secretary, will you please call upon the commanding officer of HMS *Narvik* and explain the position. In strict confidence, of course. Brigadier, I leave the military arrangements in your hands. Superintendent, you will know what to do.' The Governor rose. He inclined his head regally in the direction of Bond. 'And it only remains to express my appreciation to Commander—er—Bond, for his part in this affair. I shall not fail to mention your assistance, Commander, to the Secretary of State.'

Outside the sun blazed down on the gravel sweep. The interior of the Hillman Minx was a Turkish bath. Bond's bruised hands cringed as they took the wheel.

Pleydell-Smith leant through the window. He said, 'Ever heard the Jamaican expression "rarse"?'

'No.'

'"Rarse, man" is a vulgar expression meaning—er—'stuff it up'. If I may say so, it would have been appropriate for you to have used the expression just now. However,' Pleydell-Smith gave a wave of his hand which apologized for his Chief and dismissed him, 'is there anything else I can do for you? You really think you ought to go back to Beau Desert? They were quite definite at the hospital that they want to have you for a week.'

'Thanks,' said Bond shortly, 'but I've got to get back. See the girl's all right. Would you tell the hospital I'll be back tomorrow? You got off that signal to my Chief?'

'Urgent rates.'

'Well, then,' Bond pressed the self-starter, 'I guess that's the lot. You'll see the Jamaica Institute people about the girl, won't you? She really knows the hell of a lot about the natural history side of the island. Not from books either. If they've got the right sort of job . . . Like to see her settled. I'll take her up to New York myself and see her through the operation. She'd be ready to start in a couple of weeks after that. Incidentally,' Bond looked embarrassed, 'she's really the hell of a fine girl. When she comes back . . . if you and your wife . . . You know. Just so there's someone to keep an eye on her.'

Pleydell-Smith smiled. He thought he had the picture. He said, 'Don't worry about that. I'll see to it. Betty's rather a hand at that sort of thing. She'll like taking the girl under her wing. Nothing else? See you later in the week, anyway. That hospital's the hell of a place in this heat. You might care to spend a night or two with us before you go ho— I mean to New York. Glad to have you—er—both.'

'Thanks. And thanks for everything else.' Bond put the car into gear and went off down the avenue of flaming tropical shrubbery. He went fast, scattering the gravel on the bends. He wanted to get the hell away from King's House, and the tennis, and the kings and queens. He even wanted to get the hell away from the kindly Pleydell-Smith. Bond liked the man, but all he wanted now was to get back across the Junction Road to Beau Desert and away from the smooth world. He swung out past the sentry at the gates and on to the main road. He put his foot down.

The night voyage under the stars had been without incident. No one had come after them. The girl had done most of the sailing. Bond had not argued with her. He had laid in the bottom of the boat, totally collapsed, like a dead man. He had woken once or twice and listened to the slap of the sea against the hull and watched her quiet profile under the stars. Then the cradle of the soft swell had sent him back to sleep and to the nightmares that reached out after him from Crab Key. He didn't mind them. He didn't think he would ever mind a nightmare now. After what had happened the night before, it would have to be strong stuff that would ever frighten him again.

The crunch of a nigger-head against the hull had woken him. They were coming through the reef into Morgan's Harbour. The first quarter moon was up, and inside the reef the sea was a silver mirror. The girl had brought the canoe through under sail. They slid across the bay to the little fringe of sand and the bows under Bond's head sighed softly into it. She had had to help him out of the boat and across the velvet lawn and into the house. He had clung to her and cursed her softly as she had cut his clothes off him and taken him into the shower. She had said nothing when she had seen his battered body under the lights. She had turned the water full on and taken soap and washed him down as if he had been a horse. Then she led him out from under the water and dabbed him softly dry with towels that were soon streaked with blood. He had seen her reach for the bottle of Milton. He had groaned and taken hold of the washbasin and waited for it. Before she had begun to put it on him, she had come round and kissed him on the lips. She had said softly, 'Hold tight, my darling. And cry. It's going to hurt,' and as she splashed the murderous stuff over his body the tears of pain had run out of his eyes and down his cheeks without shame.

Then there had been a wonderful breakfast as the dawn flared up across the bay, and then the ghastly drive over to Kingston to the white table of the surgery in the emergency ward. Pleydell-Smith had been summoned. No questions had been asked. Merthiolate has been put on the wounds and tannic ointment on the burns. The efficient Negro doctor had written busily in the duty report. What? Probably just 'Multiple burns and contusions'. Then, with promises to come into the private ward on the next day, Bond had gone off with Pleydell-Smith to King's House and to the first of the meetings that had ended with the full-dress conference. Bond had enciphered a short signal to M via the Colonial Office which he had coolly concluded with: 'REGRET MUST AGAIN REQUEST SICK LEAVE STOP SURGEONS REPORT FOLLOWS STOP KINDLY INFORM ARMOURER SMITH AND WESSON INEFFECTIVE AGAINST FLAME-THROWER ENDIT.'

Now, as Bond swung the little car down the endless S-bends towards the North Shore, he regretted the gibe. M wouldn't like it. It was cheap. It wasted cipher groups. Oh well! Bond swerved to avoid a thundering red bus with 'Brownskin Gal' on the destination plate. He had just wanted M to know that it hadn't quite been a holiday in the sun. He would apologize when he sent in his written report.

Bond's bedroom was cool and dark. There was a plate of sandwiches and a Thermos full of coffee beside the turned-down bed. On the pillow was a sheet of paper with big childish writing. It said, 'You are staying with me tonight. I can't leave my animals. They were fussing. And I can't leave you. And you owe me slave-time. I will come at seven. Your H.'

In the dusk she came across the lawn to where Bond was sitting finishing his third glass of Bourbon-on-the-rocks. She was wearing a black and white striped cotton skirt and a tight sugar-pink blouse. The golden hair smelled of cheap shampoo. She looked incredibly fresh and beautiful. She reached out her hand and Bond took it and followed her up the drive and along a narrow well-trodden path through the sugar cane. It wound along for quite a way through the tall whispering sweet-scented jungle. Then there was a patch of tidy lawn up against thick broken stone walls and steps that led down to a heavy door whose edges glinted with light.

She looked up at him and from the door. 'Don't be frightened. The cane's high and they're most of them out.'

Bond didn't know what he had expected. He had vaguely thought of a flat earthen floor and rather damp walls. There would be a few sticks of furniture, a broken bedstead covered with rags, and a strong zoo smell. He had been prepared to be careful about hurting her feelings.

Instead it was rather like being inside a very large tidy cigar-box. The floor and ceiling were of highly polished cedar that gave out a cigar-box smell and the walls were panelled with wide split bamboo. The light came from a dozen candles in a fine silver chandelier that hung from the centre of the ceiling. High up in the walls there were three square windows through which Bond could see the dark blue sky and the stars. There were several pieces of good nineteenth-century furniture. Under the chandelier a table was laid for two with expensive-looking old-fashioned silver and glass.

Bond said, 'Honey, what a lovely room. From what you said I thought you lived in a sort of zoo.'

She laughed delightedly. 'I got out the old silver and things. It's all I've got. I had to spend the day polishing it. I've never had it out before. It does look rather nice, doesn't it? You see, generally there are a lot of little cages up against the wall. I like having them with me. It's company. But now that you're here . . .' She paused. 'My bedroom's in there,' she gestured at the other door. 'It's very small, but there's room for both of us. Now come on. I'm afraid it's cold dinner – just lobsters and fruit.'

Bond walked over to her. He took her in his arms and kissed her hard on the lips. He held her and looked down into the shining blue eyes. 'Honey, you're a wonderful girl. You're one of the most wonderul girls I've ever known. I hope the world's not going to change you too much. D'you really want to have that operation? I love your face – just as it is. It's part of you. Part of all this.'

She frowned and freed herself. 'You're not to be serious tonight. Don't talk about these things. I don't want to talk about them. This is my night with you. Please talk about love. I don't want to hear about anything else. Promise? Now come on. You sit there.'

Bond sat down. He smiled up at her. He said, 'I promise.'

She said, 'Here's the mayonnaise. It's not out of a bottle. I made it myself. And take some bread and butter.' She sat down opposite him and began to eat, watching him. When she saw that he seemed satisfied she said, 'Now you can start telling me about love. Everything about it. Everything you know.'

Bond looked across into the flushed, golden face. The eyes were bright and soft in the candlelight, but with the same imperious glint they had held when he had first seen her on the beach and she had thought he had come to steal her shells. The full red lips were open with excitement and impatience. With him she had no inhibitions. They were two loving animals. It was natural. She had no shame. She could ask him anything and would expect him to answer. It was if they were already in bed together, lovers. Through the tight cotton bodice the points of her breasts showed, hard and roused.

Bond said, 'Are you a virgin?'

'Not quite. I told you. That man.'

'Well . . .' Bond found he couldn't eat any more. His mouth was dry at the thought of her. He said, 'Honey, I can either eat or talk love to you. I can't do both.'

'You're going over to Kingston tomorrow. You'll get plenty to eat there. Talk love.'

Bond's eyes were fierce blue slits. He got up and went down on one knee beside her. He picked up her hand and looked into it. At the base of the thumb the Mount of Venus swelled luxuriously. Bond bent his head down into the warm soft hand and bit softly into the swelling. He felt her other hand in his hair. He bit harder. The hand was holding curled round his mouth. She was panting. He bit still harder. She gave a little scream and wrenched his head away by the hair.

'What are you doing?' Her eyes were wide and dark. She had gone pale. She dropped her eyes and looked at his mouth. Slowly she pulled his head towards her.

Bond put out a hand to her left breast and held it hard. He lifted her captive, wounded hand and put it round his neck. Their mouths met and clung, exploring.

Above them the candles began to dance. A big hawkmoth had come in through one of the windows. It whirred round the chandelier. The girl's closed eyes opened, looked at the moth. Her mouth drew away. She smoothed the handful of his hair back and got up, and without saying anything took down the candles one by one and blew them out. The moth whirred away through one of the windows.

The girl stood away from the table. She undid her blouse and threw it on the floor. Then her skirt. Under the glint of moonlight she was a pale figure with a central shadow. She came to Bond and took him by the hand and lifted him up. She undid his shirt and slowly, carefully took it off. Her body, close to him, smelled of new-mown hay and sweet pepper. She led him away from the table and through a door. The filtering moonlight shone down on a single bed. On the bed was a sleeping-bag, its mouth laid open.

The girl let go his hand and climbed into the sleeping-bag. She looked up at him. She said, practically, 'I bought this today. It's a double one.

It cost a lot of money. Take those off and come in. You promised. You owe me slave-time.'

'But . . .'

'Do as you're told.'